K. Mengel and E.A. Kirkby   Principles of Plant Nutrition

Principles of Plant Nutrition

Dr. Konrad Mengel
Professor in Plant Nutrition, Justus Liebig University,
Giessen/Federal Republic of Germany

Ernest A. Kirkby
Senior Lecturer in Plant Sciences, Department of Plant Sciences, The University,
Leeds/England

3rd Edition (completely revised)

Publisher:
International Potash Institute
P.O. Box, CH-3048 Worblaufen-Bern/Switzerland
1982

Preface

(3rd edition)

The large demand for the 1st Edition of 'Principles of Plant Nutrition' resulted in a new edition having to be made in the two years following publication in 1978. During this period translations into other languages were also undertaken. This world-wide response confirmed our view that there was indeed a need for a book such as ours which bridged the disciplines of soil science, plant physiology and agronomy in considering principles of plant nutrition. The success of the book also encouraged us to revise and update the text for a new edition.

Most of the reviews of the 1st edition were kind and some provided useful constructive criticism of great value in the preparation of this edition. In this respect too we are particularly grateful to our friends and colleagues who tactfully pointed out mistakes and to our students who made helpful suggestions and searched the text for printing errors. In this new third revised edition which covers the literature up to the end of 1981 a more thorough treatment is given to certain aspects including root growth and processes in the rhizosphere.

New photographs for this edition have kindly been provided by J.C. BROWN, Beltsville, M.C. DREW and M.J. GOSS, Letcombe, R.F. EVERT, Madison, A. GUCKERT, H. BREISCH and O. REISINGER, Nancy, A. KRAUSS, Stuttgart-Hohenheim, F.E. SANDERS, Leeds and G. TROLLDENIER, Hannover. To these authors we express our sincerest thanks.

We have been proud to regard the production of 'Principles of Plant Nutrition' as an international venture, for not only are the two authors and publisher each from a different country but also in the coverage of the book an attempt has been made to present a world-wide approach. We are delighted therefore that the book has been of use in so many different parts of the world.

Again we should like to express our most grateful thanks to our publisher, the International Potash Institute for always keeping an open mind to our wishes concerning the book.

Giessèn, Winter 1981   *Leeds, Winter 1981*

K. MENGEL   E. A. KIRKBY

Preface

(1st and 2nd edition)

Man's survival has always been dependent on plant life as a source of food, raw materials and energy. This lies in the ability of green plants to transform light energy into chemical energy. In the process of photosynthesis, the very low concentrations of carbon dioxide of the atmosphere are accumulated by plants and converted into sugars. This is the basis for the synthesis of vital natural raw materials, including starch, fibres, vegetable oils, and gums, as well as a vast array of organic compounds some of which, like essential amino acids, essential fatty acids and vitamins are indispensable in the mammalian diet. It is the photosynthetic process too that accounts for the worlds energy stores of fossil fuels on which man so heavily relies.

The increasing world population is now confronted by a major shortage of plant products, and there is a world-wide need to produce higher yielding quality crops. One important aspect of plant production is that of plant nutrition as high productivity can only be achieved if plants are properly fed. It is the aim of this book to present '*Principles of Plant Nutrition*' which may be applied in the production of more and better food and plant products. This, then, is the main purpose of the book, to provide information to help solve practical problems. In this respect we endorse the view of the great French microbiologist, *Louis Pasteur*, who once said that 'there is no Applied Science but only the application of scientific knowledge, thinking and technique to practical problems'.

The subject of plant nutrition is concerned with the provision of plants with nutrients as well as nutrient uptake and distribution in plants. Plant nutrition is clearly very closely related to plant metabolism. Thus in a broader sense the assimilation of nutrients, their functions in metabolism and their contribution to growth and yield production may also be considered as part of plant nutrition. The practical side of plant nutrition is fertilizer application. These are the main themes of the book.

The book presents a wide spectrum of topics which cut across the boundaries of Soil Science, Plant Physiology and Biochemistry. We are optimistic enough to believe that such a broad treatment will provide to a better understanding of 'Plant Nutrition', although we are fully aware that in a book of this scope and

5

for the purposes for which it is to be used, some simplification is unavoidable. In our opinion, this is justifiable in order to present a clear picture that can be understood by students.

The book is essentially a text-book for students of agriculture, horticulture and forestry. In addition, it should also serve as a guide to all those who are interested in plant science and crop production. For this reason, more literature is cited than is usually found in student text-books. In view of the vast number of papers produced over the past decade it is not possible to present a detailed literature survey of all the topics which are discussed. Nevertheless, we believe that the references cited will provide a useful introduction to those who intend to study a particular topic in more detail. In citing references, we have deliberately chosen literature from different countries in order to show the extent of research activities and to present a world-wide picture of the subject.

We should like to express our gratitude to all those people who helped us to complete this book. We are indebted to Mr. *D.R. Holdford*, Mr. *W.N. Townsend* and Dr. *P.B. Tinker* who had the unenviable task of reading sections of the book in first draft. Their stimulating comments and valuable suggestions were most appreciated. We are also grateful to Dr. *F.E. Sanders* and Professor *H.W. Woolhouse* for useful discussions.

A number of authors were kind enough to allow us to use their original photographs. These included Dr. *H. Ahmed* and Dr. *H.E. Evans*, Professor *S.A. Barber*, Dr. *M. Beck*, Dr. *J.A. Becking*, Dr. *J.B. Bole*, Dr. *C. Bould*, Professor *E. Brandenburg*, Dr. *P.C. De Kock*, Dr. *A.P. Draycott*, Dr. *D.B. Fisher*, Professor *W. Gartel*, Dr. *D. Kramer*, Dr. *O. Machold* and Dr. *G. Scholz*, Dr. *G. Mix*, Dr. *P. Ruckenbauer*, Dr. *F.E. Sanders*, Dr. *G. Trolldenier*, Dr. *H.P. Pissarek*, Dr. *C.B. Shear* and Dr. *B. Walter*.

One of the most arduous and time-consuming tasks in the production of a book is that of the preparation of the manuscript. Special thanks are therefore due to Miss *R. Gerke* and Mrs. *J. Andrew* for typing and to Mrs. *K. Mengel* who was much involved in the work of this book and checked and arranged the literature section.

We should also like to thank the International Potash Institute for complying with our wishes on the format of the book, and for publishing the book so quickly.

Giessen and Leeds, 1978   *K. Mengel*   *E.A. Kirkby*

6

Contents

Chapter 1:

Plant Nutrients

1.1 Definition and Classification

An outstanding feature of life is the capability of living cells to take up substances from the environment and use them for the synthesis of their own cellular components or as an energy source. The supply and absorption of chemical compounds needed for growth and metabolism may be defined as nutrition and the chemical compounds required by an organism termed nutrients. The mechanisms by which nutrients are converted to cellular material or used for energetic purposes are metabolic processes. The term 'metabolism' encompasses the various reactions occurring in a living cell in order to maintain life and growth. Nutrition and metabolism are thus very closely interrelated.

The essential nutrients required by higher plants are exclusively of inorganic nature. This exclusive requirement of higher plants for inorganic nutrients basically distinguishes these organisms from man, animals, and a number of microorganisms which additionally need organic foodstuffs. For an element to be considered an essential plant nutrient, three criteria must be met. These are:
1. A deficiency of the element makes it impossible for the plant to complete its life cycle.
2. The deficiency is specific for the element in question.
3. The element is directly involved in the nutrition of the plant, as for example as a constituent of an essential metabolite or required for the action of an enzyme system.

Based on these criteria as proposed by ARNON and STOUT [1939], the following chemical elements are now known to be essential for higher plants:

Carbon	C	Potassium	K	Zinc	Zn
Hydrogen	H	Calcium	Ca	Molybdenum	Mo
Oxygen	O	Magnesium	Mg	Boron	B
Nitrogen	N	Iron	Fe	Chlorine	Cl
Phosphorus	P	Manganese	Mn	(Sodium)	Na
Sulphur	S	Copper	Cu	(Silicon)	Si
				(Cobalt)	Co

Sodium, Si and Co have not been established as essential elements for all higher plants. These elements are therefore shown above in brackets. In the case of Na there are some plant species, particularly the *Chenopodiaceae* and species adapted to saline conditions that take up this element in relatively high amounts. Sodium has a beneficial effect and in some cases is essential. The same is true for Si which is an essential nutrient for rice. Chlorine is the most recent addition to the list of essential elements for the growth of all higher plants (BROYER *et al.* [1954]). The list of essential elements shown above may well not be complete and other elements, in very low concentrations, may yet be shown to be essential for higher plants. For some microorganisms, for example, vanadium (V) has now been established as an essential element (NICHOLAS [1961]).

The plant nutrients may be divided into macronutrients and micronutrients. Macronutrients are found and needed in plants in relatively higher amounts than micronutrients. The plant tissue content of the macronutrient N, for example is over a thousand times greater than the content of the micronutrient Zn. Using this classification based on the element content in plant material, the following elements may be defined as macronutrients: C, H, O, N, P, S, K, Ca, Mg (Na, Si). The micronutrients are: Fe, Mn, Cu, Zn, Mo, B, Cl. This division of the plant nutrients into macro- and micronutrients is somewhat arbitrary and in many cases differences between the contents of macronutrients and micronutrients are considerably less well defined than the example cited above. The Fe or Mn content of plant tissues for example is sometimes nearly as high as the content of S or Mg. The content of the micronutrients is also often far in excess of physiological requirements. This is true for Mn for example. Chloride also occurs in many plant species in comparatively high concentrations. For its probable role in photosynthesis, however, it is needed only in minute quantities within the entire plant. This particular example demonstrates clearly that the nutrient content of plant organs (leaves, stems, fruits, roots) provides little indication as to the nutrient quantity needed for physiological and biochemical processes. Plants may even contain high concentrations of non essential elements some of which may be toxic (Aluminium Al, Nickel Ni, Selenium Se, and Fluorine F).

From a physiological viewpoint it is difficult to justify the classification of plant nutrients into macronutrients and micronutrients depending on element concentration in plant tissues. Classification of plant nutrients according to biochemical behaviour and physiological function seems more appropriate. Adopting such a physiological approach one possible classification of plant nutrients is shown in Table 1.1. The first group includes the major constituents of the organic plant material: C, H, O, N, and S. Carbon is taken up in the form of CO_2 from the atmosphere and possibly in the form of HCO_3^- from the

Table 1.1 Classification of plant nutrients

Nutrient Element	Uptake	Biochemical Functions
1st group C, H, O, N, S	in the form of CO_2, HCO_3^-, H_2O, O_2, NO_3^-, NH_4^+, N_2, SO_4^{2-}, SO_2. The ions from the soil solution, the gases from the atmosphere.	Major constituent of organic material. Essential elements of atomic groups which are involved in enzymic processes. Assimilation by oxidation-reduction reactions.
2nd group P, B, Si	in the form of phosphates, boric acid or borate, silicate from the soil solution.	Esterification with native alcohol groups in plants. The phosphate esters are involved in energy transfer reactions.
3rd group K, Na, Mg, Ca, Mn, Cl	in the form of ions from the soil solution.	Non-specific functions establishing osmotic potentials. More specific reactions in which the ion brings about optimum conformation of an enzyme protein (enzyme activation). Bridging of the reaction partners. Balancing anions. Controlling membrane permeability and electro-potentials.
4th group Fe, Cu, Zn, Mo	in the form of ions or chelates from the soil solution	Present predominantly in a chelated form incorporated in prosthetic groups. Enable electron transport by valency change.

soil solution. These compounds are assimilated by carboxylation, with the formation of carboxylic groups. This incorporation of C is also accompanied by the simultaneous assimilation of O, for not only C but CO_2 or HCO_3^- are metabolized. Hydrogen is taken up in the form of water from the soil solution or under humid conditions from the atmosphere. In the course of photosynthesis H_2O is reduced to H (photolysis). This is transferred via a series of steps to an organic compound resulting in the reduction of nicotinamide adenine dinucleotide ($NADP^+$) to a reduced form (NADPH). This is a very important coenzyme of universal significance in oxidation-reduction processes as the H from NADPH can be transferred to a large number of different compounds. Plants take up nitrogen in the nitrate or ammonium form from the soil solution or as gaseous NH_3 and N_2 from the atmosphere. This latter process, termed fixation of molecular N_2, is dependent on the presence of specific microorganisms some of which *(Rhizobium, Actinomyces alni)* are symbiotically associated with higher plants. The N of NO_3^- is assimilated in the process of reduction and subsequent amination. Ammonium-N assi-

Gains H^+ & $2e^-$; is reduced

milation also involves an amination process. The incorporation of N from molecular N_2 depends on an initial reduction of N_2 to NH_3, which is again metabolized by the amination process. The assimilation of sulphate-S is analogous to NO_3-N incorporation, *i.e.* a reduction of SO_4^{2-} to the SH-group. Sulphur is not only taken up from the soil solution in the form of SO_4^{2-}, but can also be absorbed as SO_2 from the atmosphere. The reactions which result in the incorporation of C, H, O, N and S into organic molecules are fundamental physiological processes of plant metabolism. These will be described in more detail later. In this context it need only be mentioned that the main constituents of the organic plant material are assimilated by complex physiological reactions, and in this respect they differ considerably from the other plant nutrients.

Phosphorus, B and Si constitute another group of elements which show similarity in biochemical behaviour. All are absorbed as inorganic anions or acids, and occur as such in plant cells or are bound largely by hydroxyl groups of sugars forming phosphate-, borate- and silicate-esters.

The third group of plant nutrients is made up of K, Na, Ca, Mg, Mn and Cl. These elements are taken up from the soil solution in the form of their ions. In the plant cell they are present in the free ionic state or are adsorbed to indiffusible organic anions, as for example the adsorption of Ca^{2+} by the carboxylic groups of the pectins. Magnesium may also occur strongly bound in the chlorophyll molecule. Here the Mg^{2+} is chelated being bound by covalent and coordinate bonds (the term chelate is discussed in more detail on p. 17). In this respect Mg more closely resembles the elements of the fourth group: Fe, Cu, Zn and Mo. These elements are predominantly present as chelates in the plant and, with the exception of Mo, are often taken up by the plant as chelate complexes. The division between the third and fourth group is not very clear-cut for Mg, Mn and Ca may also be chelated.

1.2 General Functions

As described above C, H, O, N and S are constituents of organic material. As well as this, however, they also are involved in enzymic processes: C and O mainly as components of the carboxylic group, H and O in oxidation-reduction processes, N in the form of NH_2-, $NH=$, and even $-N^{\pm}$ and S in the form of the SH group. They are therefore reactants in fundamental biochemical processes. Some general examples of the reactions involved are shown below.

Carbon is assimilated by plants as CO_2. This process is called carboxylation and provides the basic mechanism by which CO_2 is fixed in photosynthesis (see p. 152). The reverse process whereby CO_2 is liberated is also very common in biochemistry and known as decarboxylation. An example of decarboxylation is the release of CO_2 from malic acid to form pyruvic acid. This is catalysed by the malic enzyme. A coenzyme, nicotinamide adenine dinucleotide phosphate ($NADP^+$), is also required in the reaction.

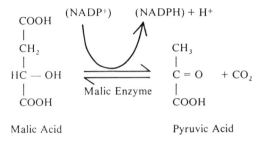

Decarboxylation

The equilibrium of this reaction is strongly in favour of pyruvic acid formation. Two H atoms from malic acid are transferred in the reaction. One is passed on to reduce the coenzyme $NADP^+$ and the other appears as a proton (H^+). The active component of the coenzyme is nicotinamide. The oxidized and reduced forms are shown below:

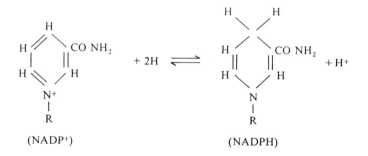

This example of decarboxylation also demonstrates the involvement of the N atom in an enzymic process. All enzymes and coenzymes contain N.

The SH-group can also be involved in oxido-reduction processes. The following equation shows the reaction of the two SH-groups of two molecules of cysteine resulting in the synthesis of one molecule of cystine, a compound characterized by the presence of an S-S-bridge. In the reaction the cysteine mole-

15

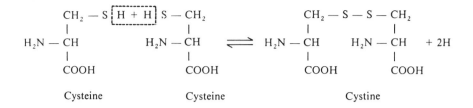

Cysteine	Cysteine		Cystine

cules are oxidized as two H atoms are removed. The S-S-group is very common in proteins, serving as a link between polypeptide strands (see p. 373).

The third and fourth group of plant nutrients (Table 1.1) have nonspecific ionic cellular functions such as establishing osmotic potentials in cell organelles or maintaining ionic balance. In addition these nutrients may carry out specific functions. In an excellent review paper CLARKSON and HANSON (1980) have adopted a system in which this third and fourth group of nutrients in our functional classification is divided into 4 categories. These are:

1. Trigger and control mechanisms (Na^+, K^+, Mg^{2+}, Ca^{++}, Cl^-) by controlling osmotic potentials, membrane permeability, electropotentials and conductance.
2. Structural influences (K^+, Ca^{2+}, Mg^{2+}, Mn^{2+}) by binding to organic molecules particularly enzyme molecules and thus altering their conformation.
3. Formation of Lewis acids (Mg^{2+}, Ca^{2+}, Mn^{2+}, Fe^{2+}, Cu^{2+}, Zn^{2+}). These ions are able to accept an electron pair and thus may catalyse or polarize reactive groups.
4. Redox reactions (Cu^{2+}, Fe^{2+}, Co^{2+}, Mn^{2+}). These ions are essential components of prosthetic groups which bring about electron transfer.

Calcium and Mg^{2+} have a rather high affinity for carboxylic and phosphate

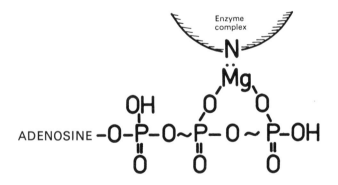

Fig.1.1 Magnesium bridging an enzyme with adenosine triphosphate.

groups, whereas the transition metals (Fe, Mn, Cu, Zn) are attracted more specifically by N and S. Since Ca^{2+} can more readily substitute its water of hydration it can react with a variety of ligands more strongly than Mg^{2+}. Calcium is thus mainly bound to cell wall material and membranes and its concentration in the cytoplasm is relatively low as compared with Mg^{2+}. When binding to an organic molecule, Mg^{2+} forms a typically strong geometrical orientation with the pyrophosphate group of the coenzyme adenosine triphosphate (ATP) to form a complex Mg ATP^{2-} which is then bound to an enzyme protein. Magnesium can also complex with the coenzyme adenosine diphosphate (ADP) although the affinity of ATP for Mg is much higher. In some reactions an $MnATP^{2-}$ complex is more active than $MgATP^{2-}$. In most enzymic reactions in which ATP acts as a phosphate donor, $MgATP^{2-}$ appears to be the active form of the coenzyme.

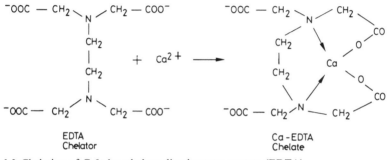

EDTA
Chelator

Ca -EDTA
Chelate

Fig.1.2 Chelation of Ca^{2+} by ethylene diamine tetra-acetate (EDTA).

The last group of plant nutrients (Table 1.1) are the heavy metals. These very often occur in a chelated form in the plant. A chelated metal atom is one that is bound to an organic compound (ligand) by two or more bonds. A ring structure is thus formed. Figure 1.2 shows an example. The Ca^{2+} is bound by ethylene diamine tetraacetate (EDTA) in such a way that the two carboxylic groups of the acid bind the Ca^{2+} by electrostatic bonds whilst two coordinate bonds are formed between Ca^{2+} and the two N-atoms. A very stable complex is formed, which is highly soluble in water and is relatively stable to changes in pH.

The most important naturally occurring plant chelates are those of the haem group and chlorophyll. The haem group is an iron porphyrin. Iron is bound to the N-atoms of two pyrrole rings by coordinate bonds and to the two remaining N-atoms of the other two pyrrole rings of the porphyrin structure by covalent bonds (Figure 1.3). The haem group forms the prosthetic group of a number of enzymes (catalase, peroxidase, cytochromes, cytochrome oxidase). The Fe present in the haem moiety can change in valency from Fe^{2+} to Fe^{3+}

$$Fe^{2+} \rightleftharpoons Fe^{3+} + e^-$$

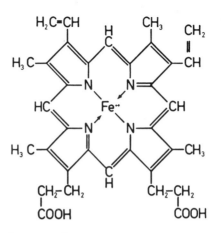

Fig.1.3 Structure of the haem complex.

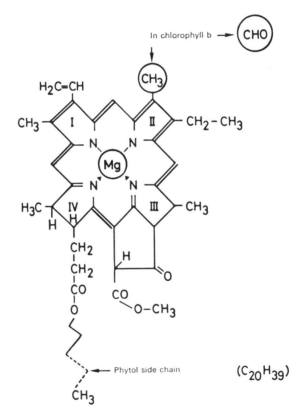

Fig.1.4 Chlorophyll a molecule. In chlorophyll b the CH_3 group is substituted by a CHO group. The 4 pyrrole rings are indicated by I, II, III and IV.

18

This enables the transfer of electrons, the principle function of this prosthetic group. In the reduced state (Fe^{II}) the group is called haem and in the oxidized state (Fe^{III}) haemin. Other metal atoms such as Cu, Co and Mo also function in enzyme systems in an analogous way to that described for Fe.

The structure of chlorophyll is similar to the haem structure (Figure 1.4). The Mg is bound to the N atoms of the porphyrin structure by two covalent and two coordinate bonds. In contrast to Fe, however, Mg is not a direct electron acceptor or donor. Chlorophyll has a function of vital importance in plant metabolism in that this organic metal complex is capable of electron emission if excited by light. This is the basis of the fundamental process of photosynthesis.

It is likely that the heavy metals are predominantly absorbed from the soil in the form of chelates. Chelation in the vicinity of the roots or even at the root surface thus probably plays a major role in their availability.

1.3   Mineral Contents of Plant Material

The material of living plants consists of organic matter, water and minerals. The relative amounts of these three components may vary, but for green plant material, water is always present in the highest proportion and the minerals in the lowest. The percentage distribution of these three components is in the following order of magnitude:

> water 70%
> organic material 27%
> minerals 3%

More detailed data showing the content of water in plant material is presented in Table 1.2. The minerals make up only a comparatively small proportion of the dry matter. They are nevertheless of extreme importance because they enable the plant to build up organic material (photosynthesis). The mineral content of plants and plant organs is therefore of physiological and practical significance.

The main factor controlling the mineral content of plant material is the specific, genetically fixed nutrient uptake potential for the different mineral nutrients. This accounts for the fact that the N and K content of green plant material is about 10 times higher than that of P and Mg which in turn is about 100–1000 times higher than the content of the micronutrients. This general pattern occurs in all species of higher plants. Within plant species, however, considerable differences in the mineral content do occur, which are also genetically determined. This question was studied by COLLANDER [1941], who grew 20 different plant species in the same nutrient solution and determined the mineral composition of the resulting plants. It was found that the content of K did not differ greatly between species but marked differences in the contents of Ca, Mg and Si occurred. The greatest interspecies differences were found for Na and Mn. Plant species with a high uptake potential for these minerals *(Atriplex hortense* and *Vicia* for Na, *Lactuca* and *Pisum* for Mn) in extreme cases contained 60 times more Na or Mn than those plant species with a low uptake for these two nutrients *(Fagopyrum* and *Zea* for Na, *Salicornia* and *Nicotiana* for Mn).

Table 1.2 Water content of various plant tissues and materials in % of the fresh weight

Young green plant material	90–95
Young roots	92–93
Old leaves	75–85
Mature cereal straw	15–20
Hay	15
Cereal grains	10–16
Rape seed	7–10
Tomato fruits	92–93
Oranges	86–90
Apples	74–81
Banana fruits	73–78
Potato tubers	75–80
Sugar beet roots	75–80

It has frequently been observed that in dicotyledenous plants there is generally a larger ratio of divalent to monovalent cations than in monocotyledons. The cation exchange capacity of the roots of dicotyledons is also usually higher than that of monocotyledons. In the older literature it was often held that there was a causal relationship between cation exchange capacity and differential uptake of divalent and monovalent cations (MCLEAN et al. [1956], DRAKE and WHITE [1961]). It is now believed for the monovalent cations at least that cation exchange properties of roots are of little significance in regulating cation uptake (MENGEL [1961], CUNNINGHAM and NIELSEN [1963]). Recent evidence indicates, however, that the cation exchange capacity of plant tissues may play a part in controlling divalent cation transport within plants (VAN DE GEIJN and PETIT [1979]).

The second factor controlling the mineral content of plant material is the availability of plant nutrients in the nutrient medium. The concentration of a particular mineral or plant nutrient in the plant increases in the form of a saturation curve as its a availability in the nutrient medium increases. (See Fig. 2.24 on page 103). The relationship between nutrient availability in the growth medium and plant nutrient content is used in leaf and plant analysis methods for diagnozing nutrient availability in the soil. This question is discussed in more detail later (p. 103). The plant needs a certain level of each nutrient in its tissues, and if this is not supplied, the plant dies. This critical level is different for each of the plant nutrients. Clearly the macronutrients are usually present in much higher concentrations than the micronutrients.

Mineral contents differ considerably between plant organs. Generally the vegetative parts of plants such as leaves, stems and roots vary to a higher extent in their mineral composition than fruits, tubers and seeds. The plant supplies its fruits or seeds with minerals and organic material at the expense of other plant organs and this generally results in only a small variation in the mineral contents of reproductive and storage parts of the plant. This relationship for Mg is demonstrated in Figure 1.5. This shows that with increasing Mg availability in the soil the Mg content of of the straw is much more affected than the Mg content of the grains (SCHREIBER [1949]). The same relationship is also true for other plant nutrients (P, N, K, Fe, Ca).

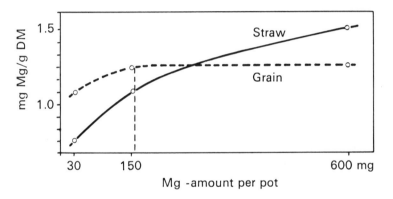

Fig.1.5 Effect of increasing Mg supply on the Mg content of cereal straw and grain (after SCHREIBER [1949]).

The mineral content of plants is also very much dependent on age. Young plants and young plant tissues have high contents of N, K and P, whereas in older plants and more mature plant parts, higher contents of Ca, Mn, Fe and B are often observed (SMITH [1962]), provided the mineral content is expressed on a dry matter basis. The typical variation in the contents of N, P and K during the growth period of cereals is shown in Figure 1.6. In the first weeks of the growing season the nutrient contents increase, due to a relatively higher nutrient uptake rate as compared with the growth rate. As soon as the tillering stage is completed, the very high growth rate of stem elongation begins. This vigorous growth causes a dramatic reduction in the mineral content of the plant by dilu-

21

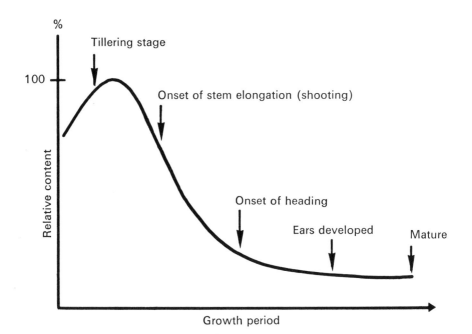

Fig. 1.6 Contents of N, P and K in oats during the course of the growing period (after SCHAR-RER and MENGEL [1960]).

tion. Once the ears are fully developed, there is little change in the content of N, P and K expressed in terms of the whole plant. Within the plant itself, however, considerable changes occur between tissues, for during this ripening period high quantities of N and P are translocated from the leaves and stems to the grain.

The mineral content of plants is generally expressed on a dry weight basis, where fresh plant material has been dried at 105 °C until all water has been removed, *e.g.* 4% K in the dry matter or 3 mg P/g dry matter or 27 ppm Mn in the dry matter. The term 'ppm' means parts per million, *e.g.* 27 parts Mn (weight) per 1,000,000 parts (weight) dry matter. Sometimes µg/g or mg/kg are used rather than ppm. This terminology is mainly applied where small quantities are being measured as in the case of the micronutrients. For the macronutrients, mineral content is usually expressed as percentage or as mg per gram plant material. Table 1.3 presents a survey of the mineral contents of various plants and plant organs. The figures given here are simply a guide. Mineral contents may vary considerably depending on uptake conditions and other factors including those mentioned above.

For practical purposes such as the calculation of the total nutrient uptake of a crop or the use of plant analysis as a tool for diagnozing nutrient availability

Table 1.3 Mineral content of different plant materials (MENGEL [1979], p. 209)

Element	Oat tops at the tillering stage	Oat grains	Oat straw	Rape at the vegetative stage
		mg/g DM		
N	39	17	4.5	56
P	4.4	4.3	1.2	4.9
S	3.2	2.8	3.3	9.3
Cl	15	2.7	14	12
K	43	6.4	14	46
Na	5.3	0.2	3	1.3
Ca	9.4	2.2	9.0	29
Mg	2.1	1.2	1.0	2.0
Si	3.5	1.8	3.3	3.4
		ppm of DM		
Fe	74	53	85	550
Mn	130	80	50	250
Cu	7	3	2.3	7
B	6	1.1	7	35
Mo	2	1.6	1.0	–

of the soil, mineral content based on dry matter is most appropriate. For physiological considerations, however, it is often more convenient to express nutrient concentrations in the plant on a fresh matter basis in the form of milli moles (mM) or milli equivalents (me), *e.g.* 2.5 me Ca/100 g fresh material. This can give a more realistic impression of the actual mineral concentration in plant cells. It is also particularly useful when expressing the concentrations or organic molecules such as free amino acids, organic acids and sugars. In addition, by basing concentrations on the fresh material and expressing the values in mM or me, it is often easier to recognize physiological relationships. One such example is the effect of age on the mineral content of plant tissues. Generally the water content of plant material is higher in younger tissues. Young tissues of plants are thus not so rich in N, P and K as is often believed from dry matter analysis. JUNGK [1970] showed in the case of *Sinapis alba* that the content of K^+ and NO_3^- based on the fresh weight remains fairly constant throughout the growing season, provided that the plants are adequately supplied with these two nutrients. Fleshy fruits and storage organs also have high water contents as compared with seeds and grains. Comparisons of the mineral compositions of dried plant material obtained from fresh material samples with very different water contents must therefore be made with caution.

General Reading

CLARKSON, D.T. and HANSON, J.B.: The mineral nutrition of higher plants. Ann. Rev. Plant. Physiol. *31*, 239–298 (1980)

EPSTEIN, E.: Mineral Nutrition of Plants: Principles and Perspectives. John Wiley & Sons, Inc., New York, London, Sydney, Toronto 1972

FLEMING, G.A.: Mineral composition of herbage. In 'Chemistry and Biochemistry of Herbage' (G.W. Butler and R.W. Bailey, eds.) pp. 529–566. Academic Press, London, New York, San Francisco 1973

GAUCH, H.G.: Inorganic Plant Nutrition. Dowden Hutchinson and Ross Inc. Stroudburg, Pa. USA 1972

HEWITT, E.J. and SMITH, T.A.: Plant Mineral Nutrition. English University Press Ltd. London 1975

LÄUCHLI, A. and BIELESKI, R.L.: Encyclopedia of Plant Physiology, Vol. 12, Inorganic Plant Nutrition New Series. Springer Verlag Berlin, Heidelberg, New York 1982

SUTCLIFFE, J.F. and BAKER, D.: Plants and Mineral Salts. Edward Arnold 1981

WALLACE, A.: Current Topics in Plant Nutrition, Department of Agric. Sciences, U.C.L.A. Los Angeles, California, USA 1966

Chapter 2

The Soil as a Plant Nutrient Medium

2.1 Important Physico-Chemical Properties

2.1.1 General

Soil is a heterogeneous material which may be considered as consisting of three major components: a solid phase, a liquid phase and a gaseous phase. All three phases specifically influence the supply of plant roots with nutrients. The solid phase may be regarded as the main nutrient reservoir. The inorganic particles of the solid phase contain cationic nutrients such as K, Na, Ca, Mg, Fe, Mn, Zn, and Co, whilst the organic particles of this phase provide the main reserve of N and to a lesser extent also of P and S. The liquid phase of the soil, the soil solution, is mainly responsible for nutrient transport in the soil, *e.g.* for the transport of nutrients from various parts of the soil to plant roots. Nutrients transported in the liquid phase are mainly present in ionic form, but O_2 and CO_2 are also dissolved in the soil solution. The gaseous phase of the soil mediates in the gaseous exchange which occurs between the numerous living organisms of the soil (plant roots, bacteria, fungi, animals) and the atmosphere. This process results in the supply of living soil organisms with O_2 and the removal of CO_2 produced by respiration from the soil atmosphere. Nutrients in the solid, liquid and gaseous soil phases are closely interrelated. These relationships and their effects on nutrient availability are considered in more detail in this chapter.

2.1.2 Cation adsorption and exchange

Colloidal soil particles are mostly negatively charged. The negative charge on clay mineral surfaces arises largely because of isomorphous replacement of cations in the crystalline lattices where trivalent cations are substituted by divalent cations. Negative charges can also result from the dissociation of H^+ from weak acids. This is particularly important in producing negatively charged sites on organic soil particles.

The negatively charged surfaces of these various soil particles attract cations such as Ca^{2+}, Mg^{2+}, K^+ and Na^+ as well as Al^{3+} and Mn^{2+}. Cations electro-

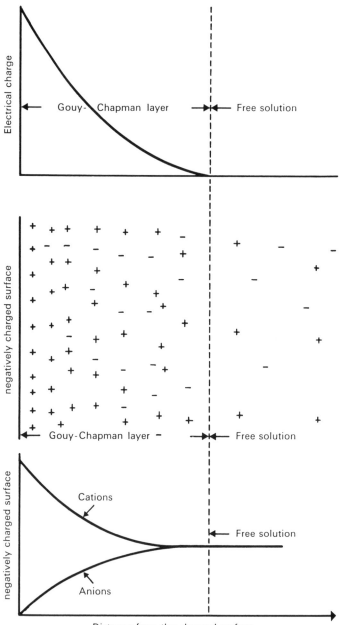

Fig. 2.1 Decline of the electrical field with increasing distance from a charged surface and the resulting ion distribution pattern (GOUY CHAPMANN-model).

statically adsorbed to the negatively charged surface of a clay particle dispersed in an electrolyte solution are subjected to both interionic (coulombic) and kinetic forces. Interionic forces tend to bind the cation tightly to the surface of the clay. On the other hand, kinetic forces in the form of thermal motion tend to dissociate cations from the surface. As a result of both these forces an electrical potential gradient is set up near the clay surface. On equilibrium a characteristic ion distribution pattern results between the clay lattice, exchangeable cations and free solution (Figure 2.1). In the immediate vicinity of the negatively charged surface there is a high concentration of cations, and the anion concentration is approximately zero. This is sometimes known as the Stern layer. With increasing distance from the colloid surface the cation concentration decreases at first rapidly and then asymptotically to the free solution where cation and anion concentrations are equal. In a reciprocal way the anion concentration increases from the surface to the outer solution. These effects are shown in the lower part of Figure 2.1. The double layer as described above contains an excess of cations and extends from the negatively charged surface to the free solution. It is known as the Gouy-Chapman layer as it was first described by these workers (GOUY [1910], CHAPMAN [1913]). Sometimes it is also referred to as the diffuse layer. Its thickness from the clay surface to the free solution is usually about 5–10 nm.

The equilibrium between ions of the diffuse double layer and the free solution is a dynamic one. Thus ions from the free solution are in rapid exchange equilibrium with ions in the Gouy-Chapman layer. When the concentration of the outer solution is diluted some ions from the diffuse double layer diffuse into the free solution thus causing a new equilibrium to be set up. Progressive dilution finally leads to a point at which the outer solution is free of ions and the total cations adsorbed to the surface are equivalent to the negative surface charge. This process occurs when a cation exchanger loaded with a salt solution is leached with water. Surplus cations and anions are washed off and finally only those cations are retained that are equivalent to the negative charge of the exchange capacity of the ion exchanger.

Cations adsorbed in the way described above can be replaced by other cation species. This reversible process usually occurring between the liquid and solid soil phases is called cation exchange. The principle of this exchange process, which is stoichiometric, is shown in Figure 2.2 where 1 Ca^{2+} is replaced by 2 K^+. Generally all cation species can exchange with each other in this way but the degree to which one cation can replace another depends on the strength of retention of the adsorbed cation. According to Coulomb's law, the interionic bond is stronger the closer the ionic partners are located, and varies inversely as the square of the distance between the charges. The binding is also stronger the higher the charge of ions. This means that trivalent cations are more strongly bound than divalent cations which in turn are more tightly held than monovalent cations. This preference increases the more dilute the system, and the higher the charge density of the clay. In addition the degree to which an ion is hydrated also influences the bonding strength. A hydrated cation can not be attracted so closely to the negatively charged surface of a clay mineral because of the presence of its hydration shell. Smaller cations have thicker hydration shells because they have a higher charge density and they are thus not so tightly bound to clay particles. Table 2.1 shows the diameters of several cations in a hydrated and nonhydrated form. Hydrogen ions do not conform to the rules of ion size and hydration largely because they induce clay breakdown with a subsequent release of Al^{3+}. The H^+ thus appears to behave as a slightly hydrated trivalent cation.

Cation species which are only weakly adsorbed can readily be exchanged and *vice versa*. Thus the relative replacing power of a particular cation species depends on its strength of binding. The following sequence of relative replacing power was established by HOFMEISTER (Hofmeister's cation sequence).

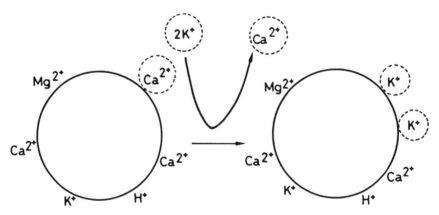

Fig.2.2 Principle of cation exchange. Ca^{2+} is replaced by 2 K.

Table 2.1 Diameter (nm) of hydrated and non-hydrated cations

	hydrated	non-hydrated
Rb^+..	0.51	0.30
K^+...	0.53	0.27
NH_4^+	0.54	0.29
Na^+..	0.76	0.20
Li^+	1.00	0.15
Mg^{2+}...	0.64	0.16
Ca^{2+}	0.56	0.21

$$Li^+ < Na^+ < K^+ < Rb^+ < Cs^+$$
$$Mg^{2+} < Ca^{2+} < Sr^{2+} < Ba^{2+}$$
$$\longrightarrow$$

Increase in the relative
replacing power
Decrease in the degree of hydration

This rule is not universally applicable as clay mineral structure also affects the binding power. This is particularly true for K^+ adsorption. SCHACHTSCHABEL [1940] investigating the release of NH_4^+ from various minerals by different chlorides observed the following sequence for the relative ease of displacement of cations.

Kaolinite	$Na^+ < H^+ < K^+ < Mg^{2+} < Ca^{2+}$
Montmorillonite	$Na^+ < K^+ < H^+ < Mg^{2+} < Ca^{2+}$
Micas	$Na^+ < Mg^{2+} < Ca^{2+} < K^+ < H^+$
Humic acid	$Na^+ < K^+ < Mg^{2+} < Ca^{2+} < H^+$

$$\longrightarrow$$

Increase in the relative ease of displacement of NH_4^+

This example demonstrates that K^+ is more strongly adsorbed by micas than can be predicted by its valency and degree of hydration. In a similar way other 2:1 clay minerals (illite, vermiculite) can also adsorb K^+ rather specifically. This is considered in more detail on page 414.

The relative replacing power of one cation species by another depends not only on the nature of the species in question but also on the concentrations or more precisely the activities of the ions present. For the sake of simplicity, ion concentrations are usually considered. It should be remembered, however, that ion activities rather than concentrations apply to exchange reactions and equilibrium conditions between adsorbed and free ions. When ion concentrations are low they approximate to their activities. At higher concentrations, however, deviation from the predicted behaviour of ideal solutions occurs. The osmotic pressure for example is lower than predicted by the concentration. Such deviations result because of interionic forces and the formation of associated ions in the solution under the higher concentration conditions. The concentration is therefore corrected by a factor (activity coefficient) which is always <1. The relationship is expressed by the equation:

$$a = f \cdot c$$

where a = activity

c = concentration

f = activity coefficient

The activity coefficient thus decreases as the ionic strength of the solution increases.

The influence of increasing activity or concentration on the replacement of one cation species by another may be considered by reference to a simple system where one cation species completely saturating a colloidal particle is being replaced by an increasing concentration of another cation species in the bathing solution. If K^+ is the ion originally saturating the colloid and Ca^{2+} the ion replacing K^+, the relationship between Ca^{2+} adsorption, K^+ desorption and Ca^{2+} activity may be represented as shown in Figure 2.3. It is clear that as the concentration or activity of free Ca^{2+} increases, the adsorption of Ca^{2+} also increases in the form of a saturation or exchange curve. This can be described in another way by saying that the lower the concentration of the replacing ion, the greater is its replacing power in relation to its concentration. This relationship between activity or concentration and adsorption as reflected in the asymptotic curve shown is applicable to all cation adsorption processes.

In the example cited above a monovalent cation (K^+) was replaced by a diva-

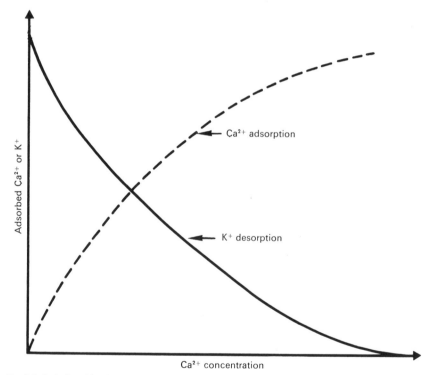

Fig. 2.3 Relationship between increasing Ca^{2+} concentration, Ca^{2+} adsorption and K^+ desorption.

lent cation (Ca^{2+}) or in other words a strongly bound cation (Ca^{2+}) replaced a less strongly bound cation (K^+). Exchange processes also occur, however, where a more strongly adsorbed cation species is replaced by a cation species which is on average less strongly adsorbed. Such exchanges occur due to the fact that kinetic as well as electrostatic forces act upon the ions. As already discussed, provided there are no specific adsorption sites on the charged surface, the binding strength of a cation species depends on its valency and on its degree of hydration. This is true, where the mean behaviour of a large number of ions is being considered as is usually the case. The relative replacing power of a single ion, however, depends on its kinetic energy. This is not the same for all ions of a given species. When a large number of ions are present, energy distribution follows the Maxwell energy distribution curve. This means that for every cation species a small proportion of so called 'high energy' cations occur which can take place in exchange reactions not open to the bulk of other ions. In the cation exchange process the energy distribution of cations is thus of particular significance as it enables the replacement of cations more strongly bound by those which are on average more weakly bound. Thus Ca^{2+} can be replaced from a clay mineral or ion exchanger by a highly hydrated monovalent cation such as Na^+, as some Na^+ is always present at a high enough energy level to replace Ca^{2+}. In order to achieve complete replacement of the more strongly bound cation, however, large amounts of the more weakly bound cation species are required. This is the principle which underlies the regeneration of a cation exchange column where the column is treated with a large excess of a replacing cation species, so that 'high energy' cations are also present in excess. In this context it should be remembered that cations are not bound tightly to the surface, but are present as a diffuse layer which facilitates exchange processes based on the individual energy levels of the cations.

Soils may differ much in their capability to adsorb cations. The so called cation exchange capacity (CEC) is a measure of the total negative charge of a soil and is expressed in terms of equivalents or more precisely milli equivalents per 100 g soil. A milli equivalent (me) is defined as 1 mg of hydrogen or the amount of any other ion that will combine with it or displace it. In the case of K^+ this would be 39 mg of K since the atomic weight of K is 39 and its valency is one i.e. one K^+ can exchange with one H^+. For Ca^{2+} (atomic wt. 40), the corresponding value is 20 mg Ca since $2H^+$ are required to displace one Ca^{2+}. Thus if 100 g soil had the following combination of adsorbed ions: 1 me Na^+, 1 me K^+, 20 me Ca^{2+}, 2 me Mg^{2+}, and 5 me H^+, it is clear that all these ions could be replaced by the sum expressed in $H^+ = 29$ me H^+. As it is possible to determine this value in practice without determining the individual elements, the milli equivalent (me) is normally used in soil analysis.

Exchangeable cations are commonly subdivided according to whether they are basic or acidic. The basic cations include Na^+, K^+, Mg^{2+}, and Ca^{++}. The acidic cations are H^+, and Al^{3+}. Thus

$$CEC = TEB + EA$$

where

CEC = Cation Exchange Capacity, me/100 g soil
TEB = Total Exchangeable Bases, me/100 g soil (Na^+, K^+, Mg^{2+}, Ca^{2+})
EA = Exchangeable Acidity, me/100 g soil (Al^{3+}, H^+)

Sometimes the term percentage base saturation is used. This represents the total exchangeable bases expressed as a percentage of the cation exchange capacity.

As the proportion of clay in a soil increases the soil system becomes more dispersed and hence the total surface area of soil particles is also increased. This means that soils rich in clay minerals are able to adsorb more water and cations than soils low in clay. Clay rich soils have thus a higher cation exchange capacity and a higher water holding capacity than soils low in clay. Cation exchange capacity values can vary considerably. BRADY [1974] gives values from 2.0 in a sand to 57.5 me/100 g in a clay soil. Values between 10 and 20 me/100 g soil are common.

2.1.3 The Gapon equation

One of the most well known equations which quantitatively describes mono-divalent cation exchange is the Gapon equation (GAPON [1933]). This may be described as follows:

$$\frac{C^+_{ads}}{C^{2+}_{ads}} = k \frac{a_c^+}{\sqrt{a_{c^{2+}}}} \; ;$$

$$\frac{a_c^+}{\sqrt{a_{c^{2+}}}} = AR$$

where

C^+_{ads}, C^{2+}_{ads} = adsorbed monovalent and divalent cations respectively
a_{c^+}, $a_{c^{2+}}$ = activity of the monovalent and divalent cations respectively (M/l)
AR = Activity ratio = ratio of the activities of the two cation species in the equilibrium solution. For a monovalent and divalent cation species, this is the ratio of the activity of the monovalent cation over the square root of the activity of the divalent cation.

The equation thus enables the ratio of the amounts of adsorbed cations to be related to the activity ratio. The value of k is a measure with which C^+ is adsorbed in comparison with C^{2+}. This could for example be K^+/Ca^{2+} or K^+/Mg^{2+}. For a given exchange system k is constant within limits, and various authors have used the equation to describe quantitative relationships between cations in adsorbed and equilibrium solution forms (BOLT [1955], LAGERWERFF and BOLT [1959], EHLERS *et al.* [1968]). The use of the Gapon equation by the US SALINITY LABORATORY for the expression of cation exchange studies in saline and alkaline soils has also meant that the equation is fairly well accepted for the prediction of adsorbed ions and solution composition of these soils (FRIED and BROESHART [1969]).

It was originally held that k should be constant. This value, however, is dependent on a number of factors including the degree of cation saturation of the clay mineral and its charge density (SCHWERTMANN [1962]). It is also considerably influenced by clay mineral structure and the presence of specific binding sites. Such specific sites particularly relate to the binding of K^+ and NH_4^+ to the 2:1 clay minerals. Where for example, K^+ is specifically adsorbed, the Gapon 'constant' for K^+/Ca^{2+} and K^+/Mg^{2+} exchange is higher (see p. 415). Because of the effects described above and the fact that k is not a constant, selectivity coefficient or Gapon coefficient are also used to describe k.

From the Gapon equation a further concept can be appreciated. This may be explained by the reference to a simple numerical example. If in the equation the two cation species C^+ and C^{2+} were Na^+ and Ca^{2+} respectively, with concentrations of $Na^+ = 1 \cdot 10^{-3}M$ and $Ca^{2+} = 3.6 \cdot 10^{-3}M$, the equation would read:

$$\frac{Na^+_{ads}}{Ca^{2+}_{ads}} = k \frac{1 \cdot 10^{-3}}{\sqrt{3.6 \cdot 10^{-3}}} = k \frac{10 \cdot 10^{-4}}{\sqrt{36 \cdot 10^{-4}}} = k \cdot \frac{1}{60}$$

Na^+_{ads} = adsorbed Na^+

Ca^{2+}_{ads} = adsorbed Ca^{2+}

A change in the concentration of cations in the equilibrium solution so that $Na^+ = 2 \cdot 10^{-3}M$ and $Ca^{2+} = 14.4 \cdot 10^{-3}M$ (*i.e.* by doubling the monovalent and multiplying the divalent concentration values by 4) would not alter the right part of the equation as

$$\frac{2 \cdot 10^{-3}}{\sqrt{14.4 \ 10^{-3}}} = \frac{2 \cdot 10^{-3}}{\sqrt{144 \cdot 10^{-4}}} = \frac{2 \cdot 10^{-3}}{12 \cdot 10^{-2}} = \frac{1}{60}$$

The use of activities rather than concentrations would have been more precise in this simplified example. However, the principal conclusion remains the same, namely that different concentrations of cations in the equilibrium solution may be associated with the same ratio of adsorbed cations. This finding was developed by (SCHOFIELD [1947]) and is called the ratio law. SCHOFIELD wrote: 'When cations in a solution are in equilibrium with a larger number of exchangeable ions, a change in the concentration of the solution will not disturb the equilibrium if the concentrations of the monovalent ions are changed in one ratio, those of all divalent ions in the square of that ratio and those of all trivalent ions in the cube of that ratio.'

2.1.4 Anion adsorption

The anion adsorption capacity of most agricultural soils is relatively small as compared with the cation adsorption capacity. However, a number of soil minerals and also amorphous soil colloids are capable of adsorbing anions very strongly. These anion adsorbers include hydrous Fe and Al oxides (haematite, goethite, gibbsite, amorphous hydroxides), 1:1 clay minerals, 2:1 clay minerals, Fe and Al organo complexes and Ca carbonates. Surface AlOH and FeOH groups are particularly important sites for anion adsorption occurring on both inorganic and organic complexes e.g. humic acids and fulvic acids. Soils rich in hydrous oxides with high surface areas are particularly efficient in anion adsorption.

Two kinds of adsorption may be distinguished, ligand exchange with OH groups and adsorption to protonated groups (PARFITT [1978]). Ligand exchange may be described in a very simplified way by the equation:

$$Me - OH + An^- \rightleftarrows Me - An + OH^-$$

Phosphate (and sulphate) adsorption by a number of Fe oxides appears to be brought about by binuclear rather than mononuclear surface bridging (ATKINSON et al. [1972], PARFITT and SMART [1978]). In this reaction two Fe atoms are involved in adsorbing one phosphate anion and a Fe(III) phosphate complex is formed. This is shown in a simplified manner below:

$$
\begin{array}{c}
| \\
Fe \\
|\ - OH \\
Fe - OH \\
|
\end{array}
+
\begin{array}{c}
HO \\ \diagdown \\ \diagup \\ {}^-O
\end{array}
P
\begin{array}{c}
\diagup\!\diagup O \\ \diagdown \\ OH
\end{array}
\rightarrow
\begin{array}{c}
| \\
Fe - O \\
| \\
Fe - O \\
|
\end{array}
\begin{array}{c}
\diagdown \\ \diagup
\end{array}
P
\begin{array}{c}
\diagup\!\diagup O \\ \diagdown \\ OH
\end{array}
+ OH^- + H_2O
$$

The second kind of adsorption mechanism, that of adsorption to protonated groups, occurs under low pH conditions. Here OH groups may become protonated (positively charged) thus allowing anion adsorption by electrostatic interaction.

34

$$\text{Me OH} + \text{H}^+ \rightarrow \left[\text{Me O}\begin{smallmatrix}\text{H}\\[2pt]\text{H}\end{smallmatrix}\right]^+$$

$$\left[\text{Me O}\begin{smallmatrix}\text{H}\\[2pt]\text{H}\end{smallmatrix}\right]^+ + \text{An}^- \rightarrow \left[\text{Me O}\begin{smallmatrix}\text{H}\\[2pt]\text{H}\end{smallmatrix}\right]^+ \text{An}^-$$

Both processes of ligand exchange and protonation are extremely pH dependent being enhanced when the H^+ concentration is raised. Highest anion exchange capacities are thus found in acid soils rich in hydrous Fe and Al oxides or in clay minerals or in both.

The two mechanisms described above for anion adsorption differ in anion specificity. Anion adsorption to protonated groups largely involves an electrostatic interaction and as such is almost totally nonspecific. Ligand exchange on the other hand is associated with a chemical interaction in which an anion becomes coordinated to a metal ion, and is for this reason much more anion specific. The pronounced specificity of anions in ligand exchange reactions is responsible for the marked differences in adsorption capacity of soils for specific anions. Phosphate which is largely adsorbed by ligand exchange is a very strongly adsorbed anion. On the other hand for nitrate and chloride where ligand exchange plays little if any role, these anions are only weakly adsorbed. PARFITT [1978] gives the probable selectivity order of anion adsorption by a soil as phosphate > arsenate > selenite = molybdate > sulphate = fluoride > chloride > nitrate.

Other anions than those mentioned above may participate in exchange reactions. Under high pH conditions boric and silicic acids may form anions.

$$H_3BO_3 + H_2O \rightarrow B(OH)_4^- + H^+$$
$$H_2SiO_3 + H_2O \rightarrow H_3SiO_4^- + H^+$$

In addition some organic anions may also compete in adsorption.

The Langmuir equation is frequently used to describe quantitative relationships in anion adsorption. This is expressed mathematically as:

$$\frac{A}{A_{max}} = \frac{K \cdot c}{1 + Kc}$$

where

A	= amount of ion adsorbed
A_{max}	= the sorption maximum
c	= solution concentration
K	= constant related to adsorption energy and is higher the stronger the adsorption.

The relationship is shown graphically in Figure 2.4. The equation is not completely obeyed for anion adsorption by soil particles since the Langmuir model is derived for monolayer gas adsorption on to solid surfaces. In anion adsorption both a charged particle and charged surface are involved. Additionally adsorption is associated with chemical reactions. Adsorption is also dependent on pH and salt conditions as both these factors affect A_{max} and K (BOWDEN et al. [1977]). As an approximate measure, however, the Langmuir equation is a valuable tool in quantifying anion adsorption processes and has been used by a number of workers including HOLFORD and MATTINGLY [1975] who investigated phosphate adsorption on calcite surfaces.

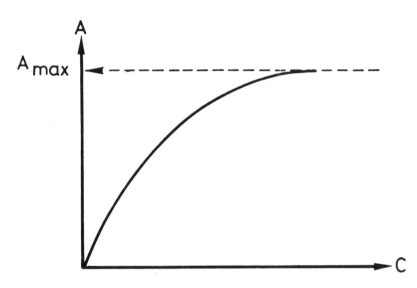

Fig.2.4 Relationship between solution concentration (c) and adsorption (A) according to the Langmuir equation.

2.1.5 Water adsorption

Dipolar molecules are also bound to surfaces. The forces which bring about adsorption, however, are van der Waal's forces. This kind of adsorption therefore differs fundamentally from cation or anion adsorption to charged surfaces, as the adsorbed molecules are not so strongly bound and there is no strong equivalency between the surface charge and the quantity of adsorbed molecules. This indicates an absence of quantitative exchange between adsorbed and free molecules. An example of this type has already been mentioned in the adsorption of water molecules by charged surfaces in ion hydration (see p. 28).

The most important example of adsorption of this kind is the adsorption of water to various particles such as clay minerals or organic matter in the soil or to protein complexes in cells. The asymmetric water molecule is a dipolar molecule, having a negative zone or side associated with the O-atom and a positive zone or side associated with the H-atoms. A negatively charged surface such as provided by a clay mineral attracts the positive sites of the water molecules and binds them strongly to its surface. The first adsorbed monomolecular layer of water molecules thus exposes another negatively charged surface. This again attracts more water molecules thus forming a series of layers of water molecules over the clay surface. The water layer in direct contact with the surface is most strongly bound. Adsorption strength decreases with increasing distance of the water layer from the adsorbing surface.

Films of water built up in the way described above are bound to soil particles and to particles in living cells. The pressure by which the first monolayer of water is held to the surface may amount to 10^3 to 10^4 bar.

Molecular adsorption of water is temperature dependent. The higher the temperature, the more thermal energy can be transferred to the adsorbed molecules. By increasing temperature a point is thus reached when the energy becomes high enough to dissociate molecules from the adsorbing surface into the vapour phase. This is one reason why soils dry out more rapidly under high temperature conditions. In this respect molecular adsorption differs basically from ion adsorption, which under soil conditions is largely independent of changes in temperature.

2.1.6 Colloidal systems

All the processes described above, involve reactions between diffusible particles (ions, molecules) and surfaces. The significance of these surface reactions is greater the larger the exposed surface area. The ratio between the surface area and the bulk of a material depends on the degree of its dispersion. Smaller particles clearly expose a relatively larger surface area. In systems made up of extremely small particles, surface forces play a dominant role. Such systems are called colloidal systems, the particles of which have a diameter in the order of 0.1–10 μm. The main feature of colloidal systems is not the composition of the particles but rather the degree to which the particles are dispersed. A colloidal system consists of a disperse phase, made up of the small particles, and dispersion medium, which can be a gas or a liquid. In soils, colloidal systems are mainly made up of clay minerals dispersed in water. Water too is the dispersion medium in plant tissues but here proteins and polysaccharides represent the disperse phase. When the particles of the disperse phase of a colloidal system are discrete and homogeneously dispersed throughout the dispersion medium the system is called a sol. If the dispersed phase is in a coagulated state it is called a gel. In many cases colloidal systems are reversible. This means that they can be converted from sol to gel and *vice versa*.

Colloidal particles in the sol form are all either negatively or positively charged, so that individual particles electrostatically repel each other. The disperse phase can thus remain in suspension and the system does not coagulate. In a system with water as the dispersion medium, the particles are surrounded by a hydration shell because of their electrical charge, and this also prevents coagulation. As a rule negatively charged particles can be neutralized by the addition of cations and particularly by H^+. Positively charged colloidal particles can be neutralized by the addition of anions, and especially by OH^-. As soon as the charge of the particles is neutralized they lose their water shell, aggregate together and coagulation occurs. This type of reaction means that the stability of a sol depends on the pH of the surrounding medium. Other ion species are also capable of coagulating colloidal systems. The extent of coagulation depends on the valency and the degree of hydration of the ion species concerned. As described above, in water systems ions are adsorbed in hydrated form. Highly hydrated ions as for example Na^+ cannot therefore be closely bound to the surface of colloidal particles because the water shell of the ion and the water layer of the surface prevent the close approach of the opposing charges. The neutralizing effect between the ion and the oppositely charged colloidal surface is thus weak. The colloidal particle, therefore, retains a relatively high amount of its charge and for this reason repels other colloidal particles, and coagulation does not occur.

In contrast, ions with a higher valency and a thinner water shell, *e.g.* Ca^{2+}, are adsorbed closely to the charged surface. They thus tend to neutralize the colloidal particles and lose their water shell; coagulation occurs and a gel system is formed. This takes place in the soil and has a very important bearing on soil structure (see p. 43). When Ca^{2+} ions are removed by leaching or exchanged by other ion species as occurs in the soil, the gel shifts over to a sol state. This transition from a gel into a sol condition is called peptization (derived from pepsin, which brings coagulated proteins into solution in the stomach). As already indicated an increase in valency enhances coagulation. According to SCHULZE-HARDY the relative coagulating capability of $Na^+:Ca^{2+}:Al^{3+}$ is in the ratios of $1:20:350$. Coagulation also increases at higher ion concentrations. This means that even ions which do not readily coagulate can induce coagulation if present in high enough concentrations. This occurs because a high ionic concentration in the vicinity of the colloidal particle surface disturbs the surface water shell and can induce neutralization. It is for this reason that proteins can be coagulated by $(NH_4)_2SO_4$.

2.2 Important Soil Characteristics

2.2.1 Soil texture and clay minerals

The solid phase of the soil is made up of inorganic and organic components. The inorganic fraction consists of particles of different sizes which range from clay ($<2\mu$ m) to silt (2 μm to 50 μm) to sand (50 μm to 2 mm) to gravel (2 mm to 2 cm) to rocks. The relative proportions of these particles determines the texture of a given soil. This soil property is of extreme importance in determining the physical behaviour of the soil (see p. 48). In addition, however, it is also very closely related to nutrient status and nutrient availability, since many plant nutrients *e.g.* K^+, Mg^{2+}, phosphate, are largely present in the clay fraction.

The most important clay minerals in soils are the layer silicates. The basic molecular building blocks of these minerals are the tetrahedron and octahedron (see figure 2.5). Tetrahedra linked together in the same plane form a tetrahedral sheet and in an analogous manner octahedra form an octahedral sheet. The tetrahedron consists of four closely packed equally spaced oxygen atoms surrounding one centrally situated atom which is usually Si. A pyramidal structure is thus formed. The octahedral structure (8 faced structure) is made up of 6 OH^- groups coordinated around a central cation. Generally the centre of the octahedron is occupied by an Al^{3+} although Mg^{2+} and Fe^{2+} may also function as central atoms of the octahedron. Sometimes this central atom may be absent.

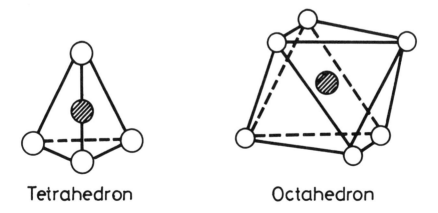

Tetrahedron   Octahedron

Fig.2.5 Tetrahedron and octahedron, structural elements of clay minerals.

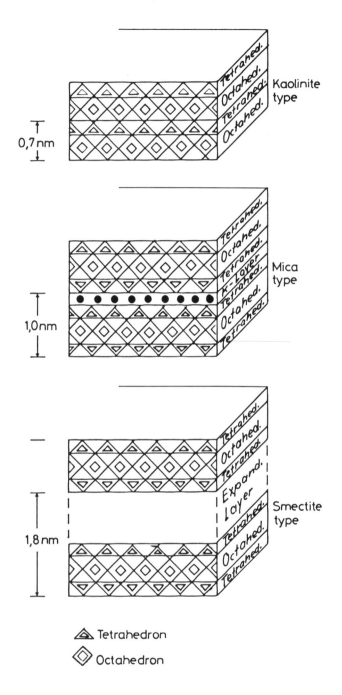

Fig. 2.6 Schematic presentation of 3 main clay mineral types.

Three major types of silicates are represented by kaolinite, mica and smectite. The clay mineral kaolinite is made up of one tetrahedral layer alternating with one octahedral layer and is hence termed 1 : 1 type crystal lattice (see Figure 2.6). Both layers form the 'unit layer' with a basal spacing between the unit layers of 0.72 nm. The tetrahedral and octahedral layers are strongly bound to each other by mutually shared O-atoms, each unit being firmly attached to the next by oxygen hydroxyl linkages. There is thus little possibility of expansion and water and cations can not move between the units.

The micas differ from kaolinite in that the unit layers are made up of two tetrahedral layers with an octahedral layer held between them (see Figure 2.6) by mutually shared O-atoms. This structure is typical of the 2 : 1 clay minerals A high negative charge occurs in the tetrahedral layer which is satisfied by K^+. This K^+ which is present in a non hydrated form binds the 2 : 1 unit layers strongly together and thus forms an integral component of the mica. The basal spacing between the unit layers is 1.0 nm.

The smectite (montmorillonite) group also has a 2 : 1 structure. The unit layers, however, are only weakly held together by hydrated cations especially Ca^{2+}. Water and cations can thus readily be absorbed by these inner surfaces and the mineral can shrink and expand with the basal spacing varying from 1 to > 4 nm. The area of the inner surfaces of this group of minerals exceeds the external surface area. The basal spacing of the fully hydrated Ca^{2+} forms which occur predominantly in soils is 1.9 nm.

Other 2 : 1 clay minerals include vermiculite (see Figure 10.1) with a unit layer distance of 1.4 nm, and illite. Illite is derived from mica and closely related to it. Illites do not have a homogenous structure. Indeed large areas of the mineral can have a similar structure to mica in which the unit layers are held together by K^+. At the edges, however, and also sometimes within this mineral, the layers can be expanded forming 'wedge zones' (see Figure 10.2) to which other cations than K^+ are adsorbed (SCHROEDER [1978]). The area of inner surfaces is comparatively smaller than that of the smectite group. The properties of these three major types of silicates are shown in Table 2.2.

The negative charge of clay minerals arises by isomorphic substitution as occurs when for example Mg^{2+} replaces Al^{3+} in the octahedral layer. In addition at exposed crystal edges negative charges may be present representing unsatisfied valences at the broken edges of tetrahedral and octahedral sheets.

The allophanes are an example of amorphous clay particles, and constitute the most important clay fraction of the so called 'anda soils' of South America. Like kaolinite, the allophanes only have 'outer surfaces'. Their cation adsorption is thus also non specific. Both allophane and kaolinite minerals

Table 2.2 Comparative properties of three major types of silicate clay (after BRADY [1974])

Property	Type of clay		
	Smectite	Illite	Kaolinite
Size (μm)	0.01–1.0	0.1–2.0	0.1–5.0
Shape	Irregular flakes	Irregular flakes	Hexagonal crystals
Specific surface (m²/g)	700–800	100–120	5–20
External surface	High	Medium	Low
Internal surface	Very high	Medium	None
Cohesion, plasticity	High	Medium	Low
Swelling capacity	High	Medium	Low
Cation exchange capacity (me/100 g)	80–100	15–40	3–15

are rather high in Al in relation to Si content, and this again induces strong phosphate adsorption in soils rich in these clay minerals.

The cation adsorption of a soil results not only from inorganic particles but also from organic matter (humic acids). The cation exchange sites of organic matter are mainly carboxylic and phenolic groups (SCHNITZER and SKINNER [1965]). These groups, when present in the dissociated form are able to adsorb cations. The adsorption is non specific and follows the Hofmeister cation sequence (see p. 28). Divalent cations are therefore preferentially adsorbed to monovalent cations. In this respect the behaviour of H^+ is exceptional because the binding of H^+ to these groups represents the formation of a chemical bond. The cation exchange capacity of the humic acids is in the range of 200–400 me/100 g. Compared with that of the clay minerals this seems very high. This exchange capacity, however, is based on weight and as the density of the organic matter is considerably lower than that of the clay minerals, organic soils *in situ* often do not have such a high cation exchange capacity as soils rich in clay. In humic mineral soils often about 50% of the exchange capacity is made up by organic matter in the surface layer. As shown in Table 2.3, however, soil organic matter levels can differ considerably depending on soil type and prevailing climatic conditions. The contribution of organic matter to the cation exchange capacity of soils can thus also vary substantially between soils.

Table 2.3 Content of organic matter in various soil types

Soil Types	% org. m. based on weight
Mineral soils	< 2%
Humic soils	2–15%
Anmoor peat	15–30%
Peat soils	> 30%

2.2.2 Soil structure

Soil structure may be defined as the arrangement of soil particles into groups or aggregates (BRADY [1974]). The capability of the soil to form aggregates, the size and shape of aggregates, and the stability of the aggregates produced is closely related to the colloid content of the soil. Light textured soils low in soil colloids are structureless as the coarse sand material does not form aggregates.

The higher the clay content the more important is soil structure. Clay minerals adsorb water which causes swelling of the soil. Swelling and shrinkage depend on the water available. Thus clay soils swell under wet conditions and shrink under dry conditions producing cracks and fissures in the profile. This behaviour is typical of soils rich in montmorillonite as this clay mineral readily adsorbs water. An example of soils in which clay swelling and drying occurs are the tropical black earths. These soils have a high clay content consisting almost exclusively of montmorillonite. In the wet season they swell and become sticky whereas in the dry season they dry out to such an extent that they become rock-hard and crack. Despite the high nutrient status of these soils the poor structure thus limits their agricultural potential because they are so difficult to work.

Shape and particle size depend to a large extent on the type of clay minerals present in the soil. Montmorillonite clays tend to produce prismatic angular structures whereas kaolinite and hydrous oxides are associated with more granular aggregates.

The stability of the aggregates depends mainly on the cations adsorbed to the soil colloids. Poor structure occurs where Na^+ is dominant in the exchange complex, as it has a dispersing effect and aggregation of soil particles is prevented. As pointed out on p. 38 divalent cations are very effective in bringing about flocculation or coagulation of soil particles. By this process smaller particles are bound together forming stable aggregates of different sizes. These aggregates from a structure containing a high proportion of pore space which can be occupied by air or water. When about 40–50% of the soil volume consists of pore space this is considered as a good structure for plant growth. Such a soil is able to store water and air and can readily be penetrated by plant roots.

In soil structure, Ca plays an important role. Due to its flocculating ability it contributes to the formation of stable aggregates with clay minerals. In combination with humic acids and clay minerals Ca also forms very stable organo-mineral complexes (SCHACHTSCHABEL [1967]). This is the reason why Ca saturation of montmorillonitic and illitic soils should be in the order of 60–80% of the exchange capacity. The corresponding value for kaolinitic soils is only about 20%

(BROYER and STOUT [1959]). These soils generally contain substantial amounts of hydrous oxides which are even more effective than Ca^{2+} in flocculation.

The cation saturation of soil colloids depends much on soil type and prevailing climatic conditions. This is shown in Table 2.4, in which cation saturation is compared in three very different soil types. In the alkali soil the soil colloids are saturated by a high proportion of alkali cations and by Na^+ in particular. Such soils obviously have a poor structure (see p. 62). The cation saturation of the chernozem soil represents and ideal situation where Ca^{2+} is the dominant cation. The particularly good granular crumb structure of these soils is well known. In the podzol H^+ and Al^{3+} ions are present in excess of other cation species. This is also detrimental to soil structure.

Table 2.4 Percentage proportions of various cations saturating the soil colloids of different soil types (HOAGLAND [1948])

Soil	Climate	Na^+	K^+	Mg^{2+}	Ca^{2+}	H^+
Alkali soils................................	arid	30	15	20	35	0
Chernozem	semi-arid	2	7	14	73	4
Podzol	humid	trace	3	10	20	67

Soil structure also depends on the vegetative cover. Under permanent grassland in particular very good soil structures occur. This results from the effect of the high organic matter content and soil fauna. In this respect the earthworm contributes considerably to the formation of stable aggregates. Arable soils are often lower in organic matter and soil fauna and for this reason often are poorer in soil structure. A useful discussion on soil structure has been presented by CROMPTON [1958].

2.2.3 Soil water

The availability of water to plants depends generally on two major soil factors. These are the total water content and its distribution within the soil profile, and the extent to which the water present is bound to soil particles. The degree to which water is bound to soil particles is expressed as soil water tension or in modern terminology as soil water potential. Water tension is generally measured in terms of pF. In this concept the suction is expressed in terms of the height (cm) of a water column the pressure of which is equal to the suction. Thus a high column is associated with a strong suction and *vice versa*. The pF value equals the common logarithm of the height of the water column measured in cm. A water column of 10 cm thus has a pF of 1. pF values are positive values in contrast to water potential values which usually are negative.

The concept of water potential has been introduced as a basic means of describing water status and water movement. The concept is particularly useful in allowing a uniform treatment of soil and plant water relations. It is considered in more detail on page 185. In this context it need only be mentioned that the water potential of a soil mainly depends on water adsorption (matric forces) and in saline soils also on the electrolytic concentration of the soil solution (osmotic forces). Water in a free state has a high water potential (zero). This is depressed when water is adsorbed or when the presence of solutes dilutes the 'water concentration'. Water flows from a higher to a lower water potential.

Water potential is expressed in terms of bar. Pure water at atmospheric pressure has a water potential of 0 bar. Water bound at a tension of pF 3 is equivalent to a suction pressure of 1 bar (1 kg/cm^2). Such water has a water potential of -1 bar. Common water potentials in soils are in a range of -0.1 to -1.0 bar. The relationship between pF and bars is given by the equation

$$-bar = 10^{pF-3}$$

To a large extent water supply to plants is regulated by water retention and water movement in the soil. As already described the water holding capacity rises as the contents of inorganic and organic colloids increase. Water can be retained by small and medium sized pores. Soil structure thus directly affects the water holding capacity of a soil. VEIHMEYER and HENDRICKSON [1931] defined the term field capacity as 'the amount of water held in the soil after the excess gravitational water has drained away and after the rate of downward movement of the water has materially decreased'. The technique of measurement of the field capacity is to saturate a soil completely with water so that all pores are water filled and then to allow the soil to drain off for a period of about two to three days under conditions where no evaporation occurs. The amount of water remaining in the soil represents the field capacity. This is expressed as a percentage of water in the dry weight or volume of the soil. If for example the soil contains 200 g water per kg dry soil the field capacity is 20%. For organic soils measurement by volume is preferable because of the high water holding capacity and the low density of the dry soil. Field capacity gives an indication of the storage potential of a soil for water. This corresponds to the capability of a soil to supply plants with water during dry seasons.

The supply of plants with water does not only depend on the field capacity but also on the strength by which water is adsorbed to the soil particles. As already pointed out on p. 37, water layers directly adjacent to the adsorbing surfaces may be bound by forces as high as 6000 bar. The strength of water binding is called water tension or suction tension, due to the fact that water is actually sucked to the surface of soil particles. Water present at field capacity includes adsorption water and water held in the capillary soil pores. This latter fraction is termed capillary water and the intensity by which it is held depends on the diameter of the pores. As the diameter decreases the water binding or suction tension becomes stronger (Table 2.5). Pores with a diameter in excess of 0.05 mm are too large to retain water after the soil has been brought to field capacity and they are termed non capillary pores. The forces binding capillary water are related to the adsorption of water molecules to the walls of the pores and the cohesive forces by which the water molecules are attracted to each other. As a result of adsorption and cohesive forces water in a soil can rise in the same way as water in a capillary tube. The height of the capillary rise increases as the diameter of the capillary becomes smaller. This capillary rise of water is of importance in the water supply of plants particularly when the water has to be transported from the deeper soil layers.

Table 2.5 Relationship between the diameter of soil pores and the suction tension of the water held in the pores (DE BOODT and DE LEENHEER [1955])

Size of Pores	Diameter in μm	Suction Tension pF
Coarse	> 50	< 1.8
Medium	50–10	1.8–2.5
Fine	10–0.2	2.5–4.2
Very fine	< 0.2	> 4.2

Plants growing in soil first absorb weakly bound water. This is the fraction with the lowest tension (low pF value) and which is most available. As water is taken up, the remaining soil water becomes progressively less available as it is more strongly held. Thus as a soil dries out the water availability declines finally reaching a point at which the water is so strongly held by adsorption that plant roots are not able to utilize it, and plants growing in the soil begin to wilt. The water potential at which wilting occurs is called the wilting point. One may distinguish between a temporary wilting point and a permanent wilting point. In the former case plants are able to recover when water is supplied to the soil, whereas when the permanent wilting point has been reached wilting is irreversible and the plant dies. The wilting point can not be precisely defined in terms of water potential or water content of the soil. Generally, however, for many plant species the permanent wilting point is reached when the water potential is in the order of about −10 to −15 bar. The exact value depends on plant species and environmental conditions.

Water which is bound by forces corresponding water potentials lower than −10 to −15 bar is thus not available to plants. The maximum amount of available water which a soil can contain is therefore the difference between the water at field capacity and the water fraction held by forces higher than −10 bar. It is clear that soils containing high amounts of clay and thus having a high surface area capable of adsorption, also contain appreciable amounts of water which is unavailable to plants.

The relationship between water content (%) and water potential (bar) is shown in Figure 2.7 for a clay soil and a silt loam soil. In the clay soil the fall in water potential from −0,2 to −0.8 bar is associated with only a small decrease in soil water content. Even at the very low water potential of −15 bar (wilting point), 26% of the water is unavailable to the plant. For the silt loam soil the relationship between soil water content and soil water potential is quite different. The drop in water potential is accompanied by a substantial decrease in soil water content and at a water potential of −15 bar the soil water content amounts to only 8%. This shows that the water in the silt loam can be depleted by plant uptake to a much higher degree than the water in the clay soil (HEATHERLY and RUSSELL [1979]).

The amount of available water that can be stored by soils is that water held between the permanent wilting point (−15 bar) and the field capacity (−0.1 bar). From Figure 2.7 it can be calculated that the storage capacity of available

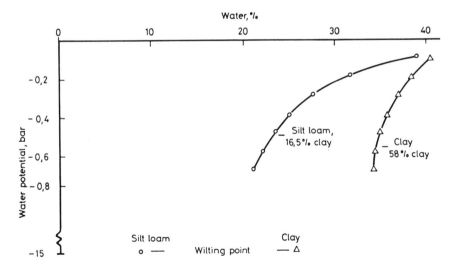

Fig. 2.7 Relationship between the water content (%) and the water potential (bar) of a clay soil and a silt loam soil (according to data of HEATHERLY and RUSSELL [1979]).

water is much higher in the silt loam soil than in the clay soil. In the latter, total water storage capacity is high, but only a small proportion of the storage water is available for plants. In sandy soils the reverse is true. Water storage capacity is low, but most of the stored water is available.

In addition to the water content and water tension in the soil, water movement also plays an important role in the water supply of plants. Downward movement caused by gravity occurs only when the upper soil layers have higher water contents than field capacity. This downward movement brings about the leaching of nutrients into the deeper soil layers and out of the profile. This excess water is usually of no great importance in plant nutrition. The upward movement of liquid water in the soil, as already described, results from capillary forces. Generally in coarse textured soils a substantial fraction of the pores are of large diameter, whereas in fine textured soils there is a higher proportion of smaller pores. The rise in water brought about by larger pores is generally more rapid but the height to which the water rises is lower than in soils containing smaller pores. This relationship was observed by WOLLNY [1885] in the last century.

This finding is of practical importance. Medium textured soils are able to transport water from the ground water table to the upper layers of the soil more readily than sandy soils. On the other hand, in fine textured soils (clay soils) the capillary rise from the ground water is often so slow that it is unable to meet the water demands of plants. Because of the higher capillary rise of water in medium textured soils relatively deep ground water may form part of the water supply of crops growing in these soils.

Water supply to plants only becomes critical when the water content of the soil is considerably below field capacity. The amount of water which becomes accessible to plants under these conditions by interception as roots force their way through the soil is relatively low in relation to the total demand. Water has therefore to be transported to the plant roots. Capillary water rise and the lateral movement of water due to capillary action are thus of importance.

2.2.4 Soil atmosphere

The composition of soil air differs from that of the atmosphere. The CO_2 level of the atmosphere by volume is about 0.03% whereas in the soil it is higher and in the order of 0.2–1% in the surface layers. Soil air also contains a correspondingly lower O_2 content of about 20.3% as compared with that of 20.99% in the atmosphere. Higher levels of CO_2 result from the respiration of living organisms in which O_2 is consumed and CO_2 released. This shows that O_2 is essential for the soil atmosphere. The respiration of plant roots depends to a high extent on the O_2 supply in the soil air. Respiration provides the energy for various metabolic processes including active ion uptake by plant roots. The partial pressure of O_2, however, required for root metabolism can be considerably lower than that of the atmosphere. Thus HOPKINS *et al.* [1950] showed that nutrient uptake of tomato plants was impaired only when the O_2 content in the root medium was lower than 10% or a partial pressure of about 0.1 bar. The main results of this investigation are shown in Table 2.6.

Lack of O_2 can directly affect the carbohydrate metabolism of roots. Oxidative degradation of sugars is depressed and ethanol is produced by fermentation (KANDLER [1958]). Ethanol has a detrimental effect on plant growth and can result in considerable yield depressions of crops (ERICKSON and VAN DOREN [1960]). Oxygen deficiency in the roots also impairs the synthesis of phytohormones such as cytokinins and giberellins.

Table 2.6 Effect of O_2 partial pressure in the nutrient solution on the relative uptake of P and K by tomato plants (HOPKINS *et al.* [1950])

| O_2 Partial Pressure | Relative Uptake | |
bar	P	K
0.21	100	100
0.05	56	75
0.005	30	37

Oxygen supply to roots and other aerobic organisms in the soil not only depends on the O_2 content of the soil air, but also on the total volume of air present in the soil. This quantity of soil air declines as the water content of the soil increases, as air which normally fills the larger soil pores is replaced by water. Thus an increase in soil water content depresses aerobic processes and favours anaerobic processes.

Under anaerobic conditions the end products of anaerobic microorganisms can be accumulated. These anaerobic metabolic end products include substances which are toxic to higher plants such as ethylene, methane, hydrogen sulphide, cyanide, butyric acid and a number of other fatty acids. Plants affected by these toxins are impaired in growth and often show wilting symptoms. The detrimental effect of poor drainage on plant growth is thus more severe than can be accounted for by a simple lack of O_2. Useful reviews dealing with plant growth and nutrient relationships in waterlogged and submerged soils have been published by MARSCHNER [1972] and PONNAMPERUMA [1972].

Plant species differ in their availability to cope with conditions of poor soil aeration (LETEY *et al.* [1961]). According to CRAWFORD [1967], some marsh plant species are able to tolerate poor aeration conditions by utilizing fermentative pathways that minimize ethanol production. This explanation has been called into question by the recent findings of SMITH and REES [1979] who have carried out detailed investigations into the pathways of carbohydrate fermentation in the roots of marsh plants. In rice and other plant species a form of adaption occurs, as demonstrated by BARBER et al. [1962] who compared the capability of rice and barley to transfer O_2 from the atmosphere through the leaves and stems to the roots. Rice plants were found to be considerably more efficient in this process and a higher proportion of air filled spaces were found in the rice roots. Rice roots are even capable of excreting O_2 into the surrounding medium. This is an important process because it renders the rhizosphere aerobic and thus protects the rice plant from anaerobic toxins. In seedlings too, O_2 can diffuse from the leaves into the roots (GREENWOOD [1971]). According to BARTLETT [1961] the ability of land plants to tolerate reducing soil conditions is linked with the capacity of the root to oxidize the rhizosphere by means of O_2 translocated from the shoots towards the roots.

Reducing conditions in the soil medium affect many inorganic and biological processes and hence have an important impact on plant growth. A useful example to demonstrate the various processes involved in waterlogged soils is provided by paddy soils. For this reason they are described in some detail.

A measure of reducing conditions in submerged soils can be assessed by the redox potential. This is regulated by the concentrations of reduced and oxidized substances according to the following equation:

$$E = E_o + \frac{R \cdot T}{nF} \ln \frac{(Ox)}{(Red)}$$

where

(Ox) = Concentration of oxidized substances   R = Gas constant

(Red) = Concentration of reduced substances   T = Absolute temperature

E_o = Standard redox potential   F = Faraday constant

E_o is equal to E, if (Ox) and (Red) are each unity. n = Valency

The redox potential in soils is generally measured using a platinum electrode against a reference electrode and is expressed in terms of voltage. Often the potential thus obtained is denoted as 'Eh' rather than 'E'.

From the above equation it can be seen that the potential decreases as the concentration of reduced substances increases relative to the concentration of oxidized substances. A low potential is thus indicative of a high reducing power or a surplus of e^- (electrons) to effect reduction, whereas a high redox-potential indicates a lack of electrons. In the presence of O_2 rather high redox potentials prevail ($+0.33$ V) due to the fact that O_2 is a powerful oxidant driving the oxidation of carbon, hydrogen, nitrogen, sulphur, iron, and manganese to the formation of the appropriate oxides (CO_2, H_2O, NO_3^-, SO_4^{2-}, Fe_2O_3, and MnO_2). During the period of submergence the soil undergoes reduction and the oxides mentioned above are reduced (PONNAMPERUMA [1972]). This reduction is often linked with the 'consumption' of H^+ as shown in the following example:

$$Fe(OH)_3 + e^- + 3H^+ \rightarrow 3H_2O + Fe^{2+}$$

It is mainly for this reason that during the period of submergence the pH of acid soils increases. Generally the redox potential of paddy soils is in the range between $+0.6$ to -0.2 volts (TAKAI et al. [1957]).

During rice cultivation paddy soils are kept under submergence to a depth of several cm. As soon as the soil is flooded anaerobic conditions set in and a specific sequence of reaction steps can be observed which can be divided into two stages. These two stages and the individual steps are shown in Table 2.7. Anaerobiosis begins with the disappearance of O_2 and the microbial reduction of NO_3^- to N_2 and N_2O. Manganese and Fe are then reduced to Mn^{2+} and Fe^{2+} respectively in accordance with the slight drop in the redox potential in the soil. This first stage of reduction is not detrimental to rice plants provided that Fe^{2+}

Table 2.7 Steps of microbial metabolism in waterlogged soils (TAKAI et al. [1957])

Step	Main Reaction	Initial Redox Potential (volts)
	First stage	
1st	O_2 disappearance	$+0.6 \sim +0.5$
2nd	Nitrate reduction	$+0.6 \sim +0.5$
3rd	Mn^{2+} formation	$+0.6 \sim +0.5$
4th	Fe^{2+} formation	$+0.5 \sim +0.3$
	Second Stage	
5th	Sulphide formation sulphate reduction	$0 \sim -0.19$
6th	H_2 formation	$-0.15 \sim -0.22$
7th	CH_4 formation	$-0.15 \sim -0.19$

and Mn^{2+} concentrations do not reach toxic levels. The second stage of reduction is associated with a substantial drop of redox potential indicating that reducing substances have been produced. At this stage sulphate is reduced to sulphide (see page 370) and at an even lower redox potential molecular H_2 and methane are formed. Accumulation of additional toxic substances such as butyric acid and fatty acids also occur at this low redox potential.

This second stage should be avoided in rice cultivation. Soils to which organic matter has been applied or which are naturally high in organic matter are prone to low redox potentials due to the fact that the organic matter favours the growth and metabolism of anaerobic microorganisms (PONNAMPERUMA [1965]). According to TANAKA and YOSHIDA [1970] soils which are rich in 'active Fe' (Fe which is easily reduced or oxidized) are able to buffer the redox potential to some extent and hence prevent the development of the second stage. This buffering capacity is due to the fact that soils high in active Fe have a high Fe^{3+}/Fe^{2+} ratio (see page 474). Sandy and silty soils are generally low in active Fe and for this reason tend to show low redox potentials. Under these conditions high Fe^{2+} concentrations can result which are harmful to the rice plant. Iron toxicity of rice is known as suffocation disease or bronzing (see page 481). The occurrence of this disease also depends on the 'oxidizing power' of the rice root. This oxidizing power results from the excretion of O_2 which induces a rise in the redox potential in the rhizosphere, and hence a decrease of the Fe^{2+} level. The Fe^{3+} is partially precipitated as oxides of Fe at the root surface giving the roots a red brown colour. This colour is indicative of healthy roots. Under anaerobic condition FeS is precipitated at the root surface and the roots are black as shown in Plate 2.1. According to TROLLDENIER [1973] the oxidizing power of the rice root depends on the K supply of the crop. Suffocation disease is thus often associated with K deficiency.

In paddy soils a characteristic profile may be observed as shown diagramatically in Figure 2.8. At the uppermost surface of the flooded soil there is a thin zone with a maximum depth of 1 cm. This is known as the oxidized layer as aerobic conditions prevail due to oxygen from the water. The layer is a reddish colour, Fe being present mainly in the Fe^{3+} form. This tendency to oxidation is also indicated by a rather high redox potential ($> +0.4$ V) and N is present as NO_3^-. Underlying this layer is a broader zone which is exclusively anaerobic and is blue grey in colour due to the presence of Fe^{2+}. It is here that NO_3^- origina-

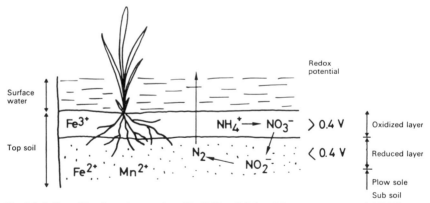

Fig.2.8 Soil profile of a submerged paddy field soil (after MATSUBAYASHI *et al.* [1963]).

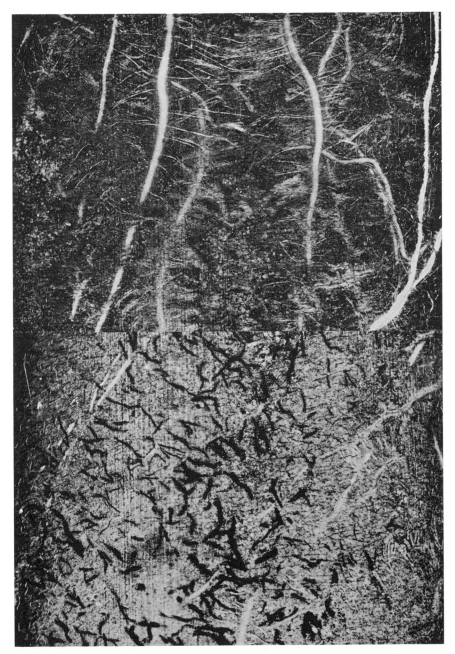

Plate 2.1 Upper part, normal rice roots growing under an optimum redox potential; lower part, rice roots affected by too low a redox potential, lateral roots are covered with a black coating of FeS. (Photo: TROLLDENIER)

ting from the oxidized layer is reduced to N_2 or the oxides of N. As these compounds are volatile they may be lost from the system. It is for this reason that NO_3^--fertilizers are not recommended for paddy soils (MATSUBAYASHI et al. [1963]). Ammonium N regardless of whether applied as fertilizer or produced during the decomposition of organic N containing compounds, can also be lost via denitrification. PATRICK and REDDY [1977] have demonstrated that NH_4^+ may diffuse from the lower layer to the oxidized thin surface soil layer where it can be oxidized to NO_3^-. If this NO_3^- is then transported back into the reducing deeper soil zone it can be denitrified and thus lost.

Submergence also influences the availability of plant nutrients other than N (PONNAMPERUMA [1978]). Generally phosphate availability increases. This is due partially to the release of occluded phosphates after the reduction of Fe^{3+} to Fe^{2+} on the Fe oxide skin and also partially to hydrolysis of $Fe(OH)_3$. In addition the decomposition of inositol hexaphosphate is promoted by submergence (DALAL [1978]). The content of soluble cations rises due to cation exchange caused by soluble Fe^{2+} and Mn^{2+}. Hydrogen sulphide produced under reducing contitions forms precipitates (sulphides) with Fe, Cu, Zn, and Mn and thus affects the availability of these nutrients. By the formation of FeS, plants are protected from toxic levels of Fe^{2+}. The formation of sulphides has no major influence on S availability, as sulphides can be oxidized in the rhizosphere by bacteria (PONNAMPERUMA [1972]). As mentioned above, flooding results in an increase in soil pH. Calcareous soils and sodic soils, however, decrease in pH when submerged. This decrease results from the dissolution of CO_2. High accumulations of CO_2 may be toxic to the rice plant (CHO and PONNAMPERUMA [1971]).

Reducing conditions as described here for paddy soils also occur in many other soils where drainage is impeded. These reducing conditions are indicated by the presence of blue grey colours in the profile resulting from Fe^{2+}. The process associated with the anaerobic conditions is called gleying. Frequently the blue colours are also associated with reddish brown colours in areas of better aeration. This often gives a mottled appearance to the soil profile which is characteristic of poorly drained soils (CROMPTON [1952], SCHLICHTING and SCHWERTMANN [1973]).

2.2.5 Soil pH

The H^+ concentration in soils as well as in physiological liquids is generally rather low and for this reason is expressed in terms of pH. pH is defined as the logarithm of the reciprocal of the hydrogen ion concentration in solution. It may be expressed mathematically as

$$pH = \log \left[\frac{1}{[H^+]} \right]$$

where $[H^+]$ is the hydrogen ion concentration in moles per litre of solution. The pH scale is a logarithmic scale ranging from 0 to 14. On the scale, 7 is neutral and $[H^+]$ is equal to $[OH^-]$. Below 7 it is acid and the $[H^+]$ is greater than the $[OH^-]$. Above 7 the reverse is the case. For each unit decrease in pH there is a 10 fold increase in $[H]$ and a 10 fold decrease in $[OH^-]$.

In the soil a distinction may be made between actual acidity, which is the H^+ concentration of the soil solution and potential acidity, which also includes H^+ ions adsorbed to soil colloids. The former can easily be determined by measuring the pH of the soil solution: the determination of the potential acidity in addition includes an exchange of H^+ by other cation species prior to the pH measurement. Generally the pH value of soils is determined in a water or in KCl extract. In the latter case some adsorbed H^+ ions are also replaced by K^+. For the same soil sample the pH of the KCl extract is therefore lower than that of the water extract.

Besides the actual soil acidity, the buffer capacity of a soil is of importance. Hydrogen ions produced by various processes in the soil are buffered by soil colloids. The principle of this buffering process is shown in Figure 2.9. Hydrogen ions exchange for other cation species adsorbed to soil colloids. From this it is clear that soils rich in organic and inorganic colloids have a high buffer capacity for H^+, provided that a high proportion of the exchange capacity is saturated with cation species other than H^+.

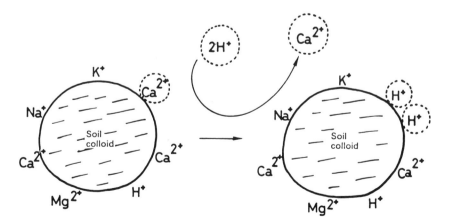

Fig.2.9 Principle of H^+ buffering, 2 H^+ exchange for another cation species (Ca^{2+}).

The pH values of soils can differ widely from values of about 3 to as high as 10, being very low in acid sulphate and podzolic soils and being rather high in calcareous and alkali soils. In alkali soils in particular very high pHs may occur as the soil solution contains weak acids (HCO_3^-) and strong bases (Na^+ or K^+).

The H^+ concentration of the soil solution has a pronounced effect on a number of soil constituents and especially on the soil minerals, soil microorganisms and plant roots. High H^+ concentrations favour the weathering of minerals resulting in a release of various ions such as K^+, Mg^{2+}, Ca^{2+}, Mn^{2+}, Cu^{2+} and Al^{3+}. The solubility of salts including carbonates, phosphates, sulphates is higher in the lower pH range. The release of Al in various forms from clay minerals is also pH dependent to a large extent. Aluminium is adsorbed by clay minerals in the form al $Al(OH)^{2+}$ or $Al(OH)_2^+$ (JENNY [1961]). As shown in Figure 2.10 from the results of LATHWELL and PEECH [1964] this adsorption becomes weaker as the pH falls, thus more soluble Al comes into soil solution in acid soils. At higher soil pH levels in the region of 6.5 to 7 the concentration of soluble Al decreases dramatically. As soluble Al can be toxic to plant growth, the pH of all

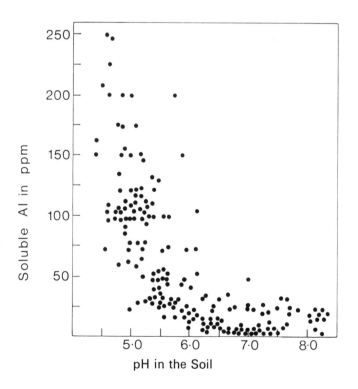

Fig. 2.10 Relationship between soil pH and soluble soil Al (after LATHWELL and PEECH [1964]).

56

soils with high clay contents should be maintained in excess of 6.5. The detrimental effect of Al on plant growth can be seen in Table 2.8 from the work of VLAMIS [1953]. The table shows the dry matter yields of barley grown in nutrient solutions at two different pH values with different levels of Al. At pH 4.2 a relatively high yield was obtained as compared with the pH 5.8 treatment, provided that the concentration of Al in the nutrient medium was low. When the Al concentration was increased in the pH 4.2 treatment there was a drastic reduction in dry matter yield. These results clearly indicate that the concentration of Al rather than the low pH of the nutrient solution was the growth limiting factor in this case. According to the investigations of ADAMS and LUND [1966] Al particularly affects root growth. In experiments with cotton these authors found considerable root damage when the soil solution contained Al^{3+} in concentrations in the order of 1.1^{-5} M.

Table 2.8 Effect of the Al^{3+} concentration and pH on the growth of barley (VLAMIS [1953])

pH	Al in ppm	Yield DM in mg
4.2	1.8	139
4.2	0.35	315
5.8	0.30	353

The optimum soil pH for crop growth is related to soil texture (SCHACHT-SCHABEL [1963]). It is rather low in organic soils and for mineral soils it rises with increasing clay content (Table 2.9). In organic soils in particular the pH should not be too high for these soils are by nature poor in a number of plant nutrients, whose availability is suppressed by high pH conditions (LUCAS and DAVIS [1961]). This is especially the case for phosphate, borate, Mn, Cu and Zn as can be seen from Figure 2.11. The pH values shown in Figure 2.11 are not completely comparable with the data of Table 2.9, as the values in Figure

Table 2.9 Optimum pH values measured in KCl extracts for various soil classes (SCHACHT-SCHABEL [1963])

Soil class		optimum pH range
	Clay content	
Sand	< 5%	5.3–5.7
Sand	5–10%	5.8–6.2
sandy loams	10–15%	6.3–6.7
silty loams and clay	> 15%	7.0–7.5
	organic matter	
humic sands	5–10%	5.0
humic sands	10–20%	4.8–5.0
peats	> 20%	3.8–4.0

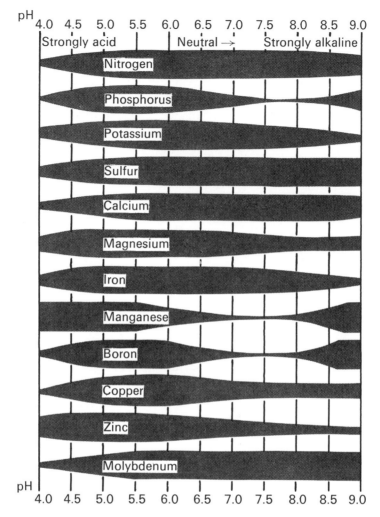

Fig. 2.11 Influence of pH on the availability of plant nutrients in organic soils; widest parts of the shaded areas indicate maximum of availability (after LUCAS and DAVIS [1961]).

2.11 refer to pH measurements in water, whereas the results of Table 2.9 are from KCl extracts. This is the reason why the optimum pH level for organic soils recommended by LUCAS and DAVIS [1961] appears somewhat higher.

Soil pH also influences the occurrence and the activity of soil microorganisms. Generally in the low pH range (<5.5) fungi dominate in the soil and in the rhizosphere, whereas at higher pH levels the bacteria are more abundant (TROLLDENIER [1971]). The nitrification of NH_4-N and NO_2-N brought by

Nitrosomonas and *Nitrobacter* depends considerably on soil pH, because these bacteria prefer more neutral soil conditions. In strongly acid soils the native nitrate content is therefore extremely low. The fixation of molecular N by free living soil microorganisms *(Azotobacter, Clostridium)* and by symbiotic microorganisms *(Rhizobium, Actinomyces)* as well as denitrifying bacteria are also favoured by more neutral pH conditions in the soil. *Beijerinckia* species which are important free living N_2 fixers in tropical soils are less sensitive to low pH levels.

The pH in the cytoplasm of plant cells is in the range of 7 to 7.5 while the pH of the sap of the vacuole is generally lower and in the range of 5 (SMITH and RAVEN [1979]). This slightly acid pH is often used in solution cultures in preference to neutral or alkaline conditions. If plants respond favourably to higher pHs as in the soil medium, this is normally because of other secondary effects resulting from the pH increase. These include the alleviation of Al or Mn toxicity or an increase in Mo or P availability.

The uptake rate of various plant nutrients is also pH dependent. Generally anions including nitrate and phosphate are taken up at a higher rate in the weak acid pH range. In the case of phosphate the pH regulates the ratio of HPO_4^-/HPO_4^{2-} in the soil solution. This also has a bearing on phosphate uptake (see page 393). The uptake rate for cations seems to be highest in the more neutral pH range (ARNON *et al.* [1942]). At very low pH levels (<3.0) cell membranes are impaired and become more permeable. This results in a leakage of plant nutrients and particularly of K^+ (MURPHY [1959]) which diffuses out of the root cells into the soil solution. This detrimental effect of high H^+ concentrations on biological membranes can be counterbalanced by Ca^{2+} (JACOBSON *et al.* [1960]). Relationships between soil pH nutrient uptake and the physiology of plants have been discussed by RORISON [1980].

Plant species are able to cope, to a varying degree, with differences in H^+ concentration in the soil solution and the accompanying effects that these pH changes induce in the soil (HACKETT [1964]). The optimum pH ranges for maximum growth of individual crops therefore differ. The pH limits presented in Table 2.10 only serve as a guideline. There is considerable variation, due to the effects of differences in crop cultivars and the influence of climate and soil conditions. The optimum pH ranges shown in Table 2.10 are from data obtained in temperate climate conditions (KLAPP [1951]). The pH limits appear rather wide, but it must be remembered that often it is not the soil pH itself that is the growth limiting factor but rather one or more secondary factors which are pH dependent. An example of this kind of relationship is shown very well from the work of EVERS [1963] who investigated the growth of *Picea* in relation to pH and the form of N-nutrition in the nutrient medium. It was found that *Picea* grows very

Table 2.10 Optimum pH ranges (pH in KCl extract) of various crop plants, according to (KLAPP [1951])

Crop	pH range
Lucerne	6.5–7.4
Barley	5.3–7.4
Sugar beet	6.4–7.4
Clover *(Trifolium pratense)*	5.3–7.4
Wheat	4.1–7.4
Peas *(Pisum sativum)*	5.3–7.4
Oats	4.0–7.0
Potatoes	4.1–7.4
Rye *(Secale cereale)*	4.1–7.4
Lupins	4.1–5.5

poorly on acid soils. In solution culture, however, the plants were observed to grow well at a pH as low as 3.3 provided that the plants were supplied with NO_3^--N. Under natural conditions in strongly acid soils the microbiological production of NO_3^- is inhibited. It was therefore concluded that the absence of NO_3^- was the cause of poor growth of *Picea* on such acid sites.

The pH of the soil can be corrected by the addition of chemicals which bring about a decrease in H^+ concentration. The most common treatment is liming of soils. This is dealt with in detail on page 454.

Most soils developing in temperate climates tend to become acidic. The production of H^+ mainly results from the decomposition of soil organic matter. The scheme in Figure 2.12 shows the main processes involved in H^+ production. Carbon dioxide produced by microbial decomposition of organic matter equilibrates with soil water thus forming H^+ and HCO_3^-. The equilibrium

$$CO_2 + H_2O \rightleftarrows H^+ + HCO_3^-$$

depends much on the pH of the soil. By increasing the pH the equilibrium is shifted in favour of H^+ production. In alkaline soils HCO_3^- can even dissociate:

$$HCO_3^- \rightleftarrows H^+ + CO_3^{2-}$$

thus producing a further H^+. On the other hand under more acid conditions (pH <5.2) hardly any H^+ is produced by the production of CO_2 due to the fact that the equilibrium is shifted in favour of CO_2.

The microbial decomposition of organic matter also produces NH_3 and H_2S. Both these compounds can be oxidized in the soil to strong inorganic acids (nitric and sulphuric) and so depress soil pH. Atmospheric SO_2 and NO_2 may also induce soil acidification as shown in Figure 2.12. In submerged soils the relative excess of electrons results in a reduction of H^+ according to the overall reaction:

60

$$2H^+ + 2e^- \rightarrow H_2$$

This process leads to a pH increase since it consumes H^+ (PONNAMPERUMA [1972]). The oxidation of Fe^{2+} to Fe^{3+} is associated with a production of H^+ (see Figure 2.12) and thus results also in acidification.

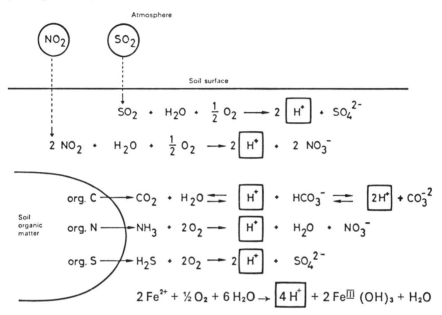

Fig. 2.12 Sources of soil acidification. Fe^{2+} or Fe^{3+} indicates divalent or trivalent Fe ions in solution while Fe^{II} or Fe^{III} indicates divalent or trivalent Fe in a complex.

In addition to the processes mentioned above, plant roots may also influence soil pH by excreting H^+ or HCO_3^-. This is of particular importance in the rhizosphere, the direct vicinity of the root, as it may in turn influence chemical and biological processes in this zone.

2.2.6 Salinity

Soil salinity is a world-wide problem. Saline habitats are characterized by an excess of inorganic salts and mainly occur in arid and semi arid regions. Under these conditions salts accumulate in the upper soil layer. This accumulation usually results from evapotranspiration causing a rise in ground water which contain salts. The effect is particularly marked where the ground water is near the surface as occurs in depression or low lying sites. Salt accumulation in soils results in a poor development in crop growth and both the yield and quality of crops are low. This problem and salt tolerance of plants has recently been reviewed by FLOWERS *et al.* [1977].

Two major soil types of salt affected or halomorphic soils may be distinguished; the saline soils (solonchak) and the alkali soils (solonetz). Saline soils contain an excess of neutral salts such as the chloride and sulphates of Na^+ and Mg^{2+}. Sometimes even NO_3^- accumulates (CHARLEY and McGARITY [1964]). According to GISKIN and MAJDAN [1969] NO_3^- accumulation occurs when organic soils are drained, the access of oxygen bringing about a vigorous microbiological mineralization of organic N. Substantial amounts of NO_3^- can thus accumulate in soils in arid regions. In dry periods saline soils often show a white efflorescence of salts on their surface. For this reason they are also sometimes known as white alkali soils. The high accumulation of neutral salts means that the clay component of the mineral soil is highly flocculated so that generally a good soil structure results which is uniform down the profile.

At a more advanced stage of leaching when some salts have been washed down the profile, the presence of more than about 15% of Na of the exchangeable ions can bring about considerable changes in soil development and the formation of an alkali soil. As might be expected from their name the alkali soils have a rather high pH (7.5–10.0). This results largely from the presence of Na_2CO_3 and $NaHCO_3$ which can be hydrolysed:

$$Na^+ + HCO_3^- + H_2O \rightleftarrows Na^+ + OH^- + H_2CO_3$$
$$2Na^+ + CO_3^{2-} + 2H_2O \rightleftarrows 2Na^+ + 2OH^- + H_2CO_3$$

thus forming OH^-. The major source of Na_2CO_3 and $NaHCO_3$ originates from the production of CO_2 by soil microorganisms and roots, which give rise to bicarbonate and carbonate ions. When appreciable quantities of Na^+ are present on exchange sites, Na^+ can come into solution and hence Na_2CO_3 and $NaHCO_3$ can be formed. These high soil pH conditions and the presence of relatively lower salt concentrations lead to the deflocculation of clay and organic matter particles. The soil structure thus becomes water unstable. The soils are black due to the dispersed humic particles and are sometimes known as black alkali soils. The movement of clay down the profile to form a pan in the B horizon means that this horizon often becomes compacted impeding plant root penetration (SZABOLCS [1971]). The black alkali soils have a poor soil structure being very sticky when wet and form hard unworkable compact clods when they dry out. This, together with the high pH conditions are the primary effects bringing about poor crop growth. Sodium and carbonates are the most abundant ions in the profile (RAIKOV [1971]).

The total ion concentration of the soil solution of saline and alkali soils can reach levels which can bring about plasmolysis of plant root cells. The radicles of germinating seeds are particularly sensitive to high ion concentrations in the soil solution. A further drawback of the high concentration of the soil solution is the resulting high osmotic pressure, which binds the soil water and renders it less available to plant roots. The mechanism of this osmotic binding of soil water is explained in more detail on page 228 along with other physiological aspects of salinity. Here it should be stressed that plant growth on saline and alkali soils is often restricted due to a lack of water (BERNSTEIN and HAYWARD [1958]). The ionic composition of the soil solution of these salt affected soils is also often imbalanced in relation to normal plant growth requirements, showing low levels of Ca^{2+} and K^+. Toxic concentrations of some other ion species may occur, such as borate, and possibly bicarbonate, chloride, Na^+ and Mg^{2+}. Under more anaerobic conditions Fe^{2+} and sulphide ions may also reach toxic levels. Several measures can be adopted to ameliorate salt affected soils. This problem is discussed on page 455.

The degree of salinity is usually measured in the water extract of a soil as electrical conductivity. This is expressed in mmhos/cm which is the reciprocal of the electrical resistance. The higher the salt concentration of the soil extract the higher is the electrical conductivity. Salt affected soils usually show conductivities in the range of 2–20 mmhos/cm in their saturated extracts. In the USA a value of 4 mmhos/cm is considered critical for crops. Salinity problems arise especially where irrigation is applied to impermeable soils. All irrigation waters contain salts and these can remain in the upper soil layer and accumulate. In this respect light textured soils are easier to handle because of their high permeability. For heavy textured soils it is often necessary to provide artificial drainage, along with irrigation. Useful discussions on halomorphic soils and the associated salinity problems have been presented by SZABOLCS [1971] and POLJAKOFF-MAYBER and GALE [1975].

2.3 Factors Relating to Nutrient Availability

2.3.1 General

The term 'nutrient availability' is an often used one in plant nutrition. It is, however, badly defined. In a simple way it may be considered as that nutrient fraction in the soil which is accessible to plant roots. The term nutrient availability thus encompasses the chemical and physical status of a nutrient in the soil as well as plant root relationships which involve plant metabolism. It is for this reason that in a strict sense the amounts of available nutrients in the soil cannot be measured and expressed in quantitative terms. Nevertheless it is expedient to know the factors and their causal relationships which contribute to 'nutrient availability'.

2.3.2 Interception and contact exchange

An important question in nutrient availability is whether nutrients need to be transported to the plant roots or whether they come in contact with roots as the roots push their way through the soil. This latter process is called root interception. One theory which held favour for many years in support of root interception, for the uptake of cations at least, was the contact exchange theory as proposed by JENNY and OVERSTREET [1938]. It was envisaged that a close contact between root surfaces and soil colloids enabled direct exchange of H^+ released from the plant root with cations from soil colloids. It was argued that by releasing H^+ produced in plant metabolism, plant roots should be able to strip off and mobilize the cationic nutrients adsorbed to clay minerals. This contact exchange process was envisaged as the first step of cation uptake by plants. Undoubtedly H^+ ions are released by plant roots, and they can exchange for the adsorbed cations on the soil colloids. What is in question is whether the process plays a major role in nutrient availability and whether contact exchange is at all important in the ion uptake process by the plant.

Figure 2.13 shows the site and dimensions of contact exchange in relation to the cell wall, and plasma membrane of a root cell. It can be seen immediately

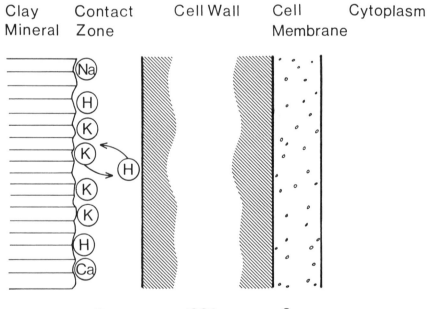

Fig. 2.13 Contact exchange between a clay mineral and an epidermal root cell, showing the dimensions involved.

that only cations at the very outer surface of the cell wall can exchange for cations adsorbed to the clay mineral. By an exchange of H^+ from the cell wall, K^+ can be mobilized from a clay mineral as indicated in Figure 2.13. Even if this does occur, however, the exchanged K^+ is still only at the outer surface of the cell wall. This is far from the real site of ion uptake. This occurs at the plasma membrane (plasmalemma) and is about 1000 nm distant from the site of contact exchange. There is no evidence that K^+ is able to move across the cell wall by further exchange processes.

In comparison with the size of inorganic ions the cell wall is immense. The fully developed cell wall is a rigid relatively thick structure which normally contains channels filled with air and soil solution. These channels almost certainly allow ions a more accessible route to the plasma membrane than the cell wall. It seems likely therefore that K^+ and other cations act as counter ions in anion transport with exchange movement being relatively unimportant.

Generally the amount of nutrients which directly contacts plant roots (interception) is small as compared with the total nutrient demand. This is particular true for nutrients required in high quantities (BARBER et al. [1963]). For this reason mass flow and diffusion rather than interception are by far the most important processes by which plant roots receive their nutrients. This view is supported by the data of DREW and NYE [1969] who found that only 6% of the total K^+ demand of *Lolium perenne* was supplied by the soil volume in the immediate vicinity of the root hair cylinder. Ninety-four % of the K^+ taken up had therefore originated from beyond the limit of root hairs, and thus must have been transported to the roots.

2.3.3 Mass-flow and diffusion

Nutrients in the soil can be transported by two different mechanisms: by mass-flow and by diffusion. Mass-flow occurs when solutes are transported with the convective flow of water from the soil to plant roots. The amount of nutrients reaching the root is thus dependent on the rate of water flow or the water consumption of the plant and the average nutrient concentration of the water. The level of a particular nutrient around the root may be increased, decreased or remain the same depending on the balance between the rate of its supply to the root by mass flow and the rate of uptake by the root.

Diffusion occurs when an ion is transported from a higher to a lower concentration by random thermal motion. Diffusion comes into operation when the concentration at the root surface is either higher or lower than that of the surrounding solution. It is directed towards the root when the concentration at the root surface is decreased, and away from the roots when it is increased. Diffusion follows Fick's law:

$$F = -D \cdot \frac{dc}{dx}$$

F = Diffusion rate (quantity diffused per unit cross section and per unit time)

$\dfrac{dc}{dx}$ = concentration gradient   c = concentration

D = diffusion coefficient   x = distance

Plant roots absorbing nutrients from the adjacent soil can thus create a sink to which nutrients diffuse (DREW *et al.* [1969]). The nutrient depletion depends on the balance between the supply from the soil and the demand by the plant. A high plant requirement or a high root 'absorbing power' as it has been termed by NYE [1968] gives rise to a strong sink. This indicates that the root itself and its metabolism also influence nutrient availability.

If diffusion is the main process by which a plant nutrient is transported to the root surface, the quantity of the nutrient absorbed by the root can be described approximately by the following equation (DREW *et al.* [1969]):

$$Q = 2\pi \cdot a \cdot \alpha \cdot \bar{c} \cdot t$$

where

Q = Quantity of nutrient absorbed per cm root length

a = Root radius in cm

α = Nutrient absorbing power of the root in cm root length

$\bar{c}$ = Average nutrient concentration at the root surface

t = Time of nutrient absorption.

The nutrient concentration (c) at the root surface may change. At the beginning of the absorption period (t) it may be relatively high and then gradually decline, the degree at which it falls depending on the capacity of the soil to replenish the soil solution with the nutrient. This capacity for nutrient replenishment is referred to as the nutrient buffer capacity and is discussed in more detail on p.73. In this context it need only be understood that the term $\bar{c}$ (=average nutrient concentration at the root surface) not only depends on the bulk nutrient concentration of the soil but also on the nutrient buffer capacity. A soil with a high nutrient buffer capacity is more capable of maintaining a high nutrient concentration at the root surface than is a soil with a low nutrient buffer capacity.

The term u (= root absorbing power) in the above equation represents the proportion of a nutrient absorbed of the total nutrient flux to the root surface. The root absorbing power is not a constant but is very dependent on root metabolism and the nutrient status of the plant (BARBER [1979]).

Nutrients taken up rapidly by plant roots and which are generally present in the soil solution in low concentrations such as NH_4^+, K^+, and phosphate are mainly transported to plant roots by diffusion. The contribution of mass flow to the transport of these nutrients can be calculated as the product of solution concentration and transpiration rate. The values are far too low to meet the needs of the plant in any of these elements (BARBER et al. [1963]). Diffusion also dominates when transpiration is low.

Mass flow plays an important role for nutrients present in soil solution in high concentration and when transpiration is high. Under such conditions considerable quantities of water are moved to the roots carrying various solutes. Occasionally ion accumulations can even occur around roots as is sometimes the case with Ca^{2+} (BARBER [1974]). Nitrate which is also present in soil solution in high concentrations, is usually transported to roots via mass flow (RENGER and STREBEL [1976]). Only under conditions where the nitrate concentration in the nutrient solution is relatively low does nitrate diffusion come into play (MENGEL and CASPER [1981]).

If the rate of nutrient uptake is higher than the rate of nutrient transport towards a plant root, nutrient depletion occurs around the root. This is typical for K^+ and phosphate (LEWIS and QUIRK [1967], BHAT and NYE [1974]). A depletion pattern resulting from diffusion is demonstrated in Plate 2.2. In this experiment from the work of BARBER [1968] a study was made on the uptake of the radioisotope Rb 86 from the soil by maize roots. Rubidium and K^+ have closely related chemical properties so that the plate can also be taken to illustrate the behaviour of K^+. A photograph of root growth is shown on the left-hand side of the plate with a corresponding autoradiograph on the right-hand side. The light areas of the autoradiograph show the depletion of the labelled Rb which follow the root growth pattern. The dark lines indicate Rb 86 accumulation in the roots.

The relative depletion of plant nutrients declines with increasing distance from the root surface (LEWIS and QUIRK [1967]). This is shown in Figure 2.14 (page 69) for two soils with high and low nutrient levels in the bulk soil. It is clear that the soil with the higher nutrient level has the steeper concentration gradient and therefore the rate of diffusion to the plant roots is greater. The higher nutrient level in the bulk soil also gives a higher concentration at the root surface which causes a more rapid uptake rate and the larger gradient allows this to be maintained. The depletion zone around the root can often be extended

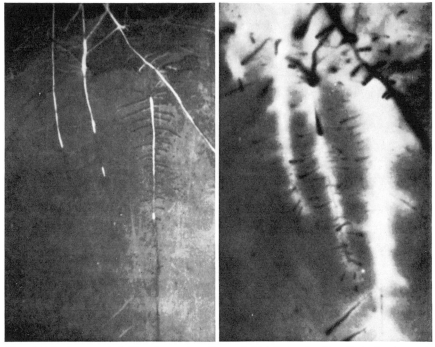

Plate 2.2 A photograph (left) and an autoradiograph (right) showing the effect of maize roots on the distribution of Rb-86 in the soil. Light areas show Rb depletion around the maize roots. (Photo BARBER)

in soils high in nutrients, since the higher nutrient level frequently implies a steeper concentration gradient. This is shown in Figure 2.14 and has been clearly demonstrated for phosphate by LEWIS and QUIRK [1967]. From Figure 2.14 it is also evident that a distinction may be made between nutrient concentration at the root surface and nutrient concentration in the bulk soil solution. The nutrient concentration at the root surface directly controls nutrient uptake as has been shown for the K^+ uptake of young maize plants by CLAASSEN and BARBER [1976]. Since it is difficult to measure nutrient concentrations at the root surface, the concentration of the bulk soil solution is sometimes used.

From Fick's law cited on p. 66 it can be seen that the rate of diffusion of a nutrient is dependent on the diffusion coefficient (D). The diffusion coefficient characterizes the diffusivity of a medium. For example O_2 diffusion in air takes place at a much higher rate than that in water because of the relatively low diffusivity of the water medium. The diffusion coefficient has often been used in soils to characterize the diffusivity of the soil medium. However, soils are not homogeneous and for this reason diffusivity may vary within the soil.

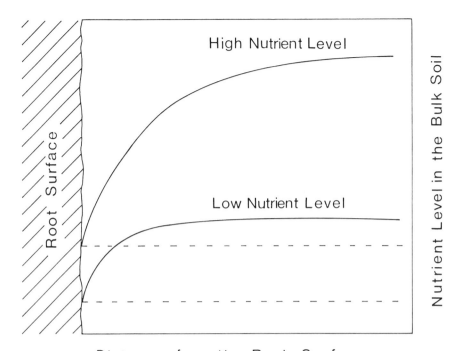

Distance from the Root Surface

Fig. 2.14 Nutrient depletion pattern at the immediate vicinity of the root for a soil with a high and with a low nutrient level in the bulk soil.

The diffusion coefficient is dependent on a number of soil factors including soil moisture and nutrient buffer capacity. These relationships have been considered thoroughly by NYE and TINKER [1977].

The rate of ion movement in the soil, whether by mass flow or diffusion, depends highly on soil moisture. Several investigations have been made showing that soil moisture affects the diffusion rate considerably. GRAHAM-BRYCE [1967] reported that a soil with a water content of 23% had a diffusion coefficient of $1 \times 10^{-7}/\mathrm{cm}^2/\mathrm{sec}$ for Rb^+. When the water content was decreased to 10% in the same soil, the diffusion coefficient fell to 5×10^{-8} $\mathrm{cm}^2/\mathrm{sec}$. The dependence of ion diffusion on soil moisture is easily understood as the removal of soil water results in an increase in air filled pores. Water channels leading from the bulk soil to the plant roots are affected. The cross sectional area of water allowing diffusion is reduced and also the pathways from the bulk soil to the plant root become less direct. Both these factors decrease the rate of diffusion. In dry soils (pF>4.1) ion diffusion is practically inhibited (ROWELL *et al.* [1967]). Under such dry conditions only very small pores with a diameter of 100 nm are filled with water.

Ion diffusion in the soil is even considerably affected at water potentials at which the water availability is still adequate for normal plant growth. It is for this reason that in dry periods poor nutrient mobility rather than the direct effect of water may often be the growth limiting factor. Very useful discussions on ion movement in soil have been presented by NYE [1966], BREWSTER and TINKER [1972] and BARBER [1974].

2.3.4 Soil solution

Nutrient mobility in the soil depends considerably on the nutrient concentration in the soil solution. As already demonstrated in Figure 2.14 the diffusion rate towards the roots is generally faster the higher the concentration of the nutrient in the soil solution.

The soil solution is not homogenous but may differ in its concentration and composition as the water filled spaces and pores of the soil are not completely interconnected. Composition and concentration of the soil solution also depend considerably on soil moisture. In a wet soil (field capacity) the soil solution is diluted and as the soil dries out the solution becomes more concentrated. Some of its ion species may even reach concentrations higher than their solubility products and precipitation of these ions can occur. Calcium, sulphate and phosphates are particularly susceptible. In order to compare soil solutions they must be based on equivalent soil moisture levels. This is usually taken at field capacity (RICHARDS [1941], MAGISTAD et al. [1945], ADAMS [1974]).

The concentrations of the ion species in the soil solution (water saturated extract) can differ widely depending on soil properties. Generally, however, the phosphate concentration is very low, the concentration of K^+ and Mg^{2+} medium and the concentration of Ca^{2+} rather high. MENGEL et al. [1969] found mean concentrations in the range of 0.015–0.030 mM P, 0.1–1.0 mM K, 0.5–1.0 mM Mg and 1.0–10.0 mM Ca in the upper layer of Central European arable soils saturated with water. Frequently NO_3^- is the anion present in highest concentrations and often occurs at levels in the same order as the sum of Ca^{2+} and Mg^{2+} (LARSEN and WIDDOWSON [1968]). The NO_3-N concentrations of the soil solution, however, can vary considerably depending on environmental conditions as free NO_3^- is not buffered (see page 76). Nitrate too is taken up rapidly by plant roots and can also be easily leached in deeper soil layers. For these reasons the NO_3^- concentration in the soil solution is subject to rapid fluctuation.

Table 2.11 shows the concentration of various plant nutrients, found in water saturated extracts (FRIED and SHAPIRO [1961]). It is obvious that these concentrations vary widely. This is particularly true for Mg^{2+}, Na^+, sulphate and chloride, and extremely high values are found for these ions in salt affected soils.

Table 2.11 Ion concentrations in the soil solution (water saturated soil) in mM (FRIED and SHAPIRO [1961])

Element	Range of all soils	An acid soil	A calcareous soil
Ca...............	0.5–38	3.4	14
Mg	0.7–100	1.9	7
K................	0.2–10	0.7	1
Na..............	0.4–150	1.0	29
N................	0.16–55	12.1	13
P	< 0.001–1	0.007	< 0.03
S	< 0.1–150	0.5	24
Cl	0.2–230	1.1	20

Generally acid soils are lower in ionic concentrations than more neutral soils. The ionic strength of the soil solution can be rather high, particularly as soils dry out, so that the activities rather than concentrations of the various ion species (see page 33) should be considered (ADAMS [1974]).

2.3.5 Intensity and quantity

Plants must be supplied adequately with nutrients during their entire growth period. For this reason the concentration of plant nutrients in the soil solution must be maintained at a satisfactory level for plant growth. Nutrient availability depends therefore not only on the nutrient concentration of the soil solution at any given time but also on the ability of the soil to maintain the nutrient concentration. This capability of a soil to 'buffer' the nutrient concentration of the soil solution is a further important factor in nutrient availability.

Generally those nutrients required by plants in high amounts, are present in the soil solution in relatively small concentrations. This is particularly the case for phosphate and K^+. Calculated on an area basis the soil solution contains in the order of only about 0.5–1.0 kg P/ha and 10–30 kg K/ha, whereas the total demand for these nutrients is considerably higher. A cereal crop for example requires about 20 kg P/ha and 100 kg K/ha. As a cereal crop growing under the soil conditions described does not necessarily become deficient in P or K, this shows that the removal of these nutrients from the soil solution by the crop must be accompanied by a substantial replenishment of the soil solution from the solid phase of the soil.

One may thus distinguish between two nutrient components in the soil: the quantity factor (Q) represents the amount of available nutrient, whereas the intensity factor (I) reflects the strength of retention by which the nutrient is held in the soil. Considered simply the intensity factor is the concentration of the nu-

71

trient in the soil solution. The concept of nutrient intensity and nutrient quantity was first proposed by SCHOFIELD [1955]. He compared the availability of phosphate with the availability of soil water. Soil water availability depends not on the total amount of water present in the soil but rather on the strength by which the water is bound to the soil particles. The same holds true for phosphate and also for some other plant nutrients. SCHOFIELD [1947] states: 'It is possible that the potash status of a soil can be better judged by finding the equilibrium concentration of potassium ions... than by finding the total exchangeable potassium.'

Nutrient intensity and quantity factors are interrelated. The main relationships are illustrated in Figure 2.15. The general concepts shown in the Figure have formed the basis of much of the very useful soil phosphate work of

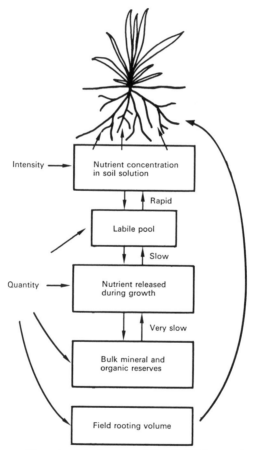

Fig. 2.15 Intensity, quantity and nutrient sources (after E. G. WILLIAMS).

72

E.G. WILLIAMS [1970]. Over the years this study has lead to a much better understanding of the behaviour of phosphate in soils and its availability to plants.

Plant roots are dependent on the nutrient intensity or soil solution concentration. This is usually regulated by a much larger labile pool of easily exchangeable or soluble nutrients. Generally this represents the main component of the quantity factor. However, this is not always the case as nutrient release from the more slowly available forms can sometimes provide a major source of nutrient supply. The extent to which this occurs is not only dependent on the particular nutrient. Soil conditions such as pH, temperature, aeration and moisture level are also important. For example, in tropical soils the rate of release of nutrients by weathering or by mineralization can be so rapid that this can form the main nutrient source. The quantity factor is therefore very much dependent on climatic and soil conditions. In addition it also depends on the volume of soil which the roots occupy. This means of course that all factors influencing the distribution of roots in the profile contribute to the quantity factor.

Another important factor in nutrient availability is the ability of the soil to maintain nutrient intensity (nutrient concentration of the soil solution). This is the buffer factor and it indicates how intensity varies with quantity. In Figure 2.16 the quantity of K^+ is plotted against intensity for two soils of differing K^+ adsorption capacity, soil A and soil B. For both soils increasing intensity (K^+ concentration of the soil solution) is accompanied by an increase in quantity. Soil A, however, shows a steeper rise in the slope than soil B. Where an equal amount of K^+ is removed from both soils by plants a similar decrease in the K^+ quantity results. This is indicated by ΔQ in the figure. The consequent reduction in intensity, however, differs considerably for both soils (compare ΔI_A with ΔI_B in Figure 2.16). This example shows that the two soils differ in their capability of replenishing the soil solution with K^+. Soil A is better able to maintain the K^+ concentration in the soil solution. Soil A is thus more buffered than soil B. In quantitative terms the buffer capacity is expressed as the ratio $\Delta Q/\Delta I$.

$$B_K = \frac{\Delta Q}{\Delta I}$$

where B_K = buffer capacity for K^+. The higher the ratio of $\Delta Q/\Delta I$, the more the soil is buffered.

Generally the rate of K^+ uptake by roots is higher than the diffusive flux of K^+ towards the roots. (see p. 67). The K^+ concentration at the root surface may thus decline during the uptake period. This fall in K^+ concentration is dependent on the K^+ buffer capacity of the soil. If this is high, the decline is likely to be small because of the efficient K^+ replenishment of the soil solution. On the other hand for soils with a poor K^+ buffer capacity, the K^+ concentration the root surface may fall considerably over the growth period.

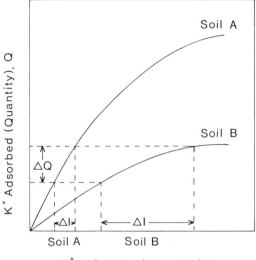

Fig. 2.16 Relationship between K^+ intensity and K^+ quantity for two soils with different adsorbing capacities (Soil A high and Soil B low).

For optimum plant growth, nutrient concentration in soil solution should be maintained above a certain level. This concentration may be termed the critical level as concentrations below this value result in yield depression. It has been shown recently by MENGEL and BUSCH [1982] that the critical K^+ level in the bulk soil solution is related to the K^+ buffer capacity (= buffer power). This relationship is shown in Figure 2.17. The critical concentration is higher, the lower the K^+ buffer capacity.

As already mentioned the quantity/intensity concept is used in soil phosphate studies. Soils can differ much in their ability to adsorb phosphate. Thus red tropical soils can generally adsorb huge quantities of phosphate whereas the phosphate adsorption potential of podzols is low. The phosphate adsorption isotherms for two such soils are shown in Figure 2.18. It can be seen that the red tropical soil requires a much higher amount of adsorbed phosphate than the podzol in order to maintain the same phosphate concentration in the equilibrated solution. From this it follows that soils with a high phosphate adsorption capacity should contain more adsorbed phosphate than sandy soils and organic soils in order to provide a satisfactory phosphate intensity. The ratio 'adsorbed

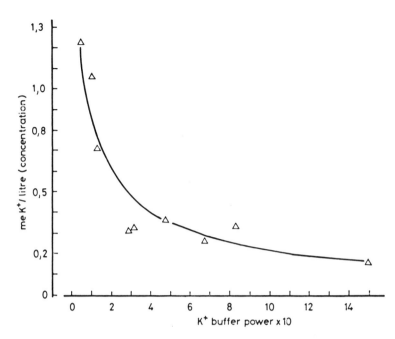

Fig. 2.17 Relationship between the critical K^+ concentration and the K^+ buffer power (Mengel and Busch [1982]).

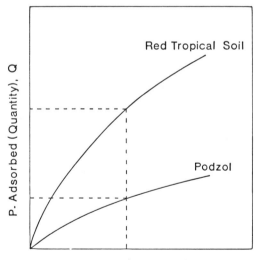

Fig. 2.18 Phosphate adsorption isotherms for two soils differing greatly in ability to adsorb phosphate.

75

phosphate/phosphate concentration in solution' usually represents the phosphate buffer capacity. In a detailed study OLSEN and WATANABE [1970] found, that the phosphate buffer capacity has a substantial impact on the P supply to plant roots and that soils with a low P buffer capacity require higher P concentrations in the soil solution and *vice versa* in order to provide adequate P to plant roots.

The quantity/intensity concept may be also applied to NH_4^+-N but not to NO_3^- supply. By far the greatest amount of soil N is present in organic form. This is biologically converted to NO_3^- which is only weakly held in the soil. The nitrate concentration of the soil solution is thus not buffered and the distinction between quantity and intensity is irrelevant.

2.3.6 Root growth and morphology

Roots have three main functions, a) anchoring the plant in the soil, b) absorption and translocation of water and nutrients, c) synthesis of phytohormones and other organic compounds. In the context considered here water and nutrient uptake are of especial interest. The capability of plants to exploit the soil for nutrients and water depends much on root morphology. This term comprises root depth, root branching, the number of root hairs, the root tips, etc. Root morphology is genetically controlled but is also influenced by a number of environmental factors. Monocotyledons and dicotyledons differ fundamentally in root growth and morphology. In the dicotyledons a tap root is formed at an early stage which extends deeply into the soil. Later lateral roots are developed. In monocots, especially in grasses lateral roots develop from the seminal roots a few days after germination and generally form a dense root system with numerous slender roots.

Root depth may also differ considerably between species. Thus perennial plants generally root deeper than annuals. For agricultural crops a rooting depth of 50 to 100 cm is common but some species may have root depths of 2 m and more. Root growth, root morphology and root depth are influenced by external factors, especially by the soil atmosphere, by mechanical impedance, and by plant nutrient status. This question has been considered by DREW and Goss [1973]. These authors stress that O_2 supply is essential to root growth and metabolism, but that low O_2 partial pressures such as 0.05 atm generally suffice for normal root development. Some of the O_2 required can be taken up from the atmosphere by the leaves and then transported into the roots (GREENWOOD [1971]). Anaerobic soil conditions, however, may not only affect O_2 supply to plant roots, but may also result in the formation of toxic substances which inhibit root growth and may lead to severe root damage. Such toxic substances include ethylene and volatile fatty acids.

Mechanical impedance may restrict root growth considerably (SCHUURMAN [1971]). Generally as roots grow through the soil they follow soil pores and fissures. In this process the roots have to enlarge some soil pores which are initially smaller than themselves. The root tip has therefore to displace soil particles. This only occurs if the mechanical impedance of the soil is not high, otherwise roots are not able to penetrate the soil (DREW and GOSS [1973]).

Root growth is unlikely to be restricted by a lack of water, provided that water can be supplied to the root tip by other plant parts. Generally roots grow better in dry soils than in wet soils (MENGEL and CASPER [1981]). Root proliferation depends much on plant nutrient distribution in the soil. Enhanced root growth in zones surrounding fertilizer granules has thus often been observed (BLANCHAR and CALDWELL [1966]). An example of such an effect is shown in Figure 2.19 from the paper of DREW and GOSS [1973]. In this culture

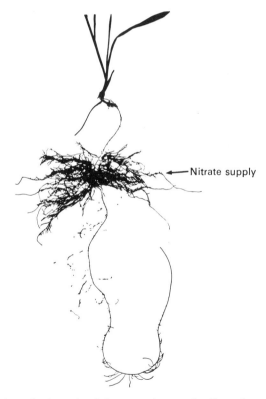

Fig. 2.19 Effect of localized supply of nitrate on the growth of lateral roots of barley (Photo: M.C. DREW).

77

solution experiment all the root system received a complete nutrient solution but only the middle zone received 1.0 mM nitrate. In the upper and lower zones the nitrate concentration was 0.1 mM. This higher nitrate supply resulted in marked root proliferation but this was restricted to the middle zone where the higher nitrate level had been provided. Too high salt concentrations in the soil medium, however, may restrict or even prevent root growth. In particular roots are sensitive to high concentrations of NH_3 (BENNETT and ADAMS 1970).

In annual crops the highest proportion of roots is generally present in the upper soil layer (0 to 20 cm). Rooting density decreases with soil depth as is shown in Figure 2.20 for maize grown at two different sites. From the Figure it is also evident that the total root mass was much greater in the brown podzolic soil (silty loam) as compared with the pelosol (loamy clay). This difference n rooting density coincides with the air pore volume of the soils which was about 13% in the upper layer of the brown podzolic soil and therefore more than twice as high as the air pore volume in the upper layer of the pelosol. MOHR [1978] suggests that especially in gleys and pseudogleys the air pore volume is a limiting factor in root growth, whereas in well aerated soils the pore volume does not restrict root proliferation.

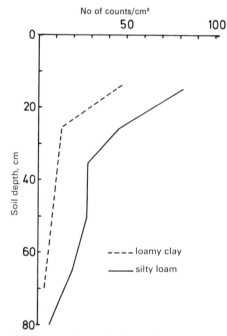

Fig. 2.20 Root density of maize grown in a silty loam with a high air pore volume and in a loamy clay with a low air pore volume. Density was measured by isotopes and is referred to as No of counts (after MOHR [1978]).

The parameters by which root systems may be measured such as root mass, root length, root surface and rooting density are of varying importance. Root weight generally is a poor parameter as old and thick roots may contribute much to the weight but play only a minor role in nutrient and water uptake. Rooting density is a more important parameter. This is the length of root (cm) per unit volume of the soil (cm^3).

$$Lv = 2\,\overline{m}$$

where Lv = rooting density and m is the arithmetic mean of the number of root axes intercepted per unit area of plane for the three principle planes. If for example the number of root axes intercepted is 6, 8 and 4 per cm^2 the rooting density is 12. Rooting density has a considerable influence on the extent at which a soil is depleted of water and nutrients. In dense rooting systems depletion zones resulting from nutrient uptake may overlap. This implies competition between neighbouring roots for available nutrients. As the depletion zones for K^+ and NH_4^+ are about 10 times higher than those for phosphate, K^+ and NH_4^+ uptake is more affected by the competition of neighbouring roots than is phosphate uptake. Thus NEWMAN and ANDREWS [1973] found that a dense rooting system provided by a limited soil volume decreased the K^+ uptake of young wheat plants to a higher degree than phosphate uptake.

A further important root parameter is root length (L_A). This is defined as the total root length per unit soil surface

$$L_A = \frac{\text{Total root length (cm)}}{\text{Soil surface (cm}^2)}$$

From this value root surface area can be calculated, if the average root diameter is known. In analogy to the Leaf Area Index the root surface per unit soil surface has been termed by BARLEY [1970] as 'Root Area Index'. Besides root length and root density the number of root tips is also of importance, since some plant nutrients such as Ca^{2+}, Mg^{2+} and Fe^{2+} are mainly absorbed by young root tissues in which the cell walls of the endodermis are unsuberized (CLARKSON and SANDERSON [1978], CLARKSON and HANSON [1980]).

Root hairs are of particular importance because of the close contact they maintain between the soil and the root (see Figure 4.4) thus forming a water continuum between the soil and the root tissue. According to CHAMPION and BARLEY [1969] root hairs are capable of penetrating moderately resistant clays and may thus contribute to nutrient exploitation of less accessible soil particles. Root hairs play a special role for nutrients which are transported towards the roots by diffusion. The life span of root hairs and their density may differ considerably between species. Generally root hairs collapse after a few days, but they may also persist for a longer period especially in grasses. Differences in root hair density may occur between the cultivars of one species (BOLE [1973]). This is shown in Plate 2.3. The wheat cultivar shown in section C of the Plate has a root hair density which is about four times greater than that of the cultivar shown in section A.

The nutrient uptake potential of a root system (roots per number of plants or roots per unit soil surface) generally exceeds by far the nutrient requirement of the plant. A small portion of the total root system is thus capable of absorbing the water and nutrients required for the whole plant provided that the root portion is abundantly supplied with nutrients and water. This has been shown by MAERTENS [1973] for maize and the same is probably also true for other crop species (DREW and GOSS [1973]). The relatively high nutrient uptake potential of root systems enables the plant to absorb adequate amounts of nutrients even under conditions, where the level of accessible nutrients in the soil is low. It must be borne in mind that under field conditions the total surface of a root system is unlikely to be in direct contact with the soil solution. The root surface, soil solution contact is mainly restricted to areas where soil pores extend to the root surface. This implies that at any given time only a part of the entire root system absorbs water and nutrients.

If one considers the nutrient demand of plants per unit root system *e.g.* per unit root length, it is obvious that it is the young plant which has the highest nutrient requirement. This question has been studied by MENGEL and BARBER [1974] with maize under field conditions. The most important results of this investigation are shown in Table 2.12. It can be seen from this Table that the nutrient requirement per m root length and per day was especially high in the early stage of growth and rapidly declined as the crop developed. Similar results have been reported by ADEPETU and AKAPA [1977] who found that the uptake rates for P and K (uptake per m root length) were four to five times higher in 5 days old cowpea plants *(Vigna unguiculata)* as compared with

Table 2.12 Nutrient requirement of maize per unit root length in relation to the age of plants (Data from MENGEL and BARBER [1974])

Age of plants days	N	P	K	Ca	Mg
	μmol/m root length/day				
20	227	11.3	53	14.4	13.8
30	32	0.90	12.4	5.2	1.6
40	19	0.86	8.0	0.56	0.90
50	11	0.66	4.8	0.37	0.78
60	5.7	0.37	1.6	0.20	0.56
100	4.2	0.23	0.2	0.08	0.29

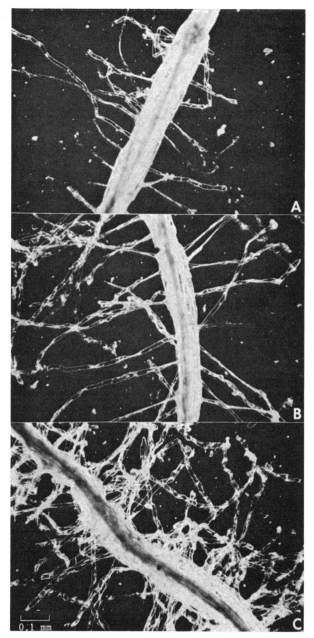

Plate 2.3 Root hair density of three different wheat cultivars.
  A: Chinese Spring (20 root hairs/mm)
  B: Chromosome substitution line (35 root hairs/mm)
  C: S – 615 (80 root hairs/mm) (Photo: BOLE)

81

30 days old plants. VINCENT *et al.* [1979] also found that the K^+ uptake rates of root tips of soya beans were much higher in the vegetative stage of plant growth as compared with the reproductive stage. From these observations it is clear that it is the young plant in particular which needs to take up a high nutrient quantity per unit root length and it is for this reason that young plants especially require a relatively high level of available nutrients in the soil.

Root studies are not easy since the measurement of root systems and root parameters is complicated. BÖHM [1978] recently described and commented on the various techniques by which root systems are measured under field conditions. A very interesting method for measuring root growth and root systems has been developed by SANDERS and BROWN [1978] in which a highly refined fiber optic duodenoscope is used for observing and photographing root development patterns within a soil profile.

2.3.7 Root exudation and rhizosphere

The immediate vicinity of plant roots is of particular importance for plant nutrient turnover and availability. This part of the soil, which is directly influenced by the roots, is called the rhizosphere and extends about 1 to 2 mm from the root surface into the bulk soil. The effect of the root on the adjacent soil medium is mainly brought about by the release of organic and inorganic material into the soil. Organic material arises from the sloughage of root material and also from direct root exudation (HALE and MOORE [1979]). As plant roots push their way through the soil some of the outer tissues are sloughed off and decomposed by autolysis or by microorganisms. The total amount of organic carbon thus released into the soil medium is considerable. One such study was carried out by SAUERBECK and JOHNEN [1976] who investigated root growth and root decomposition in pot experiments with mustard and wheat plants supplied with labelled CO_2 (C-14). The soil used was a loamy sand. For wheat at maturation the root mass still present in the soil amounted to about 30% of the total C translocated from the tops to the roots. Of the remaining 70% about 20% was released in the form of CO_2 by root respiration. Thus about 50% of the organic C translocated from the tops to the roots was released in the form of organic C to the soil during the total growing period. This and other similar observations indicate that plant roots transfer large amounts of organic matter to the soil. This organic material is readily decomposed by rhizosphere microorganisms.

Root sloughage is considered to be the main source of carbon released by roots. Besides this the production of mucilage contributes much to the transfer of organic carbon from roots to the soil. Mucilage is a layer of granular and fibrillar material covering the surface of roots and root hairs. This slimy material consists mainly of polysaccharides with galactose, fucose and uronic acids as the most important monomeric building blocks (PAUL et al. [1975]). It is now well established from the investigations of PAUL and JONES [1975, 1976] with maize root cap slime, that the polysaccharides are produced in the root cap cells. It is believed that the dictyosomes are the site of polysaccharide synthesis and that these microbodies are also involved in polysaccharide transport and secretion.

Bacteria may feed from the slimy material excreted by roots. As shown in Plate 2.4 from the work of GUCKERT et al. [1975] bacteria are embedded in the slime and may dissolve the polysaccharides by lytic enzymes. The mucilage is capable of adsorbing clay minerals (BREISCH et al. [1975]) and thus brings about a close contact between the root and the soil, with the slime filling the spaces between roots and soil particles. This close contact is of importance for nutrient and water supply. If for example a plant is moved from one soil to another the close contact formed by slime between root hairs and soil particles is destroyed. On replanting, this has to be re-established by the production of slime and the development of new root hairs. The period following replanting is thus a critical one because of this absence of a close contact between roots and soil.

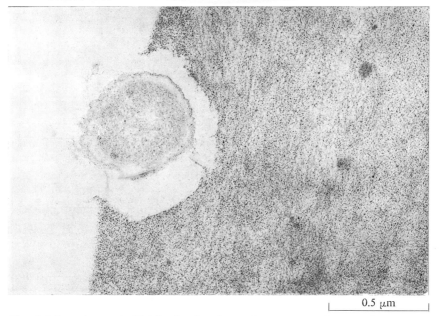

0.5 µm

Plate 2.4 Bacterium embedded in the slime layer of a root. The slime (mucigel) has been dissolved around the bacterium. (Electronmicrograph: GUCKERT, BREISCH and REISINGER).

Besides polysaccharide excretion, roots exude a number of other organic compounds of which amino acids, sugars and organic acids are the most frequent in occurrence. The release of these compounds by plant roots is of direct importance to microorganisms living in the rhizosphere as these organisms feed from the exuded organic material. This microbial activity in the rhizosphere is to a large extent dependent on plant metabolism. Plants growing under favourable conditions for example translocate considerable quantities of photosynthates to the roots so that root metabolic activity is high and the rhizosphere is well supplied with organic carbon compounds.

The enrichment of the rhizosphere with organic compounds (sugars, amino acids) which can readily be utilized by microbes results in a considerably higher microbial density in the rhizosphere than in the bulk soil. The ratio between the microbial densities of the rhizosphere and soil (rhizosphere = R, bulk soil = S) may be as high as 100 (KATZNELSON [1946]). Table 2.13 shows this R/S ratio and the bacterial density in the root free soil and in the rhizosphere for a number of crops (ROVIRA and DAVEY [1974]).

Table 2.13 Bacterial colony counts in the rhizosphere of crop plants and in the root free soil (after ROVIRA and DAVEY [1974])

Crop	Colony count 10^6 g^{-1} soil		R/S ratio
	Root free	Rhiszosphere	
Red clover.....................	134	3,255	24
Oats	184	1,090	6
Flax	184	1,015	6
Wheat........................	120	710	6
Maize........................	184	614	3
Barley	140	505	3

Rhizosphere microorganisms may be grouped into bacteria fungi and actinomyces. Bacteria thrive especially under neutral pH conditions, whereas the relative proportion of fungi is higher under acid conditions (TROLLDENIER [1971]). Exudation of organic compounds by plant roots can have a specific as well as general effect on the microbial population. Thus amino acids and sugars selectively stimulate the gram negative bacteria. Chemotactic relationships between root exudates and particular soil bacteria have also been observed, as for example between individual strains of *Rhizobium* and root exudates of legumes (CURRIER and STROBEL [1976]). *Actinomyces* may produce antibiotics and thus suppress bacterial and fungal growth in the rhizosphere.

Microorganisms directly involved in the turnover of plant nutrients are of particular importance for plant nutrition. These microorganisms include the free living N_2 fixers, the ammonifying bacteria and the denitrifying bacteria.

The N_2 fixers live in close association with the plant root. Under favourable conditions they may fix considerable amounts of nitrogen (NEYRA and DÖBEREINER [1977]). This particular question is considered in more detail on p. 337 The ammonifying bacteria produce NH_3 from the exuded amino acids and the proteins present in the debris of root cells. Ammonia thus released may be reabsorbed by the plant, incorporated into microbial bodies or even fixed by clay minerals. The denitrifying bacteria produce volatile N compounds under anaerobic conditions (see p. 343). Species of *Nitrosomonas* and *Nitrobacter* which produce nitrite or nitrate respectively are less frequent in the root vicinity (ROVIRA and DAVEY [1974]).

The question of whether rhizosphere microorganisms are strong competitors with plant roots for inorganic nutrients has been a matter of controversy. BARBER and FRANKENBURG [1971] claim that under low phosphate availability conditions, microorganisms may successfully compete with plant roots for phosphate. EPSTEIN [1972] holds the view that the competitive effect of the rhizosphere microorganisms must be negligible, as the biomass of the rhizosphere amounts to only 0.01% of the root biomass, with the demand of rhizosphere organisms for inorganic nutrients being low in absolute terms. Whether organic compounds such as acids and chelates produced by the rhizosphere organisms have a major influence on nutrient dissolution and nutrient availability is still an open question. It may be supposed that nutrients such as Fe, Cu and Zn at least which are chelated by organic compounds produced by microorganisms are rendered more available to higher plants (LINDSAY [1974]).

The pH of the rhizosphere is very much dependent on the form of nitrogen supply to the plant. Plants supplied with NO_3-N take up more inorganic anions than cations with a net excretion of OH^- (HCO_3^-) ions. For NH_4-fed plants a higher uptake of cations than anions occurs with a net efflux of H^+ into the rhizosphere (see p. 137). The pH of the rhizosphere may thus be up to one unit higher than the bulk soil for plants supplied with NO_3-N and one unit lower for NH_4-fed plants. For legumes fixing N_2 there is also a similar drop in the pH in the root vicinity (STEFFENS [1981]). The importance of these pH shifts in influencing phosphate availability has been convincingly demonstrated by RILEY and BARBER [1971].

Plant roots also exude organic acids. RIVIÈRE [1960] detected a number of different organic acids including acetic, propionic, butyric, and valeric acids. The more recent results of MOGHIMI *et al.* [1978] are of particular interest since these authors isolated 2 keto-gluconate from the rhizosphere of wheat roots in amounts that could solubilize considerable amounts of phosphate from hydroxyapatite. It remains to be seen whether this or other acids play an important role in enabling roots to acquire phosphate.

2.3.8 Mycorrhizae

Mycorrhizal fungi occur in soils in close association with plant roots. These fungi may be divided into two groups, the ectotrophic and the endotrophic mycorrhizae. The ectotrophic mycorrhizae cover roots and rootlets with a thick mantel of hyphae. This is shown in Plate 2.5 for roots of *Pinus silvestris* (TROLLDENIER [1971]). The fungal sheath spreads between the cortical cell of the roots thus enabling the fungus to maintain a close contact with the plant. These fungi which belong to the *Basidiomycetes*, are dependent on carbohydrates which are supplied by the root. It has been shown that C-14 labelled photosynthates are rapidly translocated not only to the roots but also into the sheath and hyphae of mycorrhizal fungi (HARLEY [1971]). Carbohydrate, mainly in the form of sucrose, obtained from the host root are rapidly converted into typical fungal sugars such as trehalose or mannitol. In this way the organic carbon is trapped because these sugars are only poorly reassimilated by the plant root. It has been shown that the transport of assimilates from the aerial

Plate 2.5 Young *Pinus silvestris* with mycorrhiza (left), hyphae mantel around root tip (right). (TROLLDENIER [1971]).

plant parts towards the roots is higher in mycorrhizal infected plants than in non infected plants. The mycorrhiza is thus a sink for photosynthates.

The thick sheath of hyphae covering the roots favours the uptake of water and inorganic nutrients, especially phosphate since it effectively enlarges the surface area of the root in direct contact with the soil. The thin mycorrhizal hyphae (diameter 2 to 4 μm) are able to penetrate soil pores not accessible to the root hairs with a diameter about 5 times greater than the hyphal diameter (SCHLECHTE [1976]). According to GERDEMANN [1974] infected roots live longer than non infected ones. The finest lateral rootlets, which have a very short life in uninfected conditions and remain unbranched, respond to mycorrhizal infection by growing for a longer period of time and by branching. In this way the mycorrhizal fungi assist the root in exploiting the soil for water and nutrients. It has been shown that phosphate taken up by the hyphae is transferred to the host root. The fungus may also accumulate plant nutrients and supply these to the plant in periods of low soil nutrient availability. It thus appears that the host plant supplies the mycorrhiza with photosynthates and the fungus in turn supplies the plant with inorganic nutrients.

Ectotrophic mycorrhizae are mainly found on the roots of trees and shrubs and are of economic importance for the growth of forest trees. Numerous investigations have shown that the ectotrophic mycorrhizae promote the growth of trees when grown on soils low in available phosphate. There are cases where the mycorrhiza is essential for growth. It has thus been reported that seedlings of *Pinus* and *Picea* planted on newly drained organic soils only grew when the roots were infected with the appropriate mycorrhizal fungus (SCHLECHTE [1976]). Similar observations have been made by HENDERSON and STONE [1970].

Fungi of the endotrophic mycorrhizae are members of the *Phycomycetes* and *Basidiomycetes*. The hyphae of these fungi, in contrast to those of the ectotrophic mycorrhizae, penetrate the cells of the root cortex forming an internal hyphal network. Some hyphae also extend into the soil (see plates 9.1b and 9.1c).

For many plant species including most agricultural crops the predominant type of fungal infection is vesicular arbuscular mycorrhiza (VAM). This name derives from the occurrence of two types of structures characteristic of the infection, vesicles and arbuscules (HARLEY [1971]). These Phycomycetous fungi belong to the family *Endogonaceae*. A diagrammatic representation of vesicular arbuscular mycorrhiza is shown in Figure 2.21. The fungus may be considered as a two-phase system with a mycelium in the cortex connected to an external mycelium in the rhizosphere and soil. The figure shows a hyphae penetrating the cortex by producing a series of branches both outside and

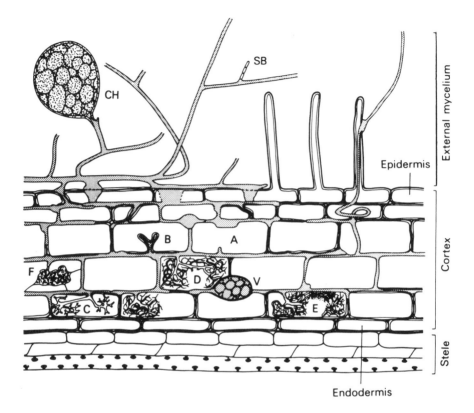

Fig.2.21 Schematic diagram of the association of vesicular arbuscular mycorrhizal fungi and a plant root. The external mycelium bears large chlamydospores (CH) and occasional septate side branches (SB). Infection of the plant can occur through root hairs or between epidermal cells. Arbusculae at progressive stages in development and senescence are shown (A–F) as is also a vesicle (V). To avoid confusion cell walls of the root are not indicated when they underlay fungal hyphae (from a drawing by F.E. SANDERS, p. 129, Plant Root Systems by R. SCOTT RUSSELL 1977 by courtesy of The McGraw Hill Book Company).

within the cortex cells. It also shows the presence of structures at different stages in development with a shrub-like appearance called arbuscules *(arbuscula,* Latin = shrub). These structures are similar to haustoria but are produced by dichotomous branching of hyphae. The second type of structure the vesicle (*vesicula* Latin = small bladder) may be formed by swelling of the hyphae and may occur within or between cells. An example of one of these thick-walled structures is shown in the Figure. External vesicles also develop on the external hyphae.

The association between the host and fungus is well co-ordinated. Young feeder roots show no sign of damage when infected. Indeed the living root is essential for the culture of these fungi (HAYMAN [1980]). This symbiotic relationship between host and fungus in principle is the same as that between the ectotropic mycorrhiza and host plant, the host plant supplying the fungus with organic carbon compounds and the fungus assisting the roots in exploiting the soil for water and inorganic nutrients. The relationship is of particular importance for phosphorus nutrition since phosphate depletion zones can readily occur around plant roots (see p. 67). The network of hyphae extending from the root into the soil, as with the ectomycorrhizae, enlarges the contact area between the soil and the fungus-host root association and hence facilitates a greater uptake rate of phosphate. This has been demonstrated by SANDERS and TINKER [1973] for onion. Recent results of CRESS et al. [1979] also indicate the possibility that rate of phosphate uptake by the hyphae may be higher than that by the root. Phosphate translocation in the hyphae appears to be rapid. According to investigations by COX et al. [1980] with onion mycorrhizae, phosphate is translocated in the form of small polyphosphate granules by cytoplasmatic streaming. Phosphate taken up by the fungi is from the 'labile pool' of soil phosphate (see p. 388), and hence from a readily available phosphate fraction. Mycorrhizal fungi appear to have little ability to utilize insoluble forms of P such as rock phosphates. Plants with root systems of low specific surface areas with fleshy roots and few root hairs profit most in phosphate uptake from the vesicular arbuscular mycorrhiza, root association. These plants include onions, citrus and grapevine. In legumes, nodulation and nitrogen fixation may be much increased in plants which are infected by mycorrhizae. The rate of absorption of Zn and Cu is also believed to be enhanced by mycorrhizal infection.

Most crop species, except those of the brassica family and sugar beet (Chenopodiaceae) have VA mycorrhizae. Infection is widespread in the Leguminosae and Gramineae and thus found in pasture and forage legumes in maize, wheat, barley and many vegetables. Plantation crops such as coffee, tea, cocoa, oil palm, papaya, and rubber are known for their heavy mycorrhizal infection (HAYMAN [1980]). Cassava is believed to be obigately associated with a vesicular-arbuscular mycorrhiza and for this reason is able to grow reasonable well even on phosphate deficient soils.

The possibility exists that inoculation of crops with appropriate strains of mycorrhizal fungi may result in significant yield increases. Best results are likely to occur on phosphate deficient soils or on soils which fix phosphate in huge quantities e.g. the ferrallitic soils of the tropics.

2.4 Determination of Nutrient Availability

2.4.1 General

Ever since man has grown crops it has been well known that soils differ widely in their fertility. Understanding the factors which underlie the phenomenon of soil 'fertility', or the capability of a soil to produce good plant growth has therefore been of interest for a very long time. It is only relatively recently, however, that it has become more and more evident that soil fertility is dependent both on physical and chemical properties of the soil. The discovery, made in the 19th century, that plants receive most of their chemical constituents from the soil, revealed that one of the components of soil fertility is the content of plant nutrients present within the soil. As already discussed in detail, however, the total content of plant nutrients in the soil is not of primary importance in this respect, but rather the content of soluble and easily accessible nutrients. The determination of this available nutrient fraction can be carried out by various techniques. These differ basically in principle and three very different approaches are provided by the methods of soil analysis, plant analysis, and plant experiments (pot and field experiments).

2.4.2 Soil sampling and interpretation of soil tests

All soil analytical methods depend very much on careful soil sampling, as the nutrient content of a soil can differ markedly not only on the same profile but even in the same horizon. For a given soil, sufficient sub-samples must therefore be collected in order to obtain a representative sample. This is particularly true for the determination of available N, as the N content of the soil can differ widely from one site to another. For phosphate and K, 25 sub-samples per ha are generally regarded as sufficient in obtaining a representative sample (HANOTIAUX [1966]).

In interpreting soil analytical data the density of the soil should also be considered. The most important factor influencing this is the soil organic matter content. Generally the higher the organic matter content of a soil, the lower is its density. For an organic soil for example, 100 g of soil implies a considerably higher soil volume than for an inorganic soil. The quantity of an available nutrient as determined by an extraction method on a weight basis thus also refers to a larger soil volume. Caution must therefore be exercised when comparing available nutrients from organic and inorganic soils. In order to overcome this difficulty calculations of available nutrients are often expressed on a unit area basis, *e.g.* 'available kg P or K per ha'. For the necessary calculation only the top 20–30 cms of the soil are taken into account.

There are other difficulties associated with the interpretation of soil analytical data. From the data alone it is not possible to say precisely what constitutes a soil of poor fertility for any given particular nutrient. The same also holds in estimating a critical level above which no further yield increase will result from additional fertilizer application. Generally values lower than 50 ppm soluble P or 80 ppm exchangeable K are indicative of soils capable of significant yield responses following application of the appropriate nutrient. Fertilizer responses may well be obtained, however, in soils with higher contents of available P and K than for the values shown above. So much depends on other factors and in particular on the soil type and textures of the soils involved. Thus as well as using soil analytical data, fertilizer recommendations should be based on the soil class and type to which the fertilizer is being applied.

As already discussed, it is necessary to distinguish between nutrient intensity and nutrient quantity (see page 71). Unfortunately most soil analytical methods give results which are dependent on both. In extreme cases two soils may have the same amount of available phosphate as determined by one particular method, but both their phosphate intensity and quantity measurements may differ considerably. For this reason application of phosphate fertilizer may give rise to quite different responses on the two soils concerned. The same is also true for K. Account must therefore be taken of both quantity and intensity measurements.

Another important aspect which must be considered in relation to nutrient availability is the difference in nutrient requirement between crops. High yielding crops and intensive cropping systems place a greater demand on available nutrients in the soil and particularly on phosphate and K. This is especially the case where high N levels are applied. Differences in nutrient uptake between crop species are considered on page 296.

For the reliable interpretation and utilization of soil analytical data for a given crop in a particular environment comparative field experiments must be carried out. Here again difficulties can arise as soil analytical data and yield responses do not always correlate. Nutrient availability is so much dependent on the plant/soil relationship as for example on soil moisture and root growth so that considerable seasonal differences may occur. It is for this reason that soil analytical data by themselves cannot provide absolutely reliable information. This in no way belittles the importance of soil testing. The data provide a relative indication of soil fertility status, particularly when regular sampling is carried out over a period of several years. It is then possible to observe the trends in fertility of a soil by recording increases or decreases in the content of 'available' nutrients. Fertilizer application generally enriches the upper soil layer with nutrients. This is especially true for K^+ and phosphate (HANITIAUX and MANIL 1963).

2.4.3 Estimation of cations

In soil analysis most methods of available nutrient estimation still involve treatment of the soil with a suitable extractant to remove an accessible nutrient fraction. This is the case for the cationic nutrients. For these nutrients the easily accessible ions in the soil are made up by cations either dissolved in the soil solution or adsorbed on inorganic and organic exchange complexes. The greater proportion are in exchangeable form. It is for this reason that the determination of available cations is based on the analysis of exchangeable cations. The extractants used contain an excess of a cation species which is able to exchange with the adsorbed cation nutrient. This principle is applied in the determination of exchangeable soil K^+ and Mg^{2+}. Using this type of extraction a high proportion of the total exchangeable and nearly all the dissolved cations of the soil solution can be removed from the soil and then determined in the extract. This estimation gives an indication of the quantity factor of the nutrient concerned. A number of different extractants are used in various methods but the principle is the same. Frequently NH_4 acetate or NH_4Cl are employed in the determination of exchangeable K^+ and Mg^{2+}. 'Exchangeable K', however, is often not a satisfactory parameter for measuring K^+ availability as it does not distinguish between the solution K^+ and adsorbed K^+. Soil K^+ availability can be assessed more reliably from the K^+ concentration of the equilibrated soil solution at a given soil moisture together with the K^+ buffer capacity. In the Netherlands available K^+ is determined by extraction of the soil sample with 0.1 M HCl. In this case H^+ is the exchanging cation. As K^+ availability also depends on the pH and on the content of clay and humus, the amount of K^+ extracted by 0.1 M HCl is adjusted by a correction factor, which takes into account the clay, pH, and the humus content of the soil. The resulting value is called the 'K-value'. The method, predominantly used in Germany for the determination of available K^+ is based on the extraction of the soil with an acid Ca lactate solution. This extractant is a 0.025 M Ca lactate made up to pH 3.6 with HCl (EGNER [1955], RIEHM [1959]). Available Mg^{2+} is usually determined by extraction with 0.0125 M $CaCl_2$ (SCHACHTSCHABEL [1954]). Details of the various methods and extractants used for exchangeable cations can be found in the standard texts on soil chemical analysis (JACKSON [1958], HESSE [1971]).

2.4.4 Estimation of phosphates

The determination of available soil phosphate is complicated, as phosphates of varying availability are present in the soil. In contrast to the available cationic nutrients, available phosphate is not only a measure of the exchangeable phosphate but of the solubility of soil phosphates. The most important soil phosphates are the Ca phosphates, phosphates adsorbed to soil colloids, and organic phosphates. The solubility of the inorganic soil phosphates not only depends on their chemical nature. The age and the surface area of the minerals are also important in this context. Generally freshly precipitated phosphates are more readily soluble. On ageing there is an increase in crystal size with a consequent decrease in surface area. Also as the phosphate minerals age some phosphates may diffuse into other minerals such as Fe and Al oxides and so become less available. The presence of other ion species in the soil solution may also affect the availability of phosphates (SCHUFFELEN [1971]). For the Ca phosphates, H^+ generally increases and Ca^{2+} decreases their solubility. The reverse is true for Al and Fe phosphates (see page 389).

It is for this reason that the choice of extractant depends very much on which phosphates are present in a particular soil. In calcareous soils the method of OLSEN et al. [1954] is particularly suitable for phosphate extraction, as this is an alkaline solution (0.5 M $NaHCO_3$, pH 8.5) and has relatively little effect on apatites in comparison with acid extractants. For more neutral and acid soils a very wide range of extractants have been used. Bray's method for example (BRAY and KURTZ [1945]), which uses a 0.03 M $NH_4F + 0.025$ M HCl solution (pH 3.5), gives reliable results for such soils (WERNER [1969]). In the USA Truog's method (0.001 $NH_2SO_4 + [NH_4]_2SO_4$, pH 3.0) and Morgan's method (Na acetate + acetic acid, pH 4.8) are also commonly used in the determination of available soil phosphate (TRUOG [1930], LATHWELL and PEECH [1964]). 1% citric acid as suggested by DYER [1894] is still frequently employed. The use of various extractants and their relative merits in available phosphate estimation have been thoroughly treated by HESSE [1971].

More recently the extraction of soil phosphate by water has proved a useful tool in determining available soil phosphate. According to investigations of VAN DER PAAUW [1962, 1969] it appears that this method is hardly affected by the soil type (content of humus, clay, lime, pH value). Unlike most of the methods described earlier water extraction gives a very good indication of the phosphate concentration of the soil solution. The extract is made up to a large extent of phosphate from the soil solution, for phosphate minerals are scarcely soluble in water. The same also holds for extraction with 0.01 M $CaCl_2$ which is sometimes used. Both methods are very useful as the separation of the soil solution itself is not easy. As the concentration of phosphate in the soil solution represents the intensity factor, estimations of water or dilute $CaCl_2$ extracts may be considered as intensity measurements. The finding that the water extraction method gives phosphate values which correlate with dry matter yield production better than with other methods (VAN DER PAAUW [1969]). OBIGBESAN [1970] indicates that phosphate intensity is frequently a more satisfactory measurement of phosphate availability than other estimations. This is supported by the findings of WILLIAMS and KNIGHT [1963] who analysed a selection of different soils using various extractants. Mild extractants of intermediate pH with fairly short extractant periods, and hence more indicative of intensity than quantity measurements, gave the highest correlations with yield. Intensity measurements are particularly useful in phosphate enriched agricultural soils where the concentration of phosphate in the soil solution can be sustained by a high phosphate capacity. The intensity factor is also important in relation to early growth and in highly responsive rapidly growing crops such as potatoes.

As already indicated absolute values for available phosphate depend very much on the type of extractant used. Table 2.14 shows the mean values of 'available' phosphate from the data of WILLIAMS and KNIGHT [1963] in which 40 different soils were treated with various extractants. The phosphate contents in air dried soil generally found by these various methods are in the range of between about 5 to 250 ppm P and more. Contents most common for arable soils are in a range of between 50 to 100 ppm P.

Table 2.14 Readily-soluble P values using various extraction methods. Results obtained from 40 soils (mg P_2O_5/100 g air dried soil) (WILLIAMS and KNIGHT [1963])

Extractant	Phosphate content
Neutral NH_4F	33.6
Acid NH_4F	16.8
Acetic acid	5.7
Sulphuric acid (TRUOG)	8.2
Lactate	2.7
Bicarbonate	5.4

Another approach to assess plant available soil phosphate status has been to extract phosphate ions from soil using synthetic anion exchange resins. Results obtained have often correlated quite well with plant P uptake (SIBBESEN [1978], and BACHE and IRELAND [1980]). The probable reason why the method gives a better correlation with P uptake than the other methods using single extractants is that the exchange resin may more satisfactorily simulate the absorbing root. The recent development by SIBBESEN [1977] to simplify the procedure of phosphate desorption by retaining the resin in nylon netting bags immersed in soil suspensions will undoubtedly assist in the development of this approach of investigating P availability.

2.4.5 Tracer techniques

About twenty years ago a new approach was made to determining available soil nutrients with the aid of radioactive elements. The technique is particularly applicable to nutrients elements with suitable radioactive isotopes such as P-32 and Ca-45 whose half lives and radioactive emission is such that it enables their fate to be followed in the soil. The principle of the methods used is based on the concept that a radioactive isotope which is added to the soil equilibrates with that fraction of its stable element in the soil which is accessible to the plant. This fraction is termed the 'labile pool' and includes nutrients which are in solution or can readily pass into it. When for example radioactive phosphate is added to a soil suspension it will mix with soil phosphate and exchange with soil colloids and with the solid phosphates such as Ca and Al and Fe phosphates. Eventually isotopic equilibrium will be attained. The study of nutrient availability and particularly that of phosphate has largely been aided by observations of dilution and exchange of isotopes under such equilibrium conditions.

If a solution of a radioactive substance is added to a solution of the same substance in unlabelled form, on the attainment of equilibrium, the ratio of labelled to unlabelled atoms will be constant throughout the system. This may be expressed as an equation:

$$\frac{\text{Total unlabelled substance}}{\text{Total labelled substance}} = \frac{\text{Unlabelled substance in any sample}}{\text{Labelled substance in any sample}}$$

The process is called isotopic dilution and it offers a very simple means of measuring the total quantity of an unlabelled substance. It is only necessary to add a known amount of a labelled form and withdraw a sample for analysis after equilibration.

Where soil is being considered, as was pointed out earlier, the presence of both a liquid and a charged solid phase, means that both dilution and exchange processes are involved. For a surface from which ions are in constant exchange with chemically identical ions in solution, the addition of an isotope to the same solution will result in the following reaction:

$$\text{E exch.} + \text{E* sol.} \rightleftarrows \text{E* exch.} + \text{E sol.}$$

where E is an ion and E* its isotope.
At equilibrium:

$$\frac{\text{E* exch.}}{\text{E* sol.}} = \frac{\text{E exch.}}{\text{E sol.}}$$

E exch. = exchangeable ion
E sol. = ion in solution

This principle was developed for the determination of phosphorus availability in soils by MCAULIFFE et al. [1947]. If P is substituted into the above equation the following holds

$$\frac{\text{P-32 exch.}}{\text{P-32 sol.}} = \frac{\text{P-31 exch.}}{\text{P-31 sol.}}$$

Using this equation P-31 exchangeable may be calculated as the other terms may be determined experimentally. P-31 (solution) and P-32 (solution) are the concentrations of stable phosphate and radioactive phosphate respectively in the soil solution after equilibration between the isotopic and stable phosphate has been attained. The term P-32 (exchangeable) is equal to the difference between the amount of P-32 added to the soil suspension and the amount in the soil solution at equilibrium.

MCAULIFFE et al. [1947] used this technique to estimate what they described as 'surface phosphate' as they held the view that the more rapid stage of isotopic dilution in a soil suspension only involved phosphates on the surface of solid particles. The work was extended by RUSSELL et al. [1954] who developed a rapid laboratory method for estimating available phosphates. These workers made no assumptions concerning the origin of the labile phosphorus. It was realised that isotope equilibration is never fully attained under laboratory conditions but recognised that after some time the rate decreases considerably. They therefore chose an arbitrary time of 48 hours for shaking suspensions of soil with radioactive phosphates and estimated total exchangeable phosphate which they termed the E or exchangeable value.

The estimation of exchangeable nutrients by this isotopic dilution procedure is not limited to phosphate. It is equally applicable to other nutrients and efforts have been made to determine available K with the use of isotopic K (GRAHAM and KAMPBELL [1968]), although the short half life of the isotope limits the method.

A further approach to determine available phosphate with the help of P-32 was made by LARSEN [1952]. This was to follow the specific activity of phosphorus taken up by a test crop grown in a labelled soil. In his method the soil is thoroughly mixed with the carrier free P-32 present as soluble phosphate. Ryegrass is usually taken as the test crop so that several cuts can be taken, the growth period of the plant allowing for isotopic dilution to occur.

Using the equation for isotopic dilution an L (labile value) can be calculated:

$$L = \left(\frac{C_o}{C} - 1\right) X$$

where C_0 and C are the specific activities of the applied phosphorus and plant phosphorus respectively, and X the amount of phosphorus added. In practice it was found that the L value was independent of the amount of P added and became independent of time suggesting that isotopic equilibrium had been attained during the growth period. The L value itself is a measure of the total quantity of plant available soil phosphorus. It has been defined as 'the amount of P in the soil and soil solution on the attainment of isotopic equilibrium that is exchangeable with orthophosphate ions added to the soil as measured by the plant growing in the system' (LARSEN [1967a]). In principle the concept of the E and L values is the same. Both are quantity measures of labile phosphorus but whilst the E value is calculated from chemical estimations on the soil solution, the plant is used for the L value. This accounts for the high correlation between both estimations. As has been pointed out by LARSEN [1967], however, the estimations are not identical, as isotopic exchange occurs under different environmental conditions for E and L values determination. The E value refers to a soil surface where no phosphorus removal takes place. For the L value the soil is at a moisture level below field capacity, and some removal of phosphorus is taking place which might well cause more extensive dilution than by isotopic exchange alone. Both procedures have been used by a number of workers within recent years (LARSEN and COOKE [1961], LARSON and SUTTON [1963], NUTTALL et al. [1967], ÖZBEK [1969]).

The L value gives the best measurement of the quantity factor. In the field this is dependent on the volume of soil effectively utilized by plant roots, soil depth, physical conditions in the profile and the quantity and distribution of moisture (WILLIAMS [1970]). The quantity of labile phosphate is especially important in relation to availability when soils are poor in phosphate and when crops have a sustained demand for phosphate supply over a long period such as in grass production. Under such conditions there is evidence of a higher correlation between phosphate uptake and quantity than between phosphate uptake and intensity measurements (WILLIAMS [1970]).

Another approach to nutrient availability in which the use of radioactive isotopes has sometimes been employed is in the determination of the availability index or A value. This concept was first put forward by FRIED and DEAN [1952]. They suggested that if a plant is confronted with two sources of a nutrient, one of which was the soil and the other which was a known amount of fertilizer standard, the amount of available nutrient can be determined provided the proportion of the nutrient in the plant derived from the standard can be determined. In putting forward this concept the authors did not include the means of measurement. It has, however, been applied to the estimation of available phosphates using P-32 supplied with fertilizer. Of necessity, the time of such estimations must be kept to a minimum because the nutrient fertilizer source will equilibrate with the soil. The original concept has been applied to the estimation of the availability of a number of nutrients including Zn, Ca, N and S. In the literature there is frequent confusion in the use of L, E and A values. The conceptual differences between these measurements have been discussed very concisely by both FRIED [1964] and LARSEN [1967].

2.4.6 Electro-ultrafiltration technique (EUF technique)

A technique has recently been developed by NÉMETH and coworkers by which different soil nutrient fractions may be obtained thus enabling the distinction between nutrient intensity (soil solution concentration) and nutrient quantity (exchangeable and easily soluble nutrients). The concept of this technique follows earlier investigations by KÖTTHEN [1933]. The principle of this method is based on the use of an electrial field to separate nutrient fractions from a soil suspension. During the separation the voltage is increased from 50 to 400 V, thus increasing the force by which plant nutrients are desorbed from soil particles. The first fraction obtained after 10 minutes at a voltage of 50 V correlates highly with the nutrient concentrations in the soil solution thus representing the intensity factor. The nutrients obtained at a higher voltage correlate with the exchangeable and easily soluble nutrients. Hence this fraction represents the quantity factor. In one extraction more than ten different plant nutrients can be determined. First results obtained by this technique are encouraging as fertilizer recommendations based on EUF data have correlated well with crop responses (NÉMETH and HARRACH [1974], NÉMETH [1975]). WANASURIA et al. [1981] reported that in flooded rice soils, EUF extractable K^+ was a better indicator of the K^+ availability than was exchangeable K^+. The EUF technique and its application have been recently described by NÉMETH [1979].

2.4.7 Estimation of available nitrogen

The estimation of available N in the soil presents even more difficulties than the determination of the availability of the other macronutrients. Soil N is not primarily affected by physical and chemical reactions, but depends very much on biological processes. Generally the bulk of soil N is present as organic N, and its availability is dependent on the process of mineralization in which organic N is converted to NH_4–N. The rate of mineralization of organic N and the further conversion by which NH_4–N is transformed to NO_3–N (see page 341) are considerably influenced by soil moisture (SABEY [1969]) and temperature. This is one of the reasons why the content of soluble N in the soil solution – mainly nitrate –

can vary so much (HARMSEN [1959]). For this reason the determination of the nitrate concentration of the soil solution does not generally provide a reliable means of estimation of the N availability of a soil, even though with modern equipment such as the nitrate electrode the nitrate content of soil extracts can very easily be determined (MYERS and PAUL [1968]). The determination of the total organic N of a soil also gives no indication of the N availability. In most cases, however, the rate of mineralization soil organic N is higher the narrower the C/N ratio of the soil organic matter. This means that for soils with a relatively high N organic matter content, the rate of release of inorganic N is also high and *vice versa*. The relationship between the rate of N mineralized and the C/N ratio of the soils (C Total/N Total) is shown in Figure 2.22 (VAN DIJK [1968]). According to VAN DIJK [1968] besides the C/N ratio of the organic matter the total amount of N in the profile controls the rate of N mineralization. For other soil classes this relationship was found to be less reliable.

The most common procedure for the determination of available soil N is the incubation method. In this estimation soil is moistened to a given water content and incubated for a period of 2 to 3 weeks at a temperature of about 25 to 37 °C, depending on the particular method used. During this incubation period mi-

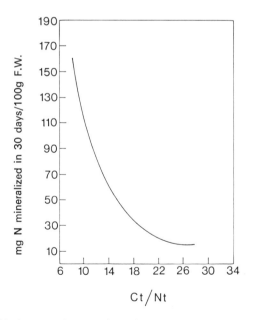

Fig. 2.22 Relationship between the rate of N mineralized and the C/N ratio of the organic matter (modified after VAN DIJK [1968]).

croorganisms are provided with optimum conditions for mineralization of soil organic N. The amount of N mineralized during the incubation period as measured by released NH_4 and NO_3–N provides a measure of the N availability of the soil concerned. Details of the various techniques based on this principle are thoroughly treated by BREMNER [1965].

The determination of the nitrate content in the rooting zone of the soil profile has been used successfully by several authors as a measure of available nitrogen (SOPER and HUANG [1962], BORST and MULDER [1971]). In recent years this technique has been applied widely in West Germany by WEHRMANN and co-workers in estimating available nitrogen for winter wheat. Soil samples are taken in early spring (February, March) from rooting depth, which may be as deep as 1 m, and the fresh samples (about 150 g non dried soil) are extracted with 600 ml $NaCl + CaCl_2$ (1 N + 0.1 N) for a period of one hour. This procedure extracts nitrate and non specifically adsorbed NH_4^+ is exchanged. Both these N fractions are determined. Generally nitrate is by far the greater fraction and only where organic manure, particularly slurry, has been applied, are high amounts of NH_4-N found. The quantity of $NO_3^- + NH_4^+$ extracted is calculated on a hectare basis allowing for the water content of the soil sample, the compactness of the soil and the rooting depth. The quantity of available N thus obtained is expressed as kg N/ha (SCHARPF and WEHRMANN [1975]) and this is used as a basis on which to make N fertilizer recommendations. Numerous field experiments carried out by WEHRMANN and SCHARPF [1979] have shown that the quantity of available N thus found in early spring must be made up by a mineral N application so that the sum of both, available N + applied N, is in the order of 120 to 140 kg N/ha. This amount guarantees optimum N supply during the vegetative growth stage of winter wheat under the growing conditions of West Germany. In addition to this early N application a further treatment of 40 to 60 kg N/ha is also recommended at a later stage in growth. This technique of estimating mineral N in the soil profile in early spring is known as the 'Nmin-method'. It has proved a useful tool in estimating available N and is now applied extensively in West Germany and the Netherlands. Only on soils which mineralize high amounts of N (>30 kg N/ha) during spring and early summer is the technique not so suitable as a basis for nitrogen fertilizer recommendation.

2.4.8 Leaf analysis, plant analysis and tissue analysis

The analysis of plant material presents another type of approach in determining the nutrient availability of a soil. This technique is based on the concept that the content of a particular nutrient in the plant is greater the higher its availability in the soil. The method was developed by LUNDEGÅRDH [1945] more than thirty years ago. In principle the concept is sound, because plant nutrients present in the plant must originally have been available in the soil. Unfortunately, however, the technique also has its drawbacks, as the mineral content in the plant not only depends on nutrient availability in the soil, but is also affected by various other factors, which will be discussed in more detail below.

There is a basic relationship between the content of a plant nutrient and the growth or yield of the plant. This is shown in Figure 2.23 (SMITH [1962]). When the nutrient content or concentration in the plant tissue is very low the rate of growth is also low. As the growth rate increases the nutrient content decreases slightly at first due to dilution brought about by the higher production of plant material. In the next stage the growth rate is improved without any marked change in the nutrient content. As the nutrient availability is increased the growth rate and nutrient content also increase until the so called critical level is attained. Further improvement of nutrient availability does not have any significant effect on the growth rate whereas the nutrient content is enhanced. For practical purposes the point of importance is the critical level at which no further yield increase results from an increase in nutrient content. Extremely high levels of nutrient supply impair growth and high nutrient contents are observed.

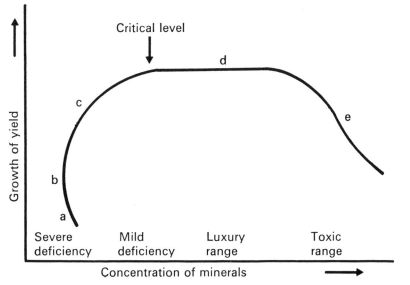

Fig. 2.23 Relationship between the nutrient content of the tissue and the growth of the plant (after SMITH [1962]).

As shown in Figure 2.23 these different stages in nutrient content correspond to severe deficiency, mild deficiency, luxury range and toxic range.

The nutrient content of a plant or a plant tissue not only reflects soil availability. It is also affected by other factors, such as the kind of plant organ or tissue, the age of the plant and the supply of the plant with other plant nutrients. A content of 0.2% P in the dry matter of straw of cereals for example may be regarded as a high P content, but the same content in the young plant would be too low to ensure optimum plant growth. A K content of 0.6% in the grain of oats is considered as high, but the same content in the vegetative plant material would also be too low for good growth. These examples demonstrate that for plant or tissue analysis the age of the plant or the plant organ in question must also be considered. Without this it is impossible to make comparisons between samples from different sites in relation to fertilizer recommendations.

Generally the contents of N, P and K decrease with the age of the plant or plant organ, whereas the contents of Ca, Mg, Mn and B often increase (Table 2.15). Young leaves therefore show relatively high contents of N, P and K, whilst in older leaves an accumulation of Ca can often be observed. For this reason leaf samples for tissue analysis should be of the same physiological age or originate from the same point of insertion in the stem.

Table 2.15 Trends of mineral content in relation to plant tissue age (SMITH [1962])

Plant	Decrease with age	Increase with age
Apple	N, P, K	Ca, Mg
Blueberry	P	Ca, Mg
Citrus	N, P, K, Cu, Zn	Ca, Mg, Mn, Fe, Al, B
Citrus (fruit)	N, P, K, Mg	Ca
Fig	N ,P, K	Ca, Mg
Peach	N, P, K, Cu, Zn	Ca, Mg, Mn, Fe, Al, B
Pine	K	Ca
Vegetables	N, P, K	Ca

In contrast to soil analysis, leaf or tissue analysis reflects nutrient uptake conditions of the soil. For example as the absorption of various plant nutrients depends on root respiration, low nutrient uptake can also result from poor soil aeration. On the other hand optimum soil moisture conditions favour the nutrient supply of the roots and hence also nutrient uptake. The resulting high nutrient contents in the plant found under such conditions may therefore result primarily from the optimum uptake conditions and only to a lesser degree from the high nutrient status of the soil (FRIIS-NIELSEN [1966]). A high content of one nutrient in the plant may also result from an inadequate supply of another plant nutrient. Where N is in short supply for example growth depressions may result in the accumulation in other plant nutrients, as N deficiency usually has a greater effect on growth rate than on nutrient uptake. In interpreting plant analytical data antagonistic and synergistic relationships between plant nutrients must also be taken into account. An antagonistic effect is one in which the uptake of one plant nutrient is restricted by another plant nutrient. A synergistic relationship is the reverse effect where the uptake of one plant nutrient is enhanced by another. The nature of antagonism and synergism is discussed more in detail on page 133.

In most cases leaf or tissue analytical data correlate fairly well with soil tests (HIPP and THOMAS [1968]), and it is therefore often held that leaf analysis can replace soil analysis and *vice versa.* As already discussed, however, leaf or tissue analysis also reflects conditions of uptake. A further difference between both techniques is the fact that the relationship between nutrient content and nutrient availability in the soil generally follows an asymptotic curve, as shown in Figure 2.24. This means that above a critical nutrient level in the plant only small changes in plant nutrient content may occur despite marked increases in nutrient availability in the soil. From this it follows that leaf or tissue analyses are

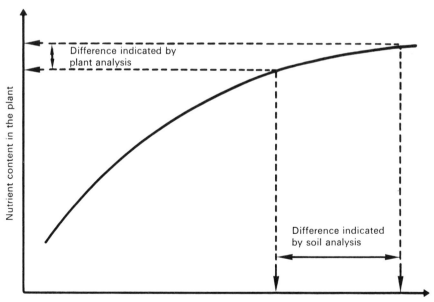

Fig.2.24 Relationship between the nutrient content in the soil solution and the nutrient content of the plant

103

particularly useful in the range of low nutrient availability. In the higher range of availability, however, leaf analysis is not sensitive enough. Here soil analysis is more appropriate.

Undoubtedly plant analysis provides a valuable tool in the determination of the nutritional status of various crops, provided that the factors mentioned above such as the specific plant tissue, the age of the plant and its supply with other nutrients are also considered. The essential feature of leaf analysis is in the determination of the critical level, above which no additional growth occurs (Figure 2.23). This has been established in numerous investigations over the past decade for various crops and nutrients (CLEMENT and HOPPER [1968], LOUÉ [1968, 1975], FINCK [1968], WARD and MILLER [1969], ULRICH and FONG [1969], GOLLMICK et al. [1970]). Table 2.16 for example shows the contents of various nutrients in maize leaves (GOLLMICK et al. [1970]). Even for the same plant species, however, critical levels may differ. Such results may originate from the wide range of environmental conditions under which these critical levels have been established. Generally it appears that with greater intensity of cropping there is a tendency for higher critical levels to be required.

Leaf or tissue analysis provides a particularly useful means of assessing the nutritional status of perennial plants such as fruit trees, vines, tea, forest trees (BAULE and FRICKER [1970]) and various plantation crops (TURNER and BARKUS [1974]). As these plants are grown for years or even decades on the same site and under the same climatic conditions, critical levels are more easily

Table 2.16 Appraisal of the nutrient status of the ear leaf of maize at the flowering stage (CHRISTENSEN cited by GOLLMICK et al. [1970])

Element	In % in the dry matter				
	Deficient	Low	Adequate	High	Excess
N..........................	<2.0	20.–2.5	2.5–3.5	>3.5	
P	<0.1	0.1–0.2	0.2–0.5	0.5–0.8	>0.8
K..........................	<1.0	1.0–1.5	1.5–3.0	3.0–5.5	>5.5
Ca..........................	<0.1	0.1–0.2	0.2–1.0	>1.0	
Mg	<0.1	0.1–0.2	0.2–1.0	>1.0	

	In ppm in the dry matter				
	Deficient	Low	Adequate	High	Excess
Mn	<10	10–20	20–200	200–350	>350
Fe	<10	10	10–300	300–550	
B	<2	3–5	6–40	40–55	>55
Cu	<2	3–5	6–50	50–70	>70
Zn........................	<15	15–20	20–70	70–150	>150

established than for annual crops. For apple trees such critical values are well established and Table 2.17 gives a range of the mineral contents of apple leaves (NEUBERT *et al.* [1970]). It must be emphasized, however, that even varieties of the same species may show considerable differences in critical levels (CHAPMAN [1966]). An example of this type of variability is presented in Table 2.18 for different citrus leaves (BAR-AKIVA [1970]). The variability of the K content of the leaves is particularly obvious. There are a number of useful texts dealing with plant analysis in relation to the diagnosis of the nutritional status of crops (CHAPMAN [1966], GOLLMICK *et al.* [1970], KOZMA [1975], BERGMANN and NEUBERT [1976]).

Table 2.17 Nutrient appraisal of apple leaves, sampled at the base of new shoots (NEUBERT *et al.* [1970])

Element	In % in the dry matter		
	Low	Adequate	High
N...	<1.8	1.8–2.4	>2.4
P...	<0.15	0.15–0.30	>0.30
K...	<1.2	1.2–1.8	>1.8
Ca..	<1.0	1.0–1.5	>1.5
Mg	<0.25	0.25–0.40	>0.40

	In ppm in the dry matter		
	Low	Adequate	High
B	<25	25–50	> 50
Cu	< 5	5–12	> 12
Mn	<35	35–105	>105
Zn..	<25	25–50	> 50
Fe	<50	50–150	>150

Table 2.18 Effect of variety on citrus leaf composition (BAR-AKIVA [1970])

(Percent in dry matter of 8–9 month-old leaves sampled from fruit-bearing terminals)

Variety	N	P	K	Ca	Mg
Shamouti orange	2.13	0.12	1.25	6.27	0.21
Washington navel orange	2.26	0.10	0.91	6.13	0.17
Valencia orange	2.10	0.08	0.56	7.02	0.23
Marsh Seedless grapefruit	1.68	0.06	0.90	6.02	0.25

As has been outlined above the use of soil analysis for estimating available N presents a number of difficulties. It is for this reason that tissue analysis for N is of special interest. ULRICH and co-workers in California have carried out numerous investigations to test whether the nitrate content of the petioles of sugar beet can serve as a guideline to evaluate the N nutrition of the crop (ULRICH et al. [1967]). The determination of 'critical values' for nitrate content is difficult, for this like soil NO_3^- can vary considerably even over short periods. The nitrate content in the petioles of sugar beet also falls with increasing age. ULRICH and HILLS [1973] report, however, that to obtain satisfactory growth recently matured sugar beet leaves must contain about 0.1% N as nitrate in the petioles.

An interesting method for the determination of the N nutritional status of the plant has been advanced by BAR-AKIVA and STERNBAUM [1965]. The concept of this method is based on the fact that nitrate reductase activity depends on the presence of nitrate in the cell. For this reason leaves abundantly supplied with nitrate have a high nitrate reductase activity and *vice versa*. The nitrate reductase enzyme assay, as the technique is called, measures the initial nitrate reductase activity in a leaf sample and the induced reductase activity resulting from the addition of nitrate to a comparative sample. The higher the induced activity as compared with the initial activity the poorer is the nitrate supply to the plant concerned. Nitrate supply is inadequate if the induced nitrate reductase activity is in excess of about 1.5 times higher than the initial nitrate reductase activity. The ratio 'induced activity/initial activity' (nitrate reductase quotient) therefore serves as measure of the N nutritional status of the plant. In crops poorly supplied

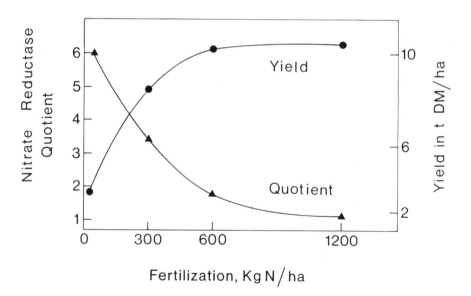

Fig. 2.25 Relationship between the nitrate reductase quotient and the yield of *Lolium* (after BAR-AKIVA *et al.* [1970]).

with N, ratios higher than 10 have been found. Interestingly enough BAR-AKIVA [1970] observed that a ratio of 1.5 can be regarded as optimum for species as different as citrus and ryegrass. The relationship between the nitrate reductase quotient and the yield of ryegrass is shown in Figure 2.25 (BAR-AKIVA *et al.* [1970]).

In some techniques the total amount of nutrients taken up by plants is used as an indicator of the soil fertility status. In the Neubauer method rye is grown for a period of two weeks in a mixture of quartz sand and of the soil under investigation. The quantities of K and P taken up from the soil by young plants over this period serve as a measure for the nutrient status of the soil (NEUBAUER and SCHNEIDER [1932]). Quantities greater than 20 mg K and 3 mg P per 100 g soil are regarded as satisfactory levels.

The Mitscherlich-method also uses a mixture of quartz sand and soil, but the plants are grown in larger pots and for a longer period as compared with the Neubauer-method. The nutrient availability of the soil is calculated (MITSCHERLICH [1954]), according to the Mitscherlich equation from the yield increments brought about by the nutrient concerned (see page 267).

2.4.9 Microbiological methods

Microbiological methods are also used in the assessment of nutrient availability in soils. Here a fungus is used rather than a higher plant. This technique has been used particularly in the determination of the availability of micronutrients such as Fe, Cu, Zn and Mo. A nutrient solution deficient in the particular nutrient in question is added to the soil under investigation. The soil suspension is then infected with a microorganism, usually *Aspergillus niger* and incubated for several days at constant temperature. The growth of the fungus as estimated by the weight of the mycelium produced is used as a measure of nutrient availability (STAPP and WETTER [1953], NICHOLAS [1960]).

General Reading

BARLEY, K.P.: The configuration of the root system in relation to nutrient uptake. Adv. Agron. *22*, 195–201 (1970)

BAVER, L.D., GARDNER, W.H. and GARDNER, W.R.: Soil Physics. John Wiley and Sons, Inc., New York, London, Sydney and Toronto 1972

BEAR, F.E.: Chemistry of the Soil. Van Nostrand Reinholt Comp., 1969

BERGMANN, W. and NEUBERT, P.: (G) Plant Diagnosis and Plant Analysis. VEB Gustav Fischer Verlag, Jena 1976

BOHN, H.L., McNEAL, B.L. and O'CONNOR, G.: Soil Chemistry. Wiley, New York, London, Sydney and Toronto 1979

BOLT, G.H. and BRUGGENWERT, M.G.M.: Soil Chemistry. Part A: Basic Elements. Elsevier Scientific Publishing Company, Amsterdam and New York, 1976

BURESH, R.J., CASSELMAN, M.E. and PATRICK, W.H. jr.: Nitrogen fixation in flooded soil systems, a review. Adv. Agron. *33*, 150–192 (1980)

CARSON, E.W., Ed.: The Plant Root and Its Environment. Univ. Press of Virginia, Charlottesville, USA, 1974

GREENLAND, D.J. and HAYES, M.H.B. Eds.: The Chemistry of Soil Constituents. Wiley, New York, London, Sydney, Toronto 1978

GREENLAND, D.J. and HAYES, M.H.B. Eds.: Chemistry of Soil Processes. Wiley, New York, London, Sydney and Toronto 1981

HALE, M.G. and MOORE, L.D.: Factors affecting root exudation II: 1970–1978. Adv. Agron. *31*, 93–124 (1979)

HARLEY, J.L. and RUSSELL, R.S.: The Soil-Root Interface. Academic Press London, New York, San Francisco 1979

HESSE, P.R.: A Testbook of Soil Chemical Analysis. John Murray, London 1971

HEWITT, E.J. and SMITH, T.A.: Plant Mineral Nutrition. English Univ. Press, 1975

JENNY, M.: The Soil Resource. Springer-Verlag, Berlin, Heidelberg, New York 1981

KOZMA, P. (F): The Control of the Mineral Nutrition of Crop Plants. 3rd European and Mediterranean Coloqu., Akademiai Kiado, Budapest 1975

MARSHALL, T.J. and HOLMES, J.W.: Soil Physics. Cambridge, 1979

NÉMÉTH, K.: The availability of nutrients in the soil as determined by electro-ultrafiltration (EUF) Adv. Agron. *31*, 155–188 (1979)

NYE, P.H.: Diffusion of ions and uncharged solutes in soils and soil clays. Adv. Agron. *31*, 225–272 (1979)

NYE, P.H. and TINKER, P.B.: Solute Movement in the Soil-Root System. Blackwell, Oxford 1977

PARFITT, R.L.: Anion adsorption by soils and soil materials. Adv. Agron. *30*, 1–50 (1978)

PONNAMPERUMA, F.N.: The chemistry of submerged soils. Adv. Agron. *24*, 29–96 (1972)

RUSSELL, E.W.: Soil Conditions and Plant Growth, Longmans, London 1973

RUSSELL, R.S.: Plant Root Systems: Their Function and Interaction with the Soil. McGraw-Hill Book Company, London, 1977

SCHEFFER, F. and SCHACHTSCHABEL, P. (G): Textbook of Soil Science. F. Enke Verlag, Stuttgart, 1976

SCHLICHTING, E. and SCHWERTMANN, U. (G): Pseudogley and Gley, Verlag Chemie, Weinheim, 1973

TAYLOR, H.M. and KLEPPER, B.: The role of rooting characteristics in the supply of water to plants. Adv. Agron. *30*, 99–128 (1978)

TINKER, P.B. Ed.: Soils and Agriculture. Critical Reports on Applied Chemistry. Vol. 2. Soc. Chem. Ind. Blackwell, Oxford 1980

TORREY, J.G. and CLARKSON, D.T.: Eds.: Development and Function of Roots. Academic Press, London, New York, San Francisco 1975

TOWNSEND, W.N.: An Introduction to the Scientific Study of the Soil. Edward Arnold, London 1973

WALSH, L.M. and BEATON, J.D.: Soil Testing and Plant Analysis, Soil Sci. Soc. of America Inc., Madison, Wisconsin, USA, 1973

WHITE, R.E.: Introduction to the Principles and Practice of Soil Science. Blackwell, Oxford 1979

(F) = original text in French
(G) = original text in German

Chapter 3:

Nutrient Uptake and Assimilation

3.1 Ion Uptake and Ionic Status of Plants

3.1.1 The plant cell

Before describing the various processes of nutrient uptake and assimilation it seems appropriate to give a simplified picture of the plant cell, for the two previous chapters have dealt primarily with inorganic materials. Ion uptake may be considered as a boundary process where the inorganic domain impinges upon the living world. The smallest viable unit of living matter is the cell. Figure 3.1

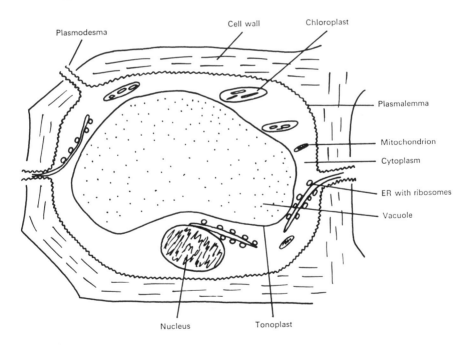

Fig.3.1 Simplified representation of a mesophyll cell (not to scale).

shows a much simplified diagram representing a mesophyll cell. The most important organelles are depicted. The cell wall structure is made up of pectic substances and cellulose. Cellulose tends to aggregate to form chain like structures known as microfibrils. Intermicrofibrillar spaces allow the entry of water, air and solute particles into the cell wall. The plasma membrane or plasmalemma is the membrane boundary between the cytoplasm and the cell wall; the tonoplast is the membrane which separates the cytoplasm from the vacuole. Membranes and their structure are considered in more detail later. Located within the cytoplasm are the most important organelles within the cell. These include the nucleus, chloroplasts and mitochondria. Chloroplasts are the organelles in which light energy conversion and CO_2 assimilation take place. In the mitochondria enzymes are present which control the various steps of the tricarboxylic acid cycle, respiration and fatty acid metabolism. The ribosomes are supramolecular assemblies composed of ribosomal nucleic acid and proteins which enable the synthesis of polypeptides from free amino acids. Many of the ribosomes are attached to the endoplasmic reticulum (ER). This is a folded sheet like structure which gives rise to a series of membranous channels permeating the cytoplasm and often leading from one cell to another. The exact function of the endoplasmatic reticulum is not clear, but it appears to play a role in the synthesis and transport of proteins through the cytoplasm. Cells are connected together by the plasmodesmata and the continuous plasmatic connection which occurs in the cells of a tissue is called the symplasm. The vacuole contains an aqueous solution consisting mainly of inorganic ions as well as some low molecular weight organic substances such as organic acids, amino acids and sugars. Dissolved O_2, CO_2 and pigments may also be present. The vacuole has an important bearing on the water economy of the cell as well as providing a site for the segregation of water and the end products of metabolism.

The size of living cells varies considerably for different tissues and plant species. Mesophyll cells and cells of the root cortex tissue are about 20–100 micron (μm) in length. The diameter of chloroplasts and plastids is in the range of 8 μm, whilst that of the mitochondria is about 1 μm and that of the ribosomes 23 nm (1 μm $= 10^3$nm). Compared with these organelles the size of the low molecular weight substances appear rather small. The diameter of a sucrose molecule is 1 nm, a glucose molecule 0,6 nm, and the various inorganic ions in their hydrated form have diameters in the order of 0.5–1.0 nm. These figures are given simply to indicate the minute size of the inorganic ions in comparison with the various cell organelles.

The cell organelles such as the nucleus, chloroplasts, plastids, and mitochondria and also the vacuole are surrounded by membranes, which are very effective barriers for water soluble substances and thus· compartmentalize the cell.

This compartmentalization is essential for the normal functioning of the cell since distinct biochemical processes occur within the different organelles (OAKS and BIDWELL [1970]). An understanding of the transport mechanisms by which organic and inorganic substances are transferred between cellular compartments is therefore of outstanding importance. It is in this context too that the transport of inorganic plant nutrients from the outer medium, the soil solution, to the cytoplasm of the cell, must be considered. The membrane which forms the boundary of the cell to the outer medium is the plasmalemma. It is this membrane and not the cell wall which presents the effective barrier to the uptake of all ions and molecules dissolved in the aqueous outer medium. The important process of ion uptake may therefore be considered basically as ion transport through the plasmalemma or in a broader sense of the phenomenon, ion transport through biological membranes.

3.1.2 Membranes

For a deeper understanding of the essential process of ion uptake some knowledge of the structure and properties of biological membranes is required. Useful reviews on this subject have been published by BRANTON and DREAMER [1972], CLARKSON [1977], WALKER [1976], LODISH and ROTHMAN [1979)]. Biological membranes consist of protein and lipid molecules in approximately equal proportions and are about 7 to 10 nm thick. For decades the lipid protein sandwich structure proposed by DANIELLI and DAVSON [1935] was considered as the universal structure model of a biological membrane. The model consists of two lipid molecular layers in which the hydrophobic tails of the fatty acids are orientated inwards towards each other. Both outer boundaries of the lipid layer are coated with a protein layer. It was argued that this type of structure could serve well as a barrier because the protein layer would enhance rigidity and the lipidic fraction prevent penetration of the membrane by hydrophilic particles including inorganic ions.

It is now generally accepted that membrane structure is more intricate than that described above. According to SINGER [1972] biological membranes consist of amphiphilic molecules. The term amphiphilic indicates the presence of both hydrophilic (OH groups, NH_2 groups, phosphate groups, carboxylic groups) and hydrophobic regions (hydrocarbon chains) in the membrane. Lipids and proteins may thus be bound by electrostatic bonds, H bonds and by hydrophobic bonds. Basically biological membranes consist mainly of a lipidic double layer composed of amphiphilic lipids. A typical example of such a lipid is phosphatidyl ethanolamine. As shown in Figure 3.2 this molecule has two lipidic tails (hydrocarbon chains) and one hydrophilic head, the phosphate

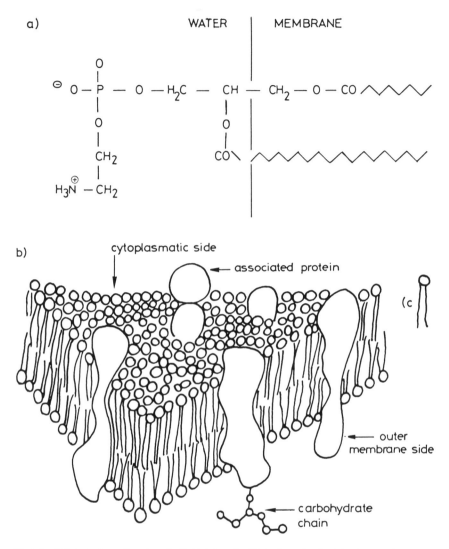

a) WATER | MEMBRANE

b)

cytoplasmatic side

← associated protein

(c

← outer membrane side

← carbohydrate chain

Fig.3.2 a) Orientation of a phospholipid (phosphatidyl ethanolamine) in the membrane
b) Membrane section
c) Symbol for a membrane lipid molecule

amino complex. This hydrophilic part of the molecule also carries a positive and a negative charge under physiological pH conditions. Recent experimental results indicate that the axis of the glycerol moiety lies vertical to the membrane plane and that the fatty acid chain at the C-2 position is located at the surface of the lipidic phase of the membrane (SEELIG [1980]). The C-3 position projects out of the membrane into the water phase (Figure 3.2a). The negatively charged phosphate group may bind cations, which probably influence the lipid conformation and membrane permeability. The lipidic monolayer consists of amphiphilic layers orientated in such a way that the heads form a plane. In the double layer or bilayer the tails are orientated towards each other (see Figure 3.2b) with each lipidic monolayer representing a two dimensional liquid. The bilayer is not symmetrical so that different types of lipids occur in the upper and lower layers. Proteins are embedded within the bilayer (LODISH and ROTHMAN [1979]), and these generally protrude from both sides of the membrane. Protein within the membrane is of hydrophobic nature, whereas the protein moieties which project out of the membrane are hydrophilic. Proteins orientated into the cytoplasm generally bind additional proteins (associated proteins), and proteins projecting out of the cell are generally associated with carbohydrates (see Figure 3.2b).

Lipids in biological membranes mainly have a barrier function preventing the diffusion of hydrophilic solutes, e.g. inorganic ions, amino acids and sugars, across the membrane. The proteins not only have a structural function but frequently are enzymes and thus responsible for particular biochemical reactions. Proteins which extend through the membrane form 'protein channels' from one side to the other. Such channels may well be of importance for the passage of small hydrophilic particles such as water molecules and inorganic ions (WALKER [1976]). In biological membranes particular arrangements and sequences of enzyme proteins are of significance in such important physiological processes as photosynthesis and respiration. The inner chloroplast membrane (thylakoid membrane) thus contains more than 40 different proteins. In addition to free chlorophyll molecules, five different chlorophyll protein complexes have been isolated (MILLER [1979]). On the periplasmatic side of the thylakoid membrane (side adjacent to chloroplast stroma, see p. 465) a rather large protein molecule has been detected, which is believed to be an ATPase. As discussed in the next sections the enzyme ATPase plays a vital role in membrane transport processes. It shoouls be stressed that biological membranes have a high turnover rate. Thus the half life of phosphatidyl choline is about 14 hours and the half life period of membrane proteins is in the range of between 2 and 384 hours (RENSING and CORNELIUS [1980]). The fluidity of membranes is very temperature dependent. At low temperatures the structure is quasi crystalline whereas at higher temperatures it is a liquid crystalline structure. These differences in structure affect membrane permeability.

The most important lipids of biological membranes are phospholipids, glycolipids and steroids. Sphingolipids are important components of animal membranes, but are probably of no major significance in plant membranes (MORRÉ

[1975]). According to VAN DEENEN [1972] the permeability of membranes to hydrophilic ions and molecules depends much on the fatty acid component. Long saturated hydrocarbon chains reduce permeability whereas unsaturated hydrocarbon chains loosen the structure and the membrane permeability is thus increased. As the proportion of steroids increases the membrane permeability decreases considerably. The phosphate group of phospholipids may be bound to the NH_3^+ group of proteins by electrostatic forces. In addition the phosphate group can be bridged by Ca^{2+} to a carboxylic group of proteins as shown below.

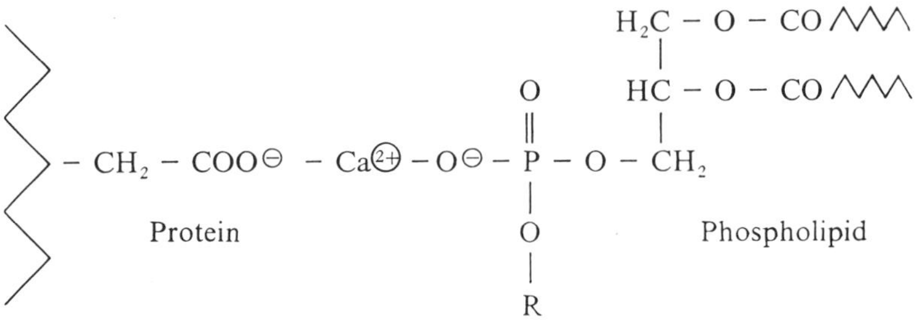

$$
\begin{array}{cccc}
& & & H_2C - O - CO \diagup\!\!\!\diagdown\!\!\!\diagup\!\!\!\diagdown \\
& & O & | \\
& & \| & HC - O - CO \diagup\!\!\!\diagdown\!\!\!\diagup\!\!\!\diagdown \\
- CH_2 - COO^{\ominus} & - Ca^{\oplus} - O^{\ominus} - & P - O - CH_2 & | \\
& & | & \\
\text{Protein} & & O & \text{Phospholipid} \\
& & | & \\
& & R &
\end{array}
$$

In an acid medium Ca^{2+} is replaced by H^+, and this bond is broken thus drastically increasing the permeability of the membrane. This effect is of importance for plant membranes as discussed in more detail on page 129.

For the understanding of the following sections dealing with ion uptake and transport it is important to keep in mind the fact that biological membranes are not completely impermeable. They may allow the diffusion of hydrophilic ions and molecules, the degree of permeability depending on the components which make up the membranes. In addition enzymes present in biological membranes may directly or indirectly be involved in the transport of ions and molecules across the membrane.

3.1.3 Ion uptake and metabolism

HOAGLAND and his co-workers carried out experiments which have had far reaching significance in all subsequent research on ion uptake by plants (HOAGLAND [1948]). In experimenting with the fresh water alga *Nitella* and the sea water alga *Valonia* they found that the ion concentrations in the vacuoles of these two algae did not correspond to the concentrations in the respective algal nutrient environments. In the vacuole of *Nitella* several ion species and particularly K^+ and Cl^- were concentrated to a considerably high degree. The same was also true for *Valonia* with the exception of Na^+ where the concentration was

114

higher in the sea water than in the vacuole (see Figure 3.3). From these findings the following important conclusions may be drawn:

1. The plant is able to take up ions selectively. Thus K+ which is lowest in concentration of all the cations in the pond water is the cation which is accumulated to the greatest extent by far in the vacuole of *Nitella*. On the other hand the concentration of Na+ in the vacuole of *Valonia* is kept to a relatively low level even though the concentration of Na+ in the sea water is high. These results support the concept that plant cells can take up certain ion species

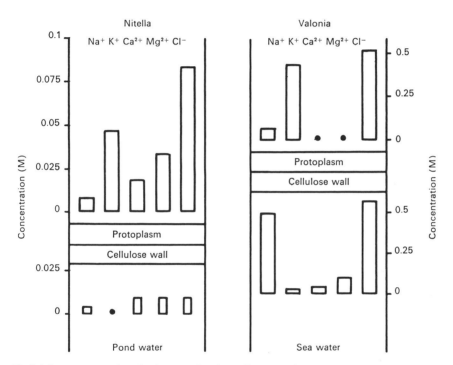

Fig. 3.3 Ion concentrations in the vacuole of *Nitella* and *Valonia* in relation to the ion concentrations in outer medium (after HOAGLAND [1948]).

from their environment and transport them into the interior of the cell whereas other ion species are in some way excluded from the cell. This phenomenon is called selective ion uptake.

2. Another major conclusion is the fact that the concentrations of several ion species are considerably higher in the vacuole than in the outer medium. This indicates that accumulation has taken place against a concentration gradient.

115

3. A further important point to be considered from these results is the fact that the uptake process itself requires energy. This is generated by cell metabolism.

The relationship between metabolism and ion uptake is not yet fully understood, although it has been known for many years that ion uptake is closely associated with respiration. An early approach to account for this relationship was put forward by LUNDEGÅRDH [1932]. The main principle of his very sophisticated concept was the linking of ion transport with electron flow in the respiration chain. LUNDEGÅRDH's ingenious ideas and experiments contributed much to our present understanding of ion uptake. It is now generally accepted, however, that cytochromes do not play any role in the ion uptake process as they are present in neither the plasmalemma nor the tonoplast.

In aerobic organisms respiration is directly related to ion uptake. Figure 3.4 from the work of HOPKINS [1956] demonstrates that O_2 supply is essential for P uptake by barley roots. The same is true for other plant nutrients. The uptake of nutrients is also found to increase simultaneously with increases in root carbohydrate content since carbohydrate acts as an energy source for ion uptake during respiration. It is of interest to note that the O_2 tension at which maximum phosphate uptake is attained is rather low (2–3%).

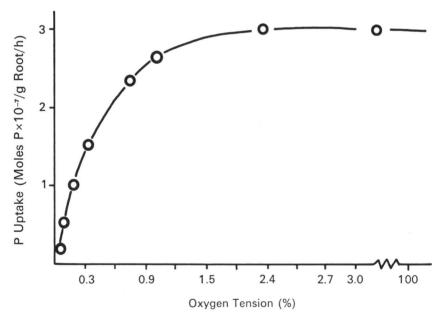

Fig.3.4 Rate of phosphate uptake by excised barley roots in relation to the O_2-tension (after HOPKINS [1956]).

The major physiological function of respiration is the synthesis of adenosine triphosphate (ATP) from adenosine diphosphate (ADP) and inorganic phosphate. All biochemical processes which need energy including the synthesis of molecules and the uptake and transport of some ion species depend on the supply of ATP or analogous compounds. ATP consists of adenine (N-base), ribose (pentose) and 3 phosphate groups.

The phosphate groups are bound to each other by energy rich bonds which are indicated by the symbol ($\sim$). This is a high energy bond and during hydrolysis it releases about 32 kJ per mol of ATP.

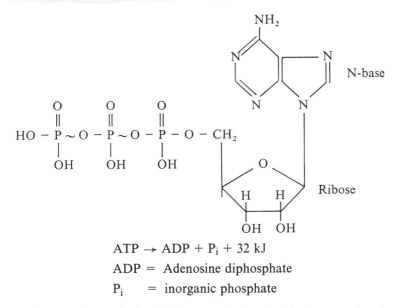

$$ATP \rightarrow ADP + P_i + 32 \text{ kJ}$$

ADP = Adenosine diphosphate

P_i = inorganic phosphate

ATP is not only synthesized during respiration (oxidative phosphorylation) but also in the glycolytic pathway (anaerobic phosphorylation) and in photosynthesis (see page 148).

As outlined above ATP appears to provide the energy for the ion uptake process. Thus when ATP formation is prevented as for example by inhibitors or uncouplers such as CO, CN$^-$, 2,4-dinitrophenol (DNP) or arsenate, ion uptake is inhibited. In roots respiration provides the main source of ATP, but in green plant tissues photophosphorylation (see page 148) also supplies ATP for the energy dependent ion uptake mechanism. This is the reason why light can directly enhance the uptake of ions by photosynthetically active tissues. This has been shown by various authors (JESCHKE [1967], NOBEL [1970]). The precise mechanism by which ATP drives the ion uptake process and particularly ion transport across biological membranes, is not yet completely clear. Recent findings indicate that ion uptake is associated with ATPase activity. ATPase is a membrane bound enzyme which splits ATP into ADP + P_i, thus providing the energy for the uptake process. The principle of this mechanism is considered below. There are currently two main although not exclusively independent directions of thought concerning metabolically driven ion uptake. One visualizes uptake in terms of carrier transport and is known as the carrier theory. The other stresses the importance of ion pumps across the membrane. Both these concepts are considered below.

3.1.4 The carrier theory

It is supposed that biological membranes contain certain molecules which are able to carry ions across the membrane. Such molecules are termed 'carriers' and it is believed that they possess specific binding sites for particular ion species, thus enabling selective ion transport through the membrane. The generation of these carriers directly or indirectly requires ATP. Figure 3.5 shows a hypothetical scheme in which the active carrier is envisaged as a phosphorylated compound. It is suggested that this carrier is diffusible in the membrane.

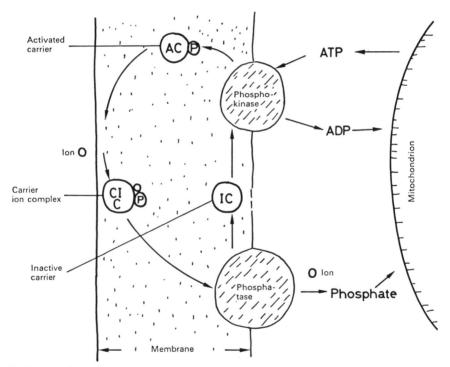

Fig.3.5 Carrier ion transport across a membrane involving energy expenditure.

At the outer membrane boundary it meets the particular ion species for which it has affinity. The ion is bound by the carrier, thus forming a carrier ion complex. This diffusible complex then moves across the membrane to a phosphatase located at the inner membrane boundary. The enzyme phosphatase splits off the phosphate group from the carrier complex. By this process the carrier is believed to lose its affinity for the ion which is released into the adjacent medium *e.g.* into the cytoplasm.

Regeneration of carrier selectivity requires ATP. This process is brought about by a 'carrier ATP kinase' which is also located at the inner membrane boundary. The phosphorylated carrier compound may then diffuse back to the outer membrane boundary, pick up another ion and the uptake cycle is repeated. The ATP required for the process may originate from respiration (plant roots), from photophosphorylation and in anaerobic organisms from glycolysis.

The whole uptake cycle may be described by the following equations:

$$\text{Car} + \text{ATP} \xrightarrow{\text{Kinase}} \text{Car} \textcircled{P} + \text{ADP}$$

$$\text{Car} \textcircled{P} + \text{Ion} \longrightarrow \text{Car} \textcircled{P} - \text{Ion}$$

$$\text{Car} \textcircled{P} - \text{Ion} \xrightarrow{\text{Phosphatase}} \text{Car} + P_i + \text{Ion}$$

$$\text{Net: Ion} + \text{ATP} \xrightarrow[\text{Transport}]{} \text{Ion} + \text{ADP} + P_i$$

The net equation shows that the transport of 1 ion through the membrane requires 1 ATP molecule. From an energetic point of view this would seem to be a reasonable energy demand. If it is assumed that the uptake of 1 ion requires 1 ATP molecule, then it follows that the ATP needed for the K uptake by a plant is less than 1% of the quantity of ATP required for CO_2 assimilation.

The concept of carrier transport as illustrated in Figure 3.5 is highly hypothetical. It does, however, cover the main experimental facts, implications and conclusions of ion uptake. These are, that energy driven ion uptake is selective, that the energy is probably in the form of ATP and that ion transport may take place against a concentration gradient. Whether a phosphatase and kinase are really involved in the ion uptake is an open question. There is considerable evidence, however, that enzymic processes are associated with ion uptake.

The barrier for hydrophilic particles is the lipid phase of the membrane, so it seems probable that carrier molecules are lipid molecules. As biological membranes are permeable to lipid molecules a carrier of this type would well be able to diffuse in the membrane. The real nature of the carrier, however, is still a matter of speculation. It is possible that carriers are derivatives of phosphatidic acid or peptides of a lipidic character. Investigations of KILBOURN *et al.* [1967], MUELLER and RUDIN [1967] and of DOBLER *et al.* [1969] have shown, that organic molecules do exist, which are highly selective in binding inorganic ions.

Antibiotics such as valinomycin, nonactin, gramicidin and enniatin B can bring about selective transport of inorganic ions through biological membranes (MUELLER and RUDIN (1967)). The transport rate of K^+, induced by valinomycin for example is about 300 times higher than that for Na^+. This example convincingly demonstrates the extremely high ability of valinomycin to discriminate between such closely related ions as K^+ and Na^+. Enniatin B and nonactin are also highly selective for K^+. According to DOBLER *et al.* [1969] 'the enniatin-K^+ complex is a charged disc with a lipophilic exterior'. Potassium is located at the centre of the disc. The nonactin-K^+ complex is described as a ball with a lipophilic exterior resulting from methyl groups (Figure 3.6), the K^+ located at the centre of the ball being surrounded by 8 oxygen atoms. Both the enniatin-K^+ and the nonactin-K^+ complexes possess the two important characteristics necessary for a carrier molecule, a specific binding site and lipophilic properties.

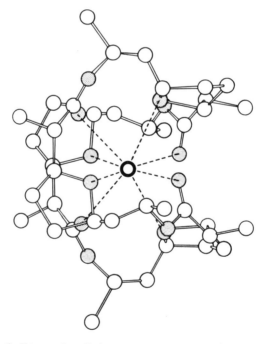

Fig. 3.6 The nonactin-K^+ complex. Carbon atoms are represented by open circles, oxygen by shaded circles and K^+ by the heavy circle (after KILBOURN *et al.* [1967]).

The K^+ specificity of ionophores, as these complexes are also called (HINKLE and McCARTY [1978]), is dependent on the thickness of the K^+ hydration shell. The formation of a complex between a cation and an ionophore is related to the degree of hydration of the cation since water molecules of the hydration shell are replaced by oxygen atoms of the organic complex. Potassium binds water less tightly than Na^+, and for this reason more readily forms a complex with an ionophore. This difference in behaviour is reflected in the much higher rates of transport of K^+ than Na^+ through biological membranes. Another type of transport through a membrane can be brought about by tunnels also formed by ionophores. Gramicidin A forms a pore in the membrane, made up of two helical molecules. This channel is highly permeable to monovalent cations and hardly discriminates between K^+ and Na^+. Whether antibiotic compounds or similar substances act as carriers *in vivo* in the sense described above is still not known.

3.1.5 Ion pumps and ATP ase

An ion pump mechanism has been proposed to account for energy dependent ion transport through animal membranes. Animal cells often contain relatively high concentrations of K^+ and Cl^-, whereas the outer solution is high in Na^+. A typical example of this type of ionic distribution is in blood. The erythrocytes contain high K^+ and low Na^+ concentrations, whereas in the plasma the reverse is the case. This asymmetrical distribution of Na^+ and K^+ has been attributed to the activity of an enzyme ATPase. ATPases are a group of enzymes which are able to split ATP into ADP and inorganic phosphate thereby releasing energy for utilization in ion transport. In animal cells the ion pump is believed to be a membrane bound protein consisting of an ATPase and a glycoprotein. It is supposed that the hydrolysis of ATP results in a conformation change of the protein which brings about cation transport across the membrane.

Membrane bound ATPases of bacteria, fungi, and higher plants differ from animal ATPases and it is unlikely that a protein conformation change is the mechanism by which solutes are transported across plant membranes. It is now generally accepted that in plant cells membrane bound ATPase and, especially the ATPase of the plasmalemma, is responsible for the negative charge of the cell. This negative charge is a universal feature of all plant cells and may be compared with ATP which represents a universal energy source (MITCHELL [1978]). A hypothetical scheme showing the possible mechanism of an ATPase is shown in Figure 3.7. The enzyme induces a pH gradient across the membrane by pumping H^+ out of the cell. By this process the cell becomes more negative and more alkaline as compared with the outer medium. The potential thus built up consists of a chemical and an electrical component, which can be described by the following equation (Poole [1978]).

$$pmf = \Delta pH + \psi$$

where

pmf = proton motive force or electrochemical gradient of H^+ ions across the membrane

ΔpH = difference in H^+ concentration at either side of the membrane

ψ = electrical potential difference across the membrane

The proton motive force (= pmf) is the force by which the protons are transported against an electrochemical gradient across the membrane. The transport process has all the characteristics of active transport, which are considered in greater detail below. The energy required is derived from ATP, and it has been shown that the potential of the H^+ (proton) pump is directly dependent on ATP supply. It is supposed that the extrusion of $2H^+$ consumes one ATP molecule. Basically the proton pump induces a pH gradient across the membrane and is the reverse mechanism of that for producing ATP in the thylakoid membrane of chloroplasts or in the inner membrane of mitochondria (see p. 148). The principle of the proton pump as shown in the hypothetical scheme of Figure 3.7 is closely related to the chemiosmotic phosphorylation process

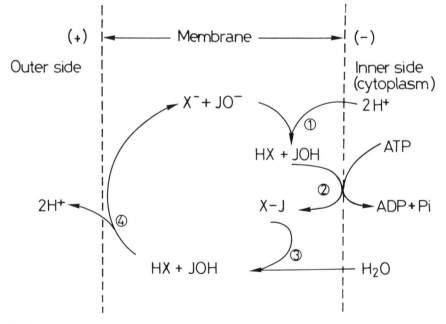

Fig. 3.7 Hypothetical scheme of an H^+ pump (ATPase) pumping $2H^+$ per 1 ATP out of the cell.

122

put forward by MITCHELL [1966]. Step 1 shows the reaction of the hypothetical membrane mobile molecules X^- and JO^- with $2H^+$ from the cytoplasm. The resulting products HX and JOH induce the hydrolysis of ATP (reaction 2) by the formation of a complex X–J. This complex is hydrolysed (reaction 3) into the two compounds HX and JOH, which are deprotonated at the outer side of the membrane (reaction 4). X^- and JO^- are thus reformed and a new cycle can begin. The net result of this reaction sequence is the transfer of $2H^+$ across the membrane associated with the hydrolysis of one ATP molecule. By this process an electrochemical potential is built up across the membrane, with the inner side of the membrane being more negatively charged with respect to the outer membrane. Cations at the outer side of the membrane are thus attracted into the cell and this entry of cations into the cytoplasm depolarizes the membrane potential. This kind of cation uptake depends much on membrane permeability which differs considerably for the various cation species. Bearing in mind the possibility that ionophores such as valinomycin may allow selective diffusion of cation species (see p. 120) the ATPase system operating in association with ionophores may induce selective cation uptake. Selective diffusion of this type is also known as facilitated diffusion. The experimental findings of RATNER and JACOBY [1976] are consistent with the view that the high rate of K^+ uptake by plant cells may be explained in terms of an ATPase driven facilitated diffusion of K^+. Such an uptake mechanism is a 'downhill' process.

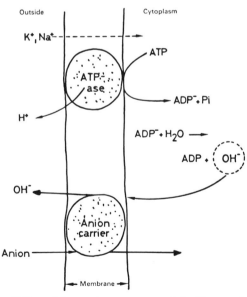

Fig. 3.8 Model of an ATPase driven cation pump coupled with an anion carrier (modified after HODGES [1973]).

There is also evidence however that K^+ is taken up actively (uphill process), a question which will be discussed in the next section.

Anion uptake cannot be explained as a downhill process, for in this case a negative charge must be moved into the negatively charged cell. It is, supposed however, that anions of the outer medium can be taken up in exchange for OH^- or HCO_3^-. HODGES [1973] has proposed a hypothetical model to account for both cation and anion absorption of plant cells. The model, shown in Figure 3.8, depicts an ATPase and an anion carrier. The ATPase renders the cytoplasm more alkaline, and the cytoplasmic OH^- drives the anion carrier. Hydroxyl ions are thus excreted and anions *e.g.* SO_4^{2-} absorbed by the cell. Whether ATPases are directly involved in active anion uptake is not yet completely clear (POOLE [1978]).

Hydroxyl ions remaining in the cytoplasm after proton extrusion may also induce the accumulation of organic acid anions and particularly malate. This occurs when the uptake of the cation in exchange for protons takes place at a faster rate than the inorganic anion uptake in exchange for OH^- (see p. 134). Organic acid anions synthesized in the cytoplasm may then be transferred into the vacuole in association with the absorbed cations. In growing plants a very significant OH^- source also arises from the reduction of NO_3^- and the decarboxylation of organic acid anions (see p. 136). Indeed in plants supplied with NO_3-N, as is usually the case, anion uptake exceeds cation uptake so that more OH^- than H^+ is generated in the exchange from the roots (KIRKBY

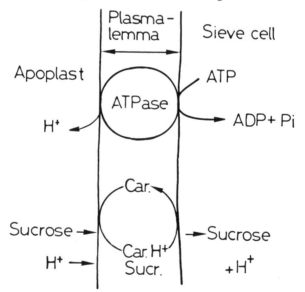

Fig. 3.9 Scheme of proton-sucrose cotransport driven by ATPase.

[1969]). According to HODGES [1973] this additional OH⁻ source should also be capable of driving the anion carrier and should be independent of ATPase activity.

The universal importance of ATPase for membrane transport is also evident from the fact, that ATPases bring about membrane transport of sugars and amino acids. The mechanism by which this may occur as proposed by GIA-QUINTA [1977] is shown in Figure 3.9 for phloem loading with sucrose. The H^+ pump (ATPase) provides an acid medium in the apoplast, which allows the protonation of a hypothetical sucrose carrier, which in the protonated form transports sucrose across the plasmalemma into the cell. The results of KOMOR and TANNER [1974] with *Chlorella* indicate that the affinity of the sugar carrier for sugar is increased about 100 fold by protonation. The hypothetical scheme depicted in Figure 3.9 is supported by recent experimental evidence of GIA-QUINTA [1979], who found that the fungal toxin fusicoccin stimulated the H^+ pump as well as the active accumulation of sucrose in sugar beet leaf tissue.

SERVAITES et al. [1979] in studying the uptake of amino acids into the phloem of soya bean suggest that amino acids are also transported into the cell by a carrier driven by an ATPase. The amino acid carrier, however, differs from the sucrose carrier. The general importance of membrane bound ATPase for membrane transport is underlined by the abundance of ATPase in plant membrane fractions as reported by various authors (LEONARD and HODGES [1973], FISHER et al. [1970], BALKE and HODGES [1975], ERDEI et al. [1979], TRAVIS and BOOZ [1979]).

3.1.6 Active and passive transport

Ions in solution are subjected to two main physical 'forces'. One arises from the chemical potential gradient and the other from the electrical potential gradient (DAINTY [1962]). Ions move down a chemical gradient, i.e. from a higher to a lower concentration. For ions acted upon by an electrical gradient, cations are attracted to a negative electropotential whereas anions are attracted to a positive electropotential. Ion movement is thus dependent on an electro-chemical potential gradient. As has been shown above, living cells are negatively charged as compared with the outer medium. For this reason the passage of ions through the plasmalemma or tonoplast must also be considered in relation to the prevailing electrical potential gradient as well as to the concentration gradient between the 'outer solution' (medium) and 'inner solution' (cytoplasm). 'Facilitated cation diffusion' discussed above is a typical example of where cations are moved along an electrical gradient. This net inwardly directed movement of cations terminates as soon as the equilibrium between the electrical and kinetic driving forces is attained. This equilibrium is described by the Nernst equation. A simple case may be considered in which an aqueous solution of KCl is separated by a membrane which is permeable to both ions, K⁺ and Cl⁻. Assuming that the electrical potential across the membrane is E, equilibrium for K⁺ and Cl⁻ is attained as soon as the concentrations of these ions at either side of the membrane satisfy the Nernst equation. This may be described as follows:

$$\psi_i - \psi_o = E = \frac{RT}{z \cdot F} \ln \frac{[K_o^+]}{[K^+_i]} = \frac{RT}{z \cdot F} \ln \frac{[Cl^-_i]}{[Cl_o^-]}$$

ψ_i = electrical charge of the inner medium e.g. cytoplasm
ψ_o = electrical charge of the outer medium e.g. nutrient solution
R = gas constant
T = absolute temperature
F = Faraday constant
z = valence of the ions

The subscripts i and o designate the inner or outer solution, the values in brackets indicate the concentrations or more precisely the activities of the ion species in question. From this equation it can be derived that when E < 0 (the cell is negatively charged) the term $[K_o^+]/[K_i^+]$ must be < 1. This means that under equilibrium conditions an accumulation of K⁺ occurs in the inner solution. It further follows that the term $[Cl_i^-]/[Cl_o^-]$ must be < 1. This implies that under equilibrium conditions the Cl⁻ concentration of the outer solution is higher than that of the inner solution. It thus appears that the cation concentration in the cytoplasm can be several times higher than that of the outer solution without requiring an 'uphill transport' of cations, i.e. a transport against an electrochemical gradient. If for example the K⁺ concentration of the inner solution is 10 times higher than that of the outer solution the term $\log [K_o^+]/[K_i^+] = -1$. The corresponding electrical potential difference is then −58 mV (DAINTY [1962]). For living cells −58 mV is a rather small electrical potential difference. This example shows that K⁺ as well as other cation species may be accumulated to a considerable extent in the cell merely by physical forces. Only, where the concentration is higher than that of the equilibrium condition, must an 'uphill transport', i.e. a transport against an electrochemical gradient, have occurred. In a strict thermodynamical sense only transport against an electrochemical gradient is called active transport, whereas the transport down or along an electrochemical gradient is passive transport. Active transport needs additional energy and cannot be brought about merely by kinetic and electrical forces (ETHERTON [1963], ETHERTON and HIGINBOTHAM [1961]).

126

In order to test, whether an ion species has been moved actively or passively into the cell, the concentrations of the particular ion species in the outer medium and in the cell must be measured as well as the electropotential (E_m) between the cell and the outer medium. This can be achieved using a microelectrode. By substituting the measured ion concentrations into the Nernst equation an electrical potential difference (E_{cal}) can be calculated. Where E_m designates the measured potential, the difference between E_m and E_{cal} indicates whether a passive or an active transport has occurred.

$$E_m - E_{cal} = E_d$$

E_d is the driving force. For cations a negative value of E_d indicates a passive uptake and a positive value an active uptake. For anions the reverse is true. A negative value is indicative of active transport, and a positive value of passive transport. It must be remembered that the test of whether an ion species has been transported actively or passively is only valid, if equilibrium conditions have been maintained in the system. This is often difficult to achieve in whole plant studies as plant tops provide a very strong sink for ions taken up by roots.

SPANSWICK and WILLIAMS [1964] measured the electropotential differences and the ion concentrations of the outer medium and in the cell of *Nitella*. The data of this experiment are shown in Table 3.1. For Na^+ at equilibrium a potential difference of –67 mV would have been sufficient for the prevailing Na^+ concentrations. As the electrical potential difference was higher (–138 mV) Na^+ uptake was passive. For K^+ an electrical potential difference of –179 mV was required for equilibrium conditions. As the measured potential difference was lower (–138 mV) K^+ uptake was active. For Cl^- a potential difference of + 99 mV (positively charged cell) would have been needed to maintain the equilibrium at the measured Cl^- concentrations. As the measured electrical potential was considerably lower, Cl^- must have been taken up actively.

Table 3.1 Measured (E_m) and calculated electropotential differences (E_{cal}) and the resulting driving forces (E_d). The data refer to experiments with *Nitella translucens* (SPANSWICK and WILLIAMS [1964])

Ion species	E_m	E_{cal}	E_d	type of uptake
Na^+	—138	— 67	— 71	passive
K^+	—138	—179	+ 41	active
Cl^-	—138	+ 99	—237	active

The fact that living cells are always negatively charged implies that anions are more subjected to active transport than cations. Whenever the anion concentration of the cell is in excess of the outer medium, active uptake must have occurred. The major anions NO_3^-, Cl^-, SO_4^{2-} and $H_2PO_4^-$ are thus all apparently accumulated against an electrochemical gradient (HIGINBOTHAM [1973]).

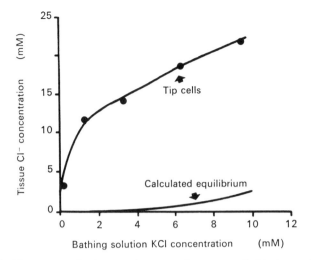

Fig.3.10 Chloride concentration in mung bean root tips compared with the maximum concentration which could be due to diffusion calculated equilibrium (after GERSON and POOLE [1972]).

Figure 3.10 shows results from mung bean root tips *(Phaseoulus aureus)* in which measured Cl⁻ uptake values are compared with calculated Cl⁻ uptake levels derived from Nernst equilibrium conditions (GERSON and POOLE [1972]). As the measured Cl⁻ concentrations are several times higher than the calculated values it can be concluded that Cl⁻ must have been taken up actively.

For cations the situation is quite different. Due to the negatively charged cell, cations may accumulate in the cell merely by physical, non metabolic forces. HIGINBOTHAM [1973] cites several experiments indicating that the concentrations of Na^+, Ca^{2+} and Mg^{2+} in plant cells do not exceed the physical equilibrium level and are thus obviously absorbed passively. Only in the case of K^+ has experimental data been obtained which are indicative of active uptake. The results shown in Table 3.1 provide evidence of this kind. A further demonstration of active K^+ transport has been provided by DAVIS and HIGINBOTHAM [1976] who showed that K^+ was transported against an electrochemical gradient from the parenchyma cells into the xylem vessels of maize roots. Experimental data of LIN and HANSON [1976] also provide evidence that K^+ is actively absorbed by maize roots.

Based on recent experimental results CHEESEMAN and HANSON [1979] suggest that in a low K^+ concentration range (<0.5 mM), K^+ is transported actively into the cell by an ATPase, whereas at higher K^+ concentration ranges, K^+ uptake is passive. This passive uptake is induced by an electropotential gradient produced by a H^+ pump which is also supposedly a membrane located ATPase.

128

According to CHEESEMAN and HANSON [1979] the active K^+ uptake mechanism is suppressed by high K^+ concentrations. Similar observations have been made by GLASS and DUNLOP [1978].

The electrical potential difference between the cell and the outer medium depends on metabolic activity. This is evident from the findings of JESCHKE [1970] who observed that the electrical potential in leaf cells of *Elodea densa* in the light was about −180 mV, whereas in the dark it amounted only to −120 mV. It is now widely accepted that the negative charge of the cells originates from so called electrogenic pumps. Such pumps transfer a net charge across the membrance. The H^+ pump described on page 122 is a typical electrogenic pump. Anion as well as cation carriers must also be considered as electrogenic pumps if an appropriate net transfer of electrical charge is induced.

3.1.7 Membrane permeability

Passive movement of ions through a membrane depends on the prevailing electrochemical gradient across the membrane and may take place in either direction. Membranes thus allow the passive influx and efflux of ions. The rate of these fluxes depends on membrane permeability. This may be defined as the quantity of ions which may be transported per unit membrane surface, per unit time. It is known that membranes differ in permeability to inorganic ions. In mitochondria for example the outer membrane is highly permeable, whereas the inner membrane presents a considerable barrier to inorganic ions. CRAM [1973] reported, that for Cl^- the plasmalemma of maize roots is much more permeable than the tonoplast. As discussed on p. 129 the permeability of the outer chloroplast membrane plays a major role in carbohydrate and energy metabolism.

Exogenous factors may also affect membrane permeability. Membrane permeability to hydrophilic compounds thus depends considerably on the concentration of H^+ and Ca^{2+} of the adjacent medium. JACOBSON *et al.* [1950] found in experiments with young barley roots that at pH values 4.5 leakage of K^+ occurred. Similar results have been reported by other investigators leading to the conclusion that H^+ increases membrane permeability. This H^+ effect is counterbalanced by Ca^{2+} (MARSCHNER *et al.* [1966]) which is more effective in a lower pH range in the medium. These data supported by the findings of other authors (JACKSON and EDWARDS [1966], MARSCHNER and MENGEL [1966]) suggest that H^+ results in a higher membrane permeability by possibly enlarging the membrane pores (KAVANAU [1965]). Many workers have shown that Ca^{2+} is required for maintaining membrane integrity. According to VAN STEVENINCK [1965], Ca^{2+} may affect permeability by binding negative charges of the plasmalemma with the cell wall. As other cations are predominantly associated with the protoplasm this would explain why they do not alter permeability characteristics of membranes to such a great extent as Ca^{2+}. The interaction between Ca^{2+} and H^+ is a classical example of ion antagonism, where two ion species act in directly opposite ways. If the Ca^{2+} of the membrane is removed by exchange for H^+ (MENGEL and HELAL [1967]) or using chelates (VAN STEVENINCK [1965]) the membrane permeability increases considerably and a leakage of ions and low molecular weight organic compounds occurs.

In this context another phenomenon known as the Viets effect should be considered. In experiments with excised barley roots VIETS (1944] found that the presence of Ca^{2+} in the outer medium stimulated the uptake of K^+ and also of bromide. Other multivalent cations such as Mg^{2+}, Sr^{2+}, Ba^{2+} and even Al^{3+} had similar but less pronounced effects. Interestingly enough, however, the internal Ca^{2+} of the roots did not influence the K^+ uptake. The presence of Ca^{2+} or the other cations mentioned above was necessary in the outer solution. This finding suggests that the influence of Ca^{2+} at the outer boundary between the nutrient solution and the plasmalemma is responsible for the Viets effect and not the metabolism of the cell. According to investigations of MENGEL and HELAL [1967], Ca^{2+} affects the efflux and not the influx of K^+ and phosphate. Deficiency of Ca^{2+} in the outer solution or at the cell boundaries results in higher efflux rates. As the net uptake results from the difference between influx and efflux, a sufficiently high enough Ca^{2+} concentration of the outer solution not only decreases the efflux rates but simultaneously increases the net uptake of ions. The interpretation of the Viets effect in this case is that Ca^{2+} decreases membrane permeability and thus favours ion retention. The Ca^{2+} concentration of the nutrient solution needed for adequate normal permeability of cell membranes is rather low (about 10^{-4} M). This is considerably below the levels of Ca^{2+} usually found in soil solution (see page 71). The Viets effect does not therefore play a major role in most soils provided that the soil pH is not too low. It is thus unlikely that a lack of Ca^{2+} in soil solution can be responsible for a leakage of nutrients from plant roots.

There are other factors, however, which can induce nutrient losses from root cell by ion leakage. Leakage is observed, when cell metabolism, and in particular root respiration is disturbed. MARSCHNER et al. [1966] reported that young root tips of Zea mays lost about 30% of their K^+ under anaerobic conditions (N_2 medium), whereas with adequate oxygen supply the K loss was about only 3%. MENGEL and PFLÜGER [1972] reported that the K^+ efflux rates of maize roots were about 5 times higher under anaerobic conditions as compared with an aerobic medium. The efflux rate decreased immediately when the roots were transferred from anaerobic conditions to aerobic conditions. In the light of the knowledge of ATPase activity and its impact on cell electropotentials (see page 123) these results may best be explained by supposing that the reduction in respiration rate depresses the activity of ATPase because of a lack of ATP. Thus as shown on page 123 the negative charge of the cell is lowered and the retention capacity for cations impaired, and cation efflux is induced.

3.1.8 Ion competition, antagonism and synergism

It has already been outlined in the previous sections that electrogenic pumps (anion carriers, H^+ pumps) generate a negative charge in the cell and that most cation species are attracted by this negative charge and are thus absorbed passively. The absorption of cations is thus more or less a non specific process, depending mainly on the concentration of the cation species in the nutrient medium and in some cases also on the specific permeability of membranes to particular cation species (facilitated diffusion). For this reason nonspecific competition between the cation species for the negative charges of the cell may occur. This is evident from the frequently made observation, that the total sum of cations in a plant or plant tissue is little changed despite variations in the levels of the individual cations in the nutrient medium. Increasing the supply of one cation species in the nutrient medium can thus depress the levels of other cation species in the plant. Table 3.2 shows a typical example of this kind. Increasing the level of Mg application to sunflower plants resulted in a decrease of Na and Ca levels and a corresponding increase in the Mg concentration thus maintaining a fairly con-

Table 3.2 The effect of an increasing Mg application on the content of various cation species in sunflower plants (SCHARRER and JUNG [1955])

	K	Na	Ca	Mg	Sum
			me/100 g DM		
Mg$_1$............................	49	4	42	49	144
Mg$_2$............................	57	3	31	61	152
Mg$_3$............................	57	2	23	68	150

stant total sum of cations in the plant of all treatments. In the results shown in this experiment the K content was not depressed by Mg applications, although this has often been observed in other investigations. The same pattern occurs when the supply of any major cation nutrient is increased. It is the general rule therefore that increasing the supply of one cation species results in lowering the concentration of other cation species. This relationship is called cation antagonism, although it is not used in the classical sense of the term, which implies that the effects of two cation species are mutually opposed.

The physiological background of the finding, that an increase in one cation species reduces the concentration of another cation species is not yet clear. Some investigators explain this effect in terms of carrier competition. If this were true, however, it would mean that the three major cations (Ca^{2+}, Mg^{2+}, K^+) were competing for the same cation carrier binding site. This seems unlikely because of the difference in size and structure of the ions. Moreover in short term experiments such cation competition effects are often not observed (LEGGETT and GILBERT [1969].

As outlined above the cell produces anionic equivalents which attract and retain cations non specifically. This attraction can be likened to a race for uptake between the individual cation species. The cation species taken up fastest will neutralize the anion equivalents first and thus reduce the electrostatic attraction for the other cation species. The uptake rate depends on the concentration of the individual cation species in the nutrient solution and also on the uptake mechanism. Potassium which is taken up by the cell rapidly either actively or by facilitated diffusion competes strongly in cation uptake. In the absence of K^+ in the nutrient solution the uptake of other cation species is thus much enhanced because competition for uptake is less severe. This relationship is shown in Table 3.3 from an experiment of FORSTER and MENGEL [1969] in which barley plants were grown in a complete nutrient solution. In one treatment K^+ was withheld from the nutrient solution for 8 days during the growth period. After this time the cation contents of roots and shoots were determined in samples of both treatments (control and interrupted supply). As shown in Table 3.3 this interruption in K supply resulted in a drastic drop in the K

Table 3.3 The effect of an interruption in the K supply on the cation content of young barley plants; interruption period 8 days (FORSTER and MENGEL [1969])

	Roots		Shoots	
	Control	Interr.	Control	Interr.
	me/100 g DM			
K............................	157	28	170	152
Ca...........................	9	12	24	66
Mg	36	74	54	21
Na...........................	3	78	trace	12
Total........................	205	192	248	251

Grain yield (g/pot): Control 108
　　　　　　　　　Interr.　　86***

levels in the roots and shoots, whereas the contents of Ca, Mg and Na increased considerably. The total content of the 4 cation species was not significantly affected by the K interruption. This indicates that the deficient equivalents of K^+ were more or less made up by the other cation species. These cations, however, were not able to substitute for the physiological functions of K^+. The yield data of Table 3.3 show that the interruption in K^+ supply, during the tillering stage, resulted in a highly significant grain yield depression.

In anion uptake, antagonistic effects are less common although Cl^-, SO_4^{2-} and $H_2PO_4^-$ uptake can be stimulated when NO_3-uptake is strongly depressed (KIRKBY and KNIGHT [1977]). The most common anion antagonism is between NO_3^- and Cl^-. High Cl^- supply in the nutrient medium lowers the nitrate uptake and *vice versa*. The effects are particularly marked in plants which accumulate NO_3^- and Cl^- such as the *Chenopodiaceae*. The basis of this non specific antagonism is probably analogous to that of cation competition.

In plant nutrition the term synergism is often used to describe the opposite phenomenon of antagonism. Thus a synergistic relationship occurs between two plant nutrients when the uptake of one is stimulated by the other. For example NO_3^-nutrition stimulates the uptake of cations. This effect is non specific. Increasing the level of NO_3^- nutrition enhances cation uptake which is associated with higher levels of organic acid accumulation (see p. 136).

The ionic interactions described above have been interpreted as non specific replacement effects and not as carrier competition processes. This does not imply that carrier competitive mechanisms do not occur in uptake. It is generally accepted that closely related ion species such as K^+ and Rb^+, or Ca^{2+} and Sr^{2+} compete for the same carrier site, and in some cases even the pattern of distribution within the plant is similar (MENZEL and HEALD [1955], MICHAEL [1959]). Other similar ion pairs include SO_4^{2-} and SeO_4^{2-} (LEGGETT and EPSTEIN [1956]) and phosphate and arsenate (MICHAEL and MARSCHNER [1958]). These interactions provide a strong argument for the existence of carriers or at least specific binding sites for which closely related ion species can compete. Because of the similar behaviour of K^+ and Rb^+ the radioactive Rb isotope (Rb-86) has often been used in labelling experiments as K radioisotopes do not have such a long half life. It is now known, however, that the behaviour of K^+ and Rb^+ is not so alike as was formerly believed (WEST and PITMAN [1967], MAAS and LEGGETT [1968]).

3.1.9 Ion uptake and organic anion accumulation

The observation that plant cells are negatively charged as compared with the outer medium implies that they contain a surplus of negative equivalents. This surplus, however, is extremely small even when electropotential differences are high in the order of 200 mV. The excess of anion equivalents is so small, that it cannot be measured by analytical methods, but only by measuring cellular electropotentials. The total sum of anion equivalents in a cell or a tissue is thus virtually equal to the total sum of cations.

Inorganic ions are taken up at different rates by plant roots. Some ions like NO_3^-, K^+ and Cl^- are taken up very rapidly whereas the uptake of others such as Ca^{2+}, SO_4^{2-} is relatively slow. This difference in uptake rate means that plants usually remove cations and anions in unequal amounts from the nutrient medium. In experiments with excised roots and young seedlings ULRICH [1941] and later JACOBSON [1955] and others, showed that the cation-anion uptake imbalance was compensated in the plant by the accumulation or degradation of non volatile organic anions and malate in particular. In the nutrient medium ionic balance was maintained by root excretion of H^+ (excess cation uptake) or OH^- (excess anion uptake). The presence of respiratory CO_2 in the root medium implies that HCO_3^- rather than OH^- occurs in the nutrient medium when plants take up an excess of anions.

The concepts discussed above are illustrated in the highly interesting and conclusive data of HIATT [1967] shown in Table 3.4. Young barley roots were in-

Table 3.4 Relationship between cation uptake, anion uptake, change of organic anion content, and CO_2 assimilation of young barley roots (HIATT [1967])

Nutrients (1 me/1)	Cation uptake	Anion uptake	Change of organic anion equivalents	rel. Ass. of ^{14}C
	in μ e/g			
K_2SO_4	17	< 1	+ 15.1	145
KCl	28	29	— 0.2	100
$CaCl_2$	< 1	15	— 9.7	60

cubated over a relatively short period in solutions of K_2SO_4, KCl or $CaCl_2$. Roots treated with K_2SO_4 absorbed K^+ at a much faster rate than SO_4^{2-} so that cation uptake greatly exceeded anion uptake (H^+ excretion into the nutrient solution). The deficit in anion equivalents in the roots was compensated for by the enhanced accumulation of organic anions. This accumulation is also reflected in the high CO_2 assimilation rate indicative of increased organic acid synthesis. In the $CaCl_2$ treatment the contrary situation occurred. Here Cl^- uptake far exceeded Ca^{2+} uptake (HCO_3^- excretion into the nutrient medium) thus resulting in an excess uptake of inorganic anions into the cell. This excess was counterbalanced by a reduction in the CO_2 assimilation rate and clearly also by a higher degradation of organic anions. In the KCl treatment, K^+ and Cl^- absorption occurred at very similar rates (little pH change in the nutrient medium) so that the level of organic anions in the roots was only slightly changed and the rate of CO_2 assimilation was relatively unaffected.

To understand the reason for the role of malate as a compensating anion in plant tissues it is necessary to know something of the biochemistry of malic acid. At the slightly acid pH of most cell saps (5–6) malic acid is present almost exclusively in a dissociated form as a divalent anion. The same must also be true in the cytoplasm where the pH is usually somewhat higher than in the vacuole (SMITH and RAVEN [1976]). There is evidence of the occurrence of separate mitochondrial, cytoplasmic and vacuolar metabolic pools for malate. Most malate, however, appears to occur in the vacuole associated with inorganic cations whereas the metabolic processes are largely associated with the cytoplasm (OSMOND [1976]). The synthesis and degradation of malate takes place in the cytoplasm and appears to be controlled by cellular pH shifts as shown below (DAVIES [1973]). Increase in pH activates PEP carboxylase which synthesises oxaloacetate from PEP by consuming HCO_3^- or $CO_2 + OH^-$. Oxaloacetate can then be reduced to malate which is accumulated. Conversely low pH promotes the reverse process, namely the oxidative decarboxylation of malate by activating malic enzyme. This 'pH stat' as DAVIES has called it is a 'fine tuning' device which enables the cell to cope with fluctuations in pH in the cytoplasm. In particular carboxylation is able to counter OH^- production by cells by the formation of malate (see SMITH and RAVEN [1979]). The reactions are presented below, oxaloacetate being shown as a possible transient intermediate in the oxidative decarboxylation of malate.

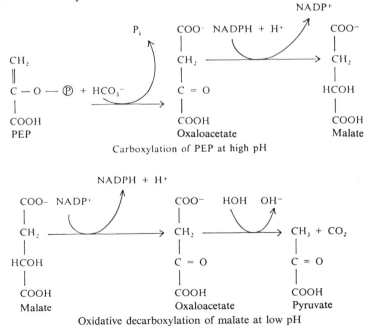

Carboxylation of PEP at high pH

Oxidative decarboxylation of malate at low pH

135

The dependence of malate accumulation on cellular pH explains the results of HIATT [1967] shown in Table 3.4. In the case of K_2SO_4 the more rapid uptake of K^+ than SO_4^{2-} induces an exchange of H^+ from the roots. The pH in the root tissue thus rises and malate is accumulated. Conversely when $CaCl_2$ is applied to the roots anion uptake exceeds cation uptake. HCO_3^- is excreted from the roots, the cellular pH falls and the level of malate drops.

The form and level of N-nutrition can considerably influence the cation-anion balance in plants (JUNGK [1967], KURVITS and KIRKBY [1980]). Plants fed with NO_3-N generally take up an excess of anions and the nutrient medium in which they are growing becomes alkaline (KIRKBY and MENGEL [1967]). The assimilation of NO_3^- after uptake leads to an alkalization effect in the plant and hence to organic anion accumulation (see p. 171). Some of the charge from NO_3^- assimilation can also appear in the nutrient medium as HCO_3^- in exchange for excess anion uptake.

In many plant species the charge transfer from NO_3^- assimilation can largely be accounted for by organic anion accumulation in the plant (DIJKSHOORN et al. [1968]). Increasing the level of NO_3^--nutrition thus stimulates organic anion synthesis and hence cation accumulation. This is demonstrated in the data of KIRKBY and KNIGHT [1977] for tomato plants shown in Figure 3.11.

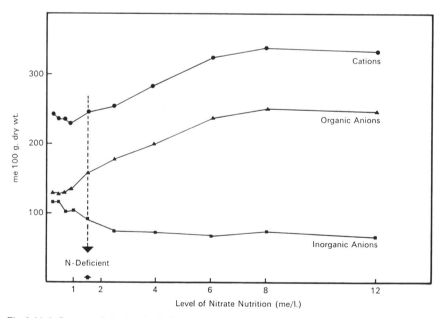

Fig. 3.11 Influence of the level of nitrate nutrition on the accumulation of cations, organic acid anions and inorganic anions in tomato plants (after KIRKBY and KNIGHT [1977]).

Although the cation level in the nutrient solution was maintained constant, concentrations of cations and organic anions increased dramatically in response to NO_3^--nutrition. Increasing the level of NO_3^--nutrition stimulated the rate of uptake and upward translocation of NO_3^- and cations as counter-ions. Following the reduction of NO_3^- in the upper plant parts organic anions were accumulated to balance the cation charge originally accompanying the NO_3^--ions.

The data of BLEVINS et al. [1974] as well as those of KIRKBY and KNIGHT [1977] are indicative of active uptake of nitrate inducing an uptake (symport) of cations. Nitrate uptake, however, may also occur in exchange for OH^- without cation uptake as has been shown by KIRKBY and ARMSTRONG [1980] in the castor oil plant (Ricinus communis). This NO_3^-/OH^- exchange (antiport) also appears to dominate in grasses where the uptake of anions is about twice that of cations (KIRKBY [1974]).

From the above discussion it is clear that plants fed with NO_3^--N contain high levels of cations and organic anions. In contrast plants supplied with NH_4^+-N often contain lower concentrations of inorganic cations (Ca, Mg, K) and organic acids whereas the elements absorbed as anions (S, P, Cl) are present in higher concentrations (Coïc et al. [1962]). This is illustrated in Table 3.5 showing the cation-anion balance of leaves of white mustard plants grown with NO_3^--N or NH_4^+-N as N source (KIRKBY [1968]).

Table 3.5   Influence of the form of N-nutrition on the cation-anion balance in white mustard leaves (KIRKBY [1968])

| | Cations | | | | | Anions | | | | | |
| | Ca | Mg | K | Na | Total | NO_3 | H_2PO_4 | SO_4 | Cl | Org. acids | Total |
	(me/100 g DM)					(me/100 g DM)					
NO_3	107	28	81	5	221	1	26	25	25	162	239
NH_4	72	22	40	7	141	1	25	25	31	54	136

The uptake mechanism for NH_4-N is not yet completely understood. According to experimental data of DEJAEGERE and NEIRINCKX [1978] and also of MUNN and JACKSON [1978] NH_4^+ is taken up in exchange for H^+. This finding is consistent with the well known observation that using NH_4-N as a nitrogen source results in a acidification of the nutrient medium (KIRKBY and MENGEL [1967]). Research work of HEBER et al. [1974] with chloroplasts, however, has led to the conclusion that it is rather NH_3 than NH_4^+ which is transported across the outer chloroplast membrane. Unpublished results of MENGEL and co-workers of uptake experiments using intact plants also indicate that NH_4^+ may be deprotonated at the plasma membrane. Ammonia may thus traverse the membrane leaving behind one H^+ for every NH_3 molecule absorbed. Deprotonation as well as H^+ exchange would of course also lead to an acidification of the root medium. If NH_4-N were mainly absorbed as NH_3 and not in ionic form, it would not be expected to participate in cation competition. This lack of competition by NH_4-N has been observed by MENGEL et al. [1976], who reported that the NH_4-N uptake by young rice plants was not competitively affected by the K^+ concentration of the nutrient medium.

Cation anion balance is of particular interest in leguminous plant species which are dependent on molecular N fixed by *Rhizobium* bacteria. Under such conditions cation uptake by far exceeds anion uptake and the cation excess is balanced by H^+ excretion from the roots. NYATASANGA and PIERRE [1973] have shown that for a lucerne crop fixing nitrogen, and producing 10 tonnes/ha of dry matter, 600 kg $CaCO_3$/ha were required to neutralize the resulting soil acidity.

3.1.10 Relationship between uptake rate and the ion concentration in the nutrient solution

The rate at which an ion species is absorbed is dependent on its concentration in the nutrient medium. This relationship is not linear but follows an asymptotic curve (see Figure 3.12). EPSTEIN and HAGEN [1952] have linked the process of carrier mediated transport of an ion across a membrane to the enzyme mediated catalysis of a substrate. Michaelis-Menten kinetics have therefore been applied to the ion uptake process. The ion being absorbed has been compared with the substrate and the carrier with the enzyme. This is expressed graphically as shown in Figure 3.12 and mathematically as

$$ I = \frac{I_{max} \cdot C}{K_m + C} $$

where

I = influx (rate of uptake)

I_{max} = maximal influx (maximal rate of uptake)

K_m = Michaelis Menten constant and is the concentration

C = Concentration of ion in solution at the root surface

when

I = $\frac{1}{2} I_{max}$. The value is characteristic for a particular ion crossing a specific membrane

138

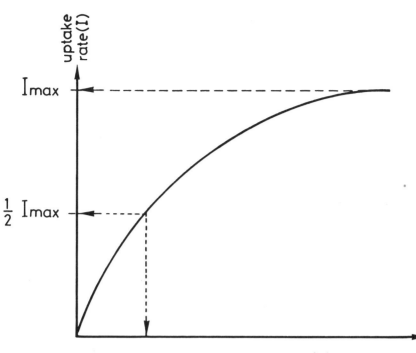

Fig.3.12 Relationship between the ion concentration and the rate of uptake.

Recently BARBER [1979] has used a modified form of the above equation to describe ion uptake by intact maize roots. This takes into account the fact that the net uptake of an ion species results from influx and efflux. When plants are allowed to deplete the nutrients from a solution until the net influx, I_n is zero, a minimum concentration C_{min} is present in the solution. At this concentration influx and efflux are equal. As C_{min} is not zero when $I_n = O$ then the above equation is modified to

$$I_n = \frac{I_{max} (C - C_{min})}{K_m + (C - C_{min})}$$

Absorption isotherms describing the demand for a nutrient as related to the concentration in solution have been obtained by measuring the rate of depletion from the solution supplying the plant (CLAASSEN and BARBER [1976]). By measurement of C_{min} and the use of the modified equation it is also possible to determine I_n, the net influx.

The concentration of C_{min} is generally low ($< 5\,\mu M$) and depends on metabolic conditions. The term 'I_{max}' is not a constant and as shown for K^+ by CLAASSEN and BARBER [1976] depends much on plant K^+ status. The higher the K^+ content of the plant, the lower is the value of I_{max}.

Some uptake characteristics for NO_3^- $H_2PO_4^-$ and K^+ are shown in Table 3.6. The data of this table probably relate to active ion uptake. The lower values for $H_2PO_4^-$ reflect the lower plant requirement of this ion than for NO_3^- or K^+. In addition these lower values also indicate that at the much lower concentrations of $H_2PO_4^-$ than NO_3^- or K^+ normally found in soil solution (see p. 71) that a higher efficiency of phosphate absorption is necessary to meet the demand of the plant.

Table 3.6 Influx characteristics of intact 18 day old maize roots growing in solution culture (BARBER [1979]).

Nutrient	I_{max} pMol, cm^{-1}, s^{-1}	K_m μM	C_{min} μM
NO_3^-	1.0	12	4
$H_2PO_4^-$	0.4	3	0.2
K^+...................................	2.0	17	2

EPSTEIN [1966, 1972] has postulated that for many nutrient ions two separate mechanisms are involved in ion transport. The occurrence of these mechanisms is dependent on the external concentration. In the case of K^+, mechanisms I operates at low K^+ concentrations (0–0.2 mM) and is highly selective for K^+ whereas mechanism II comes into play at higher concentrations (1–50 mM) and has a much lower affinity for K^+. EPSTEIN argues that these findings may be explained by the presence of two carrier systems located in the plasmalemma. On the other hand this K^+ uptake pattern may be accounted for simply by the presence of an active uptake mechanism at low K^+ concentrations with the involvement of a diffusion component (passive uptake), at higher external K^+ concentrations. This interpretation is consistent with K^+ uptake studies on maize roots by CHEESEMAN and HANSON [1979] (see p. 418).

In evaluating numerous ion uptake curves (uptake rate vs. ion concentration in the nutrient medium, NISSEN [1974] has concluded that ion uptake is 'multiphasic'. This term is used to describe absorption of a particular ion species, mediated by only one carrier where the affinity of the carrier for the ion is dependent on the ion concentration in the external medium. Uptake curves with a number of 'shoulders' are thus obtained. Whether these 'shoulders, actually result from a change in carrier affinity has yet to be established.

3.1.11 Recent developments in ion uptake

The intact root system of a plant exposes a very large surface area to the soil (see p. 76). How much of this root surface is capable of absorbing ions is an important question in plant nutrition, which has only recently been investigated. It is clearly of great interest to know which parts of the roots absorb and translocate nutrients and whether there are differences in behaviour between nutrients in this respect.

Research along these lines has been developed by CLARKSON and his colleagues in England. The basic technique employed by these workers has been to expose a small section of root from the intact plant to a radioactive tracer whilst supplying the rest of the plant root with the same solution but without the radioactive source. This has been achieved by passing the radioactive tracer through an incised plastic pipe containing the root section. From such studies it has been possible to investigate the uptake of a series of nutrients from different root sections of intact plants. Several important findings have resulted from such experiments probably the most important of which is that individual ions differ considerably in behaviour. Experiments with barley and marrow roots have shown that the movement of Ca^{2+} to the shoots is restricted to the young plant parts whereas for K^+ and phosphate the radial movement across the root and transport to the shoots takes place readily throughout the length of the root. The basic difference in behaviour of Ca^{2+} on the one hand and K^+ and phosphate on the other can be explained in terms of root structure, and especially on the development of the endodermis. This as well as the apoplast and symplast pathways are considered in more detail on p. 194.

Evidence that K^+ and phosphate are taken up over the whole length of the root suggests that these ions move *via* the symplast. On the other hand, as Ca^{2+} uptake and translocation are restricted to the root-tip region, this indicates that Ca follows the apoplast pathway. Clearly, if this is the case the radial movement of Ca^{2+} from cortex to stele should be restricted progressively as the endodermis becomes more suberized. Evidence of this kind has been provided by ROBARDS *et al.* [1973].

The significance of CLARKSON's work is that it has established a clear link between ion uptake and root structure. In addition by use of the intact plant it has taken into account the strong possibility that transport between shoot and root might provide the message to coordinate root activity with shoot demand. These messages may be hormonal (see CLARKSON and HANSON [1980]). Besides this, however, the control of NO_3^- uptake may be dependent on HCO_3^- exchange from HCO_3^- derived from NO_3^- assimilation in the shoots. This has recently been established in the castor oil plant (KIRKBY and ARMSTRONG [1980]).

These root-shoot relationships were either ignored or not appreciated in many earlier investigations in ion uptake studies in which workers used excised roots or discs.

Another aspect of ion uptake studies which has been receiving considerable attention is the use of flowing dilute nutrient solutions. In normal static water culture experiments the concentrations of ions and particularly phosphate and K^+ are usually very much in excess of values found in soil solution (see p. 71). In these experiments too nutrient fluctuations and depletions may occur so that interpretation of results is difficult. The use of nutrient solutions with low but constantly maintained concentrations of ions simulates the soil solution. Here a continuous supply of ions replaces those ions removed by the root as a result of the demand for nutrients created by plant growth. The technique of closely monitoring ions around the roots and relating these values to nutrient uptake and plant growth allows this dynamic equilibrium to be studied. Such experiments have revealed that plant roots are extremely efficient in the uptake of K^+ (WILD et al. [1974]), NO_3^- (CLEMENT et al. [1978]), and other ions (see CLARKSON and HANSON [1980]). It now remains to relate these findings to the soil/plant system in the field.

3.2 Photosynthesis and CO_2 Assimilation

3.2.1 General

Nutrition has already been defined as the supply of an organism with its essential foodstuffs. For all animals and most microorganisms these foodstuffs not only contain essential chemical elements but are also a source of chemical energy by which the energy demands of the organism are satisfied. For green plants the situation is quite different because the nutrient sources, CO_2, H_2O and inorganic ions, are of low energy status and therefore not able to meet the plants energy requirement. The assimilation of these inorganic nutrients does, in fact, need energy. In green plants this requirement is satisfied primarily by the absorption of light. This unique ability of green plant cells to absorb light energy and convert it into chemical energy is one of the most important biological processes. All other organisms with the exception of a few microorganisms are dependent on this energy conversion.

The conversion of light energy into chemical energy is closely related to the conversion of CO_2 into organic compounds. For decades both reactions – energy conversion and CO_2 fixation – were regarded as one reaction complex described by the equation:

$$6 \text{ CO}_2 + 6 \text{ H}_2\text{O} \xrightarrow{\text{light energy}} \text{C}_6\text{H}_{12}\text{O}_6 + 6 \text{ O}_2$$

A clear distinction is now drawn between energy conversion and CO_2 assimilation. In modern terminology, the term photosynthesis has been applied to the process whereby a pigment system absorbs electromagnetic radiation and converts this into chemical forms of energy which are available for growth in a particular environment.

3.2.2 Light absorption and electron flow

In higher plants light absorption is brought about by chlorophylls and carotenoids (Figure 3.13). These are constituents of the grana lamellae (thylakoids) of the chloroplasts (Plate 4.4). The unique feature of these pigments is the ability to absorb light and convert it to chemical energy. Other coloured particles are also capable of light absorption but the energy is dissipated either as heat or as light in the form of fluorescence or phosphorescence.

The basic process in photosynthesis is the absorption of light by pigments which induces an electron flow (kinetic energy), which is converted into chemical energy. The ultimate forms of chemical energy built up in this process are ATP and NADPH. In higher plants two photosystems are responsible for this energy conversion; photosystem I and II. Both these photosynthetic units consist of about 400 chlorophyll molecules and additional pigments such as carotenes and carotenoids. In some algae phycobilins are also present and function as light absorbers. The function of these pigments consists of absorbing light energy and transferring it by inductive resonance to a special chlorophyll a

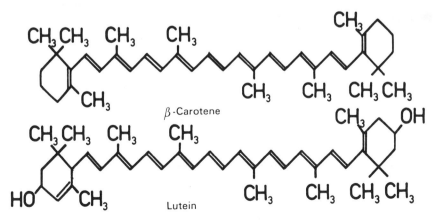

Fig.3.13 Molecular structure of carotenoids, β carotene and lutein.

143

molecule, which has a unique function in the photosystem. In photosystem I this particular chlorophyll a molecule is known as pigment 700 (= P-700) as its absorption maximum is at 700 nm. P-700 differs from the bulk of chlorophyll a molecules in that it has an absorption maximum at a somewhat longer wavelength. The light energy absorbed by the carotenes, carotenoids, chlorophyll b and by 'normal' chlorophyll a molecules in photosystem I is transferred to P-700 so inducing the emission of an electron.

$$\text{Energy} + \text{P-700} \rightarrow (\text{P-700})^+ + e^-$$

This is the basic process that initiates electron flow. The pigments in the photosynthetic unit thus act as a funnel directing absorbed energy to one P-700 molecule. This brings about the oxidation of P-700 and the release of an electron.

The electron acceptor in this particular process is supposed to be bound ferredoxin (TREBST [1974]). Its standard redoxpotential is low (–0.44 V) in comparison with that of P-700 (+0.46 V). The electron ejected from P-700 has thus to be moved against an electrical gradient.

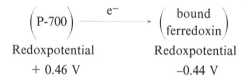

$\left(\text{P-700} \right) \xrightarrow{\ e^- \ } \left(\begin{array}{c} \text{bound} \\ \text{ferredoxin} \end{array} \right)$

Redoxpotential   Redoxpotential

+ 0.46 V   –0.44 V

This 'uphill transport' requires energy which is ultimately derived from the light energy absorbed by the pigments of photosystem I.

Photosystem II functions in an analogous way to photosystem I. In photosystem II the electron emittor is also a chlorophyll a molecule but in this case the absorption maximum is at 682 nm. It is hence known as P-682. The electron acceptor of P 682 is usually designated as Q (= quencher) due to the fact that its presence 'quenches' the fluorescence. It is supposed that this primary acceptor of photosystem II is a plastoquinone (AMESZ [1977]). As the standard redoxpotential of P-682 is +0.8 V, electron transfer from P-682 to Q is also an uphill transport requiring energy, from the light absorbed by the pigments of photosystem II.

$(\text{P-682}) \xrightarrow{\ e^- \ } (\text{Q})$

Redoxpotential   Redoxpotential

+ 0.8 V   –0.1 V

In higher plants these two photosystems function in series and are components of an electron transport pathway transferring electrons from water to $NADP^+$. This means that ultimately water is the electron donor and $NADP^+$ the

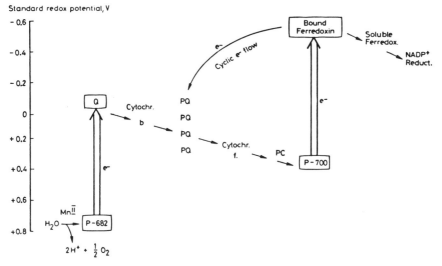

Fig.3.14 Photosynthetic e⁻ transport chain.

electron acceptor in the overall process. Figure 3.14 shows this electron transport chain and its redoxsystems. Photosystem II is closely associated with the splitting of water which serves as the electron donor. P-682 in its oxidized form $(P-682)^+$ is a very strong oxidant and thus capable of oxidising H_2O. In this reaction H_2O is split in O_2, H^+ and electrons.

$$2H_2O \rightarrow 4H^+ + 4e^- + O_2$$

This process is called photolysis and this is the origin of O_2 produced in photosynthesis. P-682 does not react directly with water. The process is mediated by unknown redox systems (RADMER and KOK [1975]). Manganese and Cl^- are involved. A bound form of Mn in the chloroplasts appears to undergo photooxidation from Mn^{2+} to Mn^{3+} (CHENIAE and MARTIN [1971]).

The electrons supplied by H_2O are transferred to P-682 and as already described are then passed on to a compound Q with a more negative redoxpotential. From Q the electrons move energetically downhill following the increasing redoxpotentials as shown in Figure 3.14. The quencher (Q) which as already mentioned is supposedly a plastoquinone transfers electrons downhill to cytochrome b and from this redoxsystem to plastoquinones (PQ) (CRAMER [1977]). These compounds are present in abundant quantities in the chloroplast membrane, and due to their lipiphilic character are believed to be rather mobile in the membrane. Plastoquinones also accept electrons from bound ferredoxin, as shown in Figure 3.14. This step in electron transfer results in

145

a cyclic electron flow which gives rise to 'cyclic photophosphorylation'. This process is considered in the next section. From plastoquinones electrons are transferred to cytochrome f and then on to plastocyanin.

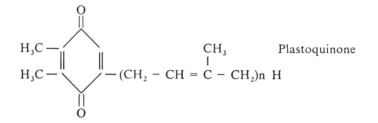

Plastoquinone

Plastocyanin is an acidic protein containing 2 Cu atoms per molecule. It is called the 'blue protein' and according to TREBST and PISTORIUS [1965] it transfers electrons directly to oxidized P-700. From P-700 a further uphill transport occurs as already indicated raising the electron from a redox-potential of $+0.46$ V to a redox-potential of -0.44 V. Both these uphill transports in the photosynthetic electron transport chain from P-7000 and P-682 are indicated by vertical arrows in Figure 3.14. Because of the zigzag pattern of the scheme it is sometimes known as the Z scheme.

The electron acceptor of P-700 is supposed to be bound ferredoxin. Electrons are then transferred to soluble ferredoxin. Ferredoxins are stable Fe-S proteins. As can be seen in Figure 3.15, Fe is coordinated to the S atoms of cysteine and also to inorganic S. Thus unlike the cytochromes, ferredoxin Fe is not present in a haem form. BOARDMAN [1975] reports that chloroplasts contain a soluble form of ferredoxin and one or more membrane bound fer-

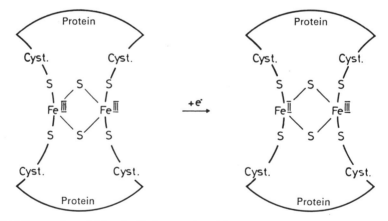

Fig.3.15 Proposed model for the Fe-S group in soluble ferredoxin, left oxidized form, right reduced form.

redoxins. The soluble form has a molecular weight of 12 000 and contains 2 atoms of Fe and 2 atoms of inorganic sulphide per molecule (ARNON [1967]). In the oxidized form both of the Fe atoms are present as Fe^{III} whereas in the reduced form one Fe atom occurs as Fe^{II}. Soluble ferredoxin thus acts as a one-electron carrier.

Ferredoxin is the first stable redox compound of the photosynthetic electron transport chain. Its high negative redox potential (-0.43 V) means that it can reduce various substances such as $NADP^+$, nitrite, O_2, sulphate and haem proteins (see Figure 3.16). In the normal course of photosynthetic electron transport, reduced ferredoxin is oxidized enzymatically by ferredoxin-NADP reductase which reduces $NADP^+$ to NADPH. Electron transport in the photosynthetic electron transport chain thus terminates with the reduction of $NADP^+$ to NADPH. In this reduced form the coenzyme nicotinamide adenine dinucleotide ($= NADP^+ =$ oxidized, NADPH $=$ reduced form) represents a high potential energy level.

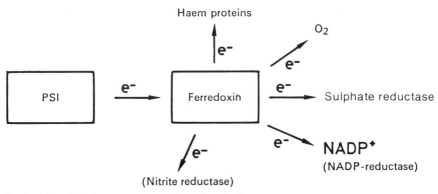

Fig. 3.16 Possible electron acceptors from ferredoxin.

As the electrons reducing $NADP^+$ to NADPH originate from H_2O the overall process of this reduction is described by the equation:

$$NADP^+ + H_2O \rightarrow NADPH + H^+ + \tfrac{1}{2} O_2$$

This is an endergonic process requiring approximately 220 kJ/mole NADPH produced. The energy is provided by the light energy trapped by photosystems I and II. It is supposed that the ejection of one electron (one photochemical event) from P-700 as well as one from P-682 each requires one photon. As the reduction of $NADP^+$ requires 2 electrons a total of 4 photons is needed. One mole of photons ($= 1$ Einstein $=$ photon mole) of red light at a wavelength of 680 nm has an energy content of about 176 kJ. Hence the total energy of 4 photon moles absorbed amounts to 704 kJ. This energy quantity exceeds the total chemical energy produced by the photosynthetic process. This total chemical energy produced is the sum of the energy required for the production of NADPH (220 kJ) and the synthesis ATP (32 kJ). Hence the Z scheme is energetically feasible, allowing a reasonable loss in the conversion of light energy to chemical energy (WALKER [1970]).

3.2.3 Photophosphorylation

In photosynthetic energy conversion, light induces an electron flow which is able to provide the energy for the synthesis of ATP and for the reduction of $NADP^+$. Both coenzymes contain chemical energy originally trapped as light by the chloroplast pigments. From the pioneer work of ARNON et al. [1961] it is now well established that photosynthetic electron transport results in the synthesis of ATP.

Three different hypotheses have been proposed to account for the mechanism of coupled electron transport and ATP synthesis (= photophosphorylation). In the first, the chemical hypothesis, it is supposed that there is a direct reaction between the electron carriers of the photosynthetic electron transport chain and enzymes synthesizing ATP, in which high energy intermediates are formed. In the second, the conformational hypothesis, it is suggested that electron transport gives rise to a conformational change of enzyme proteins bringing about the phosphorylation of ADP to ATP. The third and now most generally accepted hypothesis is that put forward by MITCHELL [1961, 1966, 1978]. MITCHELL has proposed that the flow of electrons through the system of carrier molecules, already described in the previous section, drives protons (H^+) across the chloroplast membrane. This results in an electrochemical proton gradient across the membrane The gradient consists of two components, a H^+ concentration and an electrical potential. The electrochemical potential difference (proton motive force = pmf) of the gradient may thus be described as

$$pmf = \Delta H^+ + \psi$$

where
ΔH^+ = proton gradient across the membrane
ψ = electrical gradient across the membrane

This proton motive force provides the energy for ATP synthesis which is the reverse of an ATPase reaction (see p. 121). (JAGENDORFF [1977]).

$$ADP + P_i = ATP + H_2O$$

The chemiosmotic hypothesis is now well supported by experimental evidence. The relationship between electron flow and the formation of a proton gradient has been especially well documented. PORTIS and McCARTY [1974] have also demonstrated that the rate of phosphorylation in chloroplasts is critically dependent on the magnitude of the pH gradient across the thylakoid membrane.

The mechanism by which electron transport is able to induce a proton gradient is dependent on the nature of the electron transport components and their location in the membrane. Figure 3.17 shows the arrangement according to a modified scheme proposed by TREBST [1974]. Proton separation comes about if a H carrier (plastoquinone) reacts with an electron carrier. This occurs when two electrons that cross the membrane from P 682 are picked up at the matrix surface (outer surface) by the H carrier plastoquinone (Figure 3.18). The electrons with two protons extracted from the matrix reduce PQ to PQH_2 (plastohydroquinone) which migrates back across the membrane to the inner surface. Here PQH_2 releases the protons internally and transfers the electrons to cytochrome f. Thus in this sequence 2 H^+ are transported across the thylakoid membrane from the matrix side to the inner side with plastoquinone serving as a shuttle, simultaneously transferring electrons from cytochrome b to cytochrome f. During photolysis as shown in Figure 3.17 two protons derived from one water molecule are also released into the inner compartment. Electron flow thus

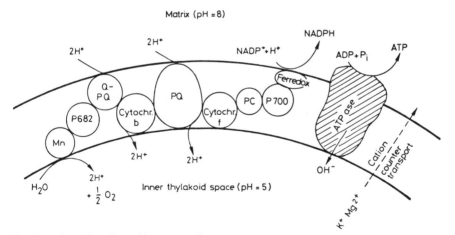

Q–PQ = Quencher plastochinone complex
PQ   = Plastoquinone
PC   = Plastocyanin

Fig. 3.17 Coupling of electron flow, proton separation and ATP synthesis in the thylakoid membrane.

results in a proton separation leading to a pH gradient across the membrane (ΔH^+) of about 2 units, with the matrix attaining a pH value of about 8.

The alkaline medium in the stroma favours ATP formation by the ATPase which appears to be located in the knob-like projections of the membrane in the matrix (see Fig. 3.17). JAGENDORF [1977] suggests that the proton gradient across the membrane enables the enzyme to split ADP into OH^- and the cation ADP^+ which spontaneously reacts with inorganic phosphate to form ATP. The OH^- is secreted into the inner space.

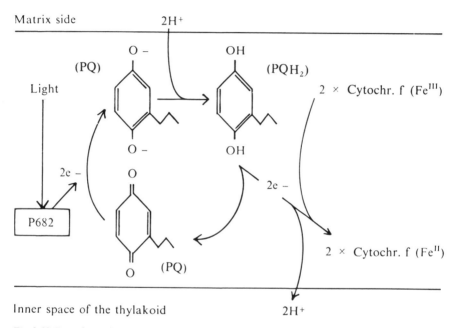

Fig.3.18 Reaction of a H-carrying redoxsystem (plastohydroquinone) with an e^--carrying redoxsystem (cytochrome f) and associated proton separation.

The dissociation of ADP into ADP^+ and OH^- is favoured by the low pH in the inner thylakoid compartment, since the OH^- formed is neutralized by the excess H^+. ATP synthesis thus discharges the electropotential and the pH gradient across the membrane. According to the scheme shown above the synthesis of 1 molecule of ATP 'consumes' 1 H^+. There is much experimental evidence, however, which is not consistent with a H^+/ATP ratio of unity, but indicates rather a ratio of 2 H^+ or even 3 H^+ per ATP produced (JAGENDORFF [1977]). If the ATPase system is as represented in Figure 3.7 a ratio of 2 H^+/ATP would be expected. From a thermodynamic approach a ratio of 3 or even 4 H^+/ATP has been suggested.

150

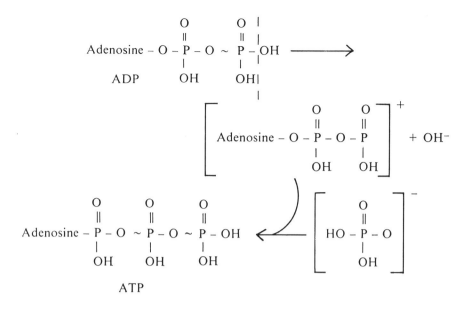

The proton gradient across the thylakoid membrane may be considered as a store of free energy with a chemical component (Δ H$^+$) and an electrical component (ψ). The measurement of this latter component is difficult. Not only do the potential gradients observed differ considerably (10 to 100 mV) but there is also some uncertainly about the results obtained. It is generally supposed that Δ H$^+$ is of more importance for ATP synthesis than is ψ.

The electrical potential gradient also depends on the counter flux of cations (antiport) induced by the H$^+$ secretion into the inner part of the thylakoid. Thus light not only triggers an electron flow in the membrane and a proton separation but also a cation flux into the stroma (PFLÜGER [1974]). This cation 'antitransport' is of physiological significance, because it prevents the establishment of too high an electrical potential gradient ($>$350 mV) across the membrane which would be detrimental to the system. The presence of high electropotential could also exert a 'backpressure' and thus impede electron flow. Electron flow is controlled by the ATP/ADP ratio in the stroma, a high ratio impeding, a low ratio promoting ATP formation and thus adjusting photophosphorylation to physiological demand. The actual enzymatic process of photosynthetic ATP formation is not yet understood and it is very well possible that besides the proton gradient, enzyme protein conformation also plays a role in the phosphorylation of ADP.

An essential prerequisite for the chemiosmotic hypothesis is the proton gradient across the membrane. This can be brought about by electron transport from water to NADP$^+$ as shown in the scheme of Figure 3.17. Besides this 'linear' electron flow, however, 'cyclic' electron flow can also occur. In this case bound ferredoxin reduces plastoquinone (PQ), which again supplies electrons into the photosynthetic electron transport chain (see Figure 3.14). Electron transport from plastoquinone to cytochrome f results in a proton separation and thus also in the build up of an electropotential across the membrane. This cyclic flow of electrons drives the so-called cyclic photophosphorylation. During cyclic electron flow no NADPH is produced. The system can thus adjust to physiological requirements (ARNON [1977]). RAGHAVENDRA and DAS [1978] have reported that the ratio 'cyclic/non cyclic' phosphorylation increases with increasing light intensity. It is suggested that under high light conditions the NADPH consumption is limited due to a lack of CO_2 and thus relatively more ATP is required.

Oxidative phosphorylation in mitochondria is brought about by an analogous mechanism. In respiration as in photosynthesis, electron flow occurs along an electropotential gradient made up of a number of redoxsystems. As electron flow in respiration is coupled with the synthesis of ATP and with the consumption of oxygen it is called oxidative phosphorylation. Both phosphorylating processes can be uncoupled by a number of chemicals. The most well known uncoupler of oxidative phosphorylation is 2.4 dinitrophenol (2.4 DNP), other uncouplers are: arsenate, ouabain and long chain fatty acids (STONER et al. [1964]). Photophosphorylation is uncoupled by a number of reagents including NH_3 and the aliphatic amines. These chemicals do not directly affect electron transport, but inhibit ATP synthesis. This effect probably depends on the capability of these compounds of decreasing the H$^+$ concentration gradient across the membrane by increasing H$^+$ membrane permeability.

3.2.4 CO_2 assimilation and the Calvin cycle

Photosynthetic CO_2 assimilation is the primary process by which inorganic C is converted into organic form simultaneously trapping energy provided by the light reaction of photosynthesis. CO_2 assimilation is thus of paramount importance for the production of organic material as well as for the storage of energy in a chemical form. CO_2 is assimilated by the carboxylation of ribulose bisphosphate (RuBP). This carboxylation reaction catalyzed by RuBP carboxylase can be described by the following reactions presented on the next page. The actual process is more complicated than that presented in the scheme below (AKAZAWA [1979]). The overall reaction shows that in addition to a CO_2 molecule, one water molecule is accepted by RuBP and required for the synthesis of 2 molecules of 3-phosphoglycerate (= PGA). According to

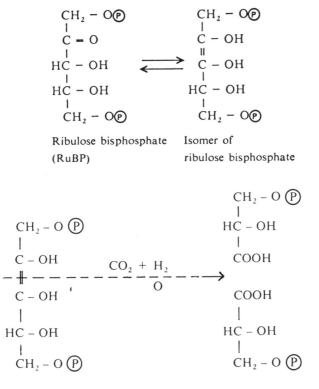

Ribulose bisphosphate
(RuBP)

Isomer of
ribulose bisphosphate

3 – Phosphoglycerate

$$RuBP + CO_2 + H_2O \rightarrow 2 \times PGA$$

COOPER *et al.* [1969] CO_2 rather than HCO_3^- is accepted by RuBP. For a long time the activity and the K_m of the catalyzing enzyme RuBP carboxylase seemed to be too low for the actual CO_2 assimilation rate measured *in vivo*. More recent research, however, has shown that the activity depends much on the pH and the Mg^{2+} concentration in the stroma (BASSHAM [1979]). As shown in Figure 3.17 the photosynthetic light reaction triggers the import of Mg^{2+} into the stroma in exchange for H^+ thus providing optimum conditions for RuBP carboxylase. Activities obtained under these conditions agree well with the CO_2 assimilation rates found *in vivo* (KELLY *et al.* [1976]). The carboxylation reaction is an exergonic reaction and therefore does not require additional energy. RuBP carboxylase catalyses the first step of a cyclic sequence of reactions which was elucidated by CALVIN and his co-workers (CALVIN [1956], BASSHAM and CALVIN [1957]). All enzymes catalyzing the various steps of this cycle are located in the stroma of the chloroplast.

The two steps following the carboxylation reaction require energy in the forms of ATP and NADPH and it is at this stage of the CO_2 assimilation process at which the products formed during the light reaction (see Figure 3.17) are required. The phosphoglycerate (PGA) is reduced to glyceraldehyde 3-phosphate. As this reduction is an energy consuming reaction the phosphoglycerate must be 'loaded' with energy before the reaction can proceed. This 'priming reaction' is brought about by ATP. The 1,3 bisphosphoglycerate thus synthesized is then reduced by NADPH to glyceraldehyde 3-phosphate. This is the first sugar (triose phosphate), synthesized in the CO_2 assimilation reaction sequence.

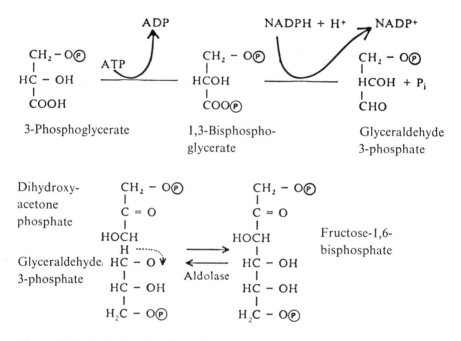

Glyceraldehyde 3-phosphate is a primary product in the synthesis of sugars. The molecule is readily converted to its isomer dihydroxyacetone phosphate, and in the presence of aldolase both molecules react to form fructose-1,6-bisphosphate a phosphorylated hexose.

Fructose-1,6-bisphosphate is a precursor of all other hexoses including glucose and its polymers. A direct series of reactions can be thus traced leading from CO_2 assimilation *via* the triose phosphates to fructose-1,6-bisphosphate and all other carbohydrates. Some of these compounds such as starch, sucrose, and inulin are energy storage compounds, whereas others like cellulose, hemicellulose and pectins play a significant role as structural cellular constituents. Triose phosphate can be used either for the synthesis of carbohydrates required in metabolism or in the regeneration of the CO_2 acceptor ribulose bisphosphate. The sequence of reaction by which ribulose bisphosphate is regenerated is known as the Calvin cycle. This is shown in Figure 3.19. The regeneration is a complex process in which sugar phosphates with different numbers of C atoms are involved. Following the reaction series as indicated by step ① in Figure 3.19 it can be seen that two triosephosphate molecules are condensed to form one molecule of fructose bisphosphate which by splitting off a phosphate group is transformed to fructose monophosphate. In the reaction indicated by ② one triose phosphate molecule reacts with fructose monophosphate to form a tetrose phosphate and

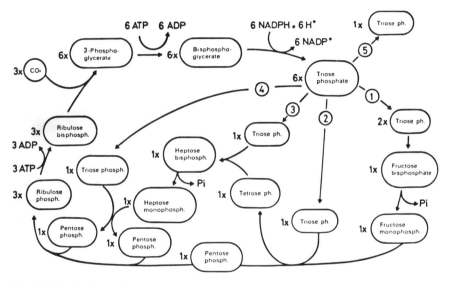

Fig.3.19 The Calvin cycle.

a pentose phosphate (xylosephosphate). The tetrosephosphate (erythrose phosphate) and a further molecule of triose phosphate are condensed to form a heptose bisphosphate (sedoheptulose bisphosphate) as indicated by ③. A phosphate group is split off from heptose bisphosphate thus forming a heptose monophosphate. This reacts with a further triose phosphate molecule as shown in reaction ④ to give two pentose phosphates (xylose phosphate and ribose phosphate). All these reaction steps ultimately result in the formation of pentose phosphates which are further converted to the isomer ribulose monophosphate. Thus in the whole reaction cycle 5 triose phosphates are converted to 3 pentose phosphates. These are phosphorylated by ATP thus forming the primary CO_2 acceptor ribulose bisphosphate.

The overall process may be written:

$$3 \, CO_2 + 3(C5) \rightarrow 6(C3) \rightarrow 1(C3) + 3(C5)$$

This assimilation of 3 molecules of CO_2 requires 9 molecules of ATP and 6 molecules of NADPH. Thus for the assimilation of 1 molecule of CO_2, 3 molecules of ATP and 2 of NADPH are needed. This shows that the process requires more ATP than NADPH. In order to supply this ratio both cyclic and non-cyclic photophosphorylation must therefore occur as non-cyclic photophosphorylation only supplies ATP/NADPH in a ratio of 1:1 (Figure 3.17). Cyclic photophosphorylation adjusts to the required ATP/NADPH ratio in the C-reduction cycle.

The levels of NADPH and ATP regulate the CALVIN cycle. In the dark the concentrations of NADPH and ATP in the chloroplasts drop so that the reduction of 3-phosphoglycerate is not only stopped, but even a reverse reaction takes place, namely the oxidation of the triosephosphate to 3-phosphoglycerate (LENDZIAN and BASSHAM [1976]). Under dark conditions fructose bisphosphate phosphatase and sedoheptulose bisphosphate phosphatase are also inactived. The CALVIN cycle is thus blocked. If the light is turned off an immediate appearance of 6-phosphogluconate is observed. This is an important intermediate of the so called oxidative pentose phosphate cycle, in which hexose phosphates are degraded and eventually intermediates of the glycollate pathway (see below) are formed. Thus dark conditions initiate respiration and accumulated chloroplast starch is oxidized, whereas under light conditions some of the triosephosphate produced is converted to starch and stored in the chloroplast. Conversely to the oxidative pentose phosphate cycle (OPP cycle) the CALVIN cycle is characterized by a reduction step and is therefore called the reductive pentose phosphate cycle (RPP cycle).

3.2.5 Photorespiration and the Glycollate Pathway

Not all the energy and reducing power produced in the photosynthetic pathway described above can be fully utilized by plants. It has been shown that although there is a net uptake of CO_2 by green plants, an efflux of CO_2 occurs which is greater in the light than in the dark. The efflux of CO_2 is accompanied by enhanced O_2 uptake. Light stimulated respiration is called photorespiration.

The C_2 pathway (glycollate pathway) in the process of photorespiration is shown in Figure 3.20. The individual steps of this reaction sequence have recently been reviewed by TOLBERT [1979]. Ribulosebisphosphate (RuBP) carboxylase, the enzyme responsible for CO_2 assimilation is also the first enzyme of the glycollate pathway (= C-2 pathway). In addition to the carboxylating function, the enzyme is also an oxygenase. It may thus oxidize RuBP especially

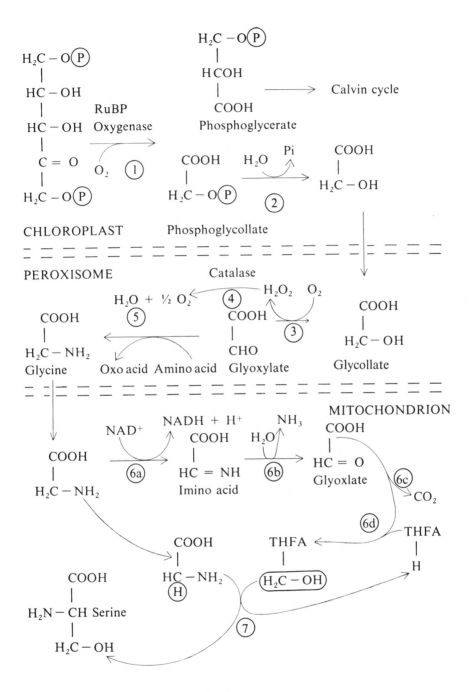

Fig. 3.20 Reaction sequence of the glycollate pathway.

under conditions where O_2 is present in abundant amounts and CO_2 is present in only low concentrations.

As shown in Figure 3.20 the first step (reaction 1) is the cleavage of RuBP into phosphoglycollate and phosphoglycerate. This step is an oxygenase reaction and consumes one molecule of O_2 per RuBP molecule split. The resulting phosphoglycerate is a metabolite of the CALVIN cycle and may thus be reduced to glyceraldehyde 3 phosphate. The phosphoglycollate is converted to glycollate by a phosphatase which splits off inorganic phosphate (reaction 2). The glycollate so formed may be released by the chloroplast and enter a peroxisome. Peroxisomes are microbodies frequently associated with chloroplasts and separated from the cytoplasm by a membrane. Peroxisomes contain several enzymes including oxidases and catalase. In the peroxisome, glycollate is oxidized to glyoxylate by a glycollate oxidase (reaction 3). The reaction consumes 1 molecule of O_2 and produces 1 molecule of H_2O_2 per glycollate molecule oxidized. The H_2O_2 formed is split into $\frac{1}{2}$ O_2 and H_2O by a catalase (reaction 4). The glyoxylate is then aminated by an aminotransferase and is thus converted to glycine (reaction 5). Glycine so formed may be transferred to a mitochondrion where it is subjected to oxidative decarboxylation. This is a complex reaction which can be subdivided into several steps. In the first step (reaction 6a) glycine is oxidized (dehydrogenated) by a glycine dehydrogenase forming the corresponding imino acid. In a second step (reaction 6b) the imino acid is deaminated. Ammonia is thus released and a glyoxylate molecule formed. This C-2 compound is then broken down into two C-1 components, namely CO_2 and $=CH-OH$ by decarboxylation (reaction 6c). The radical $=CH-OH$ is transferred to tetrahydrofolic acid (THFA), which is a coenzyme involved in the transfer of C-1 groups (reaction 6d). THFA transfers this C-1 group (hydroxymethyl) to a further glycine molecule and serine is thus formed (reaction 7). Serine may then be converted by a series of steps to phosphoglycerate which may be taken up by the CALVIN cycle.

From the reaction sequence of the glycollate pathway as shown in Figure 3.20 it is clear that O_2 is absorbed and CO_2, H_2O and NH_3 are released. This ultimately results in a loss in organic C and organically bound N. Photorespiration thus appears to be a wasteful process and may drain off nearly 50% of the C assimilated. The physiological significance of this process is not yet clear. Suggestions that it is important in amino acid synthesis, the disposal of excess reducing power or protection of the plant from high O_2 toxicity have been considered (JACKSON and VOLK [1970], TOLBERT [1979], ZELITCH [1979]). WOOLHOUSE [1978] has discussed the impact of photorespiration on crop production.

It should be emphasized that in the final part of the glycollate pathway in the mitochondria, NH_3 is released by the degradation of glycine (reacion 6b). It is believed that this NH_3 is reassimilated (KEYS *et al.* [1978]). As the turnover in the glycollate pathway can be very high under optimum conditions, it is feasible, however, that some of the NH_3 produced may be released into the atmosphere. This suggestion is consistant with recent results of STUTTE *et al.* [1979], who found that the loss of gaseous N of soya beans increased linearly with an increase in temperature.

Photorespiration is influenced to a marked extent by external factors. Generally all factors which favour the light reaction of photosynthesis such as high light intensity and high temperature lead to conditions which are favourable for the glycollate pathway. High light intensity combined with high temperature results in an abundant level of RuBP. This is associated with a high level of O_2 produced by photolysis, and a low level of CO_2 because of a high CO_2 assimilation rate. These conditions are exactly those which promote the reactions of the glycollate pathway. In addition when photosynthetic activity is high it results in an increase in Mg^{2+} concentration and a raised pH level in the stroma of the chloroplast, conditions which are essential for the activity of phosphoglycollate phosphatase (Figure 3.20 reaction 2). These stromal conditions provide a regulatory mechanism switching on the enzyme and thus the glycollate pathway under light conditions and blocking it in the dark.

Depressing photorespiration, *e.g.* by the inhibitor glycidate ($= 2,3$-epoxy-propionate), results in an increase in net CO_2 assimilation. Whether glycidate is an actual inhibitor of photorespiration has been questioned by POSKUTA and KOCHANSKA [1978]. These authors found that glycidate favours both net CO_2 assimilation and photorespiration. According to ZELITCH [1979] intermediates, such as glutamate, aspartate and glyoxylate are natural inhibitors of photorespiration.

The most important 'natural' inhibitor of photorespiration is CO_2. In C-4 plants, a category of plant species which is considered in more detail in the following section, photorespiration is practically absent. In these species high CO_2 concentrations prevail in those chloroplasts in which the CALVIN cycle reactions take place. These high CO_2 concentrations result from a particular CO_2 trapping mechanism (see Figure 3.21).

3.2.6 C-4 pathway

Ribulose bisphosphate is not the only CO_2 acceptor in photosynthesis. In a relatively wide range of plant species including maize, sugar cane, and tropical grasses as well as some temperate species, phosphoenolpyruvate (PEP) is the primary CO_2 acceptor. These species are characterized by a particular form of carboxylation (CO_2 assimilation) and decarboxylation (release of CO_2). Carboxylation and decarboxylation occur at different sites in the leaf tissue, carboxylation in the mesophyll cells and decarboxylation in the bundle sheath cells. In most plant species in which the C-4 pathway is operative (= C4 plants) these two cell types are arranged in the so called Kranz type leaf anatomy. This anatomy is shown in Plate 3.1. The vascular leaf tissue, comprising phloem and xylem strands is surrounded by large bundle sheath cells, virtually forming a 'Kranz' or wreath. The bundle sheath cells are surrounded by two layers of mesophyll cells in which the C-4 pathway is operative. $HCO_3^- + H^+$ react with phosphoenolpyruvate (= PEP) thus forming a primary C-4 intermediate, oxaloacetate (OAA).

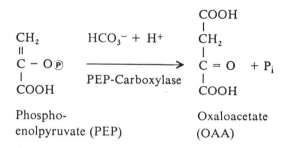

The enzyme catalysing the reaction is PEP carboxylase. The reaction which is very effective in CO_2 fixation is strongly exergonic as the high energy phosphate bond is split off from PEP. In the fixation reaction sequence oxaloacetate is converted to another C4 acid either by reduction to form malate or by transamination to produce aspartate. Because of the involvement of these C4 dicarboxylic acids as precursors of sugar phosphates this type of photosynthetic CO_2 fixation is known as the C4 pathway. Plants in which it operates are known as C4 plants to distinguish them from the more usual C3 plants in which PGA is the primary fixation product and RuBP is the primary CO_2 acceptor.

The generally accepted C4 pathway built up mainly from the work of HATCH and his colleagues is shown in Figure 3.21 and is as follows (SLACK and HATCH [1967], ANDREWS and HATCH [1971]:

① PEP is formed by the phosphorylation of pyruvate with ATP and Pi. The cyclic regeneration of PEP is dependent on the ATP requiring enzyme pyruvate phosphate dikinase. This enzyme occurs in all C4 plants and during the reaction the ATP is split into adenosine monophosphate (AMP) and pyrophosphate as indicated by the symbol Ⓟ ∼ Ⓟ.

a)

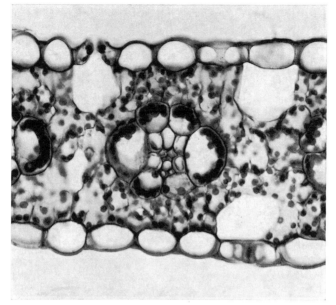

b)

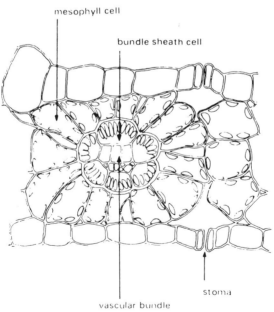

mesophyll cell

bundle sheath cell

stoma

vascular bundle

Plate 3.1 Transverse section of a young maize leaf showing characteristic 'Kranz' anatomy as seen under a light microscope
  a) Photograph (Photo: EVERT)
  b) Diagramatic representation indicating the main feature (courtesy of Dr. A.J. KEYS).

161

② PEP reacts with HCO_3^- and H^+ to yield oxaloacetate as already described. The assimilated C is marked with an asterix.

③ Oxaloacetate may be reduced to malate by the NADPH specific malate dehydrogenase.

④ Oxaloacetate may be transaminated to aspartate by the enzyme aspartate aminotransferase. In this case CO_2 assimilation is linked directly to amino acid metabolism.

⑤ Malate produced in reaction ③ is decarboxylated by the NADPH specific malic enzyme to produce CO_2 and pyruvate.

Pyruvate is then recycled as shown in step ① and CO_2 is fixed by RuBP into PGA and metabolized in the CALVIN cycle as already described above (Figure 3.19). Details of the pathway and the enzyme systems involved have been discussed by KELLY et al. [1976], RAY and BLACK [1979] and COOMBS [1979].

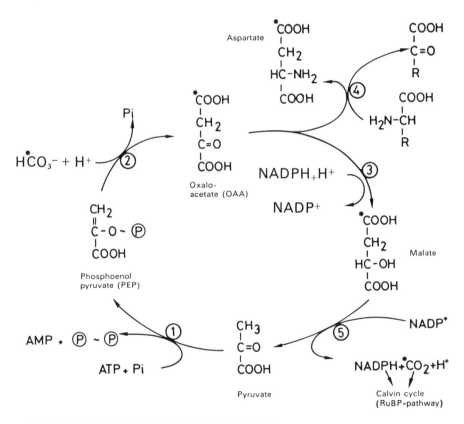

Fig. 3.21 CO_2 assimilation of C-4 plants (C-4 pathway).

The reaction sequence shown in Figure 3.21 occurs in the 'malate' type of C-4 plants. For this C-4 plant type the NADPH malic enzyme is characteristic and malate is the major form in which the trapped C is translocated from the centres of CO_2 assimilation (mesophyll cells) to the centres of decarboxylation (bundle sheath cells, see Plate 3.1 and Figure 3.22). In some C-4 plant species aspartate rather than malate is the main transport form. Decarboxylation of aspartate may be brought about by a NADH malic enzyme or by a PEP-carboxykinase. These reactions have not yet been worked out in detail. COOMBS [1979] suggests that aspartate is converted to oxaloacetate in the mitochondria of the bundle sheath cells. Oxaloacetate thus formed may be reduced to malate which is eventually decarboxylated by NADH specific malic enzyme in the chloroplasts of bundle sheath cells. The pyruvate porduced is recycled to the mesophyll cells (see Figure 3.22).

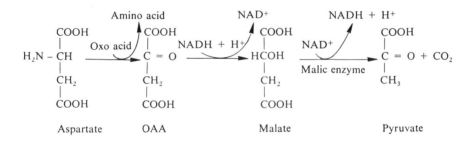

Pyruvate may also be aminated by an alanine aminotransferase to alanine, which then may be recycled to the mesophyll cells.

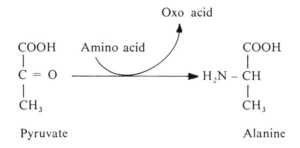

Oxaloacetate produced by the transamination reaction may also be directly decarboxylated by PEP carboxykinase of the bundle sheath cells. As shown below the reaction requires ATP:

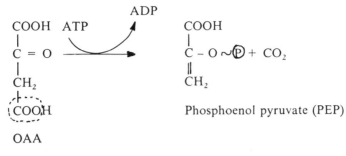

$$COOH \quad ATP$$

OAA

Phosphoenol pyruvate (PEP)

The PEP thus produced may be recycled to the mesophyll cells where it functions directly as a CO_2 acceptor.

According to the above reactions, C-4 plants may grouped into three categories as shown in Table 3.7. Often, however, all three forms of decarboxylation may occur in one species (EDWARDS and HUBER [1979]). In all three types, CO_2 or more precisely HCO_3^-, reacts with PEP carboxylase (COOMBS [1979]) to form a C-4 product which is finally decarboxylated. No net CO_2 assimilation is thus achieved (KELLY et al. [1976]), and an additional amount of energy (ATP) is required for this form of CO_2 assimilation. Netherless this C trapping mechanism has an important advantage as decarboxylation is

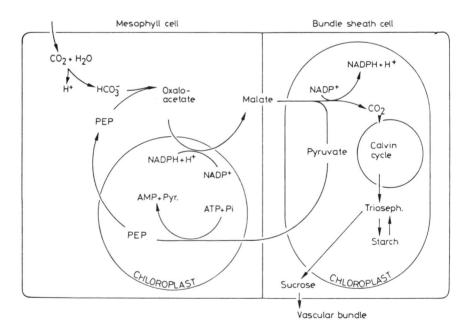

Fig. 3.22 Carbon pathway and compartmentation in C-4 plants.

164

concentrated in particular cells, the bundle sheath cells. Here optimum CO_2 levels are produced which prevent RuBP carboxylase from oxidizing RuBP and thus major losses by photorespiration are avoided. As a result of this optimum CO_2 level at the centre of the C_3 pathway (CALVIN cycle), C-4 species are not light saturated and are thus far better able to exploit high light intensities than C-3 species.

The main reason why C-4 species are so efficient in CO_2 assimilation is the strict compartmentation of the enzymes involved in the C-4 pathway. PEP carboxylase is located in the cytoplasm, malate dehydrogenase and pyruvate phosphate dikinase are located in the chloroplasts of the mesophyll cells. Malate dehydrogenase uses photosynthetically produced NADPH for the reduction of oxaloacetate to malate; the dikinase is driven by photosynthetically produced ATP. The system may adjust to the required ATP/NADPH ratio by non cyclic, cyclic, and pseudocyclic photophosphorylation (EDWARDS and HUBER [1979]). In this latter type of phosphorylation the electrons are transferred through photosystem I and II and finally to O_2 instead of NADP$^+$.

The decarboxylation enzymes, NADPH malic enzyme, NADH malic enzyme and PEP carboxykinase are located in the bundle sheath cells.

Table 3.7 Variations in the biochemistry in C-4 species (after RAY and BLACK [1979])

Decarboxylation	Energetics of decarboxylation	Major substrate moving from MC to BSC	from BSC to MC	Representativive species
NADPH malic enzyme	Production of 1 NADPH/CO_2	Malate	Pyruvate	*Zea mays, Digetaria sanguinatis*
NADH malic enzyme	Production of 1 NADH/CO_2	Aspartate	Alanine Pyruvate	*Atriplex spongiosa Portulaca oleracea*
PEP carboxykinase	Consumption of 1 ATP/CO_2	Aspartate	PEP	*Panicum maximum Sporobolus poiretti*
MC = Mesophyll cells, BSC = Bundle sheath cells				

Each of the two kinds of cells contains morphologically distinct kinds of chloroplasts. The chloroplasts of the bundle sheath cells are larger, can accumulate starch and in some cases they do not contain grana. In contrast, the smaller chloroplasts of the mesophyll cells always contain grana. How the transport of malate and/or aspartate from the mesophyll cells towards the bundle sheath cells is brought about, is not yet understood. The presence of plasmodesmata connecting the two cell types has led to the supposition that C-4 intermediates are transported through the plasmodesmata. As yet, however, direct experimental evidence to support this speculation is lacking. The suggestion of LAETSCH [1974] that the CALVIN cycle of C-4 species is located in the chloroplasts of the mesophyll cells, has not been substantiated. There is now evidence that these chloroplasts do not contain RuBP carboxylase and are thus not capable of initiating CALVIN cycle reactions (RAY and BLACK [1979]).

The C-4 pathway is light dependent as the NADPH malic enzyme and the pyruvate phosphate dikinase are light activated. The latter is also sensitive to cold temperatures and this may be the reason, why under cold climatic conditions, C-4 species do not thrive so as well as C-3 plants. Bundle sheath cells are surrounded by mesophyll cells rich in PEP carboxylase. Thus CO_2 released by mitocondrial respiration or even photorespiration will be rapidly refixed by PEP carboxylase. This and the low oxygenase activity of the RuBP carboxylase in C-4 species explains, why these species have a low CO_2 compensation point (CO_2 level at which CO_2 consumption and CO_2 production are in equilibrium). C-4 plants can therefore use relatively low atmospheric CO_2 concentrations. The compensation points of C-4 plants is as low as 0–10 ppm CO_2. For C-3 plants the values are in the order of 50 ppm (KRENZER et al. [1975].)

One reason to account for the evolution of plants with an extremely efficient CO_2 fixing system may relate to their water economy. Many C-4 plant species occur naturally in arid, semi-arid and tropical conditions, where the closure of stomata to prevent water loss is essential for growth and even survival. CO_2 entry must thus also be restricted. Under such environmental conditions species may well have evolved which are very efficient utilizers of water and CO_2. This view is consistent with the findings of DOWNES [1969] who observed that the ratio of weights of CO_2 assimilated to water transpired (the water use efficiency) of C-4 plants was often twice that of C-3 plants. Another environmental feature of C-4 plants is their frequent occurrence in saline habitats. In this context it is of interest that Na is now established as an essential nutrient for some C-4 plants (BROWNELL and CROSSLAND [1972]) and there is evidence that Na may increase the in vivo activity of PEP carboxylase, the primary carboxylating enzyme in C-4 photosynthesis (SHOMER-ILAN and WAISEL [1973]).

3.2.7 Crassulacean acid metabolism

A number of plant species adapted to arid conditions including species of *Crassulaceae*, *Cactaceae* and *Euphorbiaceae* are able to assimilate CO_2 during the night. As this form of CO_2 assimilation was first discovered in *Bryophyllum calycinum* a member of the *Crassulaceae* it has become known as Crassulacean

Acid Metabolism (CAM). The most important feature of CAM is that by maintaining stomata open during the night CAM plants can assimilate CO_2 which is stored in the vacuoles as malic acid. During the day when the stomata are closed malic acid is then decarboxylated and the resulting CO_2 used for the synthesis of sugars *via* the CALVIN cycle. This mechanism of CO_2 assimilation is well suited to protect the plant against water loss during the day. CAM may thus be considered as an adaptation to arid conditions. Most species which exhibit CAM are succulent and semi succulent species and therefore well adapted to survive periods of water stress.

As in the C-4 pathway, carboxylation is brought about by PEP carboxylase which is probably located in the cytoplasm and closely associated with the enzyme malate dehydrogenase which converts oxaloacetate to malate. De-carboxylation of malate is achieved by the NADH malic enzyme. In some species carboxykinase is the decarboxylating enzyme. The oxaloacetate used for this reaction is produced by the oxidation of malate (OSMOND [1978]). During the net CO_2 assimilation period the CO_2 acceptor (PEP) must be ge-nerated in high quantities. It is now generally accepted that PEP is produced by the glycolytic breakdown of starch. This is the reason why the starch level in the cells drops considerably during the night.

A simplified scheme of the biochemistry of CAM is shown in Figure 3.23. During the night malic acid is stored in the vacuole and may attain concentra-

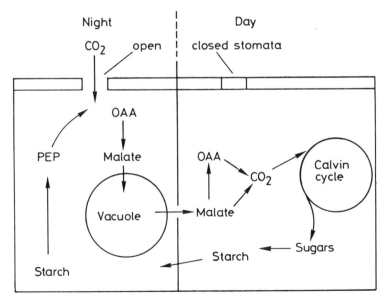

Fig. 3.23 Scheme of Crassulacean Acid Metabolism.

167

tions as high as 200 mM. The accumulation of the acid is an active process, but as yet is not completely understood. LÜTTGE *et al.* [1975] suggest that malic acid accumulation is regulated by turgor. According to OSMOND [1978] the plant water potential is the main factor controlling CAM. Under water stress conditions plants may shift over to CAM metabolism with stomata closed during the day and open at night. Under such conditions CAM plants are capable of maintaining a water potential (see p. 185) of −5 to −10 bar even if the soil water potential is as low as −22 bar. During the periods of CAM the net CO_2 assimilation rates are low and the growth rate of plants is much lower than in periods of direct CO_2 assimilation (stomata open at day).

3.3 Nitrogen and Sulphur Assimilation

3.3.1 General

The acquisition of CO_2 is not the only process of assimilation by which plants are able to synthesize large amounts of organic compounds from an inorganic source. The same is also true for the assimilation of both N and S which are essential elements for all organisms. Nitrogen is present in all amino acids, proteins and coenzymes; sulphur occurs in some of them. The processes by which plants convert inorganic N (NO_3^-, NH_4^+, N_2) and inorganic S (SO_4^{2-}) to organic forms are important in biology, for animals are dependent on a dietary source of organic N and S originating from plants and microorganisms.

3.3.2 Nitrate reduction

Nitrate is often the major source of N available to plants. Before this can be metabolized, however, it must be reduced to NH_3. This important process, called nitrate reduction, consists basically of two steps, the reduction of NO_3^- to NO_2^-, and the further reduction of NO_2^- to NH_3. The generally accepted basic mechanism of NO_3-assimilation in green plant tissues in the light is shown in Figure 3.24. The two enzymes involved in the process are nitrate reductase and nitrite reductase (HEWITT [1975], BEEVERS [1976]). Nitrate reductase catalyses the first step from NO_3^- to NO_2^-, which takes place in the cytoplasm. The further reduction of NO_2^- to NH_3 occurs in the chloroplasts and is brought about by the enzyme nitrite reductase. Both enzymes, nitrate reductase and nitrite reductase, function in series so that no appreciable nitrite accumulation occurs.

Nitrate reductase activity has been detected in a number of plant organisms including bacteria, blue green algae, green algae, fungi and higher plants (GUERRERO *et al.* [1981]), although the molecular weight as well as other

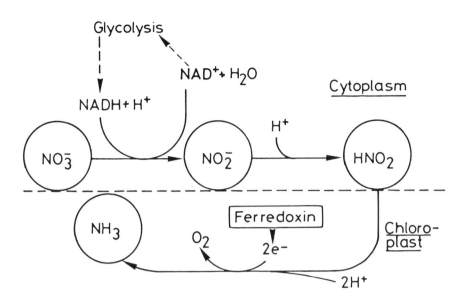

Fig.3.24 Scheme of nitrate and nitrite (nitrous acid) reduction.

properties of the enzyme appear to differ in these various plant types. Nitrate reductase found in spinach has a molecular weight of about 200 k dalton. It has three prosthetic groups: FAD, cytochrome b and Mo which function in series as shown in Figure 3.25. The reducing power required is NADH which may originate from glycolysis. NADH may also indirectly be supplied by the chloroplast *via* the oxaloacetate-malate shuttle (Figure 4.8). Oxaloacetate is taken up by the chloroplast and reduced by photosynthetically supplied NADPH to malate. This is exported into the cytoplasm and here oxidised to oxalo-acetate in which process NAD^+ is reduced to NADH. This shuttle mechanism is of particular importance for C-4 plants (see p. 163) as it links photosynthetic activity with nitrate reduction.

In bacteria, some algae and in fungi NADPH as well as NADH may function as a source of reducing power for the enzyme. Even in some species of higher plants NADPH dependent nitrate reductase has also been reported. The nitrate reductase of blue green algae is tightly bound to chlorophyll containing membrane fractions and directly utilizes electrons supplied by ferredoxin in the reduction of nitrate. There is thus a very close interrelationship between photosynthesis and nitrate reduction in this organism.

Cytochrome b transfers electrons from FAD to Mo which reacts directly with nitrate (see Figure 3.25). The oxidation change of Mo associated with the reduction is not yet clear. According to GUERRERO *et al.* [1981], electron

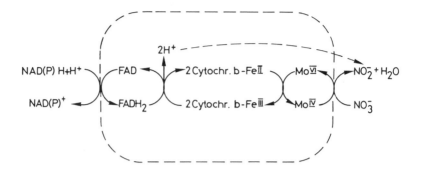

Fig.3.25 Phrosthetic groups of the nitrate reductase and the sequence of reactions (according to GUERRERO *et al.* [1981]). NAD(P)H denotes that both coenzymes NADH and NADPH may function as H donors.

transfer is mediated by an $Mo^{VI} \rightleftarrows Mo^{IV}$ change. It is generally accepted that nitrate reductase is an inducible enzyme or in other words that nitrate induces the synthesis or activity of the enzyme. However, nitrate reductase activity has been found in the absence of nitrate and the question of inducibility of the enzyme merits further study. In most cases the activity of nitrate reductase is increased by nitrate and depressed by NH_4^+ and various amino acids.

The NO_2^- produced by nitrate reductase is the anion of a weak acid and for this reason is partially protonated according to the equation:

$$NO_2^- + H^+ \rightleftarrows HNO_2$$

HEBER and PURCZELD [1977] have suggested that it is HNO_2 rather than NO_2^- which is transported across the chloroplast membrane and thus it is HNO_2 which enters the chloroplast stroma to be reduced to NH_3:

$$HNO_2 + 2e^- + 2H^+ \rightarrow NH_3 + O_2$$

The reaction is probably located on the outer side of the thylakoid membrane. In this step a powerful reductant is required and in green cells this is furnished by the low molecular weight Fe containing compound, ferredoxin (see page 147). Ferredoxin receives its electrons directly from the photosynthetic electron transport chain (Photosystem I – see Figure 3.14). Nitrite reductase of higher plants consists of a single polypeptide strand to which an iron sulphur complex and a sirohaem are attached. Sirohaem is a particular haem form which is supposed to bind the NO_2^-. Both groups of the enzyme are involved in the e^- transfer. Synthesis and activity of nitrite reductase depend on the supply with NO_2^-.

Nitrate reduction can also take place in roots. The NADH requirement in the reduction step to NO_2^- is supplied by root respiration. The reduction of NO_2^- occurs in the proplastids (DALLING et al. [1972]). According to SPILLER [1976] nitrite reduction under dark conditions is also associated with ferredoxin, which receives its electrons from NADPH. This is consistent with the observation that proplastids are potentially a good source of NADPH as they are enriched with enzymes of the pentose phosphate pathway (BEEVERS [1976]). In addition, NADPH may be produced in roots by transhydrogenation (NADH → NADPH) associated with the dark CO_2 fixation and decarboxylation, (TING and DUGGER [1965]).

The combined effects of both nitrate and nitrite reductases may be written as follows:

$$NO_3^- + 2H \rightarrow NO_2^- + H_2O \text{ (nitrate reduction)}$$

$$NO_2^- + H^+ \rightarrow HNO_2 \text{ (nitrite protonation)}$$

$$HNO_2 + 2H \rightarrow NH_3 + O_2 \text{ (nitrous acid reduction)}$$

$$\text{net: } NO_3^- + 4H + H^+ \rightarrow NH_3 + H_2O + O_2$$

Besides the consumption of 4 reducing equivalents (4H), one proton (H^+) is consumed per NH_3 produced. This protonation, which occurs in the cytoplasm, is the process responsible for the alkaline effect associated with nitrate nutrition. If NO_3^- reduction occurs in the green plant parts this stimulates malate accumulation in the cytoplasm and vacuoles. This is very closely associated with ion uptake and translocation (see page 136).

Light plays an important role in NO_3-assimilation. When green plants are transferred from the light to dark conditions, the activity of nitrate reductase is depressed even when nitrate is present in adequate amounts (BEEVERS and HAGEMAN [1972], HAGEMAN and FLESHER [1960]). This effect, together with a decrease in reducing power because of the absence of light, is the main reason for the accumulation of nitrate when light intensity is low. Nitrate accumulation can frequently occur in crops as a result of low light intensity and high NO_3-fertilization. This can be a hazard in farm animal and human nutrition (see page 327).

The assimilation of nitrate by plants is influenced by mineral nutrition and in particular by Mo. As already mentioned, Mo is an essential constituent of nitrate reductase. When Mo is deficient, nitrate accumulation takes place and the contents of soluble amino N compounds are depressed (POSSINGHAM [1956]) because of the lack of NH_3 available for amino acid synthesis (see page 528). Manganese can also indirectly influence nitrate assimilation. It is essential in photosystem II and hence in the flow of electrons from water *via* ferredoxin to NO_2^- reductase.

Nitrate reductase occurs predominantly in the cytoplasm of meristematic cells. Young leaves and root tips are thus rich in the enzyme. VAN EGMOND and BRETELER [1972] reported that the nitrate reductase activity in fully developed young sugar beet leaves was about 10 times higher than in older leaves. According to HEWITT [1970] nitrate reductase tends to rise to a maximum in moderately young leaves. In roots maximum activities occur in the younger tissues and decline markedly in the older root regions (HEWITT [1970]). The turnover of the enyme is rapid (OAKS *et al.* [1972]). According to SCHRADER *et al.* [1968] the half-life is about 4 hours.

The site of NO_3-reduction differs between plant species. In tomato plants, for example, between 80–90% of the N in the xylem sap is present in the form of NO_3-N (LORENZ [1976]) so that NO_3-reduction must take place primarily in green plant parts. Similar findings have been reported by WALLACE and PATE [1967] in cocklebur *(Xanthium pennsylvaticum)*. In this species nitrate reductase activity was found to be absent in the roots. Most plant species however, are able to reduce NO_3^- both in the roots and the upper plant parts. According to PATE [1971] who investigated NO_3-reduction in a number of crop plant species, the proportions of NO_3^- reduced in the roots decreased in the following sequence:

Oats > Maize > Sunflower > Barley > Oil Radish

The leaves of trees and shrubs do not contain nitrate, and according to SANDERSON and COCKING [1964] nitrate reduction takes place exclusively in the roots. KLEPPER and HAGEMAN [1969], however, were able to detect nitrate in the leaves of apple trees which had been subjected to high levels of nitrate fertilizer. As these leaf tissues were able to bring about nitrate reduction it seems probable that the leaves of other trees are also potentially capable of inducing nitrate reductase activity. If this is true, it is clear that the level of NO_3-nutrition can determine the distribution of NO_3-reductase activity within the plant. This has been shown in peas by WALLACE and PATE [1965]. At low levels of NO_3^- supply about half the nitrate reductase activity was accounted for in the roots but at higher levels the shoot was the principal site of NO_3-reduction.

The activity of nitrate reductase is potentially capable of influencing yield production, as to some extent it controls the rate of assimilation of nitrate. EILRICH and HAGEMAN [1973] reported that nitrate reductase activity in the flag leaf of wheat was dependent on the level of nitrate supply. Increased enzyme activities were associated with higher contents of grain proteins. On the other hand, CROY and HAGEMAN [1970] investigating the nitrate reductase activity in the leaves of 32 different wheat cultivars found no clear relationship between the enzyme activity and the grain protein content. These authors suggest that besides the nitrate reductase activity in the flag leaf, the translocation rate of amino compounds to the grains is a major factor influencing grain protein content.

3.3.3 Nitrogen fixation

The atmosphere provides a vast reservoir of molecular N_2. However, this is not directly available for use by higher plants. Before assimilation can occur it must first be converted to a so-called fixed form either by oxidation to NO_3-N or by reduction to NH_4-N. As molecular N_2 is highly inert, these conversions are not readily brought about, and indeed require a considerable amount of energy. Several species of microorganisms occur, however, which are able to reduce atmospheric N_2 to NH_3 at the ambient temperatures and pressures in the soil. These microorganisms play a unique role in the whole N-cycle of nature for by the conversion of molecular N_2 into an organic form, atmospheric N is rendered available to other organisms. This process is called N_2-fixation. The quantity of N_2 reduced in this way on a world scale is immense. According to CHATT [1976] total world biological fixation amounts to about 17.2×10^7 tonnes *per annum*. This figure which is about four times the amount fixed by chemical industry demonstrates the outstanding significance of biological N_2 fixation.

Microorganisms capable of N_2 fixation may be divided into those which are free living and those which live in symbiosis with higher plants. From an agricultural viewpoint the symbiotic *Rhizobium* bacteria-legume association is of particular significance. This is considered in Chapter 7.

The main features of the biochemistry of N_2 fixation have been fairly well established in recent years. It seems probable that the mechanism by which the N_2 fixing system operates is the same for all N_2 fixing microorganisms. Figure 3.26 shows a simplified scheme from a publication of SHANMUGAM *et al.* [1978]. The bacteroid, as the active *Rhizobium* is called, is enveloped by a membrane and embedded in a host cell. It is thus comparable with other energy converting organelles, *e.g.* with mitochondria. The membrane controls the import and export of metabolites. Photosynthate import supplies the tricarboxylic acid cycle (TCA cycle) with metabolites. The reducing equivalents (NADH) pro-

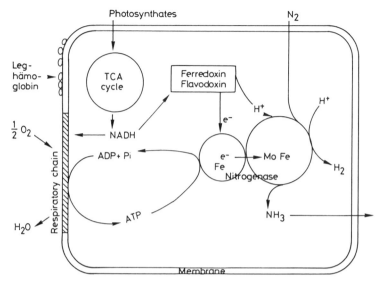

Fig.3.26 Major reactions involved in N_2 fixation.

duced by the TCA cycle are required by ferredoxin and by a respiratory chain, the latter probably being located in the membrane. The respiratory chain provides the ATP, and the ferredoxin or flavodoxin supplies the electrons to the nitrogenase system. This is the unique system which brings about the reduction of N_2 to NH_3 according to the overall equation:

$$N_2 + 6e^- + 6H^+ \rightarrow 2NH_3$$

The nitrogenase system consists of two protein complexes, one with a molecular weight of about 180 000 containing Fe and Mo in a ratio of 9:1 per molecule, and the other with a molecular weight of about 51 000 with one Fe atom per protein molecule. The Mo-Fe-containing enzyme is the nitrogen reductase, while the smaller enzyme provides the electrons for this reduction. This electron transfer from the smaller to the larger protein complex of the nitrogenase system requires ATP. According to WINTER and BURRIS [1976], Mg^{2+} forms a bridge between the smaller protein complex and ATP which lowers the redox potential of the enzyme (becomes more negative) by an allosteric effect. This drop in the redox potential allows the transfer of electrons from the Fe protein complex to the Fe Mo complex. The electron transfer is associated with the splitting of ATP into ADP and inorganic phosphate. The quantity of ATP required per N_2 reduced is not yet well established. According to SHANMUGAM et aï. [1978] the requirement amounts to 15 to 30 ATP per N_2 molecule reduced. This shows that N_2 reduction demands a high amount of ATP. The reduction step is not yet well understood. It is supposed that the N_2 is bound by the Fe and Mo of the complex and then reduced (PARTHIER [1978]). According to WINTER and BURRIS [1976] the whole reaction is a 3 step, 2 electrons per step mechanism. Whether diimide and hydrazine are intermediates of the reduction process is not yet clear.

The NH_3 produced by nitrogenase is mainly released from the bacteroid into the host cell (ANTONIW and SPRENT [1978], where it is used for the synthesis of amino acids. The enzymes responsible for this synthesis are glutamine synthetase and glutamate synthase. The reactions are considered in more detail on p. 177. Glutamate and glutamine do not occur in high levels in the bacteroid cell, and this has a physiological implication because high levels of both metabolites depress the so called 'nitrogen fixation genes' (= nif genes). These genes are located in the genom of the bacteria and they code the synthesis of the nitrogenase proteins. The bacteroid may provide the host plant with more than 90% of the NH_3 produced. This is one reason, why symbiotic living N_2 fixing bacteria are so efficient in N_2 fixation in comparison with free living bacteria in which nitrogenase activity is strictly controlled by the endogenous level of glutamate. It is supposed that the formation of nitrogenase also depends on the NH_3 level in the bacteroid, high levels inhibiting nitrogenase synthesis. Exogenous NH_3 may also enter the bacteroid and thus affect the intensity of N_2 fixation (LATIMORE et al. [1977]).

Nitrogenase not only reduces N_2 but is also capable of reducing H^+ to H_2, thus producing molecular hydrogen (see Figure 3.26). Molecular nitrogen (N_2) and H^+ therefore compete for the electrons from nitrogenase and for this reason the N_2 reducing efficiency can be affected considerably by the presence of H^+ (SCHUBERT and EVANS [1976]). Some *Rhizobium* strains are capable of splitting the H_2 produced by an enzyme (hydrogenase):

$$H_2 \rightarrow 2H^+ + 2e^-$$

Electrons so produced may be recycled to the nitrogenase and used here for the reduction of N_2. SCHUBERT et al. [1978] found that this recycling of electrons to nitrogenase contributes much to the N_2 fixing efficiency of *Rhizobium* bacteria.

The intensity of N_2 reduction depends on carbohydrate supply. This is true for free living N_2 fixing microorganisms as well as for bacteria in symbiosis with higher plants. According to experiments of ANTONIW and SPRENT [1978] with nodules of *Phaseolus vulgaris*, sucrose, fructose, glucose, malate, and other as yet unidentified substances may serve as an energy source for the bacteroid.

The energy status of the host plant, which is mainly determined by light intensity and K^+ supply to the plant, has an impact on nitrogenase activity.

This has been shown by various authors (MENGEL *et al.* [1974], BETHLENFALVAY and PHILLIPS [1978], WAHUA and MILLER [1978], FEIGENBAUM and MENGEL [1979]). The nitrogenase system is extremely sensitive to oxygen and one purpose of the membrane is the strict control of oxygen supply (PARTHIER [1978]). This is achieved by leghaemoglobin which is located at the outer side of the membrane and binds O_2. It thus strictly controls O_2 supply to the respiratory chain in the membrane (see Figure 3.26) and is responsible for ATP synthesis. In free living N_2 fixing microorganisms, high O_2 partial pressures inhibit nitrogenase (NEYRA and DÖBEREINER [1977]). *Azotobacter* has developed a highly active respiratory system which consumes considerable amounts of oxygen and thus protects nitrogenase against high O_2 pressures. In some N_2 fixing bacteria and blue green algae, flavodoxin can replace ferredoxin. Flavodoxin is a flavoprotein (MW 20 000) which is even more sensitive to oxygen than ferredoxin (BOTHE [1977]).

It is well established that *Rhizobium* bacteria require Co. From the reports of EVANS and RUSSELL [1971] Co is essential in the propionate pathway which probably controls the synthesis of leghaemoglobin (see page 554). Copper appears to be essential in N_2 fixation and it is also most likely involved in leghaemoglobin synthesis or with enzymes associated with electron transfer to molecular oxygen (see page 517).

3.3.4 Ammonia assimilation

Both the assimilation of nitrate and the fixation of molecular N_2 give rise to ammonia. For its assimilation three enzymes are of importance:

Glutamate dehydrogenase
Glutamine synthetase
Glutamate synthase

Glutamate dehydrogenase catalyzes the reaction between NH_3 and α-oxoglutarate. The enzyme has been shown to be present in many higher plants and it contains Zn (VALLEE and WACKER [1970]). It is supposed that in the reaction the substrates combine to yield an α-imino acid which is then reduced to glutamate in a subsequent reaction additionally requiring NAD(P)H. Both these steps are reversible as shown in the reaction sequence on the next page.

This process results in an amination of the α-oxoglutarate coupled with a reduction brought about by NAD(P)H. For this reason it is termed reductive amination.

Until relatively recently the reductive amination of α-oxoglutarate catalyzed by glutamate dehydrogenase was considered to be the major reaction responsi-

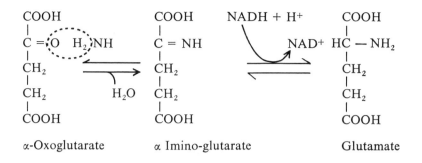

α-Oxoglutarate   α Imino-glutarate   Glutamate

ble for the assimilation of NH_3 into amino acids in higher plants. The work of LEA and MIFLIN [1974], MIFLIN and LEA [1977] and SKOKUT et al. [1978] has demonstrated the occurrence of an alternative and generally more important pathway involving two reactions operating in series in the chloroplasts and catalyzed by glutamine synthetase and glutamate synthase. This is shown in Figure 3.27. Glutamine synthetase brings about a reaction in which glutamate functions as an NH_3 acceptor to produce glutamine. The reaction is an endergonic process needing ATP and also Mg^{2+}. ATP is supplied by photosynthetic phosphorylation. In the presence of a reducing source the glutamine transfers its amide group to α-oxoglutarate. The enzyme catalyzing this reaction is glutamate synthase. It is now known as GOGAT which is an abbreviation for Glutamine Oxoglutarate Amino Transferase. In higher plants ferredoxin provides the reducing power (electrons) necessary for this reaction.

The two reactions may be written

Glutamate + NH_3 + ATP → Glutamine + ADP + P_i

Glutamine + α-oxoglutarate + 2e– + $2H^+$ → 2 Glutamate

NH3 + α-oxoglutarate + ATP + 2e– + $2H^+$ → Glutamate + ADP + Pi

One glutamate molecule is thus produced from one molecule of α-oxoglutarate and NH_3. The system is therefore more similar to the glutamate dehydrogenase mediated reductive amination process than would appear at first sight. The major difference between both systems is in their affinity for NH_3. This is much higher for glutamine synthetase which is capable of incorporating NH_3 present in very low concentrations into α-amino N (MIFLIN [1975]). The presence of glutamine synthetase in the chloroplasts ensures that the concentration of NH_3 formed by nitrite reductase can be incorporated without building up levels which would uncouple photophosphorylation (see page 148). LEA and MIFLIN [1974] suggest that glutamine synthetase is the major NH_3 acceptor in chloroplasts and that the enzyme provides the most important route of NH_3 assimila-

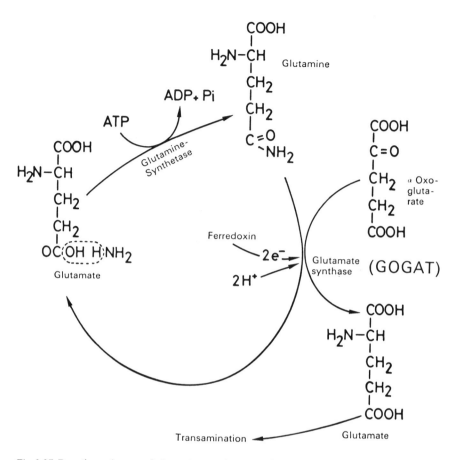

Fig.3.27 Reaction schemes of glutamine synthetase and glutamate synthase.

tion in green plants. According to WEISSMAN [1976] glutamine synthetase plays a major role in root metabolism. The system is also operative in bacteria, yeast, and free living N_2 bacteria. As yet glutamine synthetase has been only found in chloroplasts and plastids. According to MIFLIN and LEA [1977], however, the enzyme could also be present in the cytoplasm. The activity of the chloroplast located enzyme is closely related to photosynthesis since the enzyme optimum is at pH 8, which implies that under light conditions highest activity is obtained. The enzyme, as shown in Figure 3.27 requires ATP and its activity is thus also dependent on the energy status of the system (WEISSMAN [1976]). The energy status can be measured by the so called energy charge, which is defined by the ratio:

$$\frac{\text{ATP} + 1/2\ \text{ADP}}{\text{ATP} + \text{ADP} + \text{AMP}}$$

A high energy charge promotes and a low energy charge restricts NH_3 assimilation.

SODEK and DA SILVA [1977] found a high glutamate synthase activity (GOGAT) in developing maize grains. These authors suggest that glutamine is rapidly imported into the endosperm where it is metabolized by glutamate synthase. The resulting glutamate may then transfer its amino group to oxo acids such as pyruvate or oxaloacetate. This finding is consistent with recent results of MENGEL et al. [1981] who have reported a particularly high N turnover of glutamine in developing wheat grains. During germination glutamine also seems to play a dominant role in mobilizing storage seed proteins (ROUBELAKIS and KLIEWER [1978]).

3.3.5 Amino acids and amides

The amino N in glutamate can be transferred to other oxo acids (keto acids) by the process of transamination. The enzymes catalyzing this reaction are amino transferases. An example is shown below where the NH_2 group from glutamate is transferred to the oxo acid pyruvate to form the amino acid alanine.

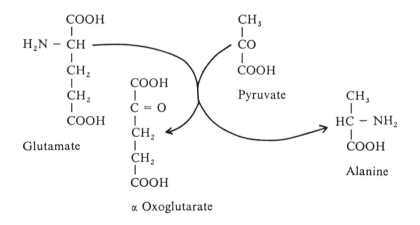

In the reaction a new amino acid (alanine) is synthesized. Transamination provides a means for the synthesis of a number of amino acids and it is probably that the NH_2 groups of many amino acids are originally derived from glutamate. The most important NH_2 acceptors (oxo acids) of the transamination process and their corresponding amino acids are listed on the next page.

Oxo acid	Amino acid
α-oxoglutarate	glutamate
oxaloacetate	aspartate
glyoxylate	glycine
pyruvate	alanine
hydroxy pyruvate	serine
glutamate γ-semialdehyde	ornithine
succinate semialdehyde	γ-amino-butyrate
α-keto β-hydroxy-butyrate	threonine

When excess NH_3 is available, glutamate and aspartate can serve as NH_3 acceptors. In this reaction the amides glutamine and asparagine are synthesized. The process requires ATP which is hydrolysed in the reaction.

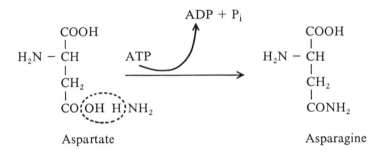

$$\text{Aspartate} \qquad\qquad\qquad\qquad \text{Asparagine}$$

As NH_3 is toxic to plant cells the synthesis of glutamine and asparagine enables the removal of a toxic substance and the process is important for this reason. Accumulation of asparagine and glutamine always occurs when plants are supplied with high levels of inorganic N, and in particular with NH_4-N. According to investigations of PLATT et al. [1977] with leaf discs of lucerne (Medicago sativa) NH_4^+ has regulatory function in promoting the formation of oxalo-acetate which is then aminated to aspartate.

3.3.6 Sulphur assimilation

The most important source of S for higher plants is sulphate. In several respects its assimilation resembles that of nitrate although the detailed mechanism is not so well understood. Sulphate taken up by plant cells must be reduced because in the major S containing organic molecules, S is present in a reduced form. These organic compounds include cysteine, cystine and methionine as well as the proteins containing these amino acids (see page 373).

A simplified scheme of SO_4-reduction in higher plants is shown in Figure 3.28 It is now generally accepted that the first step of S incorporation is a reaction between H_2SO_4 and ATP as shown in Figure 3.28a. The sulphuryl group of H_2SO_4 replaces the pyrophosphoryl group of ATP, thus forming adenosine phosphosulphate and pyrophosphate. The reaction is catalyzed by an enzyme called ATP sulphurylase. The sulphuryl group of adenosine phosphosulphate (APS) is transferred to an SH-carrier complex. In this process, catalyzed by an APS transferase, the H of the carrier SH-group is replaced by the sulphuryl group. This is then reduced to -SH, the reducing power being provided by ferredoxin (see Figure 3.28b). In a further step the SH group of the carrier complex is transferred to

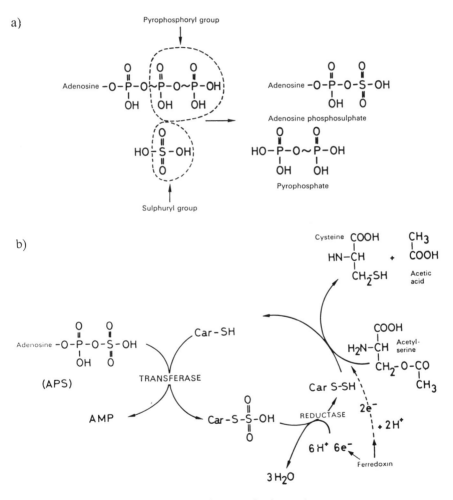

Fig.3.28 Simplified scheme showing the sulphate reduction pathway
a) ATP sulfurylase reaction producing adenosine phosphosulphate.
b) Transfer of the sulphuryl group to the Car-SH complex and reduction steps.

acetyl serine and in this process the original carrier SH-complex is regenerated. Acetyl serine is split into cysteine and acetate. This splitting reaction requires 2 additional reducing equivalents, which probably also originate from ferredoxin. The net process of the whole reduction cycle may be described by the following equation:

$$H_2SO_4 + ATP + 8H + \text{acetyl serine} \rightarrow$$
$$\text{cysteine} + \text{acetate} + 3H_2O + AMP + \textcircled{P} \sim \textcircled{P}$$

This equation shows that the sulphate reaction needs energy in the form of ATP and reducing equivalents. Hence the reduction process depends on photosynthesis and, especially on the level of ATP (SCHIFF and HODSON [1973]). Sulphate is mainly reduced during the light period, due to the fact that the enzymes of sulphate reduction are located in the chloroplast membrane. Whether other organelles are also capable of reducing sulphate is not yet known. Since isolated roots can also grow on sulphate as a sole sulphur source, it has been suggested that sulphate reduction occurs in nongreen tissue, probably in proplastids (SCHMIDT [1979]).

Sulphate reduction is carried out by a number of organisms including higher plants, algae, fungi, blue-green algae and bacteria. Animal metabolism, however, is dependent on the intake of a source of reduced S and hence on the S-assimilation of the organisms mentioned above. Cysteine is the first stable product in which S is present in a reduced organically bound form. Cysteine is a precursor of methionine, another important S-containing amino acid.

General Reading

ANDERSON, J.W.: Sulphur in Biology. Studies in Biology, p. 101 Edward Arnold, London 1978

ANDERSON, W.P.: Ion Transport in Plants. Proc. Intern. Meeting University of Liverpool, Academic Preas, London, New York and San Francisco 1972

ARNON, D.I.: Photosynthesis 1950–1975: Changing concepts and perspectives. In: Photosynthesis I, Plant Physiol. New Series, Vol. 5 (A. TREBST and M. AVRON, eds.) p. 7–56. Springer-Verlag Berlin, Heidelberg, New York 1977

BAKER, D.A. and HALL J.L.: Eds.: Ion Transport in Plant Cells and Tissues. North Holland Publishing Co, Amsterdam 1975

BASSHAM, J.A.: The reductive pentose phosphate cycle and its regulation. In: Photosynthesis II. New Series, Vol. 6 (M. GIBBS and E. LATZKO, eds.) p. 9–30. Springer-Verlag Berlin, Heidelberg, New York 1979

BAUMANN, G.: (G) Photorespiration and glycollate metabolism in higher plants. Biol. Rdsch. 18, 1–12 (1980)

BEGG, J.E. and TURNER, N.C.: Crop water deficits. Adv. Agron. 28, 161–217 (1976)

BLACK, C.C.: Photosynthetic carbon fixation in relation to net CO_2 uptake. Ann. Rev. Plant Physiol., 24, 253–286 (1973)

Bowling, D. J. F.: Uptake of Ions by Plant roots. Chapman and Hall, London 1976

Chatt, J., Richards, R.L. and G. da Camara Pini, L.M.: New Trends in the Chemistry of Nitrogen Fixation. Academic Press, London, New York and San Francisco 1980

Clarkson, D.T.: Ion Transport and Cell structure in Plants, McGraw Hill, 1974

Clarkson, D.T.: Membrane structure and transport. In: The Molecular Biology of Plant Cells (H. Smith, ed.) p. 24–63. Blackwell, London 1977

Edwards, G.E. and Huber, S.C.: C-4 metabolism in isolated cells and protoplasts. In: Photosynthesis II, New Series, Vol. 8 (M. Gibbs and E. Latzko, eds.) p. 102–112. Springer-Verlag Berlin, Heidelberg, New York 1979

Epstein, E.: Mineral Nutrition of Plants: Principles and Perspectives. John Wiley and Sons, Inc., New York, London, Sydney, Toronto 1972

Guerrero, M.G., Vega, J.M. and Losada, M.: The assimilatory nitrate reducing system and its regulation. Ann. Rev. Plant Physiol. 32, 169–204 (1981)

Hatch, M.D., Osmond, C.B. and Slatyer, R.O.: Photosynthesis and Photorespiration. Wiley Interscience, New York 1971

Hiatt, A.J. and Leggett J.E.: Ionic interactions and antagonism in plants, p. 101–134. In E.W. Carson: The Plant Root and Its Environment. University Press of Virginia, Charlottesville 1974

Higinbotham, N.: Electropotentials of plant cells. Ann. Rev. Plant Physiol., 24, 25–46 (1973)

Higinbotham, N.: The mineral absorption process in plants. Bot. Rev. 39, 15–69 (1973)

Hodges, T.K.: Ion absorption by plant roots. Adv. Agron., 25, 163–207 (1973)

Höll, W.: (G) The symbiosis between legumes and bacteria of the genus Rhizobium. Naturw. Rdsch., 8, 281–289 (1975)

International Potash Institute: Fertilizer Use and Protein production. 11th Colloquium Intern. Potash Inst., Berne 1975

Jagendorf, A.T.: Photophosphorylation. In: Photosynthesis I, Plant Physiol. New Series Vol. 5 (A. Trebst and M. Avron, eds.) p. 307–337. Springer-Verlag Berlin, Heidelberg, New York 1977

Jensen, R.G. and Bahr, J.T.: Ribulose 1,5-bisphosphate carboxylase-oxygenase. Ann. Rev. Plant Physiol. 28, 379–400 (1977)

Kelly, G.J., Latzko, E. and Gibbs, M.: Regulatory aspects of photosynthetic carbon metabolism. Ann. Rev. Plant Physiol. 27, 181–205 (1976)

Kluge, M.: The flow of carbon in Crassulacean Acid Metabolism (CAM). In: Photosynthesis II, Plant Physiol, New Series, Vol. 6 (M. Gibbs and E. Latzko, eds.) p. 112–123. Springer-Verlag Berlin, Heidelberg, New York 1979

Lüttge, U. and Pitman, M.G., eds.: Transport in Plants II, Part A, Cells; Part B, Tissues and Organs. Encyclopedia of Plant Physiology, New Series Vol 2, Springer-Verlag Berlin, Heidelberg, New York 1976

McLachlan, K.D.: Sulphur in Australasian Agriculture. Sidney Univ. Press 1975.

Miflin, B.J.: Potential for improvement of quantity and quality of plant proteins through scientific research, p. 53–74. In Fertilizer Use and Protein Production. 11th Colloquium Intern. Potash Inst., Berne 1975

Mitchell, P.: Protonmotive chemiosmotic mechanisms in oxidative and photosynthetic phosphorylation. Trends in Biochemical Sciences 3, N58–N61 (1978)

Mortenson, L.E. and Thorneley, R.N.F.: Structure and function of nitrogenase. Ann. Rev. Biochem. 48, 387–418 (1979)

Neyra, C.A. and Döbereiner, J.: Nitrogen fixation in grasses. Adv. Agron. 29, 1–38 (1977)

Osmond, C.B.: Crassulacean acid metabolism: A curiosity in context. Ann. Rev. Plant Physiol. 29, 379–414 (1978)

Parthier, B.: (G) The biological fixation of atmospheric nitrogen. Biol. Rdsch. 16, 345–364 (1978)

Phillips, D.A.: Efficiency of symbiotic nitrogen fixation in legumes. Ann. Rev. Plant Physiol. 31, 29–49 (1980)

POOLE, R.J.: Energy coupling for membrane transport. Ann. Rev. Plant Physiol. *29*, 437–460 (1978)

RADMER, R. and KOK B.: Energy capture in photosynthesis: Photosystem II. Ann. Rev. Biochem., *44*, 409–433 (1975)

RASCHE, K.: Stomatal action. Ann. Rev. Plant Physiol., *26*, 309–340 (1975)

SCHIFF, J.A. and HODSON, R.C.: The metabolism of sulphate. Ann. Rev. Plant Physiol., *24*, 381–414 (1973)

SHANMUGAM, K.T., O'GARA, F., ANDERSEN, K., and VALENTINE, R.C.: Biological nitrogen fixation. Ann. Rev. Plant Physiol. *29*, 263–276 (1978)

SHAVIT, N.: Energy transduction in chloroplasts: Structure and function of the ATPase complex. Ann. Rev. Biochem. *49*, 111–138 (1980)

SMITH, F.A. and RAVEN, J.A.: Intercellular pH and its regulation. Ann. Rev. Plant Physiol. *30*, 289–311 (1979)

STOCKING, C.R. and HEBER U.: Transport in plants III. Intracellular Interactions and Transport Process. New Series, Vol. *3*, Springer-Verlag Berlin, Heidelberg, New York 1976

TOLBERT, N.E.: Glycolate metabolism by higher plants and algae. In: Photosynthesis II, Plant Physiol. New Series, Vol. 6 (M. GIBBS and E. LATZKO, eds.) p. 338–352. Springer-Verlag Berlin, Heidelberg, New York 1979

WALKER, D.A.: Three phases of chloroplast research. Nature *226*, 1204–1208 (1970)

WINTER, H.C. and BURRIS, R.H.: Nitrogenase. Ann. Rev. Biochem. *45*, 409–426 (1976)

WOOLHOUSE, H.W.: Light gathering and carbon assimilation processes in photosynthesis; their adaptive modifications and significance for agriculture. Endeavour, New Series 2, 35–46 (1978)

ZELITCH, I.: Photorespiration: Studies with whole tissues. In: Photosynthesis II, Plant Physiol. New Series, Vol. 6 (M. GIBBS and E. LATZKO, eds.) p. 351–367. Springer-Verlag Berlin, Heidelberg, New York 1979

Chapter 4

Plant Water Relationships

4.1 Basic Processes in Plant Water Relationships

4.1.1 General

Life is intimately associated with water, and particularly with water in its liquid phase. Water is the form in which the H atom, an essential element of all organic molecules, is absorbed and then assimilated in the course of photosynthesis (p. 145). Water may thus be considered as a plant nutrient, in the same way as CO_2 or NO_3^- are also plant nutrients. The quantity of water required for the photosynthetic process, however, is small and amounts to only about 0.01% of the total quantity of water used by the plant. Most functions in which plant water is involved, are of a physical nature. Water is a solvent for many substances such as inorganic salts, sugars and organic anions. It is also the medium in which all biochemical reactions take place. Water molecules are adsorbed at the surfaces of particles forming hydration shells, which influence physical and chemical reactions. Water in liquid form allows the diffusion and mass flow of solutes, and for this reason is essential for the translocation and distribution of nutrients and metabolites throughout the entire plant. Water is also important in the vacuoles of plant cells as it generally exerts pressure on the protoplasm and cell wall (turgor pressure) thus maintaining the rigidity of leaves, roots and other plant organs. These few examples indicate the overall importance of water in plant physiology.

4.1.2 Water potential

For a more basic understanding of the processes in which water is involved it is important to appreciate the concept of water potential (SLATYER [1967]). The term water potential describes the energy status of water and was introduced into the literature to provide a unified terminology for studies in soil-plant-water relationships. It may be defined as the difference in chemical potential per unit volume between a given water sample and pure free water at the same temperature. This may be expressed in an equation as follows:

$$\Psi = \frac{\mu_w - \mu^o_w}{v_w}$$

where Ψ = water potential

μ_w = chemical potential of the water being considered

μ^o_w = chemical potential of pure free water at the same temperature

v_w = partial molar volume of water in the system

The units of chemical potential are Joules per mole, whereas the partial molar volume of water is expressed in terms of volume (m³) per mole. Substituting these units into the above equation it becomes:

$$= \frac{J/mole}{m^3/mole} = \frac{J}{m^3}$$

Energy (J) = Force (N) × distance (m)

where

N = The Newton, the unit of force

Substituting this expression for J in the above equation the water potential is given by the following term:

$$= \frac{N \times m}{m^3} = \frac{N}{m^2}$$

This represents force per unit area and as such is the definition of pressure the international standard unit of which is the Pascal (P_a).

$$P_a = N \times m^{-2}$$

As the Pascal is a very small unit, the bar is the most frequently used unit in water potential measurements.

$$1 \text{ bar} = 10^5 P_a$$

The water potential of pure water is by definition zero.

Water may be exposed to hydrostatic pressure or suction; in the former case the water potential is positive, in the latter negative. Water potential is also influenced by solutes dissolved in the water. These solutes dilute the 'concentration' of water molecules and thus decrease the water potential. Taking into account these 3 components hydrostatic pressure, suction, and solute concentration, the water potential can be described by the following equation:

$$\Psi = \psi_p + \psi_s + \psi_m$$

ψ_p the pressure potential is numerically equal to the hydrostatic pressure. Increasing the hydrostatic pressure increases the water potential and for this reason the term ψ_p has a positive sign.

186

ψ_s is the potential resulting from the presence of solutes, and is called the osmotic potential or solute potential. The introduction of solutes into water
reduces the water concentration or more precisely the activity of the water
molecules. This decreases the water potential. A 0.1 M sucrose solution, for
example, has a water potential which is 2.27 bars lower than pure water
at the same temperature and pressure. The osmotic° potential (ψ_s) is always
a negative value being lower than zero, the water potential of pure water.

ψ_m is the matric potential. It represents suction. This is the component of the
water potential made up by the effects of solid surfaces on the water phase.
Water can be bound to large molecules such as proteins and polysaccharides
by means of H bonding. In this way water can be held to cell walls and membranes. Besides this adsorptive effect, water is also held in capillaries by
surface tension effects. These forces are called matric forces and as they
restrict the mobility of water, tend to lower the water potential. The sign
of ψ_m in the above equation is therefore negative.

In fresh plant material the proportion of matric bound water is usually very
low (WIEBE and AL-SAADI [1976]). In many plant species therefore the matric potential (ψ_m) only plays an important role where tissues have been depleted of
more than 50% of their normal water content (HSIAO [1973]). In plants the matric potential can thus often be neglected. In the soil system, however, the matric
potential is an important component of the soil water potential (GARDNER
[1965]).

If we consider the water potential of a plant tissue as for example the mesophyll cells of a leaf, a high proportion of the water is present in the vacuoles
(90%) which also contain substantial amounts of solutes. Water is also present in the cytoplasm (5%) and cell walls (5%) where it is exposed to matric
forces. Both the solutes and matric forces lower (make more negative) the water
potential. For this reason the water potential of plant organs (leaves, stems and
even roots) is usually negative. Under certain conditions, however, the hydrostatic pressure in vacuoles may be high and the water potential may thus attain a
positive value.

Water potentials in plants are usually in the range of –1 to –15 bar. In extreme cases values as low as –30 bar have been recorded. These values are very
much dependent on the plant environment. Slight water losses from fully turgid
tissues for example which may have little effect on the tissue water content can
decrease the water potential considerably. This results mainly from a decrease in
hydrostatic pressure (ψ_p). Different plant tissues tend to have characteristic water potentials. The water potential of leaves is usually lower (more negative)
than roots.

One of the most important aspects of the use of water potential is that it represents the driving force for water transfer. Water movement in cells, tissues and whole plants takes place from a higher to a lower water potential. According to the catenary hypothesis of VAN DEN HONERT [1948] water movement between any two points depends on the difference in water potential and on the resistance to flow. Such resistances in plant systems are cell walls, membranes, cuticles, etc. Thus the rate of water flow may be described by the equation

$$F = \frac{\Psi'_1 - \Psi'_2}{R}$$

where Ψ'_1 and Ψ'_2 = the difference in water potential between two points
   F = flow rate
   R = resistance

4.1.3 Osmosis

Osmosis occurs when two solutions with different water potentials are separated by a semi-permeable membrane, which allows the penetration of water molecules but not the penetration of the solutes dissolved in the water. This is demonstrated in Figure, 4.1. For the sake of simplicity in the example presented in the Figure one part of the system consists of pure water (left hand side of the Figure 4.1) and the other of a sucrose solution (right hand side of the Figure 4.1). Provided that both the pure water and the sucrose solution are exposed to the same temperature and atmospheric pressure, the water potential of the sucrose solution is lower than that of the pure water. In order to attain equilibrium net water movement through the semi-permeable membrane proceeds from the pure water to the sucrose solution which is shown schematically in Figure 4.1a. Net water movement ceases as soon as the chemical potential of water is the same on both sides of the membrane. At this stage as shown in Figure 4.1b the turgor of the sucrose solution is raised.

The plant cell may be considered as an osmotic system. If a living cell is exposed to pure water there will be a net uptake of water by the cell. This results because the presence of solutes in the cell means that the water potential of the cell is lower than the water potential of the pure water. The net uptake of water influences the water potential in the cell in two ways. It dilutes the cell solute concentration so that the osmotic potential (ψ_s) in the cell increases (it becomes less negative). It also increases the hydrostatic pressure or turgor pressure in the cell. Both these effects raise the water potential of the cell. The load from the turgor pressure is carried by the cell wall and neighbouring cells. In fully turgid cells, water molecules exert a high pressure on cell walls. Cell walls, however, are elastic and can enlarge the cell volume as much as 20 to 30%. Figure 4.2

188

shows the changes which take place in turgor (hydrostatic pressure ψ_p), osmotic potential (ψ_s) and water potential ($\psi_p + \psi_s$) when cell swelling occurs. Very clearly

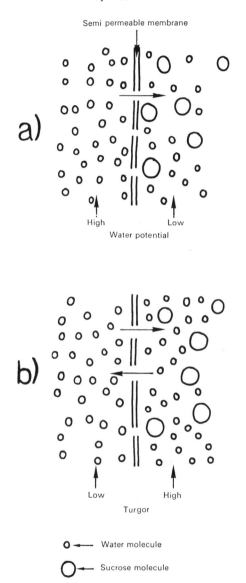

Fig.4.1 Osmotic system:
   a) Net water movement from a higher to a lower water potential.
   b) Equilibrium between both water potentials due to the high turgor in the sucrose solution – no net water movement.

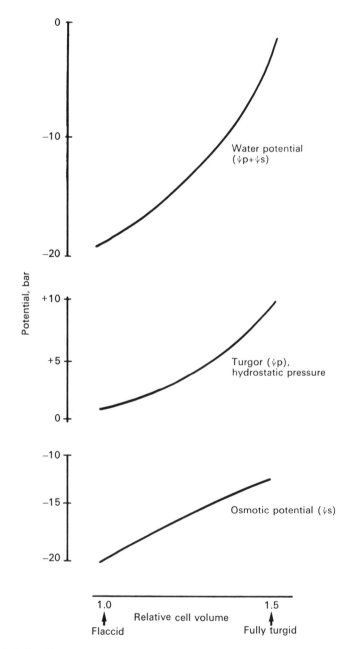

Fig.4.2 Relationship between cell volume, turgor, osmotic potential and water potential.

the increase in water potential is more marked than the osmotic potential increase. This is due to the fact that the osmotic potential is also affected by the increase in volume of the cell as it swells.

When the water potential of the ambient medium is lower than that of the cell (hypertonic solution) net water movement proceeds from the cell into the outer medium. This water loss results initially in a shrinkage of the cell volume, which at a later stage is followed by a contraction of the cytoplasm and by its separation from the cell wall. This phenomenon is called plasmolysis. If the cell has not been damaged, the process can be reversed and such plasmolyzed cells are able to attain their full turgor when exposed to pure water or to hypotonic solutions. The concentration of solutes in plant cells is usually in the range of 0.2 to 0.8 M. Higher concentrations in the outer solution cause plasmolysis.

Both inorganic and organic solutes affect the osmotic potential of plant cells. According to ZIMMERMANN [1978] the inorganic solutes, and particularly K^+, Na^+, and Cl^- occur predominantly in the vacuoles, whereas in the cytoplasm organic molecules such as glycerol, glycine-betaine, amino acids, and sucrose mainly contribute to osmotic potential. These organic solutes are so called 'compatible solutes', as they are not detrimental to the cytoplasm, even in high concentrations. Both types of osmotica (= osmotically active solutes) inorganic as well as organic play a major role in osmoregulation (ZIMMERMANN [1978]). This may be defined as an adjustment of the cell to ambient water conditions. If for example the water potential of the outer medium (soil medium) is low, the concentration of osmotica may be increased thus decreasing the water potential in the cell and promoting water uptake. This osmotic adjustment is of particular importance for plants growing under saline conditions (see p. 228) or subjected to water stress. The reverse process may also occur if the water potential of the outer medium is high. Too much water may be taken up into the cell and cell swelling may even result in membrane damage. To avoid such damage plants can decrease their concentration of osmotica thereby lowering water influx and retention.

Sometimes older terminology is still used in describing osmotic relationships in plants. The main terms are osmotic pressure, turgor pressure and suction pressure. The osmotic pressure (OP) is the pressure component exerted on the cell from the outer side of the cell wall. The turgor pressure (TP) acts in an opposite direction from the inner side of the cell wall. The difference between both is the suction pressure (SP). This is responsible for net water movement and may be expressed as follows:

$$SP = OP - TP$$

If the suction pressure is positive it infers that water is taken up and when it is negative it means than water is being lost from the cell. The suction pressure has also been termed diffusion pressure deficit (DPD) (MEYER [1945]). The comparison between the modern and older terminology is shown in Table 4.1 modified from NEWMAN [1976].

Table 4.1 Terms used in water potential terminology compared with older terms (after NEWMAN [1976])

Term	Range	Old term	Range	Any sign difference?
Osmotic Potential	Below O	Osmotic Pressure	Above O	Yes
Matric Potential	Below O	No term in plants Soil suction (in soils)	Above O	Yes
Pressure Potential	Above or below O	No general term but includes Turgor Pressure	Above or below O	No
Water Potential	Usually below O but can be above	Suction Pressure Diffusion Pressure Deficit	Usually above O	Yes

4.1.4 Adsorption and imbibition

As has already been mentioned, a small fraction of water in fresh plant tissues is adsorbed to the surfaces of cell walls, cell organelles, molecules and ions. Dry plant material also tends to adsorb water molecules from its surroundings. This is a process of biological significance. Dry seeds as for example seeds embedded in soil, rapidly adsorb water from the surrounding medium. Water molecules penetrate the intercellular spaces of the cell wall and also other cell compartments due to adsorption forces. These forces cause the swelling of the seed which, if confined, can exert pressures in the order of several hundred bar (SUTCLIFFE [1979]). This kind of water uptake provides seeds with enough water for the biochemical reactions which initiate the germination process. The swelling of gelatine brought about by water is an analogous process. Uptake of water resulting from adsorption forces is called imbibition.

4.2 Water Balance

4.2.1 General

The water potential of the atmosphere is usually lower than the water potential of the soil. This difference in water potential is the driving force which brings about the translocation of water from the soil solution through the plant to the atmosphere. Generally, the leaf water potential is not very much lower than that in the soil. However, a large potential difference occurs across the boundary layer around the leaf and stomatal cavities and the atmosphere. The rate of water transfer across this leaf-atmosphere interface is proportional to the vapour pressure difference between both sides of the boundary. The soil-plant-atmosphere continuum is of utmost importance in the water supply of all plant organs and tissues. On its path from the soil to the tips of stems and leaves, water has to overcome a number of resistances. These and the forces involved in the water translocation process will be discussed subsequently.

Three main steps in water translocation may be distinguished; the centripetal transport from the soil solution through the cortex tissue of the roots towards the xylem vessels of the central cylinder, the vertical transport from the roots towards the leaves, and the release of water as gaseous molecules at the plant atmosphere interfaces. These three principal steps are illustrated in Figure 4.3.

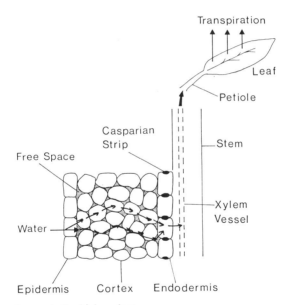

Fig.4.3 Water pathways in the higher plant.

4.2.2 Water uptake by roots

Figure 4.4 shows schematically the tissues of a young root including the cortex tissue, the endodermis, and the central cylinder with the vascular tissues of the xylem and phloem. The endodermis which separates the cortex from the central cylinder (stele) is generally characterized by a suberized layer. This layer which occurs on the radial and transverse cell walls, is known as the

193

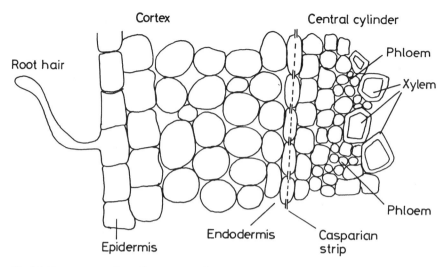

Fig.4.4 Transverse section of a young root.

Casparian strip and is made up of lipid material and lignin. It thus presents a high resistance to water and solute transport.

In the root tissues as well as in all other tissues of higher plants a distinction may be made between cell wall and cytoplasmatic fractions in relation to water and solute transport. The cell wall fraction is also called the apoplast (apo, Greek = away, away from the plasma) and comprises all parts of the tissue open to solutes and water without their having to cross a membrane. The pores and intercellular spaces of the apoplast allow the 'free' movement of water and solutes and for this reason the apoplast is sometimes referred to as 'free space' or 'apparent free space' as this cell wall part of the tissues appears to be 'free'.

The cytoplasm of one plant cell is generally connected to the cytoplasm of neighbouring cells by numerous plasmodesmata. This forms a cytoplasmatic continuum which is called the symplast (ARISZ [1956]), and provides another transport pathway for water and solutes.

The apoplast of the root cortex is in close contact with the soil medium, the contact often being enhanced by numerous root hairs. Thus soil water extends into the free space of the cortex tissue, which is characterized by relatively large cells and numerous intercellular spaces.

The uptake of water from the soil medium into the cortex results mainly from capillary action and osmosis. Capillary forces arise because of the narrow pores and channels of the cell wall material. Thus some of the free space water is bound very strongly and has a very low water potential (about –100 bar) largely

194

as a result of matric forces. This low potential means that the water can be very strongly withheld. This implies that the free space of the root tissue presents a considerable resistance to water flow (NEWMAN [1974]). Because of the narrow pores of the cell wall material (most pores have a diameter <10 nm), the matric potential of the root may be considerably lower (more negative) than that of the surrounding soil. Therefore, at the same water potential the water content of the cell wall material is about 10 times higher than that of a medium textured soil. Thus at a water potential of -1 bar, cell walls contain about 2 g H_2O/g dry matter, whereas the water content of a medium textured soil is only 0.1 to 0.2 g H_2O/g dry matter.

Water can be taken up from the free space into the cytoplasm. This uptake mainly results from osmosis. Biological membranes, such as the plasmalemma which separate the free space from the cytoplasm, are permeable to water molecules, although they present a considerable resistance to water flow. These membranes function as semi-permeable membranes and allow osmotic water movement. The osmotic potential in the cytoplasm depends on metabolism. Processes such as the active uptake of ions and the synthesis of organic acids and sugars decrease the osmotic potential in the cell and thus result in an increased net uptake of water. This shows that water uptake is linked to metabolism and therefore all factors influencing root metabolism may have an indirect impact on water uptake. Low temperature, lack of oxygen and toxic substances depress water uptake, because of their detrimental effect on metabolism (KRAMER [1955]). Thus EHLER [1962] found a reduction of about 70% in water uptake when lucerne plants were subjected to a low temperature of about 5°C. A significant positive correlation between water uptake and O_2 uptake by the roots of bean plants *(Phaseolus vulgaris)* has been reported by HOLDER and BROWN [1980]. It should be borne in mind that the effect of metabolism on water uptake and retention is an indirect one. Metabolism generates osmotic potential. Solutes arising from metabolism decrease the cell water potential. Thus the water potential difference between the cell and the outer medium is raised and a higher water uptake results. Water flow between the cytoplasm and the vacuole is also controlled by the water potential difference ($\Delta\Psi$) between these compartments. As the tonoplast functions as a semi-permeable membrane, osmotic forces are also mainly responsible for the net movement of water between the cytoplasm and the vacuole.

Water flow from the soil medium into the central cylinder is known as centripetal water transport. It may follow various pathways as indicated in Figure 4.5. The upper part of the Figure (Figure 4.5a) shows a young plant root in which the endodermis cells are still unsuberized (no Casparian strip). This lack of a Casparian strip allows water movement to take place from the

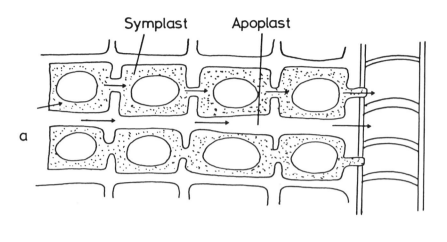

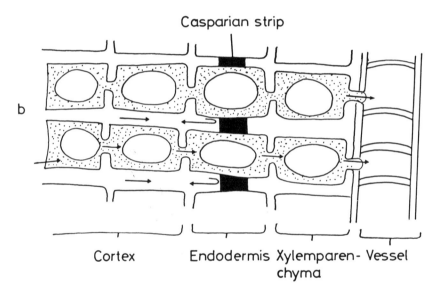

Fig.4.5 Centripetal transport of water through the root towards the vessel
   a) Young unsuberized root allowing apoplastic and symplastic transport.
   b) Suberized root with Casparian strip allowing only symplastic transport.

soil solution into the vascular tissues (vessels) in either the apoplast or the
symplast. Figure 4.5b shows the pathways of water transport for a root at a
more advanced stage in growth, where the endodermis has a well developed
Casparian strip. This suberized zone of the endodermis cell walls represents a
strong barrier to water and solute movement and therefore continuous water
flow from the soil through the apoplast to the central cylinder is prevented.

196

Water flow across the endodermis to the central cylinder has thus mainly to follow the symplastic pathway as shown in Figure 4.5b. Since the endodermal cell walls are rich in plasmodesmata, water and solute transfer between the cortex tissue and the central cylinder appears to be mainly be brought about through these plasmatic strings (CLARKSON et al. [1971]). NEWMAN [1974] who has also very throughly discussed water pathways through roots concluded that the symplastic pathway is the most important one for centripetal water transport. Only in very young plant roots in which the Casparian strip has not developed does the apoplastic pathway seems to play a major role. This pathway is of particular importance for the uptake and transport of Ca^{2+} (see p. 446).

In total, epidermis, cortex, endodermis, and central cylinder represent a considerable resistance to water transport from the soil medium into the xylem. This is particular evident for plants with a high water consumption growing in dry soils (about −3 bar water potential of the soil). Under such conditions the root water potential may become considerably lower than the soil water potential. The high resistance of roots to centripetal water transport is also the reason for diurnal shrinking and swelling of roots. Under high transpiration conditions at noon, the rate of water transport out of the roots into the upper plant parts exceeds that of water uptake from the soil, and root shrinking occurs. The reverse process takes place as transpiration declines during the late afternoon and evening when the water deficit of the roots is made up and the roots swell (TAYLOR and KLEPPER [1978]). The soil water potential is clearly reflected by the water potential of the plant. The relationship is shown in Table 4.2 for the leaf water potential of soya beans (ADJEI-TWUM and SPLITTSTOESSER [1976]).

Table 4.2 Relationship between soil water potential and the water potential of soya bean leaves

Soil water potential, bar	Leaf water potential, bar
0 to −0.1	− 2
0 to −0.2	− 4
0 to −0.4	−12
0 to −1.0	−19

4.2.3 Water release into the xylem vessels

The mechanism by which water is released into the xylem is not yet completely understood. It is generally accepted, that this is controlled by osmosis and therefore closely linked to ion transport. The question of whether inorganic ions are actively secreted or passively leak into the xylem vessels is not clear.

LÄUCHLI [1972] who discussed this problem in detail, supposes that the xylem parenchyma cells play a crucial role in secreting inorganic ions into the vessels. Plate 4.1 shows a metaxylem cell and bordering parenchyma cells. In the

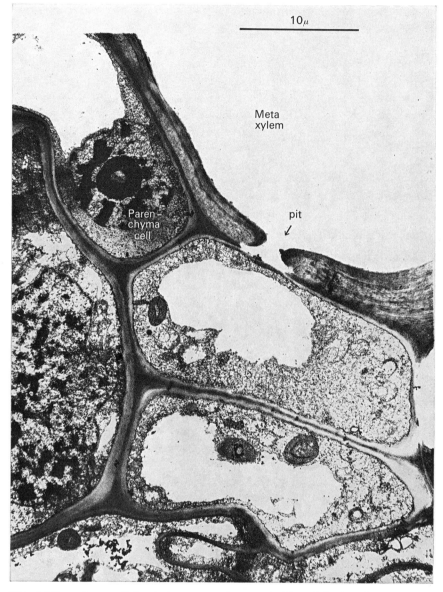

Plate 4.1 Parenchyma cells bordering a metaxylem vessel with a pit in the cell wall. (Photo: KRAMER)

thickened cell wall of the metaxylem a pit is visible and at this point the meta-xylem is separated from the parenchyma cell only by the plasmalemma. It is believed that ions are secreted from the parenchyma cells into the xylem vessels through such pits. This is the case for K^+ which accumulates in the parenchyma cells as has been shown by LÄUCHLI et al. [1974] using electron probe analysis. These outer metaxylem vessels appear to be the major functional xylem elements in the upward transport to the shoot. The secretion of ions into the vessel causes a fall in the water potential in the vessel and hence induces a net water flow in the xylem. In contrast to normal cells, where water uptake is limited by cell volume, the xylem vessels show no major restriction as absorbed water can move in an upward direction. For this reason when water uptake is in-creased the hydrostatic pressure (ψ_p) in the vessels does not rise to such an extent as is the case in living cells. Water is thus absorbed comparatively easily by the xylem vessels as a consequence of ion uptake.

4.2.4 Root pressure

The mechanism described above is responsible for a phenomenon called root pressure. This can be demonstrated by observing the exudation sap accumulat-ing on the stumps of decapitated plants. The rate of exudation depends consid-erably on prevailing metabolic conditions. It is decreased by the effects of in-hibitors or anaerobiosis which depress metabolically mediated ion uptake (KRAMER [1955], VAADIA et al. [1961]). The rate of exudation is also influenced by the presence of specific ion species and their concentration in the nutrient so-lutions. MENGEL and PFLÜGER [1969] found highest exudation rates when KCl was present in the external solutions due to the fact that both K^+ and chloride are taken up rapidly. Lowest exudation rates were observed when the external solution was of pure water. The promoting effect of K^+ on water uptake and transport has also been demonstrated by BAKER and WEATHERLEY [1969] in ex-uding root systems of Ricinus communis. These observations agree well with the results of LÄUCHLI et al. [1971], discussed above.

The importance of root pressure is difficult to assess. Undoubtedly in young plants root pressure contributes to the upward translocation of soluble organic and inorganic material, particularly under conditions where transpira-tion is low (LOCHER and BROUWER [1964]). Root pressure, however, is far too weak to transport water through the xylem vessels to the upper plant parts.

In seedlings root pressure can often cause guttation. Water is pumped through the entire plant and released as droplets at the leaf tips. Guttation is in-dicative of intense root metabolism and a high root pressure. It is often observed in the early morning partly as a result of the low water deficit of the atmosphere during the night which restricts evaporation. The droplets contain solutes and OERTLI [1962] has reported that young plants exude boron by this means. Generally, however, with the exception of a number of tropical rain forest trees which guttate continuously, guttation is of little significance in older plants.

4.2.5 Transpiration and water movement in the xylem

Root pressure and capillary forces are too weak to play a major role in the upward transport of water in the xylem. In tall trees, for example, water may be raised to a height of almost 100 m. To understand this movement we must consider several aspects of plant water. In the first place a continuous water phase – the so-called soil plant atmosphere continuum – extends from the soil solution through the entire plant (see Figure 4.3). The water molecules in this continuous phase are bound by cohesive forces. At the leaf atmosphere boundary, water is present in the fine channels and the intercellular spaces of cell walls in the stomatal cavities (see Figure 4.6). As evaporation into the atmosphere takes place, capillary action and the cohesive properties of the water ensure that water flows through the plant to replace that water which is being lost. This normally means that as water is evaporated at the leaf surface, water moves into the root from the soil. This concept of water movement is called the cohesion hypothesis.

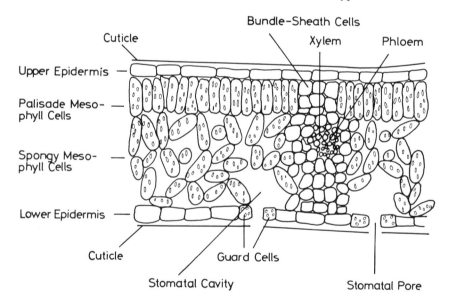

Fig.4.6 Schematic cross section of a leaf showing guard cells, stomatal pores, stomata cavity, bundle-sheath cells, xylem and phloem.

The rate at which water molecules evaporate from the plant atmosphere boundary increases with temperature and is higher when the water potential of the atmosphere is low (higher atmospheric water deficit). The process of evaporation described above is called transpiration. It exerts a tension or suction in the water columns of the xylem. This tension is higher under conditions of rapid transpiration or low water availability in the root medium. The xylem tissue is well equipped for this 'water suction' or more precisely the reduction in hydrostatic pressure of the water column. The wooden elements of the xylem cell walls are rigid enough to prevent any major compression of the xylem vessels by adjacent cells. If this were not so, too great a drop in the hydrostatic pressure of the xylem water could result in a break in the water file and a blockage in the transpiration stream by air bubbles. The fall in the hydrostatic pressure in the xylem induces a small but detectable shrinkage of the stems. In tree trunks there is often a typical diurnal variation in circumference, a maximum being observed in the early morning, when the water deficit is at a minimum (AHTI [1973]). The circumference also depends on the water availability in the root medium. The higher the water tension of the soil, the more the circumference of the trunk is reduced (AHTI [1973]).

The resistance to water flow along the xylem vessels is relatively low. For this reason the main water flow is along the xylem vessels and follows the major and minor vein systems of the xylem. Xylem cell walls, however, are permeable to water molecules. Some water is imbibed into the cell walls of the xylem and the free space of adjacent tissues. Water uptake by neighbouring tissues can then occur by osmosis. The resistance to water flow in the walls of the xylem vessels is considerably higher than in the xylem vessels themselves (NEWMAN [1974]). Lateral movement of water in plant tissues thus proceeds at a much lower rate than the upward translocation.

Higher plants expose a considerable leaf surface area to the atmosphere. This is necessary for the capture and assimilation of CO_2. On the other hand it means that the rate of water loss by transpiration is high. Many higher plants, therefore consume large quantities of water. A mature maize plant, for example, contains about 3 litres of water although during its growing period it may have transpired more than a hundred-fold that amount.

HOLDER and BROWN [1980] have recently demonstrated that water loss by transpiration is much dependent on root metabolism and to a lesser extent on leaf area. Using entire bean plants *(Phaseolus vulgaris)* these authors obtained a good correlation ($r = 0.89$) between oxygen uptake by the roots and water uptake. Measuring transpiration rates at successive stages of defoliation it was also observed that as the leaves were removed the transpiration rate per unit leaf area of the remaining leaves increased. This indicates that for plants well supplied with oxygen root uptake and not leaf surface area controls the water flux.

4.2.6 Stomatal opening and closure

By far the largest amount of water transpired by crop plants is released through the stomatal pores. Figure 4.6 shows a section of a mesophyll leaf with open stomata. Stomata are mainly located on the undersides of leaves and enable gaseous exchange between leaf and atmosphere. It can be seen that intercellular air spaces are interspersed between the parenchymatous cells of the mesophyll. The pores represent the main pathway for the transpiration of water, because the upper and lower epidermis of a leaf are generally covered by a waxy layer, called the cuticle. This consists of a lipidic material and presents a considerable barrier to the transpiration of water molecules. Thus, for most crop plants, up to 90% of the transpiration water passes through the stomata. Stomatal opening and closing is therefore an important process, not only for CO_2 assimilation but also for the water balance of the plant.

It has long been known that the opening-closing process of stomata is dependent on changes in turgor of the guard cells. High turgor results in opening and low turgor in closure. Experimental data of FISCHER [1968] and FISCHER and HSIAO [1968] have shown that the turgor of guard cells is related to metabolically dependent ion uptake and particularly to the uptake of K^+ (HUMBLE and HSIAO [1969]). FISCHER [1968]) reported that with an increasing concentration fo labelled K^+ in the guard cells the stomatal openings of *Vicia faba* became wider. This finding was supported by electron probe analysis of HUMBLE and RASCHKE [1971] who demonstrated that K^+ is accumulated in the guard cells of open stomata, whereas in closed stomata no K^+ accumulation was observed (see Figure 10.4). The mechanism thus depends primarily on the accumulation of K^+ in the guard cells and not on the hydrolyzation of starch to sugars as was formerly believed. According to FISCHER and HSIAO [1968] the starch/sugar reaction is only a secondary reaction and therefore of minor importance.

The actual mechanism of stomatal opening and closure is not yet completely understood. PENNY and BOWLING [1974] in studying the K^+ concentration in guard cells of *Commelina communis* found that stomatal opening is associated with an increase of K^+ in the guard cell of about 35 mM. The K^+ required for this accumulation is partially provided by the vacuoles of the outer lateral subsidiary cells and partially by the epidermal cells. The transfer of K^+ is reversed on stomatal closure, the K^+ accumulating in the epidermal cells. As no major electropotential differences were found between any of the cells of the leaf epidermis, regardless of the state of the stomata, the authors suggest that the K^+ transport is an active process and that stomatal opening as well as closure require metabolic energy. The K^+ flux rates required are about 50 to 100 times greater than normal rates of transmembrane fluxes into plant cells. For this reason PENNY and BOWLING [1974] raise the question of whether such fluxes occur *via* plasmodesmatal connections rather than across cell membranes.

High temperatures may also cause stomatal closure. This probably results from enhanced respiration and increased levels of CO_2 in the stomatal cavities. High temperatures are often associated with high water consumption. Stomatal closure thus protects the plant against excessive water loss. This mechanism of opening and closing provides a very efficient means of regulating the water balance of the entire plant. According to investigations of STOCKER [1967] grasses in particular possess a very sensitive stomatal regulatory mechanism. As K^+ plays a dominant role in stomatal opening, the K nutritional status of the plant affects water loss by transpiration. ZECH *et al.* [1971] observed enhanced rates of transpiration in *Pinus silvestris* suffering from K deficiency. The beneficial effect of K^+ preventing water loss has been reported by BRAG [1972] for *Triticum aestivum* and *Pisum sativum*. Phytohormones also affect the closure and opening of stomata. Generally cytokinins favour opening, whereas abscisic acid has the reverse effect (MIZRAHI *et al.* [1970]).

4.3 Long Distance Transport

4.3.1 General

In higher plants it is essential that there is adequate means of transporting materials between sites of production and sites of consumption. In this transport process water plays a dominant role. The most important pathways for long distance transport are the vascular tissues of the xylem and phloem. The main materials which are transported are water, inorganic ions and organic compounds. Water and minerals are taken up from the root medium and predominantly translocated towards the upper plant parts by the xylem. Organic compounds are mainly transported in the phloem and are translocated both in an upward and downward direction.

4.3.2 Xylem transport

We have already dealt in some detail with the movement of water in the xylem (see page 200). In this section water movement is therefore considered only in so far as it affects nutrient transport.

The relatively high rate of water flow along the xylem vessels in an upward direction causes a rapid translocation of solutes dissolved in the xylem sap. Inorganic ions once secreted into the xylem vessels (see page 199) are thus quickly transported to the upper plant parts. This effect was clearly demonstrated by RINNE and LANGSTON [1960] in an experiment in which one part of the root system of a peppermint plant was fed with labelled phosphate (P–32). Labelled phosphate was detected in the upper plant after a short time but only in those plant parts directly supplied by xylem vessels from that portion of the root system which had received labelled phosphate. This is shown schematically in Figure 4.7. The shaded parts of the leaves show the accumulation of labelled P. The distribution pattern of P-32 observed in the leaves is typical for this

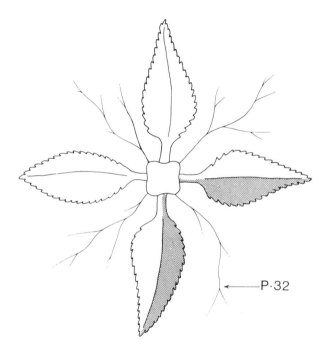

Fig.4.7 Distribution of labelled P in the leaves of a peppermint plant. P-32 was supplied to only one part of the root system (after RINNE and LANGSTON [1960]).

kind of labelling experiment. It also demonstrates that inorganic ions are mainly distributed along the vascular xylem system and that lateral movement proceeds from here into adjacent cells.

The transport mechanism for solutes in the xylem sap is predominantly one of mass flow, where cations and particularly divalent cations may be adsorbed to cell wall surfaces and exchanged for other cations (BIDDULPH *et al.* [1961], ISER-

MANN [1970]). The xylem sap is a rather dilute solution, which is largely made up of inorganic ions. Table 4.3 shows the rate of exudation and inorganic ion composition of xylem sap of tomato plants in relation to the level of K nutrition (KIRKBY et al. 1981). The ions present in highest concentrations are K^+, NO_3^- and Ca^{2+}. The level of Ca^{2+} was probably unusually high in this experiment as the level in the nutrient medium was also very high (10 me/l). It should be noted that the level of K nutrition had relatively little effect on the ionic concentration of the sap. Increasing K levels in the nutrient medium did, however, considerably increase the volume of sap exuded and thus enhanced the uptake of the ions. The concentrations of the individual inorganic ions depend on their rates of uptake, their concentration in the nutrient medium, the uptake of water, as well as on the intensity of transpiration.

Nitrogen may be transported in the xylem in the form of NO_3^-, NH_4^+, and as amino acids. The proportion of organic N depends much on the nitrate reductase potential of the roots and is generally high in woody plant species and lower in herbaceous species. The main types of amino acids found in the xylem sap are glutamine and asparagine and their precursors glutamate and aspartate (PATE [1980]). In some species, such as tropical legumes, ureides (allantoin and allantoic acid) are the most important N forms of the xylem sap. Basic amino acids, e.g. arginine, are quickly absorbed by the tissue surrounding the xylem; asparagine and glutamine are absorbed by stems at a moderate rate, while aspartate and glutamate are hardly absorbed at all and are thus transported to the leaves. Here they are used for the synthesis of proteins or even transfered to the phloem and then exported out of the leaf.

Table 4.3 The rate of exudation and inorganic ion composition of xylem sap of decapitated tomato plants in relation to the level of K-nutrition (Exudates taken in the first hour after decapitation – sulphate varied in nutrient solution) (KIRKBY et al. 1981)

Nutrient level of K	Vol. of exudate ml/hr/10 plants	Ionic composition (me/l)									
		K^+	Na^+	Ca^{2+}	Mg^{2+}	Total	NO_3^-	SO_4^{2-}	$H_2PO_4^-$	Cl^-	Total
		Cations					Anions				
K_1	46.5	17.3	0.3	10.8	3.9	32.3	26.1	3.1	0.4	1.7	31.3
K_2	50.6	21.7	0.2	10.6	4.0	36.5	30.8	3.5	0.4	1.3	36.0
K_3	55.9	21.4	0.2	11.8	4.2	37.6	31.6	3.0	0.5	1.1	36.2

Amino acids absorbed from the stem tissue are mainly used for storage. The level of amino acids in the xylem sap also depends on physiological age. It is often high in spring, when storage proteins of roots and stems are mobilized for the formation of young leaves (SAUTER [1976]).

Some inorganic nutrients can be taken up rapidly from the cells adjacent to the xylem vessels. They thus decrease in concentration as they are transported along the xylem vessels. This is true for the major plant nutrients, such as NO_3^-, $H_2PO_4^-$ and K^+. On the other hand, other nutrients are absorbed relatively slowly from the xylem sap by adjacent cells. They are thus translocated to the uppermost tips and margins of leaves and in some cases can even give rise to tip burning.

Long distance transport takes place in both the upper plant parts and in the roots. In both cases the transport rate is affected by an axial (vertical) resistance which differs between plant species and organs. Because of this resistance the water potential of upper plant parts (leaves and stems) is lower than that of plant roots. TAYLOR and KLEPPER [1978] emphasize the fact that the resistance to water transport is higher the deeper the soil layer from which the roots absorb the water. For this reason water depletion from the upper soil layers occurs earlier than that of deeper layers. Plant species which are able to take up water from deeper soil layers are believed to have lower axial root resistances to water.

The rate of upward translocations depends mainly on the transpiration intensity and water uptake by roots. This is not only true for water transport, but also for the translocation of solutes dissolved in the xylem sap. Thus LINSER and HERWIG [1963] showed with young maize plants that reducing the rate of transpiration resulted in a decrease in phosphate translocation from the roots to the upper plant parts. MICHAEL et al. [1969] growing tobacco in a growth chamber at extremely low transpiration rates induced B deficiency in the youngest leaves, because of the low rate of B translocation in the transpiration stream. Not all plant nutrients are dependent on transpiration when translocated in an upward direction. Some of the major plant nutrients are also transported in the phloem sap. This kind of transport is treated in more detail on page 213.

Although water movement in the plant and particularly in the xylem can considerably affect the transport of plant nutrients, it should be remembered that water uptake and ion uptake are two separate processes, and that a high rate of water uptake need not necessarily be associated with a high rate of ion uptake. HANSON and BONNER [1954] thus demonstrated with artichoke tubers, that lowering the rate of water uptake by a low water potential in the outer solution, did not affect the uptake of Rb^+. Under conditions, where water has to pass through a biological membrane, ion uptake precedes water uptake thus enabling osmotic water transport (see page 197). Where water movement is unimpeded, however, as in the transpiration stream, plant nutrients may be translocated along with the water by mass flow.

4.3.3 Phloem tissue and phloem loading

The phloem tissue contains the pathways in which organic material in particular is translocated. This tissue often runs parallel with the xylem strand. Phloem tissue contains sieve cells (sieve elements), companion cells and parenchyma cells. The most important are the sieve tubes or sieve elements. These elongated cells contain porous sieve like areas or sieve plates at their ends which separate the cells from one another. In the upper plant organs the sieve elements are present in the cortex, the petioles and in the major vein system of leaves. The roots contain the sieve elements in the central cylinder. The sieve element is a highly specialised long stretched cell with a thin layer of cytoplasm, pressed to the cell wall. Cell nucleus and mitochondria are degenerated.

It is now generally accepted that during metabolic activity the pores of the sieve plate are open. Thus FISHER [1975] showed that in the petiole tissue of soya bean about 70% of the sieve plate pores were essentially free from obstruction. Plate 4.2 shows an example of this investigation. The light areas of the plate show the open pores.

Sieve cells differ from the sieve elements in so far as they are still developing and not so highly specialized as the sieve elements. In comparison with the sieve elements, sieve cells contain more mitochondria, have a smaller diameter (2.5 μm) and, unlike the sieve element, are located in the minor vein system of leaves. Plate 4.3 shows a cross section of a minor vein of *Tagetes patula* from the work of EVERT [1980]. The vein comprises a tracheary element (xylem), a vascular parenchyma cell, sieve elements, phloem parenchyma cells and companion cells. These latter cells do in fact 'accompany' the sieve cells and are derived from the same meristematic cells from which the sieve cells are developed. Companion cells play an essential role in phloem loading. Thus TRIP [1969] observed that in sugar beet leaves newly synthesized assimilates are predominantly accumulated in the companion cells. Sieve elements and companion cells are connected by numerous plasmodesmata and both cell types are often considered as a functional unit called the sieve element companion complex (GEIGER [1975]).

The minor vein system which comprises sieve cells and companion cells may be compared with a rather fine net mesh (Plate 4.4). In sugar beet leaves for example the total length of this fine vein system amounts to about 70 cm per cm² leaf area (GEIGER and CATALDO [1969]). This total length is about 10 times greater than that of the corresponding major veins. This demonstrates the importance of the minor vein system in the collection of photosynthates. The mean distance of the mesophyll cells from these fine veins is only about 70 μm or the length of about two cells. Photosynthates are thus easily accessible to the

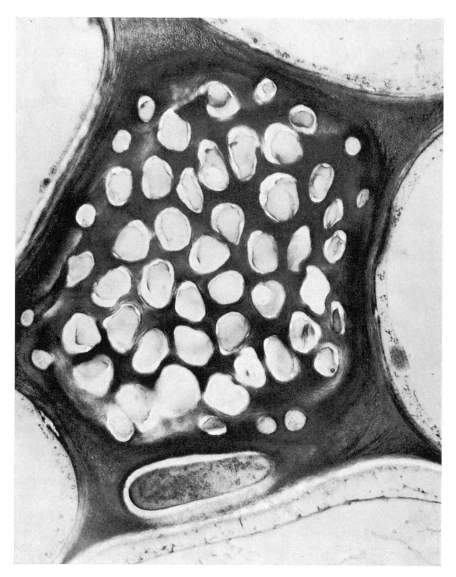

Plate 4.2 Sieve plate in a soya bean petiole which was quickly frozen *in situ*. The functional condition of this sieve tube was established by microautoradiograph. (Photo: FISHER)

companion cells. Assimilates are transported from these minor veins to the major veins. Minor veins may therefore be regarded as 'contributory streams' to the major vein system.

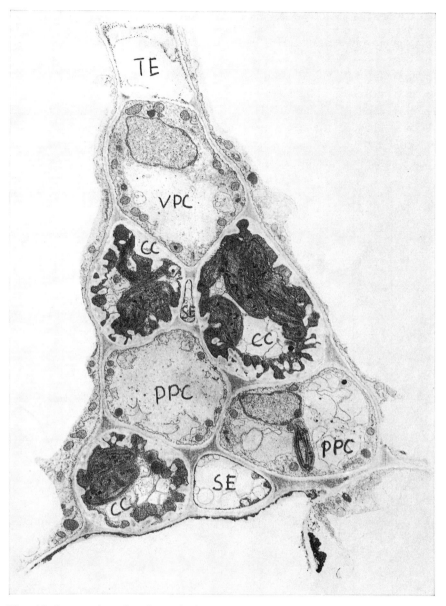

Plate 4.3 Cross section of a minor vain from leaf of *Tagetes patula* (Photo: EVERT)

TE   = Tracheary element (xylem)
VPC = Vascular parenchyma cells
CC   = Companion cell
SE   = Sieve cell
PPC = Phloem parenchyma cells

4.3.4 Export of photosynthates out of the chloroplast and phloem loading

Organic solutes transported in the phloem tissue are mainly produced in the chloroplast. The chloroplast may thus be considered as the source of organic material. This is shown in Figure 4.8. The chloroplast imports inorganic phosphate, CO_2, NH_3, and HNO_2 and exports triosephosphates and amino acids. The uptake of CO_2, NH_3, and HNO_2 probably takes place by diffusion through the outer chloroplast membrane (HEBER and PURCZELD [1977]). On the other hand the transport of both inorganic and organic phosphates across the membrane, is brought about by a so called phosphate trans-

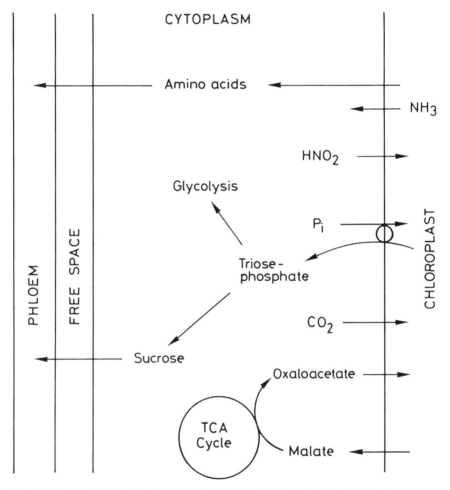

Fig.4.8 Scheme of chloroplast import and export and phloem loading. TCA cycle enzymes are located in the mitochondria.

locator, which couples the uptake of inorganic phosphate with the export of triosephosphates (HELDT et al. [1977]). The export of photosynthates such as glyceraldehyde-3-phosphate (GAP) and dihydroxy-acetonephosphate (DHAP) thus depends on the concentration of inorganic phosphate in the cytoplasm (WALKER [1980]). Too low a phosphate level may result in a reduction in the export of triosephosphates out of the chloroplast and lead to an accumulation of starch in the chloroplast, as occurs when plants are grown under conditions of phosphate deficiency.

Inorganic phosphate also has a considerable influence on starch synthesis in the chloroplast. ADP-glucose pyrophosphorylase is a key enzyme in starch synthesis and is allosterically regulated by inorganic phosphate (P_i) and PGA (PREISS and LEVI [1979]). The absolute concentrations of these compounds is of lesser importance than the relative concentrations the enzyme being 'switched on' when the PGA/P_i ratio is high. According to HELDT et al. [1977] highest rates of starch synthesis are obtained with a PGA/P_i ratio of about 1.7.

Starch degradation in the chloroplast is associated with an increase in the concentrations of hexosephosphates, DHAP, and PGA. Triosephosphates thus formed can be released into the cytoplasm. Starch degradation in the chloroplast is probably brought about by a phosphorylase according to the reaction

$$(\text{Glucan})_n + P_i \rightleftarrows (\text{Glucan})_{n-1} + \text{glucose-1-phosphate}$$

The equilibrium of this reaction depends on the level of P_i and glucose-1-phosphate, high levels of P_i favouring starch degradation.

The export of photosynthates from the chloroplast not only represents the removal of organic carbon but also the export of energy. This is present in triosephosphates and also in malate which may be produced in the chloroplast by the reduction of oxaloacetate (see p. 164). These constituents may be incorporated into the glycolytic pathway (triosephosphates) or TCA cycle (malate) and thus contribute to the energetic requirement of the cytoplasm. A considerable proportion of triosephosphates released by the chloroplast is used for the synthesis of organic compounds. Triosephosphates are thus also precursors of sucrose which is synthesized in the cytoplasm. In most plant species this is the quantitatively most important organic constituent which participates in long distance transport. In addition some organic carbon is transported in the form of amino acids (see Table 4.5).

The transport pathway from the mesophyll cells to the minor veins is not yet completely clear. The pathway may be a symplastic one following the endoplasmic reticulum extending from the mesophyll cells through the plasmodesmata to the sieve cell companion cell complex (GEIGER [1975]). The experimental evidence of GEIGER *et al.* [1974] obtained with sugar beet leaves, however, indicates that the free space (apoplast) of the mesophyll tissue is an essential part of the pathway photosynthates follow when transported from the mesophyll cells towards the sieve cell companion cell complex. It is supposed that sucrose leaks into the apoplast, and diffuses along a concentration gradient towards the minor veins. This supposition is supported by the range of sucrose concentrations found in the various tissues of sugar beet (KURSANOV [1974]) shown in Table 4.4.

Table 4.4 Sucrose concentrations in various tissues of sugar beets (KURSANOV [1974])

	Concentr., M 10^{-3}
Mesophyll	3– 3.5
Minor veins	20– 25
Major veins	50– 80
Phloem sap	200–300
Storage tissue of the root	400–600

The sucrose concentration of the phloem sap is almost 100 times higher than that of the mesophyll cells, which means that an uphill transport must occur and that energy is required. It is now generally accepted that the plasma membranes of the sieve cell companion cell complex represent the main resistance to the process of phloem loading. Experiments of SOVONICK *et al.* [1974] have shown that for phloem loading with sucrose, ATP is required. Analogous results have been obtained for phloem loading with amino acids by SERVAITES *et al.* [1979]. Transport across the membrane is brought about by a carrier system driven by an ATPase. The mechanism of this carrier transport has already been described on p. 118. Phloem transport has been discussed recently at a symposium published in the *Berichte Deutsch. Bot. Ges.* in Vol. 93 [1980].

Phloem loading depends on energy supply, on the water potential of the leaves and on the K nutritional status of the plant. Whether K^+ has a direct influence or whether it functions indirectly by providing a higher energy level, is not yet clear (MENGEL [1980]). GEIGER [1979] suggests that phloem loading is controlled by the turgor of the sieve cells, higher turgor depressing, and lower turgor promoting the process of loading. It is well known from the experiments of WARDLAW [1969] and BREVEDAN and HODGES [1973] that water stress affects the long distance transport of assimilates. It is, however, not yet clear whether this depression in long distance transport is due to a reduction in phloem loading or to an inhibition of assimilate transport through the apoplast.

The process of phloem unloading is not yet well understood. A number of authors suppose that unloading is a passive process so that sucrose and amino acids leak out of the sieve cells into the surrounding apoplast following a concentration gradient, controlled by the consumption of photosynthates by adjacent cells (JENNER [1980], MENGEL [1980]).

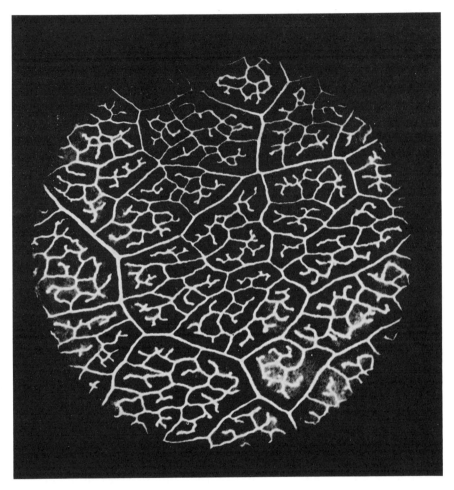

Plate 4.4 Autoradiograph showing the minor vein system of a sugar beet leaf (magnification × 10). The autoradiograph was obtained after treating the leaf with C-14 labelled sucrose and finally removing the free space sucrose by rinsing. (Photo: GEIGER)

4.3.5 Mechanism of phloem transport

It is more than 50 years ago since MÜNCH [1930] proposed a 'Pressure flow hypothesis' to account for phloem transport as a mass flow phenomenon. Stated simply, this is as follows: Phloem loading of solutes increases the pressure in the sieve tubes and this is responsible for a mass flow action. The process of loading and 'deloading' of phloem affects the water status of the sieve tubes. Loading results in a decrease in osmotic potential. Hence the accumulation of sucrose in sieve tubes is associated with water uptake by osmosis. The sieve tube thus takes on a rather high turgor, which may amount to about +10 bar or even higher (WRIGHT and FISHER [1980]). The reverse situation occurs when sieve tubes are 'deloaded'. Loss of sucrose results in a decrease of the solute concentration (an increase in osmotic potential) and hence also in a loss of water. If one imagines two sieve tubes in the same phloem strand, in which one sieve tube being loaded and the other deloaded, it is easy to envisage mass flow along a pressure gradient (Figure 4.9), provided that the sieve plates do not present too great a resistance to the mass flow process. As we have already seen however, evidence now suggests that in normal functioning sieve pores are open.

The possible mechanism of phloem transport has been discussed very thoroughly by GEIGER [1975]. He concludes that it is mainly a mass flow phenomenon in which phloem loading exerts the 'push' of the mechanism and deloading the 'pull'. Thus despite 50 years of research, the MÜNCH hypothesis – with modifications – is still generally held by a number of eminent plant physiologists to be the most acceptable mechanism to account for phloem translocation (BIDDULPH [1969], ZIMMERMANN [1969], EPSTEIN [1972], ZIMMERMANN and MILBURN [1975]). It should be mentioned, however, that besides the modified mass flow theory discussed above other hypotheses have been put forward to explain phloem transport. One such proposition is the electro osmosis theory of SPANNER [1975].

Phloem loading needs energy as has been already mentioned. Energy is also probably needed for the release and consumption of photosynthates in so-called 'physiological sinks' (plant tissues in which the assimilates are stored or used for growth). Whether the transport of solutes itself is also an energy consuming process is not yet clear. Experiments of COULSON et al. [1972] suggest that the ATP consumed in the phloem tissue is required for maintaining the tissue but not for the translocation process. Effects of temperature on the rate of translocation in the phloem cannot be used as an argument in favour of energy involvement because of the induced changes in viscosity of the phloem sap. Such changes can be considerable as the phloem sap contains large concentrations of sucrose. Low temperature ($0\,^\circ$C) may also result in blockage of the sieve plates by plasmatic material (GIAQUINTA and GEIGER [1973]). From the results available it would appear that phloem transport itself does not require energy. The idea that the translocation process is not directly driven by energy is consistent with the concept of the pressure flow theory.

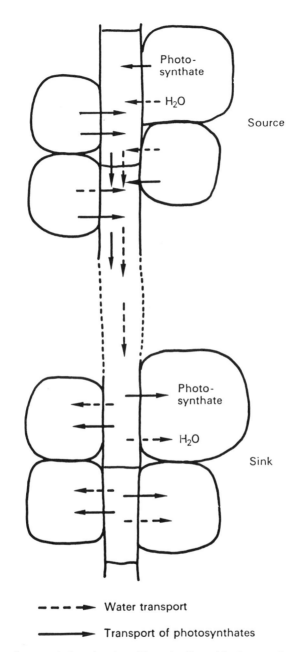

Photo-
synthate

H_2O

Source

Photo-
synthate

H_2O

Sink

- - - ▶ Water transport

───────▶ Transport of photosynthates

Fig.4.9 Schematic presentation showing phloem loading with photosynthate at the source and deloading at the physiological sink. Loading induces water uptake into the phloem and deloading water release. Thus resulting in a water movement from source to sink.

4.3.5 Redistribution

Table 4.5 shows the composition of the phloem sap of the castor oil plant (HALL and BAKER [1972]). Phloem saps obtained from other plant species differ only in detail from the results presented here. The main pattern is always the same: sucrose is the dominant component by far with concentrations in the range of 200 to 400 mM. The concentrations of amino acids can vary considerably depending on physiological conditions (MENGEL and HAEDER [1977]). Of the inorganic ions, K^+ in particular and to a lesser extent Mg^{2+} occur in relatively high concentration. Sucrose is the most important form in which carbon is translocated in the plant. There are some plant species, however, in which the sugar alcohols mannitol or sorbitol are translocated instead of sucrose. The phytohormones such as auxins, gibberellins and cytokinins also occur in the phloem sap, as can be seen from Table 4.5. The pH of the phloem sap is relatively high (about 8), probably due to the presence of K^+ and HCO_3^-.

Table 4.5 Composition of phloem sap of *Ricinus communis* according to HALL and BAKER [1972]

Dry matter	10–12.5%
Sucrose	234–304 mM
Reducing sugars	–
Amino acids	35.2 mM
Keto acids	30–47 me/l
Phosphate	7.4–11.4 me/l
Sulphate	0.5–1.0 me/l
Chloride	10–19 me/l
Nitrate	–
Bicarbonate	1.7 me/l
Potassium	60–112 me/l
Sodium	2–12 me/l
Calcium	1.0–4.6 me/l
Magnesium	9–10.0 me/l
Ammonium	1.6 me/l
Auxin	0.60×10^{-4} mM
Gibberellin	0.67×10^{-5} mM
Cytokinin	0.52×10^{-4} mM
ATP	0.4–0.6 mM
pH	8.0–8.2
Osmotic potential	–14.2 to –15.2 bars
Conductance	13.2 microohms
Viscosity	1.34 cP at 20°C

Unlike higher animals, which have a closed system of circulation, the main transport pathways in higher plants, the phloem and the xylem, are not directly linked to one another. Thus in the translocation between these two pathways water and solutes must pass through the connecting tissues. The phloem absorbs water from the surrounding tissues which in turn obtain water from the xylem. Thus on average about 5% of the water transported in an upward direction in the xylem is retranslocated *via* the phloem to the lower plant parts (ZIMMER-MANN [1969]). The water potential in these connecting tissues may exert an influence on the flow rate in phloem and xylem. A high rate of transpiration lowers the water potential of tissues surrounding the xylem and thus also depresses water transport into the phloem and the turgor of sieve tubes.

The translocation of plant nutrients *via* the phloem depends much on the capability of sieve tubes to take up nutrients rapidly. Potassium, as can be seen from Table 4.5 is present in the phloem sap in a high concentration and for this reason it can be translocated to various plant parts very quickly. Retranslocation of K^+ from older to younger leaves in barley plants has been shown by GREENWAY and PITMAN [1965]. Magnesium is also translocated in the phloem and is thus rather mobile throughout the whole plant (STEUCEK and KOONTZ [1970]). SCHIMANSKI [1973] reported that the translocation pattern of Mg^{2+} in the phloem is similar to that of the photosynthates. Because of the high concentrations of K^+ and Mg^{2+} in the phloem sap, fruits and storage tissues, which are all mainly supplied by the phloem sap, are relatively rich in K^+ and Mg^{2+}. Thus tomato fruits (VIRO [1973]) and potato tubers (ADDISCOTT [1974]) are comparatively rich in Mg as compared with Ca. Like the transport of photosynthates (see page 422), Mg^{2+} translocation in the phloem seems to be enhanced by K^+ (AD-DISCOTT [1974]). Calcium occurs only in minute concentrations in the phloem sap. Thus Ca^{2+} translocated by the transpiration stream to the upper plant parts, is scarcely moved in a downward direction in the phloem (LONERAGAN and SNOWBALL [1969]). The difference in behaviour between K^+ and Mg^{2+} on the one hand and Ca^{2+} on the other, in relation to phloem transport, is also reflected in the appearance of deficiency symptoms. Calcium deficiency first appears in the youngest leaves because Ca cannot be retranslocated from the older leaves. This means that it cannot be transported against the transpiration stream. For K^+ and Mg^{2+} the reverse holds true. Both ion species can be removed from older plant parts *via* the phloem pathway and thus translocated to the younger tissues. When K^+ or Mg^{2+} supply is inadequate, the K and Mg in the older plant parts are mobilized and used in the younger growing tissues. This is the reason why K- and Mg-deficiency symptoms appear first in the older leaves.

As the Ca supply to a plant organ mainly depends on transpiration intensity, the transpiration rate of a given plant organ is of particular importance in determining its Ca^{2+} content. Where transpiration is low, Ca supply may be inadequate and Ca deficiency may thus result. Fruits generally have a lower transpiration rate than leaves. This gives rise to blossom end rot in tomatoes and bitter pit in apples (see page 452). Both of these physiological disorders are caused by a lack of Ca.

Phosphate may be translocated in the phloem in inorganic and organic forms. Quite a substantial amount of P in the phloem sap is present in the form of ATP (GARDNER and PEEL [1969]). Redistribution of nitrogenous compounds is an essential part of N metabolism in most plant species. Many species are capable of storing N in the form of proteins at early stages in development, which at a later stage are hydrolyzed and translocated *via* the phloem to the fruits (PATE *et al.* [1979]). C-3 plants in particular store high amounts of leaf protein as RuBP carboxylase which may also serve as a storage protein, as well as a CO_2 fixing enzyme. BROWN [1978] argues that C-4 plants have a greater N use efficiency (biomass production per unit of N in the plant) than C-3 plants because of the smaller investment of N in the photosynthetic carboxylation enzymes. Fruits are mainly nourished by phloem sap. In an excellent review paper PATE [1980] notes that phloem sap provides 98% of the C, 89% of the N and 40% of the water of the fruits of *Lupinus albus*. Relatively high contents of amino acids in the phloem are often observed at the end of the growing period, as proteolysis occurs during leaf senescence. The resulting amino acids are transported from the leaves to storage tissues.

In contrast to translocation in the xylem, which occurs only in one direction, phloem transport is bidirectional. Generally photosynthates synthesized in the older leaves are translocated in a downward direction mainly to the roots, whereas younger leaves mainly supply photosynthates to the apex and fruits.

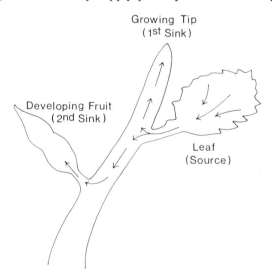

Fig.4.10 Distribution of photosynthate in relation to the strength of the physiological sink.

This pattern of distribution has been shown by MAJOR and CHARNETSKI [1976] in rape plants. The direction of transport also depends on physiological conditions. An example of this kind is shown in a schematic way in Figure 4.10. An old leaf is shown first to provide assimilates for a young leaf (1st sink). This means that assimilates from the old leaf are transported in an upward direction. As fruit setting begins a new physiological sink develops and the assimilates are diverted in a downward direction to the young developing fruit (2nd sink). Such source-sink relationships are of major importance in crop production as discussed in Chapter 5. The green plant parts providing the photosynthates are regarded as the source, whereas tissues in which the assimilates are stored or consumed are termed 'sinks'.

4.4 Physiological Aspects of Water Stress

4.4.1 Processes and parameters of water stress

Water stress in plants is one of the major factors limiting crop production throughout the world. The physiological relationships associated with water

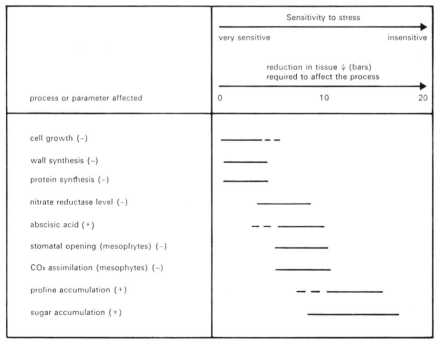

Fig.4.11 General sensitivity of some metabolic processes and parameters to water stress; (–) reduced, (+) increased (after HSIAO *et al.* [1976]).

stress therefore merit serious study. Water loss from plant tissues may cause a number of effects. It can lead to a reduction in hydrostatic pressure (ψ_p) inside cells. It can result in an increase in concentration of macromolecules and solutes of low molecular weight. The spatial relations of cellular membranes may be altered. In addition, a reduction in the chemical potential activity of plant water occurs. All these effects can influence metabolic processes. When plants are subjected to water stress it is thus not surprising that many plant processes are affected. This occurs even when only small changes in plant water status are involved. In mesophytic crop plants, for example, a water loss of 10–15% which corresponds to a lowering of the water potential (Ψ) by only about 6 bar can markedly influence metabolic processes (HSIAO *et al.* [1976]). Figure 4.11 from the review of HSIAO *et al.* [1976] indicates the generalized sensitivity of some plant processes to water stress. These are discussed below in relation to the water stress phenomenon.

4.4.2 Cell expansion and division

The most sensitive process to water stress is cell growth. The primary effect appears to be a physical one. When the turgor pressure in a plant cell falls, as happens in water stress, cell expansion is also decreased because of lack of pressure within the cell. There is thus a close correlation between decrease in cell size and the degree of water stress in plant tissues. A high turgor in plant tissues is sometimes only attained at night. This results in an enhanced growth rate at night as compared with during the day (BOYER [1968]). As soil water influences the leaf water potential, leaf enlargement also depends on soil water availability (MARC and PALMER [1976]). Thus ACEVEDO *et al.* [1971] reported that the elongation of young maize leaves was depressed when the water availability of the root medium decreased from –0.1 to –0.2 bar (= pF 2.0 to 2.3) (see p. 45). The corresponding leaf water potentials were –2.8 to –7.0 bar respectively.

In addition to cell enlargement, cell division can also be affected by water stress. From an extensive survey of the literature, HSIAO [1973] suggests that if stress is prolonged, cell division can be inhibited. It is not clear whether this is a direct effect of water stress or is rather an indirect effect of stress restricting meristematic cells from enlarging to a size minimal for cell division to take place.

4.4.3 Cell wall and protein synthesis

Cell wall synthesis has been measured by the incorporation of labelled glucose into wall material. This is substantially depressed by water stress by a drop of only a few bar (CLELAND [1967]). Water stress is reported to inhibit the incorporation of amino acids into proteins (BEN-ZIONI *et al.* [1967]) and causes a decrease in protein content of the tissues (MIZRAHI *et al.* [1970]). Results of DHINDSA and CLELAND [1975] using a double labelling radio technique (C-14, H-3) with *avena* coleoptiles showed that water stress induces both a qualitative change in the types of protein produced as well as a quantitative reduction in the rate of incorporation of leucine into proteins. Little is known of how the water stress brings about its effects on protein synthesis, but it appears not to depend on phytohormone activity.

Plants can to some degree adapt to water stress. Thus SIMMELSGAARD [1976] found in his investigation with young wheat plants that a low water availability in the nutrient medium (−7 bar) resulted in a gradual decline in the osmotic potential in the leaves from −14 to −25 bar with a concomitant decrease of the water potential from −8 to −16 bar. The hydrostatic pressure (ψ_p) which can be calculated from these data was thus higher in the water stressed than in the control treatment. This increase in the ψ_p (turgor) was due to smaller vacuoles developed under water stress.

4.4.4 Enzymes

Severe water deficits directly affect enzyme levels in plants. Under moderate stress some enzyme levels are raised as, for example, the enzymes involved in hydrolysis and dehydrogenation. In general, however, water stress results in a decrease in enzyme level. In particular, this is the case with nitrate reductase. It has been suggested that this relates to the suppression of protein synthesis (BARDZIK *et al.* [1971]). It is argued that an enzyme with a short half life such as nitrate reductase would be particularly dependent on protein synthesis. When considering enzyme activity it should be borne in mind that water stress is unlikely to exert any direct influence on enzyme conformation. Water loss to the point of desiccation is required before enzyme conformation is affected.

An intriguing question is whether enzymes located in the plasma membrane are affected by the turgor (ψ_p) which presses the membrane to the cell wall. ZIMMERMANN [1978] discussing the question in a useful review paper suggests that the pressure results in a change of membrane thickness which in turn could influence the membrane located enzymes. It is thus feasible that the activity of the membrane ATPase is controlled to some extent by the turgor, which also implies that membrane potentials are dependent on turgor. ZIMMERMANN and BECKERS [1978] suppose that these changes in membrane potentials are a general means by which plant tissues can control physiological reactions, *e.g.* uptake of solutes. The relationship between sucrose uptake and the turgor of sieve tubes has already been mentioned. A similar relationship was found between the turgor and K^+ uptake in *Valonia utricularis* (ZIMMERMANN [1978]).

K^+ uptake increased as the cell turgor decreased and *vice versa*. It thus appears that turgor pressure has a dual function in growth processes. It is required to stretch the walls and to facilitate the breaking of chemical bonds and in a following phase it controls the uptake of solutes required for growth.

4.4.5 Plant hormones

The relationships between water stress and phytohormones are complex. Some general points are, however, fairly clear. It is well established for example that even under moderate water stress there is a rapid and dramatic accumulation of abscisic acid (ABA, formula see page 238) (MIZRAHI *et al.* [1970]). In wilted leaves it appears that the higher levels of ABA are maintained by an increase in both the rate of ABA synthesis and metabolism (HARRISON and WALTON [1975]). ABA accumulation induces stomatal closure and inhibits transpiration (BEARDSELL and COHEN [1975]). As plant senescence is accelerated by ABA, the general phenomenon that plants become senescent more rapidly under water stress is almost certainly related to ABA synthesis and content.

Ethylene is well known in its ability to induce abscission. In cotton production this is a particular problem as it can result in the loss of developing flowers and young fruits. Evidence of McMICHAEL *et al.* [1972] suggests that water stress predisposes leaves to ethylene action, ethylene production occurring in the petioles of cotton plants within hours of the development of a water deficit. In some cases, but not all, their findings showed that ethylene production declined on rewatering. The influence of water stress on the cytokinins is not so clear, although low amounts of cytokinins have been observed in root exudates of plants which have undergone a period of water stress (ITAI *et al.* [1968]).

4.4.6 Photosynthetic activity

It is well known that water stress inhibits stomatal opening and photosynthesis. Mild water stress, however, appears to have little effect on stomatal closure (HSIAO [1973]). Soya beans for example, showed no reduction in gaseous exchange, indicative of substantial closure of stomata, until the water potential of the leaves had fallen to as low as −10 bar. The corresponding values for sunflowers and maize were −7 bar (BOYER [1970]). These so-called 'threshold values' indicate, that very low water potentials are required to inhibit gaseous exchange and thus also the diffusion of CO_2 from the atmosphere through the stomata into the leaf tissue. The results of BOYER [1970] for sunflower plants provide evidence that changes in the leaf water potential are more sensitively registered by changes in leaf enlargement than by net photosynthesis. As can be seen from Figure 4.12 leaf enlargement which, as we have seen, is very sensitive to water stress, dropped rapidly when the water potential was depressed below –3 bar. Net photosynthesis, however, was not lowered appreciably until values under –8 bar were reached. In experiments with *Phaseolus vulgaris* O'TOOLE *et al.* [1977] found highest CO_2 uptake and transpiration rates at a leaf water potential of –3 bar. At a potential as low as –9 bar, CO_2 absorption and transpiration were almost inhibited.

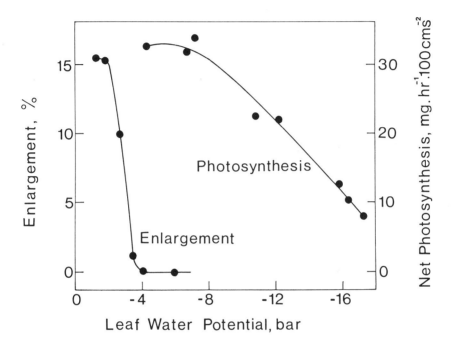

Fig.4.12 Effect of leaf water potential on leaf enlargement and net photosynthesis in sunflowers (after BOYER [1970]).

When water stress is more severe there is a reduction in the uptake of CO_2. Moreover, photophosphorylation and photolysis are also impaired (SANTARIUS [1967]). BREVEDAN and HODGES [1973] found that maize grown under field conditions with water stress resulting in a water potential of –17 to –22 bar showed an inhibited CO_2 assimilation rate. A reduction in translocation rate of photosynthates from the leaves to other plant parts was also observed. These authors claim that translocation of photosynthates responds more sensitively to water stress than to photosynthesis. Low plant water potentials may also reduce respiration (BELL *et al.* [1971]).

223

4.4.7 Proline accumulation

When water stress is more pronounced free amino acids and particularly proline can accumulate in plant tissues. The results of SINGH et al. [1973] suggest that this accumulation of proline is linked with the ability of the plant tissue to survive under conditions of water stress. Table 4.6 shows the proline contents and leaf survival percentage of 5 different cultivars of barley subjected to 73 hours of osmotic stress. The barley plants which were first grown in nutrient solution were transferred to a solution of osmotic potential –20 bar. The increase in proline levels was dramatic, rising from about 1 mg/g dry weight to the values shown in Table 4.6. The interesting point from these results is that there was no significant difference between cultivars in leaf water potential, dehydrogenase activity or leaf chlorophyll content during the period of osmotic stress. However, there was a positive correlation between the level of proline accumulation and leaf survival. In field conditions too, drought tolerant barley cultivars have been shown to accumulate higher proline contents. One possible reason to account for the accumulation is that proline is synthesized to depress the internal osmotic potential and so maintain a positive gradient for water uptake under the water stress conditions. This osmotic adjustment may well be an adaptive mechanism by which the plant is able to withstand water stress conditions.

Table 4.6 Percentage leaf area survival and proline contents of leaves from different cultivars of young barley plants subject to 73 hours osmotic stress (SINGH et al. [1973])

Variety	Proline (mg/g dry wt.)	Leaf survival (%)
Prior	18.5	54
Ketch	15.6	41
CI 3576	13.5	36
CI 5611	11.3	27
Asahi-2	7.5	16

4.4.8 Water stress development in plants

From the above discussion it is clear that water stress can bring about very different physiological effects. In an excellent review on plant response to water stress HSIAO [1973] has suggested the following very tentative scheme of the development of these effects in tissues with water stress. The first change suggested is the reduction in shoot and leaf growth brought about by a reduced water potential. This is followed very closely by a decrease in cell wall and protein synthesis in tissues with high growth potential. With a further decrease in water potential, cell division may decline and the levels of some enzymes such as nitrate reductase decrease. Stomata may then close with a consequent reduction in transpiration and CO_2 assimilation. At this stage, secondary and tertiary changes begin to develop and other features associated with water stress occur such as a decline in respiration and translocation of photosynthates. Accumulations of sugars and proline are observed and CO_2 assimilation falls to a very low level. These physiological effects are accompanied by anatomical changes including cavitation of the xylem, and blockage by vapour space. Older leaves become senescent and are shed as the process continues, and finally the plant dies.

4.5 Practical Aspects of Water Stress

4.5.1 Water potential values and irrigation

When the water availability in the soil is poor and transpiration is high, a negative water balance results, *i.e.* the loss of water by the plant is greater than its uptake (Ψ falls – it becomes more negative). If the loss becomes excessive the plants at first wilt and water stress inhibits growth.

Obviously the most usual way of balancing a water deficit and avoiding water stress is by irrigation. According to PADURARIU *et al.* [1969] the leaf water potential for maize during the main growing period should not be lower than about –6 to –7 bar. The respective value for sugar beet is –5, showing that the latter crop responds more sensitively to water stress. For most crop species optimum soil moisture conditions are in a range of –0.2 to –0.5 bar (~pF 2.3 to 2.7). Insufficient water supply has a tremendous impact on the growth of most crop species (see Figure 5.13 on p. 271).

The water requirement of crops differs between growth stages. Maize, for example, is particularly sensitive to water stress at the tasseling stage. Irrigation at this growing stage has a substantial effect on grain yield under conditions where soil water supply is poor. An example of this kind is shown in Table 4.7. Irrigation of 150 mm water in July-August raised grain yields considerably (BUCHNER and STURM [1971]). Increasing the rate of nitrogen application had a similar effect provided that it was accompanied by irrigation. In the treatment without irrigation, nitrogen application depressed grain yield.

Table 4.7 Interactions between N application and irrigation and the effect on the grain yield of maize (BUCHNER and STURM [1971])

Rate of N appl. kg N/ha	grain yield, tonnes/ha			
	1969		1970	
	without	with irrigation	without	with irrigation
60	5.1	8.8	3.4	6.1
120	3.8	9.7	3.7	8.7
120 + 60	3.3	9.6	2.3	10.0

SIONIT et al. [1980] reported that wheat was especially sensitive to water stress during anthesis. At this period of development the plants were less capable of adjusting to low water availability in the soil than at an earlier growth stage. Water stress at anthesis lead to a reduction in the number of ears and number of grains per ear and was thus detrimental to grain yield.

4.5.2 Antitranspirants

Most crop plants have a high water demand. Water loss by transpiration by far exceeds the amount of water required for transport processes and other physiological needs. As the plants need open stomata in order to absorb CO_2, however, water loss due to stomatal transpiration seems unavoidable. Under more humid climatic conditions this problem is not of great importance as water deficits are not common, particularly under conditions where the soil water capacity is high (see page 47). Under arid conditions, however, water stress of crop plants is of major significance. Here efforts have been made to achieve partial closure of stomata by chemicals or so-called antitranspirants. These compounds are used in order to depress water consumption without affecting CO_2 assimilation to any major extent (GALE and HAGAN [1966]). WAGGONER and ZELITCH [1965] have reported that the monomethyl ester of decenyl succinic acid is particularly effective in stomatal closure. FULTON [1967] used this chemical and found the relationship between the concentration of the compound and the width of stomata openings as listed in Table 4.8. In a field experiment with potatoes, however, the compound had no effect on the evaporation regime. More work is needed for the successful utilization of these compounds in agriculture.

Table 4.8 Relationship between stomatal aperture and concentration of the antitranspirant applied (FULTON [1967])

Concentration (M)	Width (μm)
0	8.9
10^{-5}	8.2
10^{-4}	4.4
10^{-3}	3.9
10^{-2}	2.9

Another method of reducing transpiration has been proposed by GALE and HAGAN [1966]. The principle of this technique is to increase the light reflection by the leaves and thus decrease leaf temperature. This is achieved by spraying the leaves with kaolinite which increases reflectivity. Using this method ABOU-KHALED et al. [1970] were successful in reducing the transpiration rate of C-4 species without affecting CO_2 assimilation. MORESHET et al. [1977], however, in spraying kaolinite found a significant decrease in CO_2 uptake and the leaves senesced at an earlier stage of growth.

4.5.3 Transpiration coefficient

For practical purposes the use of the transpiration coefficient provides a valuable means of expressing the efficiency by which consumed water is used for crop production. The transpiration coefficient may be defined as the amount of water in litres used for the production of 1 kg plant dry matter. Table 4.9 shows that the transpiration coefficients differ markedly between crops (SHANTZ, quoted by RÖMER and SCHEFFER [1959]) and are higher for C-3 crops than for C-4 crops (see page 159). Per unit dry matter production lucerne therefore consumes more water than maize and sorghum. The transpiration coefficients are not absolute values and depend on climate and soil conditions as well as on the nutrition of the crop. Under conditions of low relative air humidity and abundant water supply, the transpiration coefficients tend to be higher. The reverse is true where water availability in the soil is poor and the relative air humidity is high. When plants are not well supplied with nutrients, transpiration coefficients tend to be higher. This means that when nutrition is inadequate, water is less efficiently utilized for crop production. This relationship results from the fact that under nutrient stress conditions dry matter production is more affected than water consumption. Table 4.10 shows this relationship from results of a field experiment of MITSCHERLICH and BEUTELSPACHER [1938] with potatoes. Potassium in particular has a beneficial effect on water utilization

Table 4.9 Transpiration coefficients of various crop plants (SHANTZ, quoted by ROEMER and SCHEFFER [1959])

Sorghum	277	Oats	583
Maize	349	Spring rye	634
Sugar beet	443	Red clover	698
Spring wheat	491	Flax	783
Barley	527	Lucerne	844
Potatoes	575		

as has been shown by BLANCHET et al. [1962] and by LINSER and HERWIG [1968]. Potassium depresses the osmotic potential (ψ_s) of plant cells and hence prevents water loss from the plant.

Table 4.10 Yield and transpiration coefficient of potatoes in relation to fertilization (MITSCHERLICH and BEUTELSPACHER [1938])

Fertilization	Yield (kg DM/m^2)	Transpiration (coefficient)
Without	450	693
Mineral	928	357
Stable manure	741	428
Mineral + stable manure	1049	320

4.6   Salinity

4.6.1   General

Soil salinity is a worldwide problem in crop production. In arid and semi-arid regions in particular soils development is characterized by high salt levels in the soil profile (see page 62). Depending on specific conditions one or more of a number of ions (Na$^+$, Cl$^-$, HCO$_3^-$, Mg^{2+}, SO$_4^{2-}$ and borate) may be present within the root range in high concentrations thus affecting crop growth.

In general the presence of soluble salts in the nutrient medium can affect plant growth in two ways. In the first place high concentrations of specific ions can be toxic and induce physiological disorders (*e.g.* Na$^+$, borate). Secondly, soluble salts depress the water potential of the nutrient medium and hence restrict the water uptake by plant roots. This second effect is less important as, to some extent, it is counterbalanced, because the higher salt concentration in the nutrient medium leads to an increase in the rate of ion uptake. This lowers the water potential in the plant roots and stimulates water uptake, which raises cell turgor and the turgidity of plant tissues. This means of maintaining a positive water balance is known as osmotic adjustment. Table 4.11 shows an example of this kind of behaviour from the data of LAGERWERFF and EAGLE [1961]. Increasing levels of KCl were supplied to bean plants growing in a saline (NaCl) medium. Higher concentrations of KCl increased plant growth as well as the levels of K and Cl and water contents of the leaves. The osmotic potential of the leaves fell by more than 3 bar as a consequence of the increased K and Cl levels. Similar osmotic adjustment effects have been observed by BERNSTEIN [1963] and MEIRI and POLJAKOFF-MAYBER [1969]. Potassium and Cl$^-$ are particularly effective in osmotic adjustment as these ion species are taken up very rapidly and can be accumulated in high concentrations in plants. For this reason, chloride salinity may be frequently less detrimental than sulphate salinity, provided that isoosmotic concentrations are compared (HENCKEL and SOLOVYOV [1968]) and that Cl⁻ does not have a direct toxic effect on the plant. The contribution of Na to osmotic adjustment of plant cells varies considerably as the uptake potential and distribution of this element within plants is very much dependent on individual plant species (see page 425).

Table 4.11 Effect of an increasing supply of KCl on the yield, K and Cl content in the leaves, and the osmotic potential of the leaf sap of *Phaseolus vulgaris* grown in a saline medium (LAGERWERFF and EAGLE [1961])

KCl-concentration me/l	FW g	K content me/g DM	Cl content me/g DM	osmotic potential (ψ_s)bars
3.5	534	1.45	1.91	–11.7
8.8	544	1.66	2.06	–12.9
14.1	562	1.92	2.27	–15.3

Plants suffering from salt stress are typically stunted with small and dull bluish-green leaves. Wilting symptoms are seldom observed (BERNSTEIN and HAYWARD [1958]). This is in complete contrast to plants suffering directly from water stress. The higher turgor of salt stressed plants as already described depends on osmotic adjustment brought about by a higher rate of ion uptake. The adequate turgor of plants growing in saline conditions implies that the detrimental effect of soluble salts on plant growth results from salt induced physiological dissorders rather than osmotic effects *per se*. This has been confirmed experimentally in culture solution studies. When mannitol or carbowax (polyethylene glycol MW approx. 20 000) are added to a culture solution the water potential is depressed. The same effect is observed on the addition of inorganic salts. It is thus possible to compare plant growth from solutions of the same low water potential with and without the effects of salts. Such experiments have shown very clearly that plant growth is poorer in the presence of high salt concentrations than with an isoosmotic solution of carbowax (LAGERWERFF and EAGLE [1961]).

4.6.2 Salt toxicity

Salinity may affect different metabolic processes, such as CO_2 assimilation, protein synthesis, respiration or phytohormone turnover. However, the question of whether these are direct effects, is often difficult to answer. Toxicity begins with an imbalance of ions in the plant tissue, often with a large excess of Na⁺. The plant can cope to some degree with this excess Na⁺ by excluding its uptake or secreting it into vacuoles (RAINS [1972]). These regulatory processes require an additional amount of energy and for this reason, plants subjected to salinity conditions show higher respiration rates (LÜTTGE et al. [1971]) and deplete storage carbohydrates to a greater extent than plants grown under non saline conditions. Plants suffering from salinity are also poor in energy status. This relationship between energy supply and salinity has been demonstrated by CHIMIKLIS and KARLANDER [1973] for *Chlorella* and by HELAL and MENGEL [1981] for *Vicia faba*. In both cases it was shown that the toxic effect of NaCl salinity was less severe when the plants were grown under high light intensity as compared to low light intensity. Under high light intensity conditions the plants were able to maintain balanced cation concentrations in the plant organs in contrast to low light intensity, where an excess of Na^+ and low K^+ concentrations were found. This imbalanced ionic status was associated with impaired CO_2 assimilation and a drastic reduction in lipid turnover (HELAL and MENGEL [1981]).

Lack of energy as a consequence of salinity may affect various energy requiring processes such as CO_2 assimilation, protein synthesis or the assimilation of inorganic N (HELAL and MENGEL [1979]). Saline conditions restrict the synthesis of cytokinins in the roots and their translocation to upper plant parts can also be inhibited (MEIRI-SHALHEVET [1973]). The synthesis of abscisic acid on the other hand is promoted by salinity (MIZRAHI et al. [1970]).

Under severe salinity stress, the cytoplasm can be overloaded with Na^+ which can affect enzymes and organelles present in the cytoplasm. Thus HECHT-BUCHHOLZ et al. [1974] reported that isolated chloroplasts of *Phaseolus vulgaris* subjected to a 25-mM solution of NaCl were found to suffer a considerable loss in fine structure (Plate 4.5). The damage was accompanied by an exchange of K^+ from the chloroplasts for Na^+ from the solution. Interestingly chloroplasts of *Beta vulgaris* was not affected by this same procedure and the K/Na exchange did not occur. As *Phaseolus* is known to be a salt-sensitive species, whereas *Beta* is a rather salt-tolerant plant, it is tempting to speculate that salt tolerance in some way relates to the stability of chloroplasts to high Na concentrations. More recently, MARSCHNER and POSSINGHAM [1975] have reported that in sugar beet and spinach, both natrophilic species, high Na levels in the outer medium enhance cell expansion and growth, although chlorophyll synthesis is impaired.

4.6.3 Salt tolerance

Marked differences in salt tolerance occur between plant species. This is roughly shown in Figure 4.13 from a useful review paper of GREENWAY and MUNNS [1980]. Line 1 in the Figure shows the growth response of the halophyte

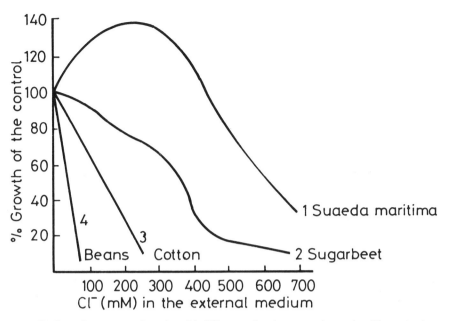

Fig.4.13 Growth response of species with different salt tolerance to increasing Cl⁻ concentrations in the external medium (modified after GREENWAY and MUNNS 1980).

Suaeda maritima in relation to the Cl⁻ concentration denoted on the x-axis. It is obvious that maximum growth was obtained at concentrations as high as 200 to 300 mM Cl⁻. Line 2 shows the growth response of sugar beet, a species which is related to the halophytes; line 3 represents cotton, a non halophytic but salt tolerant species and line 4 represents beans recognized as a salt sensitive plant. Halophytes are able to cope with high electrolyte concentrations in the nutrient medium due to their capability of taking up large amounts of ions and sequestering them into the vacuoles, where they contribute to the osmotic potential. Halophytes even need an excess of salts for maximum growth and for attaining osmotic potentials as high as –20 to –50 bar (FLOWERS *et al.* [1977]). The main mechanism on which the salt tolerance in these species depends is the compartmentation of inorganic ions. Thus according to KYLIN and QUATRANO [1975] the active secretion of Na⁺ into the vacuole protects the cytoplasm against too high a concentration of Na⁺.

    Non halophytic species (glycophytes) may possess the same mechanism to a less well developed degree, but there are other species which prevent excess salt uptake and thus protect the cells against too high ion concentrations. In such species, however, a lack of solutes may result in poor turgor, so that water deficiency rather than salt toxicity may be the growth limiting factor (GREENWAY

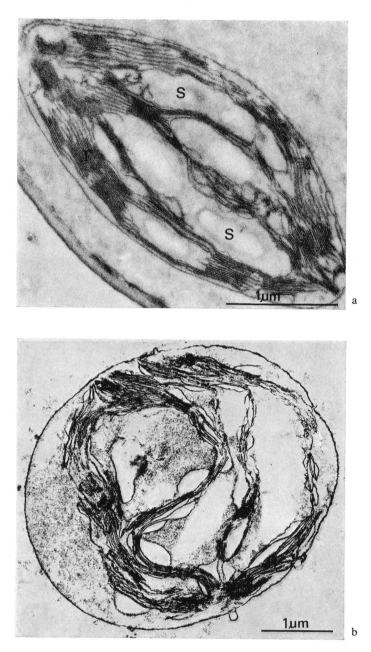

Plate 4.5 Chloroplasts of *Phaseolus vulgaris*. a) normal; b) damaged by 25 me/l NaCl. The intact chloroplast (a) shows starch inclusions (S) and thylakoids (T). (Photo: Mɪx)

and MUNNS [1980]). Salt tolerance may also be brought about by reabsorption of Na+ from the xylem vessels in the basal part of the roots. Such an example has been described for two soya bean cultivars by LÄUCHLI [1975]. A striking example of salt tolerance of closely related plant species was reported by RUSH and EPSTEIN [1976] for tomato. The salt tolerant ecotype *Lycopersicon chees-manii* was able to survive in a full strength sea water nutrient solution whereas *Lycopersicon esculentum* was not able to withstand more than 50% of sea water. The salt tolerant ecotype accumulated large concentrations of Na+ in the leaves (up to 7% in the dry matter). Salt accumulation in leaves, however, is not a reliable indicator of salt tolerance. This is evident from the work of LESSANI and MARSCHNER [1978] who reported similar high contents of (Na + K) in the salt sensitive pepper plant and the salt tolerant sugar beet. It is rather the ability to secrete the excess of ions into the vacuole than the overall salt content of leaves which plays a role in salt tolerance. If high levels of salts remain in the leaf free space they may be detrimental to the water status of the cell. On the other hand if high salt levels are present in the cytoplasm they may affect enzyme activity. Damage resulting from excess salt levels occurs particularly in young expanded leaves, where too low a turgor affects plant growth (GREENWAY and MUNNS [1980]).

It is still an open question as to what extent organic solutes can protect the cytoplasm from the detrimental effect of high salt levels. The high concentrations of organic solutes needed for a protective effect makes such a function doubt-ful. GREENWAY and MUNNS [1980] have suggested, however, that glycine-betaine plays such an adaptive role in some halophytes. The function of proline in this role is dubious. According to GREENWAY and MUNNS [1980], this reason is not considered as a typical solute of salt tolerance. In halophytes organic solutes are essential osmotica of the cytoplasm which have to balance the low osmotic potential (= high concentration of solutes) of the vacuole (FLOWERS *et al.* [1977]). These organic solutes of the cytoplasm comprise amino acids, betaines, sugars, and organic acids. As they are not toxic to the cytoplasm they are termed 'compatible solutes'.

4.6.4 Crop production

In crop production studies soil salinity is measured as the electrical conduc-tivity of a water saturated soil extract. The conductivity, expressed in mmhos/cm, is higher the more concentrated the ionic composition of the ex-tract. Table 4.12 gives a survey showing the degree of salinity in terms of electri-cal conductivity (EC) in relation to crop species (BERNSTEIN [1970]). Considerable differences occur between crop species and cultivars in relation to salt tolerance. Generally, most fruit crops are more sensitive to salinity than are field, forage or vegetable crops. Table 4.13 shows the response of various field crops to salinity decreasing from the top of the table downwards (BERNSTEIN [1970]). The detrimental effects of salinity are also often dependent on the stage of plant growth. For many species the seedling stage is very sensitive to salinity. In most cereal crops grain yields are less affected than straw yields. For rice, however, the reverse is true, as this crop is particularly sensitive at the flowering and seed setting stage. Salinity may also affect crop quality. In sugar beet, for example, very low levels of sugar may result.

Table 4.12 Crop response to salinity (BERNSTEIN [1970])

Salinity (EC mmhos./cm at 25° C)	Crop responses
0 to 2	Salinity effects mostly negligible
2 to 4	Yields of very sensitive crops may be restricted
4 to 8	Yields of many crops restricted
8 to 16	Only tolerant crops yield satisfactorily
Above 16	Only a few very tolerant crops yield satisfactorily

Table 4.13 Salt tolerance of various field crops as conductivity at which the yield is reduced by 25% (data of BERNSTEIN [1970])

	EC		EC
Barley	15.8	Rice (paddy)	6.2
Sugar beet	13.0	Maize	6.2
Cotton	12.0	Sesbania	5.8
Safflower	11.3	Broadbean *(Vicia)*	5.0
Wheat	10.0	Flax	4.8
Sorghum	9.0	Beans *(Phaseolus)*	2.5
Soybean	7.2		

EPSTEIN and co-workers have suggested that there is a very great need to breed economic crops which are salt tolerant. RUSH and EPSTEIN [1976] argue that by generating strains of crops capable of coping with salinity, that, 'what is now a problem could become a vast opportunity for crop production by tapping the immense wealth of water and mineral nutrients of the oceans without the energy-costly process of industrial desalination'. In view of the enormous expanses of saline soils and the necessary increase in crop production to meet the world's expanding population such a breeding programme may well prove to be of extreme importance.

General Reading

ADDISCOTT, T.M.: Potassium in relation to transport of carbohydrate and ions in plants, p. 175–190. In: Potassium Research and Agricultural Production, 10th Congr. Intern. Potash Institute, Berne, 1974

ARANOFF, S., DAINTY, J., GORHAM, P.R., SRIVASTAVA, L.M. and SWANSON, C.A.: Phloem Transport. Plenum Press 1975

EPSTEIN, E.: Mineral Nutrition of Plants: Principles and Perspectives. John Wiley and Sons, Inc., New York, London, Sydney, Toronto, 1972

ESCHRICH, W.: Biochemistry and fine structure of phloem in relation to transport. Ann. Rev. Plant Physiol. *21*, 193–214 (1970)

FLOWERS, T.J., TROKE, P.F. and YEO, A.R.: The mechanism of salt tolerance in halophytes. Ann. Rev. Plant Physiol. *28*, 89–121 (1977)

GREENWAY, H. and MUNNS, R.: Mechanism of salt tolerance in nonhalophytes. Ann. Rev. Plant Physiol. *31*, 149–190 (1980)

HEBER, U. and HELDT, H.W.: The chloroplast envelope: structure, function and role in leaf metabolism. Ann. Rev. Plant Physiol. *32*, 139–168 (1981)

HSIAO, T.C.: Plant responses to water stress. Ann. Rev. Plant Physiol. *24*, 519–570 (1973)

LÄUCHLI, A.: Translocation of inorganic solutes. Ann. Rev. Plant Physiol. *23*, 197–218 (1972)

MEIDNER, H. and SHERIFF, D.W.: Water and Plants, Blackie, 1976

MILBURN, J.A.: Water Flow in Plants. Longman, London and New York, 1979

MONTEITH, T.L. and WEATHERLEY, P.E.: A discussion on water relations of plants. Phil. Trans. Royal Soc. of London B *273*, 433–613 (1976)

MOORBY, J.: Transport Systems in Plants Longman, London, New York, 1981

NEWMAN, E.J.: Root and soil water relations. In: E.W. Carson, (ed.): The Plant Root and its Environment, p. 362–440, University Press of Virginia, Charlottesville, 1974

PATE, J.S.: Transport and partitioning of nitrogenous solutes. Ann. Rev. Plant Physiol. *31*, 313–340 (1980)

PEEL, A.J.: Transport of Nutrients in Plants. Butterworths, London, 1974

PITMAN, M.G.: Ion transport into the xylem. Ann. Rev. Plant Physiol. *28*, 71–88 (1977)

RAINS, D.W.: Salt transport by plants in relation to salinity. Ann. Rev. Plant Physiol. *23*, 367–388 (1972)

SLAYTER, R.O.: Plant-Water Relationships. Academic Press, London, New York, 1967

SUTCLIFFE, J.F.: Plants and Water, Edward Arnold, London, 1979

TAYLOR, H.H. and KLEPPER, B.: The role of rooting characteristics in the supply of water to plants. Adv. Agron. *30*, 99–128 (1978)

WARDLAW, I.F.: Phloem transport: Physical, chemical or impossible. Ann. Rev. Plant Physiol., *25*, 519–539 (1974)

WARDLAW, I.F. and PASSIOURA, J.B.: Transport and Transfer Processes in Plants. Academic Press 1976

ZIMMERMANN, M.: Translocation of nutrients, p. 383–417. In: M.B.Wilkins, Ed., Physiology of Plant Growth and Development. McGraw Hill, 1969

ZIMMERMANN, M.H. and MILBURN, J.A.: Transport in Plants I, Phloem Transport. Encyclopedia of Plant Physiology, New Series Vol. I. Springer Verlag, Berlin, Heidelberg, New York, 1975

ZIMMERMANN, U.: Physics of turgor- and osmoregulation. Ann. Rev. Plant Physiol. *29*, 121–148 (1978)

Chapter 5

Nutrition and Plant Growth

5.1 Essential Growth Stages and Yield Components

5.1.1 General

The life cycle of a plant starts with germination. In this process the soil embedded seed requires an optimum temperature as well as a supply of water and oxygen, and the presence of favourable endogenous factors within the seed itself. These endogenous factors are mainly phytohormones such as abscisic acid (ABA), gibberellic acid (GA_3) and indole acetic acid (IAA). The germination process is dependent on their synthesis or decomposition. Optimum temperatures for germination promote the synthesis of gibberellins and indole acetic acid, which stimulate germination, but favour the decomposition of the germination inhibitor abscisic acid. The molecular structures of the most important phytohormones are shown in Figure 5.1. Phytohormones are produced in plants in low concentrations, and regulate physiological processes usually moving within the plant from a site of production to a site of action.

Germination begins with the uptake of water. The swollen seed provides the necessary conditions for respiration. With the uptake of oxygen the seed reserves of carbohydrates, fats and sometimes even proteins are oxidized to CO_2 and water, and energy is released in the form of ATP and NADH (see p. 143). This form of energy is essential for growth processes. The storage proteins in seeds are mainly hydrolyzed and the resulting amino acids used for the synthesis of enzyme proteins and nucleic acids. Both are essential components in the formation of meristematic cells and for cell division, the process which initiates growth.

The first plant parts to be developed are the roots. This means that at an early stage of development of the plant, the organ is formed which is responsible for the uptake of water and nutrients. Shoot growth then starts and as soon as the shoot breaks through the soil surface, the synthesis of chlorophyll is induced by light. From this point onwards two further growth factors come into play, namely, light and the CO_2 of the atmosphere. The importance of these two factors increases the more the seed is depleted of its storage material. Young leaves are not self-sufficient. They must be supplied with carbohydrates and

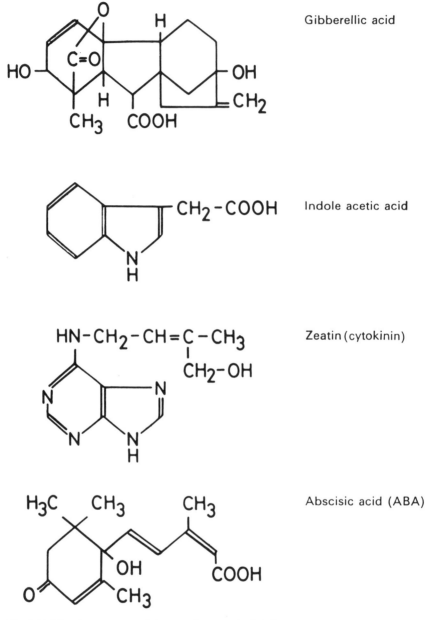

Gibberellic acid

Indole acetic acid

Zeatin (cytokinin)

Abscisic acid (ABA)

Fig.5.1 Molecular structure of the most important phytohormones.

amino acids. In seedlings this supply of organic material is provided by storage compounds present in the seeds. However, with the onset of the vegetative stage which is characterized by the rapid development of leaves stems and roots, the sources of organic material for growth shifts from the seeds to the leaves. Photosynthates assimilated in the older leaves provide the source for younger tissues. Young leaves import carbohydrates until they have reached about one-third of their final size. The net import of amino acids into young leaves continues longer and even until they are fully developed (MILTHORPE and MOORBY [1969]). Mature leaves export about 50% of their photosynthates. The remainder is needed for leaf metabolism itself and is mainly respired. As in the seed, carbohydrates are oxidized to CO_2 and water. In the process the energy released from the carbohydrates is converted to ATP.

The vegetative stage is followed by the reproductive stage. This begins with flower initiation and it is succeeded after pollination or anthesis, by the maturation stage. In determinate plants such as cereals, the vegetative and reproductive stages are quite distinct but for indeterminate plants such as tomatoes they overlap. As plant growth progresses from the vegetative stage to maturity, photosynthates are more and more directed away from younger meristematic tissues towards storage tissues.

5.1.2 Growth rate and nutrient supply

The yield of a crop may be considered in biological as well as agricultural terms. Biological yield has been defined as the total production of plant material by a crop whereas the 'economic yield' or 'commercial yield' (HOLLIDAY [1976]) takes into account only those plant organs for which particular crops are cultivated and harvested. Obvious examples include cotton bolls, cereal seeds, tobacco leaves, potato tubers, etc. For a number of crop plants such as forage crops and some vegetables, the amount of plant material produced above ground during the vegetative growth stage is equivalent to the economic yield. For most crop plants, however, this is not the case and plant development during the vegetative stage controls both the biological and economic yields. This dependence on the vegetative growth stage lies in the fact that during this period green plant tissues are formed which provide photosynthates for seeds or storage tissues. HOLLIDAY [1976] denotes the economic or commercial yield (Y_c) as the product of the total yield (Y_t) and the 'crop index' (I_c). This latter term denotes the proportion of harvested crop, *e.g.* grains, of the total yield: $Y_c = Y_t \cdot I_c$. As a result of plant breeding, modern cultivars often have higher crop indices than older ones. The crop index of modern wheat cultivars is thus about 35 to 40%, whereas older cultivars have indices in the range of 23 to 30%.

Vegetative growth consists mainly of the growth and formation of new leaves, stems and roots. As meristematic tissues have a very active protein metabolism, photosynthates transported to these sites are used predominantly in the synthesis of nucleic acids and proteins. It is for this reason that during the vegetative stage, the N nutrition of the plant to a large extent controls the growth rate of the plant. A high rate of growth only occurs when abundant N is available.

Table 5.1 shows the influence of N nutrition on the growth and contents of organic constituents of ryegrass *(Lolium perenne)* (HEHL and MENGEL [1972]). In the treatment with the low level of N nutrition (0.5 g N/pot), the dry matter yield was very much lower than in the treatment with abundant N supply (2.0 g N/pot). It can also be seen that the plants with the low N supply accumulated carbohydrates, particularly starch and polyfructosans, whereas the content of crude protein was very much depressed. This clearly demonstrates that where N-nutrition is inadequate, photosynthates can only be utilized to a limited extent in the synthesis of organic N compounds. The remainder is stored in the form of starch and polyfructosans (MINOTTI *et al.* [1969]). In this example the carbohydrate contents of the N deficient plants were particularly high even though the samples were taken at the very beginning of vegetative growth.

Table 5.1 Effect of N supply on the yield and organic constituents of young ryegrass plants *(Lolium perenne)* ; (HEHL and MENGEL [1972])

	N supply (g N/pot)	
	0.5	2.0
Yield (g DM/pot)	14.9	26.0
Crude Protein (% DM).......................................	12.3	26.4
Sucrose (% DM)	7.7	6.3
Polyfructosans (% DM)	10.0	1.0
Starch (% DM)	6.1	1.4
Cellulose (% DM)	14.4	17.6

As vegetative growth proceeds the carbohydrate levels of annual plants generally increase. The effect of N nutrition on carbohydrate accumulation is therefore often less marked towards the end of the vegetative period and the onset of flowering. When the level of N nutrition is inadequate, the life cycle of the plants is shortened; plants mature earlier and the resulting economic yield is generally poor. Early senescence under N-deficiency conditions does not result from a lack of N for protein synthesis. It is induced by a depression in cytokinin synthesis (MICHAEL and BERINGER [1980]). Amino acids are required for the synthesis of cytokinins so that cytokinin metabolism is very closely related to N-nutrition (WAGNER and MICHAEL [1971]).

The example presented above demonstrates that for optimum growth of plants there must be a balance between the rate of photosynthate production and the rate of N assimilation. Under conditions where high photosynthetic activity can occur (high light intensity, optimum temperature, absence of water stress), the level of N nutrition must also be high and *vice versa*. In plant species in which the rate of CO_2 fixation is high and particularly species which assimilate CO_2 *via* the C_4 pathway the N demand is considerable when growth conditions are optimum (see Figure on p. 271).

The level of N-nutrition required for optimum growth during the vegetative period must also be balanced by the presence of other plant nutrients in adequate amounts. The synthesis of organic N compounds depends on a number of inorganic ions, including Mg^{2+} for the formation of chlorophyll, and phosphate for the synthesis of nucleic acids. Both the uptake of nitrate, and especially its assimilation into protein, are also considerably influenced by plant K status. In general it may be concluded that mineral nutrient requirement during the

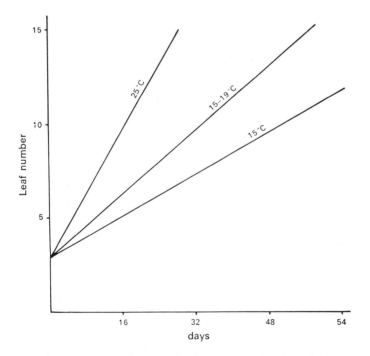

Fig.5.2 Effect of temperature on the rate of leaf appearance of maize (after BROUWER *et al.* [1973]).

241

vegetative growth period is primarily determined by the rate of CO_2 assimilation. If the rate of photosynthate production is high, the amounts of inorganic nutrients must also be correspondingly high in order to convert the photo-synthates into the numerous metabolites needed for vegetative growth.

Growth and development at this early stage are very much dependent on temperature. BROUWER et al. [1973] reported that the rate of leaf appearance of young maize plants was mainly controlled by temperature, whereas light intensi-ty had hardly any effect. The essential results of this experiment are presented in Figure 5.2. Temperature increases tend to stimulate growth which in turn results in a dilution of carbohydrates and chlorophyll. This occurs particularly when the light intensity is low (cloudy weather). Very often under these conditions large pale-green leaves with long stems are produced (WARREN-WILSON [1969]). On the other hand, high light intensity and lower temperatures especially during the night, result in smaller, more fungal disease resistant plants with higher con-tents of chlorophyll and carbohydrates.

5.1.3 Grain crops

Grain yield depends on three main yield components: number of ears per ha, number of grains per ear and the single grain weight. The number of ears per ha in a cereal crop depends on seed density and tillering capability. Tillering capability is genetically controlled, but is also much dependent on environmental factors. Short day conditions associated with high light in-tensities, low temperatures and ample nitrogen supply favour tillering (EVANS et al. [1975]). These environmental conditions considerably influence phyto-hormone activity. Long day conditions and high temperatures are associated with a high auxin (IAA) production in the apex of the young primary cereal shoot (MICHAEL and BERINGER [1980]). IAA or related compounds induce the production of ethylene, which inhibits the growth of lateral buds and thus the formation of tillers. This action of auxin produced in the apex restricting the development of lateral buds is called 'apical dominance' and occurs very strongly in monoculm varieties. Cytokinins function in a converse manner to auxins as they promote the growth of buds and tillers (BRUINSMA [1979]). Cytokinins are purine or pyrimidine derivatives, both of which are N contain-ing ring structures and are synthesized from amino acids. The stimulating effect of N nutrition on tillering is thus probably due to the effect of N on cytokinin synthesis. Unter the climatic conditions of Central Europe, maximum grain yields of wheat (6 to 7 tonnes grain/ha) are obtained, when the number of ears is about 500 to 600/m^2. Such a high plant density is not always desirable. In more arid climates, a lower density often produces higher grain yields, as lower plant densities do not require so much water. In critical growing phases such as heading and flowering, the possibility of water stress is thus reduced. According to DAY and INTALAP [1970] water stress at heading results in a reduction in the number of ears per unit area and also in grains per ear. Water stress during flowering accelerates the maturation process thus leading to smaller grains and lower grain yields. This observation is consistent with the findings of PELTON [1969] made under the arid conditions of South-Western Saskatchewan in the U.S.A., that lower plant densities were associated with longer ears, larger grains and thus higher grain yields of wheat.

Several investigators have shown that nutrient supply exerts a considerable influence on the yield components of cereals. FORSTER [1973] reported that interrupting K nutrition during the tillering stage decreased the number of ears and the number of grains per ear of wheat and oats. Similar observations were made by CHAPMAN and KEAY [1971]. The importance of adequate N-nutrition at an early growth stage in determining the number of ears per unit area, has also been reported by STOY [1972].

The number of grains produced per ear is not only affected by nutrition but also by other environmental factors. MICHAEL and BERINGER [1980] suggest that spikelet formation in the ears is controlled by a type of 'apical dominance' or more precisely 'medial dominance', as the spikelets located in the middle of the ear develop more strongly. These middle spikelets are believed to suppress to some extent the formation and development of other spikelets. The number of grains per ear is also related to the action of gibberellins. Semi-dwarf mutants of cereals are characterized by a blocking of gibberellin function, which is associated with a reduction in culm length and a higher number of grains per ear (GALE [1978]). The finding that chlorocholine chloride (CCC), an inhibitor of gibberellin synthesis, has the same effect, adds support to the idea that high levels of gibberellins can reduce the number of grains per ear. The longer the period of ear formation the more spikelets can be developed and the greater is the chance of producing long ears containing a large number of grains (EVANS et al. [1975]). However, as the duration of ear development is inversely related to the duration of grain filling, a high number of grains per ear is often associated with a low single grain weight. This is shown in Table 5.2 in which some yield components of an old and a modern cultivar of spring wheat are compared (HAEDER et al. [1977]). Grains are developed within the spikelets which are initiated at an early stage in cereal growth. During subsequent development, a considerable proportion of spikelets degenerate. In the case of rice, degeneration can account for as many as 50% of the original number of spikelets (YOSHIDA [1972]). Degeneration is promoted when N-nutrition is inadequate and by low light intensity or low temperatures at the time of spikelet development (FUCHS [1975]). These environmental factors can thus considerably affect grain formation. Plate 5.1 shows a developing ear of barley at the 6th leaf stage.

Table 5.2 Grain yield and yield criteria of an old and a modern wheat cultivar (HAEDER et al. [1977])

	Hohenheimer Franken old cv	Kolibri modern cv
Duration from anthesis until maturation, day ..	56	47
Grain yield, g/ear............................	1.12	1.12
Single grain weight, mg	48.2[++])	44.2
No. of grains/ear	23[++])	28
Crop index, %	29.3[+++])	37.7
Significant difference[++]) 1%, [+++]) 0.1% level		

The third important component of cereal yield, the grain size or single grain weight, is genetically controlled as well as depending on the environmental factors which influence the process of grain filling during maturation. In the filling process the ears or grains act as a physiological sink. The source for this sink is provided by the leaves and to a much lesser extent by hulls and awns. After the onset of flowering, photosynthates are used more and more for the grain filling process. This is shown in Figure 5.3 in which the distribution of photosynthates in a wheat plant is shown for the various stages from flowering until maturation. The arrows indicate the direction in which the photosynthates are translocated. The plant parts shown in black are the most important for assimilation. In the later stage, the flag leaf in particular provides photosynthates for grain filling (EVANS and RAWSON [1970]). In awned wheat varieties photosynthates from the flag leaf contribute to about 70% of the total grain filling, whereas in varieties without awns about 80% may originate from this source. The remainder of assimilates mainly comes from the ear itself. Not all the photosynthates required for grain filling are photosynthesized during the reproductive period (after flowering). Some of the carbohydrates are synthesized before flowering and stored in stems and leaves during the vegetative growth stage. The proportion of stored assimilates used in grain filling can vary from 0 to 40% for rice, 5 to 10% for wheat, 12 to 15% for maize and be in the region of 20% for barley (YOSHIDA [1972]). These values depend to a large extent on photosynthetic activity after flowering. If for some reason this is low, as for example, because of water stress or nutrient deficiency, the assimilates synthesized before flowering contribute to a great extent in the grain filling process and vice versa.

An intensive rate of grain filling is obtained if the level of N-nutrition is high during the grain filling period and the K status of the plant is at an optimum lev-

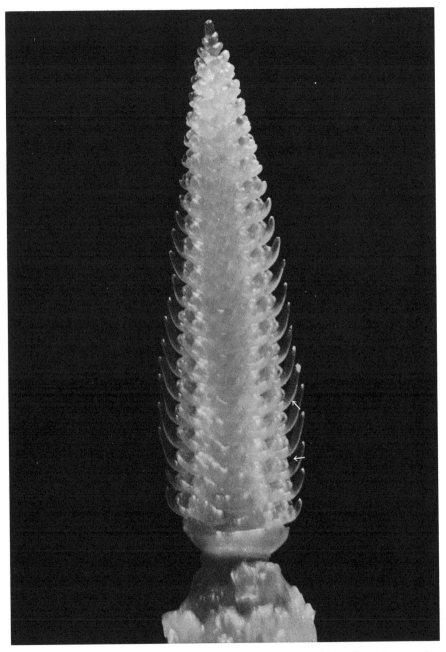

Plate 5.1 Young developing ear of barley in the 6th leaf stage at which spikelet degeneration frequently occurs. The arrows indicate an awn primordia (above) and a spikelet primordia (below). (Photo: RUCKENBAUER)

245

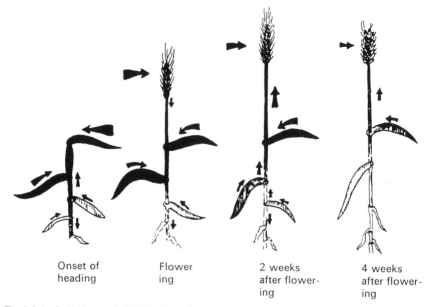

| Onset of heading | Flowering | 2 weeks after flowering | 4 weeks after flowering |

Fig.5.3 Assimilation and distribution of photosynthates at different stages in growth (after STOY).

el (MENGEL and HAEDER [1974]). In plants well supplied with N, senescence of the flag leaf is delayed and respiration losses are low (ORLOVIUS and HÖFNER [1976]). Potassium has a similar effect, but in addition increases the CO_2 assimilation rate (WATANABE and YOSHIDA [1970]). Table 5.3 shows the influence of dropping the level of N nutrition during the grain filling period on the grain yield of spring wheat (FORSTER [1973]). The nutrient solution in the control treatment was maintained at a NO_3-concentration of 6.2 mM whereas in the comparative treatment it was lowered to 1.2 mM NO_3^-. This lower level of N-nutrition during the grain filling period resulted in a yield reduction, which

Table 5.3 Effect of N supply in the grain filling stage on the yield of spring wheat (FORSTER [1973])

mM NO_3^-/l nutrient sol.	grain yield g/16 plants	TGW	crude protein %
6.2	51.4 (100)	38.2 (100)	20.6 (100)
1.2	46.6 (91)	35.4 (92)	18.9 (92)

1000 grains of the '6.2' treatment contained $\rightarrow$ 7.9 g Cr. Pr.
1000 grains of the '1.2' treatment contained $\rightarrow$ 6.7 g Cr. Pr.
Difference $\rightarrow$ 1.2 g

was largely accounted for by the smaller grains, obtained in this treatment. The content of crude protein in the grain was also lowered. The yield reduction, however, cannot be explained solely by the lower crude protein content in the grains. This amounted only to 1.2 g per 1000 grains, whereas the yield depression (difference between the thousand grain weights) was 2.8 g per 1000 grains.

Most usually, grain filling is not primarily limited by photosynthate supply to developing grains (JENNER and RATJEN [1975], MENGEL and HAEDER [1976]). It is the 'sink' and not the 'source' that is the controlling influence in grain filling. MICHAEL and BERINGER [1980] hold the view that this influence is to a large extent that of phytohormone activity. Recent investigations have shown that during the grain filling process the activities of each of the phytohormones in the grain reaches a maximum value at different times between anthesis and maturation. This is shown in Figure 5.4 from the data of WHEELER [1972] and GOLDBACH and MICHAEL [1976] which have recently been presented by MICHAEL and BERINGER [1980]. From this Figure it is clear that cytokinins reach a peak at about 1 week after anthesis. Cytokinins are believed to control the formation of grain endosperm cells and thus have a marked influence on grain size. This view is consistent with findings of AUFHAMMER and SOLANSKY [1976] with spring wheat and HERZOG and GEISLER [1977] with spring barley, that cytokinin application increased grain yield exclusively by increasing single grain weight. The peaks of gibberellic acid (GA) and indole acetic acid (IAA) occur about 4 and 5 weeks respectively after anthesis. These two types of phytohormones also probably promote grain growth, while abscisic acid (ABA) has the reverse effect. As can be seen from Figure 5.4 the ABA peak coincides with the peak of grain fresh weight. This finding may be interpreted as an inducing effect of ABA in the maturation process which is in accordance with the well known effect of ABA in promoting senescence in other tissues. The content of ABA in grains is also controlled by exogenous factors such as water supply and temperature. High temperatures (about 26°C) are associated with high contents of ABA, a shorter period of grain filling, and thus lower single grain weights (GOLDBACH and MICHAEL [1976]). Nitrogen deficiency and water stress also induce the synthesis of ABA and thus lead to smaller grains (GOLDBACH et al. [1975]). HAEDER [1980] has recently reported that K nutrition influences the ABA concentration in developing barley grains, highest ABA levels being found in the K deficient plants. Abscisic acid is closely related to the carotenoids. It is mainly produced in chloroplasts and is often translocated via the phloem from the older leaves towards the apex.

In contrast to the other cereals, grain yields of rice can only be improved to a very limited degree by increasing grain size. This is because grain growth is physi-

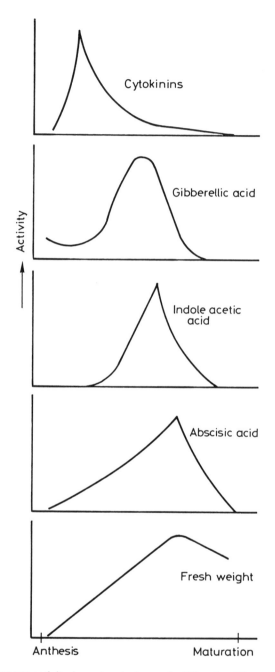

Fig. 5.4 Phytohormone activity in grains during grain filling (modified after MICHAEL and BERINGER [1980]).

cally restricted by the size of the hulls (YOSHIDA [1972]). If the nutrient status of the plant is adequate it is not the rate of photosynthesis (physiological source) that restricts growth, but rather the physiological sink which is the limiting factor in rice yields. The strength of the physiological sink is dependent on the number of grains per unit area (TANAKA [1973]). This number can be raised either by increasing the plant density or by increasing the number of grains per panicle and panicles per plant. The number of panicles per plant is initiated fairly late in tillering, and the number of spikelets per panicle is determined about 10 days before flowering. These critical stages are important for the grain yield of rice and only under optimum nutritional and weather conditions are a high number of fertile spikelets developed. When this occurs a strong sink capacity results which requires an abundant supply of carbohydrates during the grain filling period. Tillering in rice is favoured by low temperature, high light intensity and an abundant N supply. Spikelet degeneration is low under conditions of high light intensity and *vice versa*. Grain filling is improved by adequate O_2 supply to the roots during the grain filling stage (MURATA and MATSUSHIMA [1975]), as O_2 retards root senescence and hence allows the roots to supply the upper plant parts with cytokinins for a longer period. The distribution of available photosynthates is affected by both the number of panicles and number of spikelets per panicle. If the rate of assimilate production is limiting, a high number of panicles per unit area is often accompanied by a reduction in the number of grains per panicle, and an increase in the number of empty hulls.

The rate of growth after flowering also has a bearing on the grain yield of rice. If the maturation period is shortened, as can occur if the crop is deficient of N, a decrease in grain yield results. After flowering, rice especially needs an abundant supply of N and K, and for obtaining top yields in the range of 10 tonnes grain/ha, a late dressing of N and K is often applied (TANAKA [1972]). Table 5.4 shows the model yield components of a high yielding rice culture (TO-

Table 5.4 The model yield components of a high yielding rice cultivar at different climatic regions (TORIYAMA [1974])

Component	Monsoon climate		Moderate climate (Japan)
	Wet season	Dry season	
Panicle number per m^2	250	375	400
Grains per panicle	100	100	80
Total number of grains per m^2	25 000	37 500	32 000
Filled grain in %	85	85	85
1000-grain weight	29.0	29.0	27.0
Computed grain yield (tonnes/ha).........	6.6	9.2	7.5

RIYAMA [1974]). In the wet season where light intensity is low, solar radiation is often the yield limiting factor, and this considerably reduces the number of panicles per unit area.

Maize can be grown under various climatic conditions provided that the temperature is not too low (ARNON [1975]). According to DUNCAN [1975] best grain yields are obtained with high temperatures during the day (30–33°C) and relatively cool nights. As maize is characterized by a high growth rate its nutrient requirements are also high as compared with other cereals. Nutrient uptake and dry matter production of maize are shown in Figure 5.5 (NELSON [1968]). Maize responds favourably to a high level of N supply (BRETELER [1976], SHIMSHI [1969], see also Figure 5.13 on page 271). Maximum grain yields are only obtained if water stress is avoided (DECAU and PUJOL [1973], BUCHNER and STURM [1971], (see also Table 4.7 on p. 225). Under temperate climatic conditions maize can mature too late, if the weather is cool. For this reason late N applications should not be recommended in regions where maturation may be a problem, as late N supply delays senescence. Inadequate K nutrition favours root and stalk rot (*Fusarium* species) (KRÜGER [1976]) and affects grain filling which may lead to deformation of the cobs (see Plate 5.2).

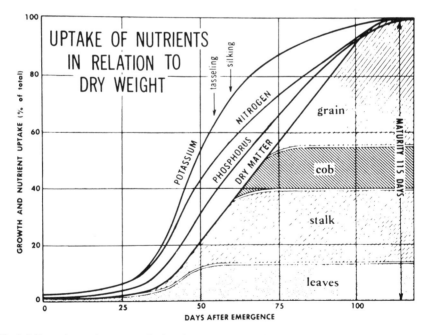

Fig. 5.5 Potassium, nitrogen and phosphorus uptake and dry matter production of maize during the growing season (Iowa State University, after NELSON [1968]).

Plate 5.2 Cob deformation in maize as a consequence of inadequate K^+ nutrition (Photo: *Kali und Salz AG, Bern*)

5.1.4 Root crops

Yield physiology of root crops differs in several respects from that of cereals. The main difference between both groups of crops is the fact that in root crops a marked competition for carbohydrates is often observed between vegetative growth and the filling of storage tissues. For potatoes and similar root crops the yield components are the number of plants per ha, the number of tubers per plant and the tuber size.

Tuber initiation is induced by plant hormones. The question has been discussed recently by KRAUSS [1980]. Abscisic acid promotes initiation whereas gibberellins (GA) have an adverse effect. The ABA/GA ratio thus controls

251

tuber setting, a high ratio favouring and a low ratio restricting tuber initiation. The ABA/GA ratio responds sensitively and rapidly to N-nutrition. A continuous N-supply results in a relatively low ABA/GA ratio with 'regrowth' of the tubers occurring (Plate 5.3a) *i.e.* tuber growth ceasing and one or more stolons being formed on the tuber apex. Interrupting the N supply increases the ABA content dramatically and thus gives rise to tuber initiation. This effect of N is sensitive enough to produce chain-like tubers (Plate 5.3c) and can happen when after a period of 'regrowth' the nitrogen supply is removed and a second phase of tuber initiation is induced. In practice this reversible cessation of tuber growth by a high level cf N nutrition often occurs at a late stage in tuber growth. This causes tuber malformaticns and the production of knobbly tubers (Plate 5.3b). The inducing effect of ABA on tuber initiation has been demonstrated by KRAUSS and MARSCHNER [1976] by treating stolons with ABA. Treatment of the tubers with chlorocholine chloride (CCC), which is known to be an inhibitor of GA synthesis, had a similar effect as ABA on tuber initiation.

The effect of day length on tuber setting can also be explained in terms of phytohormone activity. Long days restrict tuber initiation whereas short days with low night temperatures promote initiation. This is understandable as long day conditions are associated with high GA and low ABA levels in the plant, whereas for short days the reverse is true.

Tuber growth is very closely related to carbohydrate supply. This depends on the intensity of CO_2 assimilation of aerial plant parts and on the translocation rate of photosynthates from the leaves to the tubers. The intensity of assimilation is a function of the leaf area per plant and its ability to bring about CO_2 fixation. The area of leaf per plant primarily depends on plant development during the vegetative growth stage (from germination until flowering). Vigorous growth is obtained if in addition to favourable climatic conditions the plant is adequately supplied with water and nutrients and especially with N. The efficiency of leaves in the transformation of solar energy into ATP, required for the assimilation of photosynthates, depends considerably on the levels of K and P nutrition (WATANABE and YOSHIDA [1970]). The beneficial effect of adequate K nutrition on tuber yield has been shown by HAEDER *et al.* [1973]).

If tuber yields are to be satisfactory, a high rate of CO_2 assimilation during the tuber filling stage is essential. The filling process, however, is not only dependent on the rate of photosynthesis but also on the translocation of photosynthates produced (HAEDER [1975]). In this respect N-nutrition is important, for in root crops unlike cereals, enhanced N nutrition after flowering can stimulate vegetative growth and the initiation of new leaves. Photosynthates can thus be diverted from the filling of storage tissues to promoting vegetative

252

Plate 5.3 Effect of N supply on tuber formation of potatoes (Photo: KRAUSS)
a) Regrowth of tubers following abundant N supply

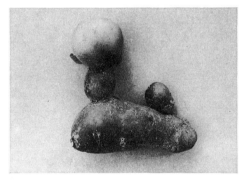

b) Malformations of tubers as a result of disturbances in tuber growth caused by N

c) Secondary growth after alterating N supply

growth. This is demonstrated for potatoes in the data of Table 5.5 obtained by KRAUSS and MARSCHNER [1971]. Tuber growth rate was considerably

Table 5.5 Growth rate of potato tubers in relation to nitrate supply (KRAUSS and MARSCHNER [1971])

Nitrate concentr. me/l	Nitrate uptake me/day	Tuber growth cm³/day
1.5	1.18	3.24
3.5	2.10	4.06
7.0	6.04	0.44
–	–	3.89

depressed by the highest level of NO_3-nutrition (7.0 me NO_3/litre)and N uptake. During the early stages of development root crops should be well supplied with N in order to develop the vegetative plant organs needed for photosynthesis. After flowering, however, the N supply to root crops should decline. This later stage should be characterized primarily by the synthesis of carbohydrates and their translocation to the tubers. Figure 5.6 demonstrates this pattern in potato

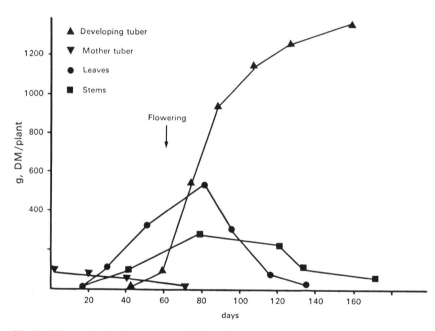

Fig. 5.6 Changes in the dry matter yield of various parts of a potato plant during the growth period.

development. Before flowering, leaf and stem material are predominantly produced. After this time, however, there is a rapid decline in the yield of leaf material and a steep increase in the dry matter production of tubers. Generally tuber initiation starts at flowering, but in modern cultivars tuber setting occurs before flower buds are developed (BOMMER and DAMBROTH [1970]). It has been shown by MOORBY [1968] in experiments using labelled CO_2 that tuber setting influences the rate of photosynthesis. After tuber setting occurs there is an increase in both the rate of CO_2 assimilation and the rate of translocation of carbohydrates from the leaves to the roots and stolons (Table 5.6). This example shows, that photosynthesis not only depends on light intensity, nutrient supply and CO_2 availability, but also on the transport of carbohydrates from the sites of production. If tubers are removed, the translocation of photosynthates is suppressed and the rate of CO_2 assimilation reduced (BURT [1964]).

Root crops of the beet family, differ from potatoes in yield physiology in so far as they are perennials, and are dormant between the vegetative and reproductive stage. Before going into the stage of winter dormancy this type of crop ac-

Table 5.6 CO_2-assimilation and translocation of labelled photosynthates to underground plant parts of potatoes (MOORBY [1968])

	before tuber formation	after setting
Assimilated C in % of applied CO_2	24	58
Translocated C in % of assimilated C	46	72

cumulates carbohydrate in the storage tissue. The economic yield of these crops thus closely relates to this accumulation process. This is the case for sugar beet where the economic yield depends on the number of plants per unit area, the size of roots and their sugar content. The number of plants per unit area, or plant density, will be discussed in more detail below. Root size is dependent to a large extent on nutrient and water supply during the early growth of the crop. Vigorous leaf growth during this stage and the development of a large leaf area per plant is essential for voluminous roots. The more quickly in the growth period the leaves are able to form a complete canopy over the soil, the better are the chances of a good yield. Satisfactory leaf growth depends very much on a high level of N nutrition during the early stages of plant development. In the later phases of plant growth, however, generally beginning at the end of July or in the beginning of August in Central Europe, the level of N supply to the plants should decline. If this does not occur, photosynthates are diverted from filling root tissue with sugar and are utilized to a marked extent for the growth of new leaves. The data of Table 5.7 illustrate this relationship (FORSTER [1970]). In one treatment of this solution culture experiment, the N concentration of the nutrient solution was reduced to one-third of the original concentration at 6 weeks prior to harvesting. This had no major effect on the root yield, but the leaf production was drastically reduced. The reduction in N supply resulted in a considerable increase in the sugar content of roots and hence an improvement of sugar yield by more than 30%. This example demonstrates, that in the final stages of sugar beet development, photosynthesis and the translocation of photosynthates towards the roots should be the main processes and not leaf growth. The same observations have been made in field trials (BRONNER [1974]). The relationship between N nutrition and sugar content in sugar beet is also dependent on phytohormone activity. KURSANOV [1974] reported that abundant N supply during the late stage of sugar beet growth enhances the auxin (IAA) level which in turn, is believed to promote root growth and to delay sucrose storage. A high rate of both CO_2 fixation and translocation are particularly necessary when voluminous roots have been developed, for considerable amounts of sugar are required in the filling process. This explains why high root yields are sometimes accompanied by low sugar contents and also why plants well supplied with K are often high in sugar content (DRAYCOTT et al. [1970]).

Sugar cane is a completely different crop type from sugar beet. There are, however, similar patterns in the production of economic yields. In sugar cane as in sugar beet, the last weeks before harvest should be characterized by synthesis and storage of sugars and not by vegetative growth. The effect of plant nutrients on these processes, especially of N and K, is basically the same as in sugar beet.

Table 5.7   Effect of lowering the N supply in the late stage of growth on the yield and sugar contents of sugar beet (FORSTER [1970])

	Roots g/Plant	Leaves g/Plant	Sugar %	Sugar yield g/Plant
Full N	957	426	16.4	93
⅓ N	955	360	19.0	125

5.1.5   Fruit crops

Yield production of perennials such as grapes and fruit trees is also characterized by a filling period which starts after flowering. In grapes, KOBLET [1969] showed that leaf position is important in the filling process. At the onset of fruit development, leaves in the direct vicinity of the fruits are the main contributors to fruit growth. As fruit development proceeds more and more of the leaves above the grape bunch provide photosynthates for fruit filling. Grape weights and sugar contents are higher the more leaf material is available to supply the grape bunches. A large leaf area is therefore important in grape production. In the early stages of fruit development this appears to be of significance in increasing the weight of grapes. Later its effect is mainly in increasing sugar contents. The filling process also depends on the photosynthetic efficiency of leaves, which is not only controlled by light intensity and temperature but also by mineral nutrition. In order to maintain the leaves in a green state for a prolonged period and thus extend their photosynthetic activity, an additional N dressing is often applied to grapes after flowering. Sucrose along with smaller amounts of fructose, glucose and organic acids are the most important photosynthates translocated from the leaves to the grapes. The predominance of sugar or organic acid synthesis depends considerably on temperature. According to investigations of KLIEWER [1964] with *Vitis vinifera*, the synthesis of organic acids is enhanced at lower temperatures, whereas sugars are synthesized to a much greater extent under warmer conditions. This may partly explain why temperature effects during growth have such a significant bearing on the taste and quality of wine.

The development of other fruit crops such as apples, pears and peaches is basically similar to that described above for grapes. A main factor in fruit yield is the quantity of fruits per tree or plant. Undoubtedly fruit setting is related to phytohormone activity and probably also to nutrition in a more indirect way. This problem is of particular significance for perennial fruit crops, which tend to bear fruits only every second season. This phenomenon, called alternance, is often observed in apple trees. WELLER [1971] reported that in years with a poor fruit yield, apple trees develop abundant fine roots during the late summer and in the beginning of autumn. Improved fruit setting is observed in these trees in the following year. The relationships between root development, phytohormone synthesis and flower setting, are by no means clear. Whether plant nutrients are involved in these relationships has yet to be firmly established.

The development of tomato fruits is in some ways comparable with the growth of grapes. Leaves located in the vicinity of the fruit truss provide the major source of photosynthates in fruit filling (KHAN and SAGAR [1967]). The filling process and also the number of fruits per plant depend on the nutritional status of the plant (FORSTER [1973]).

Plantation crops such as oil palm, coconut, rubber trees, bananas and pineapple are not so strictly bound to seasons. Their growth and yield depend considerably on an ample supply of plant nutrients. FRÉMOND and OUVRIER [1971] reported that the onset of fruiting of coconut palms was considerably earlier provided that the young plants were abundantly supplied with nutrients.

5.1.6 Growth regulators

In recent years growth regulators have been used in agriculture in increasing amounts. These chemicals are not native plant compounds but can influence phytohormone turnover. Table 5.8 shows some examples of the antagonistic, synergistic, and inhibitory behaviour of these growth substances on phytohormone activity.

Table 5.8 Synergists, antagonists and inhibitors of phytohormones

Phyto-hormones	Analogous substances	Synergists	Antagonists & Inhibitors
Auxins	Arylalkane carboxylic acids	Monophenols	Coumarins
		Brassins	2,3,5-Triiodobenzoic acid (TIBA)
	Aryloxyalkane carboxylic acids		
			Naphthylphthalamic acid
	Derivates of benzoic acid		Chlorflurenol
Gibberellins	Cyclic adenosine monophosphate	Catecholamines	Onium compounds – quaternary N compounds – Sulphonium & Phosphonium derivatives Pyrimidine derivatives Succinic acid-N-dimethylhydrazide
Cytokinins	Benzyladenine Furfuryladenine	–	Pyrrolo- & Pyrazolo pyrimidines
Abscisic acid	Xanthoxin Phaseic acid	Farnesol	Fusicoccin
Ethylene	1-aminocyclopropane 1-carboxylic acid 2-chloroethyl-phosphonic acid	Auxins Glyoxime	Aminoethoxyvinylglycine

The aim of growth regulator application is often to influence vegetative growth therby controlling culm length or shoot/root ratio, but it may also be focussed on flower or fruit formation. The most widely applied growth regulator is a choline derivate, chlorocholine chloride (= CCC) known commercially as 'Cycocel'. TOLBERT [1960] found that this chemical depresses shoot growth in wheat. The application of CCC to cereals was first introduced by LINSER et al. [1961].

$$[ClCH_2 - CH_2 - N^+(CH_3)_3] Cl$$
Chlorocholine chloride ($=$ CCC)

According to Wittwer and Tolbert [1960] chlorocholine chloride restricts the synthesis of gibberellins which in turn results in a reduction in the length of the culm. The basal internodes in particular are shorter (Primost and Rittmeyer [1969]) and the diameter of CCC treated culms is thicker. The number of vascular bundles is increased, cell walls are more developed and the elasticity of the culm is improved (Koch [1968]). Table 5.9 shows the effect of a CCC-treatment at three different growth stages on culm length and on the yield of spring wheat grown in a pot experiment (Linser and Kühn [1963]). At all three stages CCC application resulted in a substantial reduction of straw length by about 24%; grain yield and root growth were improved and straw yield was depressed. Normally, however, applications of CCC do not increase grain yield directly. The reduction of straw length results in a substantial increase in resistance to lodging as has been observed in numerous field experiments (Bachthaler [1967]). Spring wheat and winter wheat in particular respond to CCC treatment, whereas the application of this chemical to other

Table 5.9   Effect of a CCC application at different stages of cultivation on the yield and culm length of spring wheat (data according to Linser and Kühn [1963])

CCC-Treatment	Grain yield	Straw yield in g DM/pot	Root yield	Mean length of culms in cm
Without...................	33.7	53.1	9.0	88.9
Before sowing	34.4	54.0	10.6	70.9
At tillering	35.2	49.4	10.6	67.4
Onset of stem elongation ...	35.9	49.3	10.2	68.0

cereals (rye, oats, barley) does not always result in an improvement in resistance to lodging. In practice CCC is sprayed on the wheat crop between the tillering and heading stages, when the plants are about 10 to 20 cm in height. As a result of the use of CCC, the levels of N application to wheat have increased in Central Europe. These are now in the order of about 120 to 160 kg N/ha, given as a split application.

In addition to choline derivatives 1,1-dimethyl-hexahydropyridazinium salts, 1,1-dimethyl-piperidinium salts and salts of thianium have been reported to have growth regulating properties (Zeeh et al. [1974]). These compounds all have an organic cation in common which is the active part of the molecule. 1,1-dimethyl-piperidinium chloride is now being used in cotton growing. This growth regulator known as 'Pix' reduces ethylene production and thus prevents the abscission of flowers and bolls.

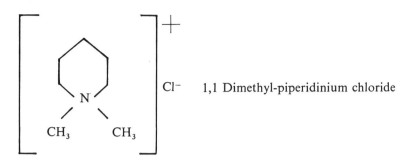

1,1 Dimethyl-piperidinium chloride

A mixture of 1,1-dimethyl piperidinium chloride and 2-chloroethyl phosphonic acid is known commercially as 'Terbal'. This growth regulator has recently been introduced in Germany. It is applied to barley and rye and reduces the hazard of lodging by restricting a stem elongation.

$$Cl - CH_2 - CH_2 - P = O \begin{array}{c} {}^{OH} \\ {}_{OH} \end{array}$$ 2-chloroethyl phosphonic acid (= ethrel)

KÜHN et al. [1977] in applying a mixture of chlorocholine chloride and 2-chloroethyl phosphonic acid, were able to reduce the culm length of winter rye significantly and thus prevent crop lodging. The application of 2-chloroethyl phosphonic acid, also known as 'ethrel', is used in rubber production (RIBAILLIER and AUZAC [1970]). It delays the formation of the wound callus and thus extends the period of latex flow. Ethrel like chlorocholine chloride blocks the synthesis of gibberellins (SADEGHIAN and KÜHN [1976]).

Another growth regulator (ancymidol) when applied together with CCC is effective in reducing the culm length of winter barley (KÜHN et al. [1978]). Besides this effect on culm length the application of the mixture resulted in prolonged reproductive growth, and the number of ears per unit area and

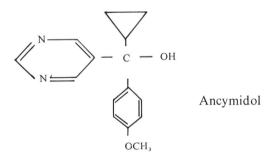

Ancymidol

number of grains per ear were increased. The single grain weight, however, was lowered (BRÜCKNER et al. [1978]).

Recently JUNG et al. [1980] have described the growth regulating effect of triazoline and aziridine derivatives of norbornenodiazitine. These compounds which promote root growth at the expense of shoot growth are especially effective both in soil and seed treatments. According to OHLROGGE [1977] some herbicides also have a growth regulating action apart from a herbicidal effect.

5.2 Nutrition and Yield Response

5.2.1 General

Since the famous experiment carried out by J.B. VAN HELMONT more than 300 years ago it has been known that the soil contributes to only a small extent to the weight of material synthesized by plants. VAN HELMONT planted a willow in a pot and found that after a growth period of 5 years the weight of soil in the pot had hardly changed whereas the willow had gained about 160 lb. VAN HELMONT suggested that the production of wood, bark and leaves resulted from water taken up from the soil. We now know that as well as water, CO_2 and mineral nutrients determine the production of plant material. Indeed CO_2 assimilation is the primary process involved in yield formation. It is for this reason that the rate of CO_2 assimilation and factors which influence it are of paramount interest.

Photosynthates can be utilized for vegetative growth, for the synthesis of storage material and for respiration. The proportion of photosynthates directed towards these three sinks depends on the physiological age of the plant (WARREN-WILSON [1969]). In young seedlings structural growth dominates and therefore more than half of the photosynthates assimilated are used for growth. In mature plants, however, the major fraction of photosynthates is used in the synthesis of storage material (Table 5.10). During the main grain filling period of wheat about 80% of photosynthates transported to the grains are used as metabolites for the synthesis of numerous organic compounds. The remainder are re-

Table 5.10 Rates of utilization of photosynthates by three types of sinks at three stages of development (WARREN-WILSON [1969])

| | mg photosynthates/g DM/day | | |
	Structural growth	Storage	Respiration
Germinating seedling	20	5*	10
Young vegetative plant	15	5	8
Mature plant with storage organ	5	10	4

* Assumes that seed reserves are not part of embryo, otherwise a negative value arise here

spired (EVANS and RAWSON [1970]). The same is also true of other plants. Tomato fruits for example respire about 30% of the photosynthates they receive (HAEDER and MENGEL [1972]). Similar values (30 to 40%) have also been obtained for ryegrass by ALBERDA [1977].

5.2.2 Net assimilation rate and leaf area index

In a crop stand CO_2 is continuously being fixed by photosynthesis and released by respiration. The net amount of C assimilated (net assimilation) is measured by the excess C gained from photosynthesis over that lost by respiration. The net assimilation rate (NAR) is often used to express the rate at which dry matter is accrued and is defined as the net assimilation per unit leaf area.

In the process of respiration, molecular O_2 is taken up by plants and assimilates are oxidized to CO_2 and water. In dark or mitochondrial respiration the oxidation process is accompanied by ATP synthesis. Some green plant cells, however, are also capable of light induced respiration (photorespiration) but in this process ATP is not produced (see page 156). Photorespiration is virtually absent in the C4 crops (maize, sugar cane). This difference is important. It means that the compensation point – the CO_2 concentration at the leaf surface at which CO_2 assimilation (fixation) and CO_2 release (respiration) are equal – is different for C3 and C4 plants. The compensation point for C4 plants is in the order of 0–10 ppm CO_2 whereas C3 plants are normally unable to diminish the CO_2 concentration to much less than 50 ppm CO_2 (KRENZER et al. [1975]). The lower compensation points of C4 plants are of importance in crop physiology, for C4 plants are able to show a net positive assimilation rate at very low CO_2 levels at the leaf surface. This physiological relationship is one of the major reasons why tropical grasses can grow at such an enormous rate under high light intensity and high temperature conditions.

Both CO_2 assimilation and respiration rates increase with temperature. The relationship between CO_2 assimilation rate and temperature is characterized by an asymptotic curve whereas the plot between respiration rate and temperature is hyperbolic (Figure 5.7). A temperature point therefore occurs at which assimilation is equal to respiration (mitochondrial and photorespiration). At this temperature net assimilation is zero and no net growth occurs. As photorespiration is virtually absent in C4 plants, the temperature at which CO_2 assimilation and CO_2 release are equal in these species, is higher than in C3 plants. This means that C4 plants are able to grow at higher temperatures than C3 plants. This of course is of major significance under tropical conditions. The temperatures at which net assimilation is highest differ between plant species and even between cultivars of the same species. EAGLES [1967] thus reported that the highest rate of net assimilation of a cultivar of ryegrass *(Lolium perenne)* originating from Denmark was in a temperature range between 10 to 15°C whereas for cultivar from Algeria it was 20°C.

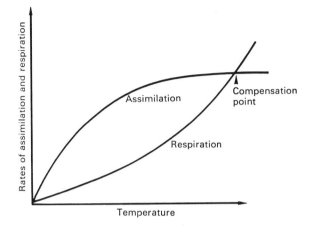

Fig.5.7 Rates of CO_2 assimilation and respiration in relation to temperature.

The higher the density of plants in a particular crop stand, the more mutual competition comes into play: competition for water, competition for nutrients, competition for light. Secondary effects may also be induced by competition. Mutual shading resulting from a high plant density may, for example, increase the susceptibility of the crop to fungal diseases and lodging. In very dense stands competition for light is often the limiting growth factor provided that water and mineral nutrients are present in adequate amounts, as is usual in fertile soils. Under such conditions the photosynthetic rate is decreased in shaded leaves whereas the rate of respiration is increased. As the crop density is increased and mutual shading is intensified, the net assimilation rate (NAR) is thus decreased.

Generally the density of a crop population is expressed in terms of 'leaf area index' (LAI). This may be expressed as the leaf area of the crop per unit soil area, on which the crop is growing (WATSON [1952]). An LAI of 4 for a given crop means that plants growing on an area of 1 m² soil have a leaf area of 4 m². The optimum LAI differs between crops. Some LAI values for different crops are given in Table 5.11. For cereals an LAI of 6 to 8.8 is usually recommended. Sugar beet requires an LAI of 3.2 to 3.7 growing under the light conditions of Central Europe (BIRKE [1966]) but at higher light intensities as in Southern Europe, optimum LAI values for sugar beet are in the region of about 6 (STANACEV [1967]). This example shows that a higher LAI value is acceptable, if the light intensity is

263

Table 5.11 Optimum LAI-values of various crops

Soyabeans	3.2
Maize	5.0
Sugar beet	3.2–6.0
Wheat	6.0–8.8
Rice (new varieties)	7
Rice (local varieties)	4

enhanced. Crop type may also be important. This is evident in Table 5.11 in the case of rice. Modern rice cultivars are characterized by short culms and erect small leaves. These types minimize mutual shading and thus allow a better light absorption (TANAKA [1972]). The view that mutual shading results in enhanced respiration has been questioned by EVANS [1975]. He suggests that old leaves respire at a low rate, and they die if the CO_2 loss by respiration exceeds CO_2 assimilation. This means that mutual shading plays no major role in CO_2 respiration loss by old leaves. Crop nutrition is also important in relation to LAI. When the LAI is optimum, excess N nutrition enhances leaf growth and the grain yields of rice are depressed because of higher mutual shading (TANAKA [1973]). High levels of phosphate and K nutrition cannot counteract this negative effect of N. This relationship between the LAI and grain yield of maize is shown in Figure 5.8 (DUNCAN [1975]).

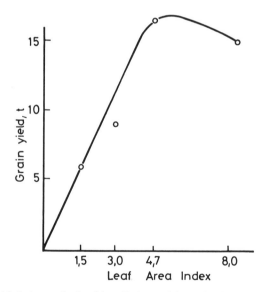

Fig. 5.8 Relationship between the Leaf Area Index and the grain yield of maize (after DUNCAN [1975]).

5.2.3 CO₂ assimilation, CO₂ concentration and light intensity

It is clear that atmospheric CO_2 concentration exerts a major influence on the assimilation rate of CO_2 and hence on yield formation. YOSHIDA [1972] reported that with a normal CO_2 concentration of 300 ppm, very high rice yields of 10 tonnes grains/ha were obtained, but when the CO_2 concentration was raised to 2400 ppm, grain yields of about 19 tonnes/ha were produced. This example demonstrates that under intensive cropping in field conditions the CO_2 concentration of the atmosphere can be a yield limiting factor. Generally it is too costly and too impractical to apply CO_2 to crops as a means of increasing crop yields. It is only under glasshouse conditions that CO_2 application to crops is of any practical importance. PENNINGSFELD [1954] obtained maximum yields for *Sinapis alba* and cucumber growing under glass with CO_2 concentrations of 30 000 ppm. Concentrations higher than 50 000 ppm were toxic. The CO_2 concentration of the atmosphere is generally about 300 ppm. In a crop stand it may vary from this level because of crop assimilation and respiration. In a stand of sugar cane for example CHANG-CHI CHU [1968] found values lower than 300 ppm during the day but higher than 440 ppm at night.

Figure 5.9 shows the effect of increasing the CO_2 concentration on the CO_2 assimilation rate (mg CO_2 per m^2 leaf area per second) in *Trifolium pratense* growing under different light intensities. Under poor light conditions (50 J/m²/s) the rate of CO_2 assimilation was only slightly increased by raising the CO_2 concentration. From the three dimensional diagram it can be seen very clearly, however, that by raising the CO_2 concentration at higher light intensities the rate of CO_2 assimilation was dramatically increased (WARREN-WILSON [1969]). This relationship shown in Figure 5.9 is an excellent example of an interaction of two factors. In this example two factors, CO_2 concentration and light intensity interact to positively influence the rate of CO_2 assimilation. From this example, it is evident that increasing one of the factors will only have a major effect provided that an adequate amount or intensity of the other factor is available. This is a general relationship which not only applies to light intensity and CO_2 concentration but also to other factors which influence growth such as the soil moisture regime, the level of N nutrition or the rate of supply of other plant nutrients. The light intensity at which the plateau of CO_2 assimilation is obtained, the so called light saturation, also depends on the age of the plants. ALBERDA [1977] found that light saturation of 7 weeks old ryegrass *(Lolium perenne)* was obtained at a lower light intensity than for 3 weeks old ryegrass.

The favourable effect of increased light intensity or CO_2 concentration or the combined effects of both on CO_2 assimilation has been observed by a number of authors (RÖMER [1971], LARCHER [1963]). BRUN and COOPER [1967] experimenting with soya beans found that when atmospheric CO_2 concentration was nor-

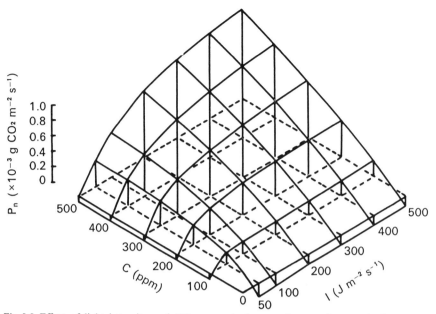

Fig.5.9 Effect of light intensity and CO_2 concentration on the net photosynthetic rate per unit leaf area of clover leaves (after Warren-Wilson [1969]):

C → concentration of CO_2
J → light intensity in Joule J m^{-2} sec^{-1}
Pn → net photosynthetic rate per unit leaf area
I (J m^{-2} sec^{-1}) = 238 lux = 22.2 fc.

mal (300 ppm), CO_2 assimilation levelled off at a light intensity of about 100 J/m²/s. For rice, higher light intensities of about 300 J/m²/s to 400 J/m²/s may be regarded as optimum (Yoshida [1972]). An idea of what is meant by these light intensity figures can be appreciated from the normal values which occur in Central Europe. On a clear day at noon in summer, light intensities as high as 300 J/m²/s may be reached. Under cloudy conditions the value is about 80 J/m²/s.

The degree of utilization of radiation energy by plants is rather low. Loomis *et al.* [1971] reported that under optimum conditions the maximum efficiency of utilization of radiation energy for crop production is about 5%, the remaining 95% being converted to heat. The 'available energy' for annual crops is even lower than 5% due to the fact that a considerable period is needed for these crops to grow to attain maximum leaf expansion. Leaf senescence in the canopy may also occur before the growing season ends. According to Holliday [1976], in an advanced agricultural system with intensive cropping, plants of the C3 type utilize about 2.7% of the available radiation energy in the production of plant dry matter. For C4 plants the comparative figure is about 4%. Gibbon *et al.* [1970] compared the growth and solar energy conversion of maize under the two very different radiation climates of England and Italy (Table 5.12). Not only were yields greater in the high radiation climate (Italy) but also the efficiency of energy conversion was higher. The percentages of energy conversion agree well with the data of HALL [1977] who quotes a 0.5 to 1% utilization for temperate crops and a 1 to 2% utilization for tropical crops.

Table 5.12 Yield and energy conversion efficiency of maize (INRA 200) at four different sites (GIBBON *et al.* [1970])

	1	2	3	4
Aerial plant parts (tonnes/ha)	8.7	11.9	24.8	25.7
% of total radiation energy utilized	0.73	0.95	1.75	1.33

Locations: 1 Leeds University Farm (UK)
2 Cawood Exp. Station (UK)
3 Turin (Italy)
4 Rome (Italy)

5.2.4 Yield curves

It has already been mentioned that improving conditions for growth by altering one growth factor can be without effect if another growth factor is limiting. This relationship which is known as the 'law of the minimum' was discovered by SPRENGEL at the beginning of the nineteenth century and its significance for crop production was particularly propagated by JUSTUS VON LIEBIG. It is still of utmost importance in crop production to know which, if any, growth factor is limiting under a given set of growing conditions. Alleviating the limiting growth factor results in a yield increase. This relationship is roughly reflected in an asymptotic curve. In other words, as the growth factor is increased to improve yield, the yield increments become smaller. This pattern of yield increase is shown in Figure 5.10 where N is used to represent the growth factor. The highest yield increment results from the first unit of N applied and with successive applications of N units the yield increments become progressively smaller (diminishing response curve). MITSCHERLICH studied this relationship in numerous pot and field experiments and concluded that the yield increase brought about by a 'unit growth factor' was proportional to the quantity of yield still required to attain maximum yield level. This is described in mathematical terms as follows:

$$\frac{dy}{dx} = k\,(A - y)$$

where y = yield A = maximum yield
x = growth factor k = constant

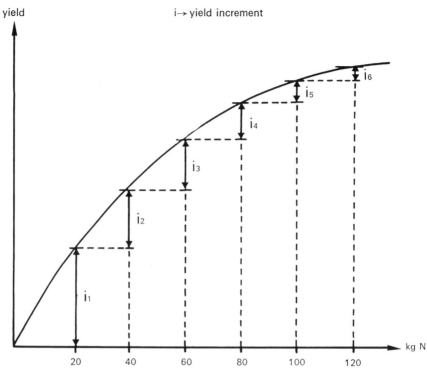

yield

i→ yield increment

i_1 i_2 i_3 i_4 i_5 i_6

20   40   60   80   100   120   kg N

Fig.5.10 Response curve showing diminishing increments.

On integration the equation below is obtained

$$\ln (A - y) = c - kx$$

The term c is an integration constant which comprises all the invariable terms, except k. If x = zero, y is also equal to zero, so that in this case the following equation is valid:

$$\ln (A - O) = c - O$$
$$\ln A = c$$

By substituting ln A for c in the integration equation the following equation is obtained:

$$\ln (A - y) = \ln A - kx$$

Converting the natural logarithms into common logarithms, the final form of the Mitscherlich-equation results:

$$\log (A - y) = \log A - cx$$

The term c in this case is porportional to k and results from the conversion of natural to common logarithms:

$$c = k \times 0.434$$

The Mitscherlich-equation is often written non-logarithmically in the following form:

$$y = A (1 - 10^{-cx})$$

Mitscherlich-curves for the growth factors N, K and P are shown in Figure 5.11 (VON BOGUSLAWSKI [1958]). The slopes of the three curves differ. The steepest gra-

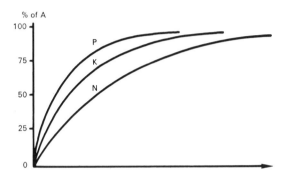

Fig.5.11 Yield response curves for N, P and K (after v. BOGUSLAWSKI [1958]).

dient is brought about by P and the flatest by N, provided that the growth factors are expressed in weight units of N, K_2O and P_2O_5 respectively. The rise of the curve is steeper the higher the 'c-value'. MITSCHERLICH [1954] considered this c value to be of fundamental importance. He believed it to be a constant term, or in other words that it should be possible to define precisely the yield curve brought about by improving a growth factor. This, however, is now known not to be the case and has been demonstrated in a number of experiments by different authors (VAN DER PAAUW [1952], ATANASIU [1954], SHIMSHI [1969]). The significance of the c value is that it gives an indication of whether the maximum yield level can be attained by a relatively low or high 'quantity of growth factor'. When the c value is low, a high quantity is required, and *vice versa*.

In Figure 5.9 it was shown that the yield response resulting from an increase in one growth factor, *e.g.* CO_2 concentration also depends on the intensity of other growth factors, *e.g.* light intensity. The same kind of relationship is also true for plant nutrients. A very good example of this kind was reported by MACLEOD [1969], the main results of which are presented in Figure 5.12. The ex-

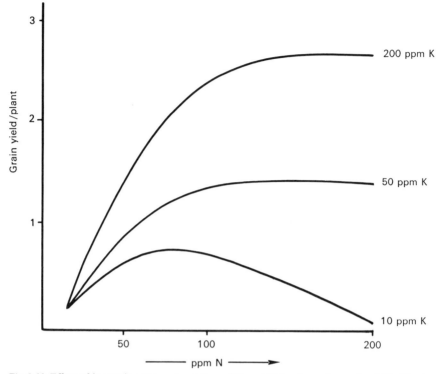

Fig.5.12 Effect of increasing N supply at three different K levels on the grain yield of barley (after MacLeod [1969]).

periments which were carried out with barley in a solution culture, show that increasing the N concentration in the nutrient solution resulted in three different 'yield curves' for the three different K levels applied. For the lowest K level a curve was obtained which showed a pronounced yield depression at high levels of N nutrition. This cannot be described by the Mitscherlich-equation for as we have seen it is an asymptotic curve in which the yield (y) approaches a maximum. Even in the other two curves of Figure 5.12, this asymptotic shape is not observable. It seems rather that they level off at a given N concentration in the nutrient solution. A similar pattern of fertilizer response by a number of field crops has also been reported by Boyd [1970] in which a linear rise with a fairly sharp transition was followed by a second linear relationship where the yield changed little or slowly decreased.

Similar results to those discussed above have been obtained by Shimsi [1969] when plotting grain yields of maize against N fertilizer application rates in relation to soil moisture level. As illustrated in Figure 5.13, when the soil mois-

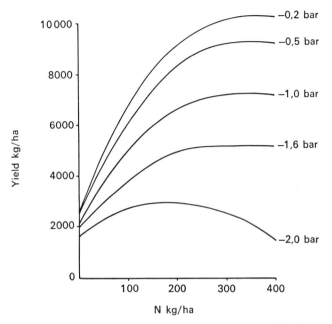

Fig.5.13 Effect of increasing the rate of N application on the grain yield of maize at different soil moisture levels (after SHIMSHI [1969]).

ture was low (low water potential), the curves show an inversion which was not observed at the higher soil moisture levels. In treating these data according to the Mitscherlich-equation, SHIMSHI found that the c-values were not constant, but increased with water stress. This means that the higher the water stress the lower was the N rate required for attaining maximum yield. In more general terms this example shows that fertilizer response will be higher where the presence of other growth factors is beneficial, such as water, temperature, light intensity and many other environmental factors. This is frequently seen in practical farming, where highest yield responses from fertilizer application are often found on soils with a high yield potential (HOLLIDAY [1963]). An example of this kind is shown in Figure 5.14. The highest NPK application to potatoes resulted in a yield depression on soils of low yield potential, whereas on the high yielding potential soils a yield response was obtained. From these and other results HOLLIDAY [1963] states 'a basic weakness of the Mitscherlich-equation for describing fertilizer responses is the fact that it gives an asymptotic type of curve'. Frequently, the yield curves resulting from fertilizer experiments show a point of inversion. For this reason some authors prefer to use a quadratic equation in describing the yield response brought about by an improvement of one growth factor.

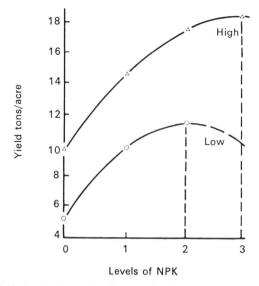

Fig.5.14 Potato yields in relation to fertilizer application (NPK) on a soil of low and high potential (after HOLLIDAY [1963]).

From a more biological point of view, the question must be answered as to why yield depression results from excess nutrient supply. A few examples may be cited. For instance, in cereals high N application rates can cause lodging or increase the susceptibility of the crop to fungal disease. In addition, more physiological disorders may occur. Increasing the level of N-nutrition may lead to an excess of soluble amino acids, which cannot be used for growth processes because of a relative shortage of other plant nutrients. In the case of K, excess supply can depress the uptake of other cation species and particularly Mg (see page 463). This can induce Mg deficiency and hence depress yield. High P dressings can depress yields by reducing the availability of heavy metals, especially Zn (GÄRTEL [1968]). High applications of mineral fertilizer in particular when applied directly before or at the time of sowing may temporarily lead to high ion concentrations in the soil solution which may be detrimental to seed germination. Ammonium N is especially harmful in this respect (BARKER *et al.* [1970]).

The examples cited above demonstrate that it is futile to attempt to describe yield response from one growth factor by a single equation valid for all conditions of crop growth. Yield production results from numerous physical, chemical, biochemical and physiological processes all of which are influenced by other factors which vary considerably during the growing period. One cannot expect therefore that a single response curve resulting from one growth factor should cover the wide variation of conditions which contribute to yield formation. This does not belittle the importance of response curves and equations and in particular the experimental findings of MITSCHERLICH [1950] and his co-workers. The main conclusion from MITSCHERLICH'S work is that as a growth factor is increased the yield increments become smaller. This 'law of diminishing yield increments' has a broader significance and is not only applicable to agricultural production, but has also been used in industrial and economic problems.

5.3   Nutrition and Plant Quality

5.3.1   General

The quality of plant products is not so easily defined and measured as yield. Quality standards depend very much on the purpose for which a plant is used. For example, very different qualities are looked for in grains of malting barley than in those used for animal feeds. The same is true for potato tubers, as to whether they are used for starch production or for human consumption. There are also other examples of this kind. Many quality factors such as flavour or taste are very difficult to measure and as these factors are also very much subjective, the absolute assessment of quality is often very difficult. For this reason the following section is restricted to considering some basic relationships between nutrition and the synthesis of organic compounds.

The major factors controlling crop quality are fixed genetically. Thus potato tuber proteins differ considerably between potato cultivars, whereas environmental factors including nutrition are scarcely able to influence protein pattern (STEGEMANN et al. [1973]). On the other hand, exogenous factors can considerably influence the levels of some organic compounds in plants. These nutritional effects are dependent on the influence of particular nutrients on biochemical or physiological processes. The content of carbohydrates or sugars in storage tissues, grains and seeds is thus related to the photosynthetic activity of the plant and to the translocation rate of photosynthates to the storage plant parts.

5.3.2   Root crops

As already pointed out above (page 246) the presence of an adequate level of K nutrition promotes CO_2 assimilation and the translocation of carbohydrates from the leaves to the tubers of potatoes. This is the reason why the starch content of the tubers is high in potatoes well supplied with K (LACHOVER and ARNON [1966]). This effect also depends on the kind of potash fertilizer used, muriate of potash (KCl) generally giving lower starch contents than the sulphate form. This difference is probably due to the fact, that chloride has a detrimental influence on the translocation of carbohydrates in the potato plant (HAEDER [1975]). Table 5.13 shows the results of long term field trials in which the effect of KCl and K_2SO_4 on the tuber yield and starch content of tubers was investigated (TERMAN [1950]). Very high K levels (>800 kg K_2O/ha) can reduce the carbohydrate content of potato tubers (VERTREGT [1968]). This is particularly the case, if K is applied in the form of KCl in Spring (WICKE [1968]).

The quality of potato tubers is not only a matter of starch content. For tubers used in starch production there should be a high degree of esterification between phosphate and the hydroxyl groups of the starch. More highly esterified starches are more viscous and of better quality. Experiments of GÖRLITZ [1966] and of EFFMERT [1967] thus showed that P fertilization not only increased the P content of potato tubers but also improved starch quality. In tubers used for human

Table 5.13 Effect of potassium sulphate and potassium chloride on the yield and starch content of potato tubers (TERMAN [1950])

Treatment	Tuber yield (tonnes/ha)	Starch %
KCl	2.81	13.3
K_2SO_4	2.82	14.6
½ KCl + ½ K_2SO_4	2.86	13.8

consumption 'blackening' of tubers is often a problem. According to investigations of HUGHES and SWAIN [1962] blackening originates from a complex formed by iron and chlorogenic acid. Citric acid inhibits this complex formation, probably by chelating the Fe. As the content of citric acid in potato tubers is positively correlated with the K content (MACKLON and DEKOCK [1967]), heavy potash dressing usually reduces the suceptibility of potato tubers to blackening (MULDER [1956], VERTREGT [1968]).

The relationship between the occurrence of black spot and the K content of potato tubers is shown in Figure 5.15 from the work of VERTREGT [1968]. Of the tubers with a K content <500 me K/kg DM more than 50% were found to be suffering from black spot, whereas of those tubers with a K content >600 me K/kg DM less than 20% showed the disease. The Figure also shows a clear negative correlation between the K content and the dry matter content of the tubers. This relationship however, is not only dependent on K nutrition but is also influenced by the physiological age of the tubers. Young tubers are high in K, low in starch and have high water contents, whereas for old tubers the reverse is true. The sensitivity of potato tubers to damage caused by mechanical harvesting or by transportation is also influenced by nutrition. Thus Pätzold and Dambroth [1964] reported that higher levels of phosphate application reduced the sensitivity of potato tubers to mechanical damage.

Tubers of other crops where carbohydrates are the main storage material, such as sweet potatoes *(Ipomoea batata)*, cassava (= manioc), yam *(Dioscorea*

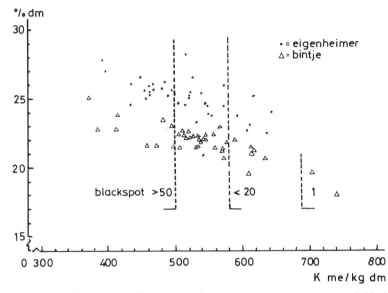

Fig.5.15 Relationship between K content of tubers, dry matter content and black spot of two potato cultivars (Vertregt [1968]).

species) and topinambur *(Helianthus tuberosus)*, respond in a similar way to nutrition. Obigbesan [1973] found that in tubers of cassava not only was the starch content enhanced by K, but the content of the poisonous cyanide was also decreased.

The quality of sugar beet depends primarily on sugar content, but is also affected by the content of soluble amino compounds, and by the content of minerals in particular K^+ and Na^+. The presence of soluble amino compounds and minerals disturbs crystallization during sugar refining and thus affects the sugar output. Increasing the K nutrition to an adequate level is generally accompanied by an increase in the sugar content (Trocmé and Barbier [1966], Gutstein [1967]) and a decrease in the contents of soluble amino compounds (Draycott et al. [1970]). On the other hand, high K levels at least slightly increase the K content of the roots, although the main response is in increasing the K content of the leaves. An increase of K in sugar beet roots is usually accompanied by a decrease of the Na content (von Boguslawski and Schildbach [1969]).

Nitrogen nutrition is of paramount importance for sugar beet quality. During the first period of beet growth abundant N supply is essential for satisfactory yields, but during the later stages (August to October) N supply should decline (WINNER [1968], BRONNER [1974]). If this does not occur leaf growth is stimulated at the expense of sugar storage in the roots (see page 256). The roots of sugar beet grown at too high a level of N nutrition during the last months prior to harvest are generally characterized by low sugar contents and high concentrations of amino compounds and minerals. This results because the storage tissue is retained in a juvenile stage (FORSTER [1970]). Late application of N and the supply of N forms, which are not directly available, as for example anhydrous NH_3, should therefore not be recommended for sugar beet cultivation (ROUSSEL et al. [1966]).

Sugar beet quality is not only dependent on mineral nutrition but is also influenced by environmental factors. In years with low rainfall and high light intensity, low root yields are generally harvested. Such roots are usally high in sugar as well as in amino acids and minerals. This pattern is typical for water stress situations, which result in poor root growth and thus in an accumulation of sugars, amino compounds and minerals in the roots. Best sugar yields are obtained when high light intensity conditions prevail during the last weeks of the sugar beet growth period and where adequate water is available for the crop. Optimum fertilizer application in combination with irrigation produces maximum root yields of satisfactory quality (VON BOGUSLAWSKI and SCHILDBACH [1969]). In Central Europe under these conditions yields of as much as 80 tonnes roots/ha or 12 tonnes sugar/ha can be harvested.

The problems of sugar cane quality are similar to those of sugar beet. Sugar cane grown on saline sites is often poor in quality, being low in sugar and containing very high amounts of minerals and amino compounds.

5.3.3 Grain crops

In cereals used for bread, grain baking quality is of particular interest. Wheat cultivars grown under the arid conditions of Canada or of South-Eastern Europe are partially of the hard wheat type possessing high baking quality properties. Cultivars grown under the more humid conditions of Western and North-Western Europe, are often poorer in baking quality, although they are characterized by a higher grain yield potential. In the past the differences between these two types was particularly pronounced. New high yielding cultivars of wheat are now available, however, which have very satisfactory baking qualities. In order to utilize this quality potential, the growing crop must be adequately supplied with nutrients and in particular with N. The most important constituent determining the baking quality of cereals is gluten. This consists predominantly of the grain protein glutelin, which is found in the endosperm of the grains. The baking quality is also related to the degree of glutelin polymerization which is brought about by disulphide bridging. According to EWART [1978] a high degree of glutelin polymerization results in an increase of dough tenacity and thus in an improvement of baking quality.

Table 5.14 Effect of an additional N application at the flowering stage on yield, protein content of grains and baking quality of winter wheat. Mean values of 10 field experiments (KÜRTEN [1964])

	Control, 80 kg N/ha as a basic dressing	+40 kg N/ha at flowering stage	+60 kg N/ha
Grain yield, tonnes/ha	4.59	4.98	5.24
Protein content, %	11.9	12.7	13.3
Sedimentation value	28	30	34

Nitrogen supplied to cereals at flowering increases the protein content of the grains substantially and thus improves baking quality. This is shown in Table 5.14 (KÜRTEN [1964]). The addition of 40 or 60 kg N/ha at the flowering stage not only increased the grain yield but substantially improved grain quality. The protein content and the sedimentation value were raised so that a better baking quality was obtained

Nitrogen taken up during the vegetative stage is used primarily for vegetative growth, whereas the N applied after flowering is mainly directed towards the synthesis of grain proteins (MICHAEL and BLUME [1960]). The beneficial effect of late N application on the baking quality of bread cereals has been confirmed by numerous experiments carried out in Central Europe (PRIMOST [1962, 1968], JAHN-DEESBACH and WEIPERT [1965]). Under more arid conditions, however, baking quality is often not improved by late N application. This was observed by MCNEAL et al. [1963] using five hard red spring wheat varieties. According to field trials of PRIMOST [1968] and SCHÄFER and SIEBOLD [1972] plants must be adequately supplied with K in order to obtain the beneficial effect of late N application on baking quality.

The feeding quality of proteins is mainly determined by the content of crude protein and the proportion of essential amino acids. These are amino acids which cannot be synthesized by humans or animals, and for this reason must be supplied as constituents of the mammalian diet (Table 5.15). Grains of cereals and maize are particularly low in lysine and therefore are rather poor in protein quality. Late N application increases the content of crude protein in the grains, but the individual grain proteins are affected to a different degree. Albumin and globulin, the main proteins of the embryo, are hardly affected, whereas the content of glutelin and especially of prolamin is increased (MICHAEL and BLUME [1960]). MITCHELL *et al.* [1952] found a similar relationship in maize grains;

Table 5.15 Essential amino acids in human nutrition

Valine	Threonine	Phenylalanine
Leucine	Methionine	Tryptophan
Isoleucine	Lysine	

N application mainly increased the content of zein (prolamin of maize grain). Prolamins are very poor in lysine, so that by increasing the prolamin content the nutritional value of the grains is reduced. This increase in the prolamin proportion occurs especially in the final stages of grain maturation. This is shown in Table 5.16 for a conventional maize cultivar (SONNTAG and MICHAEL [1973]). The same has been found for wheat where the glutelin concentration was only slightly increased during the final stage of the grain filling period whereas the prolamin content rose markedly (MENGEL *et al.* [1981]). Late N application to wheat, barley and maize thus usually increases the content of grain crude protein, but its nutritional value is reduced.

Table 5.16 Change of protein proportions during the maturation of maize grains of a conventional cultivar (SONNTAG and MICHAEL [1973])

Days after flowering	16	24	28	42	70
	% of total grain N				
Albumin + globulin	31	32	26	18	18
Prolamin	3	20	34	43	43
Glutelin	12	13	13	16	19
Water soluble N...........................	49	28	23	15	12
Residue	5	6	4	5	8

According to investigations of VÖLKER [1960] with wheat and barley, increasing the content of crude protein results in a reduction of the proportions of various essential amino acids. Similar results have been reported by KEENEY [1970] for maize who found that high rates of N application resulted in a substantial increase in the crude protein of grains, but this was accompanied by a reduction of the proportions of lysine, threonine, cysteine, arginine, asparagine and glycine in the total grain proteins. HOJJATI and MALEKI [1972] also reported that in wheat grains an increase in the crude protein content was particularly accompanied by a reduction in the proportion of lysine and methionine. Similar relationships have been found for the proteins of rye grains (BAYZER and MAYR [1967]). With oats and rice the situation is different. Here high or late N fertilizer dressings predominantly increase the content of glutelin, a grain protein with a moderately high proportion of lysine. For these crops therefore an increase in grain proteins does not result in a reduction in nutritional value. This finding has been confirmed in feeding experiments using pigs and rats. It was observed that the protein quality of barley and wheat grains was impaired, but that of oat grains was improved by high N application (BRUNE et al. [1968]).

From the foregoing discussion it can be seen that poor quality grain proteins of wheat, barley and maize can be little improved by plant nutrition. As these grains play a major role in human nutrition, especially in the developing countries, the improvement of grain proteins is a challenging target for plant breeders. One important advancement in this direction has been made by MERTZ et al. [1964]. These workers obtained strains of maize and barley with relatively high contents of lysine in the grain, due to the fact that the storage proteins consist mainly of glutelin and not of prolamin. Increasing the level of N nutrition to these strains therefore mainly results in an increase of glutelin rather than prolamin content (DECAU and POLLACSEK [1970], SONNTAG and MICHAEL [1973]). Unfortunately, these lysine rich cereals are not so high yielding as conventional cereal cultivars. This means that any increase in lysine content in the grains is offset by a lower grain production. An example of this kind may be cited from the field experiments of DECAU and POLLACSEK [1970]. These workers showed that increasing the level of N application from 0 to 300 kg N/ha to a conventional maize cultivar increased the zein fraction of the total grain protein from 28 to 43%. Lysine production was thus decreased. In the lysine rich cultivar 'Inra O_2' the zein level remained constant at 15%, despite the increased N application. The lysine content was thus not diluted. In terms of total lysine production, however, there was not a great difference between the two cultivars although the grain yield of the lysine rich cultivar Inra O_2 was 20 to 30% lower than the conventional cultivar. In spite of this lower grain yield, however, the lysine rich cultivar yielded 36.8 kg lysine/ha as compared with 32.1 kg lysine/ha for the conventional cultivar.

The lower grain yields of the lysine rich cultivars (opaque, flowry) of maize and barley (hiproly) are mainly due to a poor single grain weight (STOY [1972], SONNTAG and MICHAEL [1973]). BERINGER and KOCH [1977] in studying the grain filling of the isogenic lysine rich barley mutant 'Ris' found that the low single grain weight resulted not because of a lack of available photosynthate but rather was related to the incorporation of amino acids into grain proteins.

A close relationship appears to occur between the protein content of cereal grains and the content of vitamins of the vitamin B group (thiamine, riboflavin, nicotinic acid). Late N application generally enhances the vitamin B content of grains (SCHARRER and PREISSNER [1954], SCHUPHAN et al. [1968], JAHN-DEES-

BACH and MAY [1972]) and thus improves their nutritional value. Vitamin B_1 mainly occurs in the aleurone layer and in the scutellum of the grains. The vitamin B content of flours is therefore lower in the higher milled grades.

In grains used for malting purposes and in particular barley, low protein and high starch contents are required. The grains should be large, as larger grains are generally richer in carbohydrates and the germination rate is higher. It has been known for many years that crops adequately supplied with phosphate and K produce better quality grains for malting barley, whereas high rates of N application impair quality due to an increase in the grain protein content. This has been confirmed in field trials by SCHILDBACH [1972]. Small scale malting tests were also carried out by the same author in which it was found that several components important for beer quality were improved by phosphate and K application.

The oil content of cereal grains is relatively low (2 to 5%) with a high proportion of grain oil being located in the embryo. WELCH [1978] found a positive correlation between the protein and oil contents of 86 barley genotypes. No relationship was observed, however, between the oil content of barley and baking quality. More than 50% of the fatty acid of barley grain oil consists of linoleic acid, as shown in Table 5.17.

Table 5.17 Percent proportion of fatty acids in oil of barley grain (WELCH [1978])

Palmitic acid	21.4–28.7
Stearic acid	0.6– 1.8
Oleic acid	10.4–16.9
Linoleic acid	52.4–58.3
Linolenic acid	4.5– 7.3

As already outlined above, the content of carbohydrates and the content of proteins in grains and cereals depend to a considerable extent on N supply during grain or seed maturation. If the N supply is low during this stage of growth, a higher proportion of photosynthates is used for the synthesis of carbohydrates, whereas if there is an abundant N supply, a fairly high proportion of photosynthates is converted to proteins. In cereals, protein synthesis and starch synthesis thus compete for photosynthates during the grain filling period.

5.3.4 Oil crops

In oil crops like grain crops, there is a marked competition for photosynthates between different metabolic sinks. This is shown very clearly in the results of SCHMALFUSS [1963] in an experiment with flax. Increasing the level of N nutrition enhanced the content of crude protein from about 22% to 28%, but lowered the fat content by several percent. Similar results have been reported by APPELQUIST [1968] for rape *(Brassica napus)*. The most important data of this investigation are shown in Table 5.18. At the low level of N nutrition the oil content was higher but both the seed yield and seed size were depressed. This beneficial effect of the lower level of N nutrition on the oil content probably resulted because the earlier senescence of leaves in this treatment reduced the rate of seed filling during seed maturation. HERMANN [1977] reported that high N fertilizer rates result in a rise of erucic acid in rape oil and thus have a negative effect on quality.

It is well known that oil seeds grown at low temperatures are comparatively richer in unsaturated fatty acids than saturated fatty acids (IVANOV [1929], BARKER and HILDTICH [1950], BERINGER [1971]). An example of this relationship is shown in Table 5.19. The more unsaturated fatty acids have higher iodine num-

Table 5.18 Effect of nitrogen supply on yield and oil content of rape seeds (APPELQUIST [1968])

Nitrogen rate	Seed yield g/pot	Seed weight mg	Oil content % DM
Low	10.0	3.0	46.8
High	18.6	3.6	41.7

Table 5.19 Effect of location on the iodine number in oil of flax seeds (IVANOV [1929])

Location	Degree of latitude	Iodine No.
Archangelsk	64	195–204
Leningrad	59	185–190
Moskow	55	178–182
Woronesh	51	170
Kuban-Odessa	45	163
Taschkent	41	154–158

bers. BERINGER and SAXENA [1968] experimenting with sunflowers, flax and oats confirmed this finding. They further showed that the content of tocopherol (vitamin E) in the seeds is increased by higher growth temperatures. The higher contents of unsaturated fatty acids found in oil seeds from plants grown at low temperatures can be explained by the greater O_2 pressure in these seeds. This favours the desaturation of saturated to unsaturated fatty acids, for oxygen is required for this oxidation (HARRIS and JAMES [1969], DOMPERT and BERINGER [1970]). Under higher temperature conditions, the O_2 pressure in the seeds is lower due to a higher rate of respiration. DYBING and ZIMMERMANN [1966] in studying the synthesis of fatty acids in maturing flax seeds found that at low temperatures (15–20 °C) the synthesis of linoleic acid (unsaturated) runs parallel with the maturation of the pods. Under high temperature conditions (30°C), however, the synthesis of linoleic acid terminated before the seed matured.

5.3.5 Forage crops

The quality of forage crops such as herbage (grasses, clover, lucerne) used as pasture or as hay depends very much on the digestibility of the fodder. Digestibility decreases as the content of crude fibre (cellulose, hemicelluloses, lignin) is increased. As these compounds are accumulated as plants age, and the content of crude protein decreases, the quality of old forage crops is generally poor. This is particularly true for grass, very young grass having a crude protein content of about 20 to 25% and crude fibre content of about 20%. In old grass the crude fibre content exceeds the content of crude protein considerably and may be in the order of 30%, while the crude protein content may only amount to 10%. Nitrogen supply increases the content of crude protein. This has been observed by numerous authors (DAM KOFOED and SONDERGAARD KLAUSEN [1969], HOOGERKAMP [1974]). Table 5.20 from the data of GOSWAMI and WILLCOX [1969] demonstrates the effect of increasing the rate of N on the various nitrogenous fractions in ryegrass. High rates of N fertilization enhanced the protein content substantially and the NO_3^- content appeared to reach a maximum at rates higher than about 400 kg N/ha. An increase in crude protein content is usually accompanied by a decrease in soluble carbohydrates and especially in polyfructosans (NOWAKOWSKI [1962]). The beneficial effect of adequate N nutrition on the yield of dry matter and particularly on the yield of starch units, in a meadow cut 3 times per year, is shown in the results of SCHECHTNER and DEUTSCH [1966] presented in Table 5.21.

The digestibility of forage may also be influenced by other forms of fertilizer practice. SCHMITT and BRAUER [1979] thus reported that potassium application to grassland had a clear effect on the digestibility of various constituents in the resulting herbage. The digestibility quotients which were estimated using animal trials are shown in Table 5.22. The application of potassium, made in addition to the phosphate of the control treatment, improved the digestibility of crude protein, protein and lipids and depressed the digestibility of crude fibre. The meadow was a mixed sward and the K^+ application greatly increased the proportion of legumes at the expense of herbs. This shift in botanical composition probably exerted an important influence on the digestibility of the herbage.

Table 5.20 Effect of an increasing nitrogen supply on the various nitrogenous fractions of ryegrass (GOSWAMI and WILLCOX [1969])

kg N/ha	Total N % DM	Protein N % DM	Free amino acid N % of DM	Nitrate and nitrite N % DM
0	1.32	0.98	0.16	0.04
55	1.53	1.10	0.16	0.04
110	1.89	1.26	0.21	0.06
220	1.69	1.75	0.31	0.17
440	3.73	2.06	0.56	0.35
880	3.93	2.34	0.59	0.35

Table 5.21 Effect of nitrogen application rate on the yield of herbage and starch units taking 3 cuts per year (SCHECHTNER and DEUTSCH [1966])

Treatment kg N/ha	Yield t DM/ha	Starch-units t/ha
PK	6.1	3.0
PK + 60 N	7.0	3.3
PK + 120 N	7.9	3.7
PK + 240 N	9.4	4.1

Table 5.22 Effect of K fertilization on the digestibility quotients of various herbage fractions (data from SCHMITT and BRAUER [1979])

| | % digestibility | |
	P	PK
Dry matter	60.5	60.3
Organic matter	63.9	62.9
Crude protein	54.1	61.3
Protein	48.0	54.9
Lipids	44.3	50.6
Crude fibre	64.5	61.6

Table 5.23 Effect of fertilizer practice on the percentage proportion of grasses, legumes and herbs in a meadow. Location 'Beerfelden'. Soil derived from Bunter sandstone mixed with some loess. (data from SCHMITT and BRAUER [1979])

	Grasses	Legumes	Herbs
No fertilizer	65.8	6.3	27.9
P + K	65.9	22.5	11.6
P + K + N	80.5	9.3	10.2

Generally high N application leads to an increase in the proportion of grasses, whereas P and K fertilization favours the legumes. This relationship is shown in Table 5.23 from a long-term field trial on a loamy alluvial soil typical of many meadows in Central Europe (SCHMITT and BRAUER [1979]). The N treatments on these sites (150–300 kg N/ha) enables at least 3 cuts per year to be taken. Where only two cuts are harvested grass is often in a senescent stage when it is cut and this results in a poorer quality (BRAUER [1960]). How many cuts can be harvested in any one year is frequently dependent on soil moisture. In arid conditions, in particular, water can often be the limiting factor to forage growth. Under these conditions, mixed swards of grasses and legumes are more resistant to water shortage and other unfavourable influences. These meadows are often not treated with N, in order to maintain a high proportion of legumes, which fix the N required by the sward. Legumes on the other hand need an abundant supply of K and P otherwise they are replaced by herbs of a poorer nutritional quality.

Forage crops contain energy (carbohydrates, fats, proteins) and the organic constituents (proteins) required for animal growth and the production of milk, eggs or wool. In addition to these organic constitutents, fodder supplies animals with the essential minerals such as P, S, Ca, Na, Mg, K, and heavy metals. In many cases, these minerals are present in forage crops in abundant quantities, but under conditions of intensive production a mineral shortage often occurs. This is especially true in milk production, as dairy cows require considerable amounts of Na, Mg, Ca and P. These minerals can be supplied as additives, but it is often also opportune to supply mineral contents in the fodder high enough to meet the normal requirement of the animals. For this reason pastures are often dressed with Na and Mg fertilizers, in order to increase the Mg and Na content of the herbage rather than to improve plant growth (FINGER and WERK [1973]). The mineral content of herbage and the requirement of dairy cows are shown in Table 5.24 (KEMP [1971]). The K content in the herbage is always higher than the requirement of milking cows, but this is needed for obtaining maximum grass yields.

Table 5.24 Mineral contents of herbage and the mineral requirements of dairy cows (KEMP [1971])

	Average content % DM	Highest and lowest content % DM	Requirement of lactating cows
K	3.0	1.0 –5.0	0.5
Na	0.2	0.01–2.0	0.10–0.15
Ca	0.6	0.3 –2.0	0.40–0.55
Mg	0.2	0.1 –0.5	0.15–0.40

The Mg nutrition of milking cows can be a problem, particularly in spring when animals are grazing young herbage. Frequently this is low in Mg content, and the Mg availability in the young plant material is particularly poor. Generally 15 to 20% of the Mg in the herbage is resorbed by the animals. In young herbage, however, this resorption percentage (availability) can drop to values below 5% (PULSS and HAGEMEISTER [1969]). Under these conditions milking cows are undersupplied with Mg, so that the Mg content in the blood serum drops below the critical level (1.0 mg Mg/100 ml blood serum) and animals suffer from the so-called grass tetany. The reason why the Mg availability is poor in young grasses is not yet clear. High K level in grass was often suggested as a cause for poor Mg resorption. The data of KEMP et al. [1961], however, show that older herbage with high K contents result in satisfactory Mg resorption in milking cows (Table 5.25). It is of further interest that low Mg resorption is only observed in young grass and not in young legumes (PULSS and HAGEMEISTER [1969]).

Table 5.25 Magnesium resorption in milking cows of freshly cut herbage in relation to the content of crude protein, magnesium and potassium (KEMP et al. [1961])

Age of the herbage	Young	Medium	Old
Crude protein, % DM	25.9	17.8	14.0
Mg, % DM	0.15	0.12	0.11
K, % DM	3.01	3.35	3.08
Mg-resorption in % of total Mg	10	16	20

5.3.6 Vegetables and fruits

Most of the plant nutrients such as P, K, Mg, Cl, S and the heavy metals are also essential elements for animals and man. In this respect NO_3^- is an exception; it is an important plant nutrient but it is not essential for the animal organism. Nitrate itself is not toxic but NO_2^- resulting from microbiological reduction of NO_3^- during storage or processing of plant material may have toxic effects (RIEHLE and JUNG [1966]). Nitrite may impair the oxygen transport of haemoglobin (see p. 327).

As yet it is not established whether NO_2^- can give rise to nitrosamine formation in the mammalian digestion tract. Carcinogenic nitrosamines are not synthesized in plants, even under conditions of a high nitrate supply (HILDEBRANDT [1979]). The recent finding that NO_3^- and NO_2^- can be produced in the human digestive tract from amino acids or NH_3 (TANNENBAUM et al. [1978]) demonstrates that hazards due to NO_2^- not only result from nitrate intake. Nevertheless plants for direct consumption, such as herbage and vegetables should thus not have too high a NO_3^- content. In vegetables and particularly in spinach, a content of 2 mg NO_3^--N per g dry matter is regarded as a critical level. In forage crops contents of up to 4 mg NO_3^--N per g dry matter are acceptable.

Nitrate contents in forage crops and vegetables depend largely on the level of NO_3^- nutrition at which they are grown (see Table 5.26). High rates of NO_3^- application in the range of 300 to 400 kg N/ha result in high levels of NO_3^- in the plant material (LAWRENCE et al. [1968], NIENSTEDT [1969], GOSWAMI and WILLCOX [1969]). On the other hand, it should be remembered that growth conditions also affect the NO_3^- content. Light intensity is particularly important in this respect. Spinach grown in spring under favourable light conditions thus generally has an NO_3^- content which is only one-fifth or even one-tenth as high as spinach grown in autumn (KNAUER and SIMON [1968]). Table 5.26 shows the effect of light intensity and NO_3^- content in the soil on the level of NO_3^- in spinach (CANTLIFFE [1973]).

The effect of light intensity on nitrate reduction is probably not a direct one, since high light intensities have no effect in the absence of CO_2. It seems feasible therefore that phytosynthates, particularly phosphoglyceraldehyde rather than light intensity *per se* is related to nitrate reduction (MAYNARD et al. [1976]). The nitrate content of plant tissues is also dependent on plant age and is usually higher in younger than in older plants. Stems, petioles, and veins of lettuce, cabbage, and other vegetables generally have higher nitrate contents than the mesophyll tissue (FRITZ [1977]). To some degree the nitrate content is also genetically controlled. Thus MAYNARD et al. [1976] quote an example in which the nitrate content of lettuce cultivars was positively related to water content.

Table 5.26 Effect of nitrogen content in the soil and light intensity on the nitrate content in spinach (CANTLIFFE [1973])

mg N/kg soil	Light intensity	
	10,800 lux	32,300 lux
	% nitrate N in DM	
0	0.14	0.09
100	1.09	0.35
200	1.61	0.72

Nitrate found in soils does not always originate from mineral fertilizers but depends on microbiological processes oxidizing organic N to NO_2^- and NO_3^-. Mineral fertilizer cannot therefore always be blamed for high NO_3^- contents sometimes found in vegetables or forage crops. MAYNARD and BARKER [1972] analysed a number of vegetables for NO_3^- and compared their results with NO_3^- contents reported at the turn of the century for the same vegetables. This comparison showed that there were no major differences between the NO_3^- contents found at the present time and those determined at the time when NO_3^- fertilizer consumption was considerably lower (see page 321). A useful review paper dealing with nitrate in vegetables was published by MAYNARD et al. [1976].

The vitamin content in forage crops, vegetables and fruits is also a quality factor. SCHARRER and BÜRKE [1953] reported that increasing levels of N supply raised the carotene content in ryegrass. A similar trend was observed by PEN-NINGSFELD and FORCHTHAMMER [1961] for tomatoes and carrots. In pot experiments with vegetables SCHARRER and WERNER [1957] found that high levels of K nutrition generally increased the content of vitamin C, whereas higher N levels resulted in the reverse effect. This finding was confirmed by PENNINGSFELD and FORCHTHAMMER [1961] for tomato fruits and carrot roots.

The quality of fruits not only depends on the contents of organic constituents, but also to a considerable extent on fruit size, colour, shape, flavour and taste. These characteristics are especially affected by nutrient deficiencies. PENNINGS-FELD and KURZMANN [1966/67] for example carried out pot experiments with apples, pears, plums, cherries and grapes, which showed that inadequate K and P nutrition produced fruits of poor quality. Small green immature fruits were obtained which contained low contents of sugars and acids and were of poor taste.

In apple production it is of utmost importance to maintain an adequate Ca supply to the fruits otherwise 'bitter pit' occurs (see page 452). This disease is characterized by small brown spots on and in the fruit resulting from a break-down of fruit tissue (Plate 11.1). Such fruits are generally low in Ca content (<200 ppm Ca in the D.M.) and may often be high in K and Mg. The Ca content of apple fruits depends considerably on transpiration conditions, as Ca is moved to the fruits almost exclusively in the transpiration stream. Apple fruits in which the transpiration rate is adequate are generally well supplied with Ca^{2+}, provided that Ca uptake by the roots is not impeded. Under moisture stress conditions, however, leaves and fruits can compete for xylem sap, and in the process the leaves are more effective. According to WILKINSON [1968] there may even be a back-flow of xylem sap from the fruits to the leaves under very dry weather conditions. BÜNEMANN and LÜDDERS [1969] have reported that 'bitter pit' occurs more frequently when fruit and shoot growth is high. It is known that Ca moves preferentially to actively growing vegetative tissues than to storage tissues. Shoot growth may therefore compete with storage tissue for available Ca in the plant and induce Ca deficiency in the fruits. This effect may be brought about by high levels of N nutrition. This may account for the well-known observation that Ca disorders are stimulated by high levels of N fertilization.

Sprays of Ca salts can be used to alleviate 'bitter pit'. Generally, however, they are not very successful, for if Ca is to be useful it must be taken up through the fruits, for it is immobilized in the leaf. Application of gypsum or other Ca salts to the soil is a more efficient means of supplying Ca, as most of the Ca in apple fruits arrives there from the roots via the transpiration stream.

SHEAR [1975] cites a list of 35 such Ca related disorders in fruits and vegetables. This demonstrates that not only apples but also other fruits and vegetables are affected in quality by conditions of localized Ca deficiency within the plant.

'Blossom end rot' of tomato fruits is also brought about by an inadequate Ca supply and has many similarities to 'bitter pit' (SHEAR [1975]). The disease is more prevalent under high levels of K nutrition. This relationship is shown in Table 5.27 (FORSTER [1973]). On the other hand, tomatoes should be well supplied with K in order to prevent so-called 'green back' (WINSOR [1966]). This disease is characterized by a delayed maturation of the fruit associated with low N/Ca and K/Ca ratios (MARCELLE and BODSON [1979]). Often the tissue around the fruit stem remains green whilst the remainder becomes a yellowish-red colour. Tissue affected by 'green back' is hard and tasteless, and for this reason such fruits are of poor quality. A number of authors have observed that abundant K supply prevents or at least reduces 'green back' in tomato fruits (WINSOR [1966], FORSTER [1973], FORSTER and VENTER [1975]).

Table 5.27 Occurrence of greenback and blossom-end rot at tomato fruits in relation to the level of potassium nutrition (FORSTER [1973]) (Number of fruits/6 plants)

me K/l nutrient sol.	1	3	9
Greenback	82	2	0
Blossom-end rot	9	15	21
Healthy fruits	96	192	221
Total No. of fruits/6 plants	187	209	242

Taste and flavour of fruits can only be influenced to a limited extent by mineral nutrition. Weather conditions and climatic factors generally play a more important role. For example apples grown under high light intensities and temperatures are sweeter and have lower acid contents than the same varieties of apples grown under more humid and cold conditions. Generally high light intensity favours the synthesis of vitamin C (SCHUPHAN [1961]) and taste and flavour constituents such as sugars, esters, aldehydes and ketones. For many fruits it is a combined effect of these and other compounds which pro-

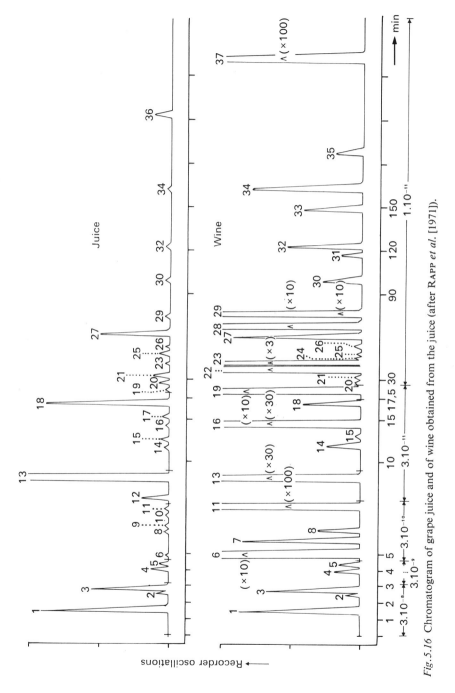

Fig.5.16 Chromatogram of grape juice and of wine obtained from the juice (after RAPP *et al.* [1971]).

289

duces the taste. The balance between the constituents is therefore important. The major components influencing quality in grapes are sugars, organic anions and organic acids. Top quality white vines are grown under more temperate climatic conditions which produce grapes with relatively low sugar and high organic acid contents. Red vines on the other hand require higher temperatures and light intensities, in order to develop a broad palette of tasting and flavour compounds together with high sugar contents, which are typically required for the production of heavy wines (wines rich in alcohol). Red wines are further characterized by a fairly high content of tannins, which have a conserving effect and by anthocyanins, which give rise to the red colour. The marginal regions between the temperate Central European climate and the Mediterranean climate offer the most favourable growing conditions for red wines. Good examples of this are found in the magnificent red wine qualities produced in the region of Bordeaux (Claret) and of Burgundy. These famous wines, of course, not only result from their advantageous growing conditions. Fermentation and processing based on long experience and tradition are also important. During fermentation many of the tasting and flavour stuffs are formed, which are essential to wine taste and quality. Figure 5.16 shows a chromatogram of flavour and tasting stuffs of grape juice before and after fermentation. As can be seen from the large number of peaks in the wine sample a considerable number of flavour compounds have been synthesized during fermentation (RAPP et al. [1971]).

General Reading

BURRIS, R.H. and BLACK, C.C., eds.: CO_2 Metabolism and Plant Productivity, Univ. Paul Press, Baltimore, London 1976

CARLSON, P.S.: The Biology of Crop Productivity. Academic Press London, New York, San Francisco, 1980

EVANS, L.T.: Crop Physiology. Cambridge University Press 1975

EVANS, L.T. and WARDLAW, J.F.: Aspects of the comparative physiology of grain yield in cereals. Adv. Agron. 28, 301–359 (1976)

INTERNATIONAL POTASH INSTITUTE: Fertilizer Use and Protein Production, Proc. 11th Coll. IPI Bern 1975

INTERNATIONAL POTASH INSTITUTE: Physiological Aspects in Crop Productivity. 15th Coll. IPI Bern 1980

LOOMIS, R.S., WILLIAMS, W.A. and HALL, A.E.: Agricultural productivity. Ann. Rev. Plant Physiol. 22, 431–463 (1971)

MAYNARD, D.N., BARKER, A.V., MINOTTI, P.L. and PECK, N.H.: Nitrate accumulation in vegetables. Adv. Agron. 28, 71–118 (1976)

MICHAEL, G. and BERINGER, H.: The role of hormones in yield formation. In: Physiological Aspects in Crop productivity p. 85–116. 15th Coll. Int. Potash Inst. Bern 1980

MOORE, T.C.: Biochemistry and Physiology of Plant Hormones. Springer Verlag, Berlin, Heidelberg, New York, 1979

SCHUPHAN, W.: Nutritional Values in Crops and Plants. Faber and Faber, London 1965

U.S. PLANT SOIL and NUTRITIONAL LABORATORY STAFF: The effect of soils and fertilizers on the nutritional quality of plants. Agricultural Information Bulletin No. 299, U.S. Department of Agriculture 1965

WAREING, P.F. and COOPER, J.P.: Potential Crop Production. A case study. Heinemann Educational Books, 1971

WARREN-WILSON, J.: Maximum yield potential, In: Transition from Extensive to Intensive Agriculture with Fertilizers. Proc. VIIth Coll. Intern. Potash Institute, p. 34–56, Berne 1969

YOSHIDA, S.: Physiological aspects of grain yield. Ann. Rev. Plant physiol., *23*, 437–464 (1972)

Chapter 6

Fertilizer Application

6.1 Nutrient Cycling

6.1.1 General

During the growing period roots act as a sink collecting available nutrients to be utilized in the synthesis of organic plant constituents. After the termination of growth and the start of decay, the process is reversed and nutrients are released into the soil from the breakdown of plant debris. Not all nutrients taken up by plants over the growth period need necessarily be released back into the soil in the same year. In forest trees, for example, about 10–20% of the annual uptake of some minerals may be retained in the bark over winter to be utilized in the spring. On the other hand, some nutrients may even be lost from growing plants by the leaching effect of rain. Senescent leaves are particularly susceptible to the loss of potassium, sodium, chloride, nitrate, and phosphate.

The turnover of nutrients in the 'soil-plant cycle', as described above, is controlled by a number of factors. In particular it is dependent on the intensity of weathering of soil particles, the nature of the soil parent material and the rate of leaching of plant nutrients from the upper soil layer. When the rate of leaching is high and the intensity of weathering is low, plant nutrients may be leached out of the soil at a faster rate than they are taken up by plants. Soils in which this occurs have a negative nutrient balance and become more and more acidic due to the leaching of Ca– and Mg– nitrates and bicarbonates (see page 301). Such soils become progressively poorer in available plant nutrients and show typical features associated with low soil pH conditions. These include low phosphate availability, high levels of soluble Al and Mn and, severe retardation or complete inhibition of N_2 fixation and nitrification (see page 342). The podzolic soils are an example of soils with the features described above. These soils are found throughout the world and develop under conditions where the parent material is poor in plant nutrients and the leaching intensity is high. On the other hand when the nutrient balance is positive, very fertile soils can develop because of the continuous accumulation of plant nutrients. The chernozem soils are typical of these natural fertile sites. Between these two extreme examples many other soil types develop, which are intermediate in their nutrient balance status. Of course not all soils with a positive nutrient balance are fertile. Toxic salt accumulations can also occur, as is the case in the saline soils (see page 62).

The development of agriculture has lead to a disturbance in the nutrient balance in soils. In the older systems of farming a high rate of recycling of plant nutrients was guaranteed. Animals were fattened by extensive grazing so that a high proportion of nutrients were returned to the soil in faeces and urine. Similarly most crops were consumed locally and mineral plant nutrients were brought back to the soil as manure. The main nutrient loss from the system therefore resulted from leaching, and to some extent this was overcome by the age-old practice of liming. With the onset of industrialization, however, the situation changed. Plant nutrients were removed from the cycle to an increasing extent in the form of crop and animal products to meet the food demands of the growing towns. Intensity and specialization in agriculture increased and farming techniques improved. All this resulted in a widening nutrient gap which was filled by the application of plant nutrients in the form of mineral fertilizers. By this means the nutrient balance between the input and removal of plant nutrient was redressed. This idea was put forward by LIEBIG [1841] in the middle of the last century, when he wrote: 'It must be borne in mind that as a principle

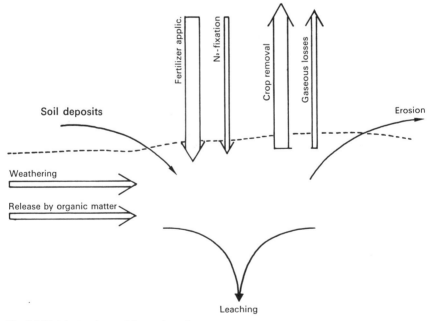

Fig.6.1 Nutrient gains and losses in soils.

of arable farming, what is taken from the soil must be returned to it in full measure'. In addition the use of mineral fertilizers improved the nutrient status of many soils which previously had been poor in plant nutrients and of little agricultural value.

The major components of the nutrient balance in agricultural soils are shown in Figure 6.1. Soil nutrient gains arise from nutrient release in the soil by weathering and mineralization, the application of mineral and organic fertilizers, nitrogen fixation, and the supply of nutrients contained in rain and snow. The main losses result from crop removal, leaching, volatilization (NH_3, N_2, N_2O) and erosion. These components are now considered in more detail.

6.1.2 Nutrient removal by crops

The quantitiy of nutrients which a crop takes up during growth depends very much on crop species and yield. Both crop yield and nutrient uptake also depend considerably on the choice of crop cultivar. This is demonstrated in the data in Table 6.1 which shows nutrient uptake by the rice crop (KEMMLER [1972]). The new high yielding cultivar has higher nutrient requirements, because of its increased yield potential.

Table 6.1 Yield level and nutrient uptake of a conventional local rice variety and the modern high yielding rice variety 'TN1' (KEMMLER [1972])

Cultivar	Grain yield Tonnes/ha	N	P kg/ha	K
Local	2.8	82	10	100
TN 1..	8.0	152	37	270

The nutrient uptake of various field crops is presented in Table 6.2. Comparative figures are given in Table 6.3 for nutrient removal by the most important plantation crops. Nutrient removal in these data is calculated on the basis of those plant parts which are generally harvested. The same also applies to the data of Table 6.4 which shows nutrient removal by fruit trees. In field crops only those plant parts of agricultural importance are usually removed from the field as, for example, grains, tubers or roots. This must be taken into account when calculating nutrient balances. The mature grains of cereal crops contain about 70% of both the total N and P of the aerial plant parts. Most K, however, occurs in the green plant parts, and as little as 25% of the total K is present in the grains. In contrast, the roots and tubers of root crops (potatoes, sugar beet) contain only about 30% of the total N absorbed, but as much as 70% of total plant K.

Table 6.2 Quantities of plant nutrients removed by various crops (calculated from data of EAKIN [1972])

Crop	Yield tonnes/ha	N	P	K	Ca	Mg	S	Cu	Mn	Zn
		kg/ha						g/ha		
Grains										
Barley (Grain)................	2.2	40	8	10	1	2	3	34	30	70
Barley (Straw)	2.5	17	3	30	9	2	5	11	360	60
Wheat (Grain)	2.7	56	13	14	1	7	3	33	100	160
Wheat (Straw)................	3.8	22	3	33	7	4	6	11	180	56
Oats (Grain)	2.9	55	10	14	2	3	6	34	134	56
Oats (Straw)	5.0	28	8	75	9	9	10	34	—	330
Maize (Grain)................	9.5	150	27	37	2	9	11	66	100	170
Maize (Straw)	11.0	110	19	135	29	22	16	55	1700	330
Hay										
Lucerne	10.0	200	20	170	125	24	21	66	500	470
Coastal Bermuda Grass	20.0	340	35	250	66	27	40	230	—	—
Red Clover	6.0	110	13	95	77	19	8	45	600	400
Timothy.....................	6.0	66	13	90	20	7	6	33	340	220
Other Crops										
Sugarcane	75.0	110	27	250	31	26	26	—	—	—
Tobacco (Leaves)	2.2	83	8	110	83	20	15	33	600	80
Cotton (Seed and Lint)	1.7	45	11	14	2	4	3	66	120	350
Cotton (Stalks, Leaves and Burs)	2.2	39	5	33	31	9	17	—	—	—
Potatoes (Tubers).............	27.0	90	15	140	3	7	7	44	100	60
Tomatoes (Fruit)	50.0	130	20	150	8	12	15	80	145	180
Cabbage	50.0	145	18	120	22	9	50	44	110	90

Table 6.3 Nutrient removal of plantation crops (COOKE [1974])

	Yield per hectare equivalent to	kg/ha				
		N	P	K	Ca	Mg
Oil palm	2.5 tonnes of oil	162	30	217	36	38
Sugar cane	88 tonnes of cane	45	25	121	—	—
Coconuts	1.4 tonnes of dry copra	62	17	56	6	12
Bananas	45 tonnes of fruit	78	22	224	—	—
Rubber	1.1 tonnes of dry rubber	7	1	4	—	—
Soyabeans	3.4 tonnes of grain	210	22	60	—	—
Coffee	1 tonne of made coffee	38	8	50	—	—
Tea	1300 kg of dried leaves	60	5	30	6	3

The data presented in the tables cited above provide only a general guide to the amounts of nutrients removed from the soil by crops. The figures can vary considerably. As well as the effects of yield differences, the use of new cultivars and modern techniques have also had a bearing on crop nutrient requirements and thus also on the amounts of nutrients taken up by the crops.

Table 6.4 Nutrient removal by fruit crops; medium yield, normal spacing (according to JACOB and VON UEXKÜLL [1963])

	kg/ha/year		
	N	P	K
Pome fruits	70	9	60
Stone fruits	85	9	65
Grapes	110	15	110
Oranges	170	23	120
Lemons	180	23	115

Data relating to nutrient removal, and fertilizer application rates in particular, are frequently given in the old oxide formulae, *e.g.* kg P_2O_5 or kg K_2O per ha. Recently it has become more common to express these values in terms of the element, *e.g.* kg P or kg K per ha. This modern nomenclature has been used in tables throughout this chapter to indicate both nutrient removal and leaching losses of nutrients. The numerical difference between the two types of nomenclature is not large for K and to calculate the 'K_2O rates', the K data must be multiplied by a factor of 1.2. The respective factors for P_2O_5, MgO and CaO are 2.29, 1.66 and 1.4. From these figures it is clear that differences in data between the two forms of terminology are greatest for phosphate. When noticing what may appear to be rather low numerical values for phosphate in the tables presented here, it should be borne in mind that these data refer to P and not to P_2O_5.

6.1.3 Nutrient removal by leaching

The extent to which nutrients are transported down the soil profile varies considerably between soils. It depends mainly on the climate, soil type and the quantity of nutrients present in the soil in readily soluble form. Freely drained soils are very prone to nutrient removal by leaching. Percolation is particularly high in pervious soil profiles under conditions of high rainfall. Nutrient losses by leaching are thus most pronounced in the tropics and in the humid temperate zones especially on light textured soils.

The rate of leaching is generally measured using lysimeters in which the flow of water and nutrients can be followed through columns of soil similar to those of the soil profile. Although movement of water in natural soils differs from water movement in lysimeters, as these generally have an artificial soil profile, leaching rates obtained using lysimeters provide a useful guide to assessing the rate at which plant nutrients are lost from the soil. Under the climatic conditions of Central Europe with a rainfall of about 700 mm per year, about 25 to 50% of

297

the rainwater passes through the soil profile to a depth of more than one meter. Higher water percolation figures are typical of sandy soils whilst the lower value is more usual in heavier soils. The quantities of nutrients transported along with the water into deeper soil layers are shown in Table 6.5 (VÖMEL [1965/66]). The data presented are the maximum and minimum values observed over a period of eight years on arable soils in Germany and agree well with leaching figures obtained in England (COOKE [1972]). The data show that the rate of leaching of nutrients is highest on light soils and the lowest on heavy soils where the rate of percolation is low.

The leaching of plant nutrients is not only dependent on the rate of percolation and on the quantity of nutrients present in the upper soil layer. The tightness and the extent to which nutrients are bound to soil particles is also important. This can be seen from the data of Table 6.5. Although the contents of exchangeable Na^+ in these soils were much lower than the contents of exchangeable K^+, the leaching rates were higher for Na^+. Both cation species, Mg^{2+} and Na^+, are only weakly adsorbed by clay minerals and for this reason they are

Table 6.5 Rates of leaching of plant nutrients from soils of different texture (VÖMEL [1965/66])

| Soil | Clay content | kg/ha/year | | | | |
		N	K	Na	Ca	Mg
Sand	<3%	12–52	7–17	9–52	110–300	17–34
Sandy Loam	16%	0–27	0–14	1–69	0–242	0–37
Loam	28%	9–44	3– 8	11–45	21–176	9–61
Clay	39%	5–44	3– 8	9–42	72–341	10–54

particularly susceptile to leaching. Calcium is also not very strongly adsorbed by inorganic colloids and, as this ion is present in most mineral arable soils in comparatively high amounts, the rate of leaching of Ca^{2+} is very high. Potassium, on the other hand, can be bound very tightly particularly to clay minerals of the 2:1 type (see page 414). For soils rich in these minerals, K leaching rates are relatively low. Clay minerals of the kaolinitic type do not absorb K^+ selectively. High rates of leaching of K have therefore been observed in kaolinitic soils (PEDRO [1973]).

Of the major plant nutrients, phosphate is leached at the lowest rate. COOKE and WILLIAMS [1970] found that on a heavy arable soil, phosphate originating from an annual dressing of 33 kg P/ha given over the past 100 years only penetrated about 20 cm below the plough layer. For grassland similar results were obtained (see Figure 6.2). The rate of removal of phosphate by leaching from the upper soil layer in mineral soils is thus rather low and amounts to about

0–1.75 kg P/ha/annum (DAM KOFOED and LINDHARD [1968]). In organic soils higher rates of phosphate leaching may occur as phosphate is less strongly bound to soil particles (MUNK [1972]).

In contrast to phosphate and the cationic plant nutrients, which are mainly involved in physico-chemical processes, the mobility of N in the soil depends

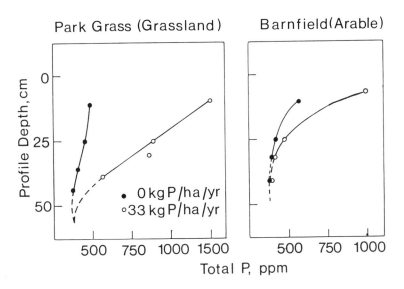

Fig.6.2 Downward movement of phosphate after a hundred years of fertilizing (after COOKE and WILLIAMS [1970]).

largely on biological processes. Nitrogen is mainly leached in form of the NO_3–N (MINDERMAN and LEEFLANG [1968]). For this reason the rate of mineralization of organic N to NO_3–N considerably influences the rate of leaching of N. PFAFF [1963] reported that N leached out by the winter rainfall mainly originated from the organic N mineralized during autumn and winter. The rate of NO_3–N leaching is thus particularly high, if organic manure is applied in autumn. Under European conditons NO_3–N is leached out of the profile to only a minor extent during summer. Even on sandy soils, which are especially susceptible to NO_3–N leaching (DAM KOFOED and KJELLERUP [1970]), NO_3–N transported into the deeper soil layers during summer remains within the range of plant roots. This observation is shown very clearly in the findings of OGUS and FOX [1970] presented in Table 6.6 The results compare the uptake of N by *Bromus inermis* for N placed at different soil depths. Even at a depth of application of 60 cm, more than half the N applied was absorbed over the experimental period of 50 days. This relatively high uptake of N may be accounted for largely by the comparative ease with which NO_3^- is translocated upwards in the soil profile. This depends very much on climatic conditions. In the temperate climatic zone alternating wet and dry periods occur during summertime. In the drier periods NO_3–N from the deeper soil layers is often conducted to the upper soil profile. As this is usually more abundant in plant roots, the N-nutrition of the crop is enhanced (HARMSEN [1959]). Similar observations have been made by NOMMIK [1966] in Sweden who reported a high crop recovery of N which had been applied in the previous year. On the other hand considerable leaching of NO_3–N may occur even on heavy soils, which are well fissured and allow a high rate of vertical water movement (SHAW [1962]). Under temperate climatic conditions, *e.g.* in Central Europe, fertilizer N leaching can be avoided to a large extent, if N application is made in spring or summer and not before winter. TESKE and MATZEL [1976] in studying the N balance in lysimeter experiments with N-15 labelled urea, found that the N leaching rate ranged from 8.8 to 16.7 kg N/ha/year. Of this quantity only 12 to 15% originated from fertilizer N.

As already mentioned, the process of leaching of plant nutrients in soils is affected by plant cover. In fallow soils in particular, high leaching rates are often

Table 6.6 Uptake of nitrogen by *Bromis inermis* from nitrate fertilizer applied at different soil depths.

Application rate: 135 kg N/ha per soil layer in the form of Ca $(NO_3)_2$.
Duration of uptake 50 days (OGUS and FOX [1970])

Depth of nitrate application in cm	Uptake by *Bromus inermis* in kg N/ha
Surface	82
30	75
60	72
105	26
150	11

found because in the absence of a nutrient demand by a growing crop, more nutrients are available for translocation. Similarly the percolation rate of water is also higher under fallow conditions because of the lack of a crop requirement. Differences in leaching between fallow and cropped land can be very clearly seen in the results of a lysimeter experiment carried out by COPPENET [1969] under the very humid conditions of the French Atlantic coast. The data of this experiment, presented in Table 6.7 are taken from observations made over a 12-year period. Leaching rates for all nutrients, with the exception of phosphate, were higher in the fallow treatment. The differences were particularly marked for N and K

Table 6.7 Leaching rates of plant nutrients from a clay loam soil (18% clay) under fallow and cropped treatments (COPPENET [1969])

| | kg nutrient ha/year | |
	Fallow	Cropped
N	142	62
P	0.3	0.3
K	46	24
Ca	310	230
Mg	24	18

which are required and taken up by plant roots at a very high rate. Crop type can also affect the rate at which nutrients are leached from the soil. For widely spaced crops, such as grapes or maize, leaching losses are generally higher than for high density crops. Under grassland, N leaching is usually quite low although higher rates occur when leguminous species are present. This was shown by the work of LOW and ARMITAGE [1970] under English climatic conditions. Nitrogen leaching rates were especially high when the deterioration of the white clover sward began, as can be seen from the data of Table 6.8.

Table 6.8 Nitrogen leaching rates in relation to soil cover (LOW and ARMITAGE [1970])

Period	White clover kg N/ha/year	Grass	Fallow
1952–1953	27	1.8	114
1953–1954	26	1.3	113
1954–1955	60[+]	3.9	105
1956	131[++]	2.0	41

[+] White clover dying out
[++] White clover removed

The movement of ions in solution involves the transport of cations and anions in equivalent amounts. In the soil profile the main cation species transported are Ca^{2+}, Mg^{2+}, Na^+ and K^+ and the major anions are NO_3^-, HCO_3^-, Cl^-, SO_4^{2-}. For soils developed under humid climatic conditions, Ca^{2+}, Mg^{2+}, NO_3^- and in some cases HCO_3^- are the ions usually transported in highest amounts. This is discussed in more detail on page 70. As might be expected from these findings, leaching contributes to a varying degree to the loss of individual plant nutrients from the soil. For both P and K, leaching plays a minor role. Removal by plant uptake is very much more important. For Na^+, Ca^{2+} and SO_4^{2-}, however, leaching losses under humid conditions can amount to more than 50% of the total removal (DAM KOFOED and LINDHARD [1968]).

The movement of ions into deeper soil layers may not only be regarded in terms of nutrient loss. Additionally, it is a process by which the accumulation of ions in the upper soil layer is prevented and hence also the development of salinity. This is an often forgotten advantage of regions of humid climate, for by appropriate fertilizer usage nutrient losses by leaching can be controlled. The retention of plant nutrients in the upper soil layers only becomes a major problem under tropical conditions where rainfall is high and soils are often very pervious. Under these conditions the use of slow-release fertilizers is likely to reduce leaching losses. The most important 'slow release fertilizers' or 'controlled release fertilizers' can be grouped into coated fertilizers and organic fertilizers. In the former, the granules are coated by a plastic film or by sulphur. Some coated fertilizers the so called 'osmocotes' release nutrients from the granule as a result of the internal pressure built up by the osmotic entry of water. Of the

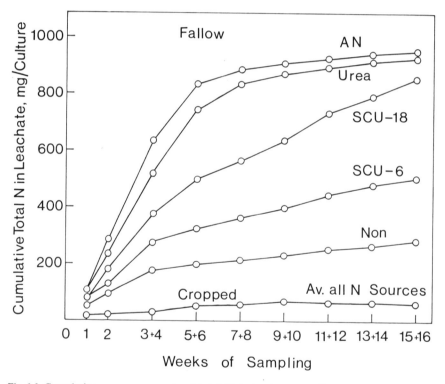

Fig.6.3 Cumulative average amounts of total N in leachates as affected by N source and cropping.
AN = ammonium nitrate, SCU = sulphur coated urea (after TERMAN and ALLEN [1970]).

organic slow release fertilizers, urea formaldehyde polymers (UF) isobutylideneurea (IBDU) and crotonylidenediurea (CDU) are the most important (see also p. 367). The aim of the slow release fertilizers, namely to adjust the nutrient release to the demand of the plant, is not always achieved.

SAN VALENTIN et al. [1978] were able to reduce K$^+$ leaching losses considerably by applying coated potassium to tobacco grown on sandy soils. MINER et al. [1978] on the other hand emphasize that the release rate of slow release fertilizers is not predictable because they are influenced by soil microbial activities as well as by physical and chemical processes. For this reason they are often inferior to conventional fertilizers. OERTLI [1980] who has considered 'controlled-release fertilizers' in a very useful review paper draws attention to the fact that the successful application of these fertilizers depends much on climatic and weather conditions as well as on crop type. He suggests that controlled release fertilizers are especially useful in greenhouse cultivation, for container grown plants, for crops grown under a plastic cover and probably also for paddy rice.

TERMAN and ALLEN [1970] carried out an experiment (Figure 6.3) in humid climatic conditions comparing sulphur coated N fertilizers with straight N fertilizers under fallow and cropped treatments. In the treatments cropped with grass, all the leachates were low in N regardless of the fertilizer applied. In the fallow treatment, however, there were marked differences between the N contents of the leachates. The much lower rates of N leaching for the two sulphur coated urea forms SCU–18 and SCU-6 over the straight N fertilizers shows the benefit of the coated fertilizers. Similar advantages of S coated KCl have also been found (TERMAN and ALLEN [1970]).

6.1.4 Volatilization and denitrification

Nitrogen may be lost from the soil in the form of gases (TERMAN [1979]). A considerable loss of NH_3 may occur when NH_4-salts are applied to calcareous soils. Such high pH soils should not be treated with NH_4-salts. The same is also true for the use of urea as a top dressing (COOKE [1972]).

Recent investigations have shown that the plant itself may also release gaseous nitrogen into the atmosphere mainly in the form of NH_3. The net rate of release depends on the NH_3 concentration of the atmosphere, temperature and transpiration conditions, high temperature and high transpiration rates increasing the net N loss. According to investigations of STUTTE et al. [1979] with soya beans carried out under field conditions, the N release of the crop may amount to about 45 kg N/ha/year under high temperature and transpiration conditions.

LEMON and VAN HOUTTE [1980] hold the view that the release and uptake of NH_3 by the crop results in a significant N transfer from sites of higher to sites of lower atmospheric NH_3 concentration. Atmospheric NH_3 concentrations may vary to a marked extent. Thus according to their observations of 'clean air' contained about 3 to 5 µg NH_3 m^{-3} whereas for an ungrazed pasture the NH_3 concentration at the canopy base was 13.5 and above the canopy 1 µg NH_3 m^{-3}. These results demonstrate that the NH_3 released by the soil was to a large extent absorbed by the grass.

The atmospheric NH_3 concentration profile for a crop stand at day and night is shown in Figure 6.4 from this work of LEMON and VAN HOUTTE [1980]. It is obvious that during the day the atmospheric NH_3 concentration in the crop stand was much reduced because of the uptake by the crop. The absorption of NH_3 occurs mainly *via* the stomata and thus higher NH_3 concentrations were found in the crop stand during the night. These values were particularly high near the soil surface showing that the soil was a major source of NH_3.

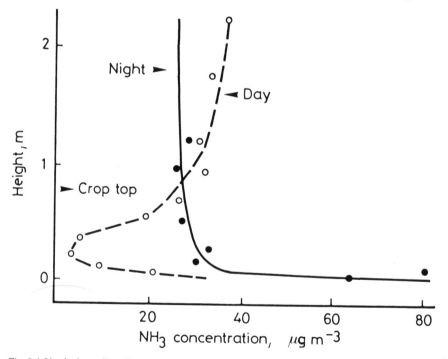

Fig.6.4 Vertical profile of atmospheric NH_3 concentration within and above a canopy of quackgrass *(Agropyron repens)* at night and day (modified after LEMON and VAN HOUTTE [1980]).

Under anaerobic soil conditions, nitrate is often reduced to volatile nitrogen forms such as N_2 and N_2O. This process, which is mediated by microbiological activity is called denitrification (see page 343). ROLSTON [1977] observed that the proportion of N_2O produced by denitrification amounted only to about 5% of the N_2 released. Denitrification occurs particularly rapidly under anaerobic conditions where a ready source of carbohydrate (straw, roots, etc.) is available for the denitrifying bacteria. According to WOLDENDORP [1968] even on grassland 10 to 40% of the applied nitrogen can be lost in this way. Denitrification losses also occur on arable land (TERMAN and BROWN [1968]). Paddy soils in particular are susceptible to denitrification as they are characterized by low O_2 partial pressures (PONNAMPERUMA [1965]). For this reason these soils should not be supplied with nitrate, but only with NH_4-N. Under low pH conditions (ph <4.5) denitrification is almost totally inhibited. Denitrification and leaching losses of soil N can be reduced by the application of nitrification inhibitors (TOUCHTON et al. [1978]). This question is considered in more detail on p. 345.

6.1.5 Erosion

An additional nutrient loss in soil can be caused by erosion. Large quantities of soil can be permanently removed from agricultural land to rivers and lakes. As this material contains a high proportion of fine soil particles, considerable amounts of plant nutrients can be lost. The degree of erosion depends on a number of factors including the rainfall and its intensity, the relief of the land and, in particular, on the soil cover. In regions where erosion is important the loss of some plant nutrients may be high. Nutrients removed from a 4% slope from the Missouri Erosion Experiment were cited by BUCKMAN and BRADY [1969]. When maize was grown continuously annual losses as high as 678 kg/ha K, 246 kg/ha Ca and 98 kg/ha Mg were reported. These levels are all well in excess of the annual uptake of these nutrients by crops (see page 296). For most soils which are not subjected to erosion to any great extent, losses of nutrients are relatively small and amount to only a few kg/ha of nutrients at the most (MILLER [1972]). Under fallow conditions the effects of erosion are more pronounced.

6.1.6 Nutrient supply by precipitation and atmosphere

It is well known that plant nutrients contained in rainwater can contribute to the nutrient supply of crops. An intensive investigation into the plant nutrient content of the precipitation from twelve different sites in Norway was carried out by LÅG [1968]. The data from the sites with the highest and the lowest rainfall are shown in Table 6.9. The Vågåmo site which is situated in the mountains is characterized by a rather low precipitation, containing very low amounts of plant nutrients. On the Lista site the pattern is quite different. Lista is on the Southern coast of Norway where the rainfall is high. The precipitation is considerably influenced by sea water and is relatively rich in inorganic ions, in particular in Na^+ and Cl^-. As well as the high levels of Na^+ and Cl^-, substantial amounts of Mg^{2+} and sulphate are also present in the rainwater at this site. The contents of Na^+, Cl^- and Mg^{2+} all decreased from the coastal districts to the interior. This observation could have a more general bearing for tropical conditions when the natural distribution of oil palms and coconut palms is restricted to coastal areas. According to OLLAGNIER and OCHS [1971] these species have a particularly high requirement for Cl^- (see page 548).

Table 6.9 Amounts of plant nutrients supplied by precipitation on two Norwegian sites (LÅG [1968])

Location	Precipitation mm/year	kg/ha/year							
		S	Cl	NO_3-N	NH_3-N	Na	K	Mg	Ca
Vågåmo	294	0.9	0.4	0.1	0.1	0.4	0.3	0.2	1.2
Lista	1871	19.2	264	3.5	2.8	147	8.6	17.8	14.2

The results from these two Norwegian sites demonstrate the great variability in the nutrient content of rainwater. It must be emphasized, however, that these are extreme sites and are therefore by no means representative. On average, the quantities of plant nutrients generally supplied in precipitation are somewhere between the values given in Table 6.9. RIEHM and QUELLMALZ [1959] found that under the climatic conditions of Central Europe, nutrients supplied from the atmosphere and as precipitation range from 1 to 30 kg/ha/annum. Table 6.10 gives the mean values obtained from 14 different stations over a period of several years. With the exceptions of S and Cl, the contents of all the nutrients in the rainwater were well below the amounts required to meet crop demand. This is

Table 6.10 Quantities of plant nutrients in the atmosphere and amounts supplied in precipitation under Central European conditions (RIEHM and QUELLMALZ [1959])

	mean values in kg/ha year							
	S	Cl	NO_3-N	NH_3-N	Na	K	Mg	Ca
Precipitation	8–13	4–6	1–3	2–4	2–4	1–2	2–3	8–16
Atmosphere	10–20	4–8	–	4–7	2–4	1–2	1–3	2–5

particularly true for N and K where rainwater can supply only in the order of a few per cent of the total crop needs. In the case of S, however, the atmospheric source can often adequately meet the requirements of even intensive cropping.

The levels of S falling annually as SO_4^{2-} in rainwater closely follows the distribution of industry and the burning of coal and oil in particular. In industrial regions as much as 100 kg S/ha/annum in rainwater are not uncommon. More generally values in Western Europe are in the range of about 15 kg S/ha/annum. This is adequate for crop growth, although it must be remembered that sulphate is very easily leached from soils. According to PFAFF [1963] a negative S balance in the soil can result even in regions where relatively high levels of S are supplied from the atmosphere (see page 384). A high proportion of sulphur may be present in the atmosphere in the gaseous form of SO_2. This can be used directly by plants (DE CORMIS [1968], FALLER et al. [1970]).

6.2 Mineral Fertilizers, Manures and Fertilization Techniques

6.2.1 Mineral fertilizers

In many soils the rate of removal of plant nutrients by crop uptake, leaching and denitrification is well in excess of nutrient release by weathering and mineralization. A negative nutrient balance thus results unless nutrients are applied in the form of fertilizers or manures to make up the difference. Generally, the more intensive the cropping system and the higher the yields, the greater must be the amounts of nutrients applied to the soil in order to maintain soil fertility. For most soils the use of inorganic fertilizers is thus almost essential and a wide range of fertilizers of different grades and nutrient ratios are now marketed. It is beyond the scope of this book to discuss these in detail. Only a brief survey of the most important fertilizer types will be given. The more common fertilizers are considered in the chapters following which deal with the individual plant nutrients.

Fertilizers contain those nutrients such as N, P, and K that are rapidly taken up and required in high quantities by crops. Nitrogen is mainly given in the form of nitrate, ammonium or urea. More specialized fertilizers contain nitrogen in a more insoluble form, such as urea formaldehyde and isobutylidene urea. These forms are slow release nitrogen sources. Phosphorus fertilizers generally contain P mainly in the form of phosphate. In a small number of phosphate fertilizers P is present as polyphosphates. An important criterium of P-fertilizers is solubility. Superphosphate for example is very soluble in water; ground rock phosphates, on the other hand, have a low water solubility. Potassium is applied to soils mainly in the chloride or sulphate forms. Potassium nitrate and potassium polyphosphate play only a minor role. Sulphur fertilizers can be obtained in the form of sulphate in ammonium sulphate, superphosphate and potassium sulphate. In addition to supplying S, these fertilizers are also a source of nitrogen, phosphorus and potassium respectively. Calcium and magnesium are applied as sulphates or in the form of carbonates or oxides. These two latter compounds have an alkaline reaction and are thus mainly used to increase soil pH (see page 454).

Although most inorganic fertilizers, such as ammonium sulphate, calcium nitrate or potassium chloride, are salts which are neutral in reaction, they can affect soil pH by their physiological reaction. Nitrates, when assimilated (reduced) by plant roots or microorganisms, yield one OH^- (HCO_3^-) for every NO_3^- reduced (see page 136). A portion of this OH^- (HCO_3^-) is released into the root medium and thus increases its pH value (KIRKBY and MENGEL [1967]). For this reason nitrate fertilizers are known to be physiologically alkaline. For NH_4^+ the reverse is true. The uptake of NH_4–N results in the release of H^+.

$$NH_4^+ \rightleftarrows NH_3 + H^+$$

Ammonium fertilizers, such as ammonium sulphate therefore have a physiological acid reaction. The potassium fertilizers, potassium chloride and potassium sulphate, tend to be neutral in reaction.

Fertilizers containing only one of the three most important plant nutrients, nitrogen, phosphorus or potassium, are called straight fertilizers. Typical examples of this group are superphosphate (P), muriate of potash (K), ammonium nitrate (N) and a mixture of ammonium nitrate with calcium cabonate (N), called 'nitro-chalk'. Compound and mixed fertilizers contain two or three of the main plant nutrients N, P and K. NPK-fertilizers very commonly differ in their NPK-ratios. An NPK compound 15–15–15, for example, means that the ratio of $N:P_2O_5:K_2O$ is equal to 1:1:1 and that the concentration (grade) of these plant nutrients in the compound is 15% N, 15% P_2O_5 and 15% K_2O. As this example shows, the nutrient content of straight and compound fertilizers is generally expressed in terms of % P_2O_5 and % K_2O and not as a percentage of the element.

6.2.2 Organic manures and crop residues

Organic manures mainly originate from the wastes and residues of plant and animal life. They are rich in water and carbon compounds but are usually comparatively poor in plant nutrients. One of the most important organic manures is farmyard manure (FYM). This is a mixture of partially decomposed straw containing faeces and urine. In recent years there has been a decline in its use as modern methods of livestock management tend to use little or no straw for bedding, the basis of FYM. The production of livestock slurries has thus increased.

The nutrient content of organic manures can vary widely depending much on their source and moisture content. Some mean values for a number of organic manures are listed in Table 6.11. The relative amounts of the major nutrients differ considerably. Farmyard manure is comparatively poor in phosphate as it contains a high proportion of straw. Sewage sludge is low in potassium as this is lost during preparation.

Table 6.11 Nutrient content of organic manures

| | Mosture % | % of the fresh matter | | | | |
		N	P	K	Ca	Mg
Farmyard manure	76	0.50	0.11	0.54	0.42	0.11
Cattle slurry	93	0.31	0.07	0.32	0.11	0.04
Pig slurry......................	97	0.20	0.10	0.20	–	–
Sewage sludge..................	55	0.83	0.22	0.04	0.07	–

The nutrient content of slurries is often difficult to assess, since slurries can differ considerably in water content. For this reason VETTER and KLASINK [1977] have proposed a calculation for the amount of plant nutrients 'produced' by farm animals on the basis of animal number. In this calculation 1 cow or 7 adult pigs or 200 hens are considered as one 'animal manure unit'. The unit is such that each animal group 'produces' about the same amount of plant nutrients. In Table 6.12 the amounts resulting in a one year cycle are shown. It can be seen that the quantity of nitrogen 'produced' by one unit is about the same for the three animal groups, but there are differences for K, P and Mg resulting from the type of food fed to the animals. Roughages and green fodder are rich in K and thus these materials give rise to relatively high K contents in slurries. On the other hand cereals are rich in P, and since they are fed to hens and pigs in relatively high amounts, the slurries of these animals have a high P concentration. In areas of intensive animal husbandry huge amounts of manure are produced, which may lead to overfertilization of soils and thus result in pollution problems (FÜRCHTENICHT *et al.* [1978]).

Table 6.12 Amounts of plant nutrients excreted by 'one animal manure unit' per year (VETTER and KLASINK [1977])

	N kg/year	P	K	Mg
Cattle (1 animal)	77	18	90	6.6
Pigs (7 animals)	75	29	34	5.4
Poultry (200 animals)	80	32	32	4.2

The value of organic manures cannot be assessed simply by analysis for the total quantity of plant nutrients. Nutrient availability to crops is highly important and this can only be determined by field trials. Most of the N in manures occurs in organic compounds. In urine it is present as urea and in poultry manure as uric acid. Nitrogen is readily available to plants from both these sources. The N containing organic compounds in FYM are much more resistant to decomposition and only about one-third of the N is easily released (COOKE [1972]). The remaining N can persist in the soil for a long period. The question of N availability in organic manure has been discussed by SLUIJSMANS and KOLENBRANDER [1977]. These authors emphasize that the direct N effect of organic matter depends much on the content of mineral N and urea. This amounts to about 10% of the total N of FYM, whereas in slurries about a half of the total N consists of mineral N and urea. This fraction is easily avaiable to plants and is almost as high in efficiency as mineral N fertilizer. The remainder of the N in FYM is of organic nature and is only gradually mineralized in the soil. Phosphorus in farmyard manure is present largely in organic form and about half the total P present quickly becomes available to crops. In contrast to the other major nutrients, K is almost totally water soluble as K^+ and is thus readily available. According to COOKE [1972], under many circumstances 25 t/h FYM supplies a first-year crop with about 40 kg N, 20 kg P and 80 kg K. This does not provide an adequate amount of N for the uptake of most crops of average yield. The same is true for K with the exception of the cereal crops (see Table 6.2).

The rate of decomposition of organic matter in the soil depends much on organic matter type and especially on the proportion of non hydrolyzable substances. These are relatively high in FYM and low in young green manure, with straw being between the two. Figure 6.5 shows the decomposition of these three organic materials over a period of 8 years (SLUIJSMANS and KOLEN-BRANDER [1977]). It is obvious that about 80% of the fresh green plant material, e.g. sugar beet leaves was decomposed during the first year after application. On the other hand only about 50% of the FYM and 60% of the straw were decomposed during the same period. For soil fertility much of the value of FYM results from the cumulative effects of one dressing after another on the structural improvement of the soil. In addition to soil structure, however, the N supplying power of the soil is also improved by long term FYM application so that treatment with FYM may be superior to an equivalent application of mineral fertilizer (COOKE [1977]).

The value of applying straw to soils is doubtful. Plant nutrients present in the straw such as K and P are available. However, straw application can considerably influence the nitrogen turnover in the soil and often leads to a re-

310

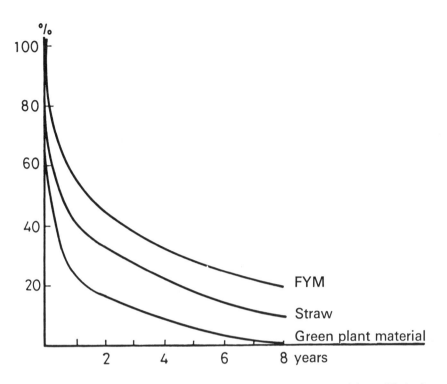

Fig.6.5 Rate of decomposition of FYM, straw, and green plant material (modified after
SLUIJSMANS and KOLENBRANDER [1977]).

duction in available nitrogen. It is usually held that this occurs because during
straw decomposition some of the soil inorganic nitrogen is fixed into organic
forms by soil microorganisms (TERMAN and BROWN [1968], MYERS and PAUL
[1971]). In the light of modern research findings, however, it is doubtful whether
N immobilization is the main cause of a reduction in N availability after straw
application. GANRY *et al.* [1978] found that the application of pearl millet
straw resulted in considerable N losses due to denitrification. Analogous
results have also been reported by GUIRAUD and BERLIER [1969]. BIEDERBECK
et al. [1980] in comparing straw application with straw burning over a period
of 20 years under the climatic conditions of Saskatchewan, found that plough-
ing straw into the soil in spring improved soil structure and reduced the hazard
of erosion as compared with straw burning. Straw burning on the other hand
resulted in an increase of available phosphate and exchangeable NH_4^+ in the
soil. The 'straw burning' treatments gave somewhat higher yields as compared
with the straw application treatments, although the difference was not significant. BACHTHALER and WAGNER [1973] carrying out straw application trials

on various sites in Bavaria, reported that on microbiologically active soils straw application generally increased crop yields. On dry or cold soils, however, straw application usually resulted in yield depressions. In this context the finding of GRAFF and KÜHN [1977] is of interest as these workers reported that the detrimental effect of straw application on yield is much alleviated, if the straw is decomposed by earthworms.

6.2.3 Liquid fertilizers

In recent years the application of fertilizer 'fluids' has become more common. The term 'fluid' includes 'liquids' in which the fertilizer is completely dissolved and 'suspensions' in which the fertilizer is present in the form of a suspension. Liquid fertilizers are generally easier to transport than solid ones and cause less of a labour problem in handling and application. A further advantage is their homogenity and the even distribution which can be achieved when they are applied to the soil. The two most important liquid N fertilizers are anhydrous ammonia and aqueous ammonia.

Anhydrous ammonia is the simplest liquid nitrogen fertilizer. It consists only of NH_3 which is present in a liquid form under pressure. Anhydrous ammonia is a high grade N-fertilizer with 82% N. This high concentration is of considerable advantage in terms of transport costs. On the other hand, the liquid under pressure requires special handling precautions and also suitable equipment for transportation and application. Its use is therefore often restricted. A special injection assembly is used to apply it into the soil at a depth of 15 to 20 cm to avoid loss of NH_3 by volatilization.

Aqueous ammonia is a solution containing about 25% NH_3. This solution is only under a very low pressure; it is therefore easier to handle and does not require the rather expensive application equipment which is needed for anhydrous ammonia. It must be remembered, however, that aqueous ammonia is a low grade fertilizer and contains only about 21–29% N. Again it is also necessary to ensure that it is applied below the soil surface in order to avoid loss of NH_3 by volatilization.

In recent years 'nitrogen solutions' have been developed by the Tennessee Valley Authority (TVA) in the USA. 'Low pressure' solutions are made up from urea, ammonia and ammonium nitrate and have about 30–40% N. They have the advantage that they are more concentrated than aqueous ammonia and more easy to handle. 'No pressure' solutions made up directly from urea and ammonium nitrate contain less than 30% N. The use of both urea and ammonium nitrate in solution is based on the fact that a mixture of these fertilizers has a higher solubility than either of its individual components.

312

Phosphorus and N containing solutions have been in use in the USA since the early 1950's. These 'NP solutions' were first produced by neutralizing ortho-phosphoric acid with an ammonium salt to produce mono- and diammonium phosphates; the standard solutions resulting from this procedure were about 8–24–0 (8% N, 24% P_2O_5, 0% K_2O). More recently by substitution of poly-phosphates for orthophosphates it has been possible to manufacture and ship higher graded fertilizers. The basic component of these solutions is super-phosphoric acid. This has a high P_2O_5 content and is made from orthophosphoric acid and a series of polyphosphoric acids. The proportion of each depends on the total P_2O_5 concentration; as this increases the proportion of longer chain acids goes up and the ortho acid content is reduced. This is illustrated in Figure 6.6 (SLACK [1967]). Superphosphoric acid is neutralized by the addition of ammonium ions (ammoniation) and NP-solutions can be obtained with grades of 10–34–0 and 11–37–0, depending on the P-content of the superphos-

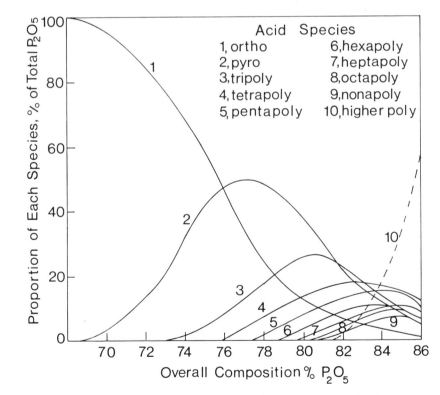

Fig.6.6 Equilibrium proportions of phosphoric acid species in the P_2O_5–H_2O system at high P_2O_5 concentration (after SLACK [1967]).

phoric acid used. These grades are based on a salting out temperature of $0°C$. This is the temperature at which crystallization occurs. As high nitrogen grade fertilizers are generally required, NP solutions are supplemented by a mixture of dissolved urea plus ammonium nitrate (28–32% N). Solutions of varying NP ratios are thus obtained. Polyphosphates tend to chelate heavy metals and Mg. This is a further advantage of NP solutions based on superphosphoric acid, because impurities of Mg, Fe or other heavy metals do not cause phosphate precipitation. Unfortunately, the addition of KCl to NP solutions results in precipitation. In solutions containing nitrate, KNO_3 crystallizes out. According to HIGNETT [1971] nitrate containing NPK solutions have a maximum grade of 7-7-7 (7% N, 7% P_2O_5, 7% K_2O), whereas for solutions containing only urea nitrogen component, a grade of 9-9-9 can be produced at a salting out temperature of $0°C$. The preparation of suitable NPK solutions by the addition of KCl is thus difficult. High graded PK solutions can be obtained by the neutralization of superphosphoric acid with KOH. Potassium hydroxide, however, is rather expensive and the resulting high production costs present a substantial drawback. For this reason most farmers using liquid fertilizers in the form of N- and NP solutions apply potassium in the solid form.

Some work has been carried out to develop suspensions in which the KCl is present as finely divided crystals, stabilized by the addition of clay (1 to 3% as suspending agent). According to SLACK [1967] high grades in the range of 15–15–15, and 10–30–10 can be obtained by this technique. Suspensions (slurries), however, are not easy to deal with and for this reason their application is limited.

Liquid fertilizers are easier to handle and to apply than solid ones, provided that suitable equipment is available for application. Once brought into contact with the soil, liquids behave in the same way as comparative solid fertilizers, and generally no differences are observed in relation to growth and crop yields.

6.2.4 Techniques of application

One of the most important aspects of fertilizer usage is to know when fertilizers should be applied. This depends primarily on the crop and on the mobility of the particular nutrients applied to the soil. Potassium and phosphates, which are hardly leached on medium to heavy textured soils are often applied in autumn and incorporated into the soil ready for crop growth in the spring. On the other hand, nitrogen fertilizers, which are generally susceptible to leaching, are applied in spring and also in the form of a top dressing during vegetative growth. Under semi-humid climatic conditions some of the nitrogen required by a crop can be applied in autumn for the following spring crop. The N-fertilizer is ploughed well into the soil, so that it is available in the deeper rooting zone in the following year.

In many cases it is not opportune to apply all the nitrogen in one dressing but rather to split the total amount into two or several applications. This type of nitrogen treatment is particularly common in intensive cropping systems where crop yields are high and where large amounts of nutrients are applied. Both in rice production in Japan and wheat production in Europe, split application is a well known fertilizer practice. Total nitrogen application rates are in the order of 100 to 160 kg N/ha for wheat. This can sometimes be split into three or sometimes four applications. The last application at the flowering stage is particularly important as it promotes grain filling and improves the grain protein content (see p. 277). Nitrogen treatment of winter crops, *e.g.* winter wheat or winter rape, can be split into autumn and spring applications. This is practised in the Mid-West (Indiana) of the USA where N application in autumn is necessary for good growth of winter wheat (HUBER *et al.* [1980]). The optimum N supply of this stage reduces the hazard of take-all root and crown rot *(Ophiobolus graminis)*. The beneficial effect of split N application on the annual yield of the grass crop has been reported by BROCKMAN [1974].

Most fertilizer applied is in solid form and is broadcast or in other words distributed uniformly on the soil. For soils of poor nutrient status the application of fertilizer in a row or a band, can often yield better results. The same is true for soils which strongly fix plant nutrients. Broadcasting phosphate fertilizers allows maximum contact between the fertilizer and soil particles so that it promotes P fixation. If the fertilizer is applied in the form of a band (placed application), the extent of contact between the phosphate soil fixing particles is reduced. Soil fixation is thus depressed and if the band is near the seed, a zone of high phosphate concentration is accessible to developing plant roots. The effect of phosphate placement is particularly noticeable on soils where P is limiting. This influence of placement was shown very clearly in experiments carried out on P deficient soils in Scotland (REITH [1972]). This is demonstrated in the data in Table 6.13. The placed application of phosphate resulted in considerable yield

Table 6.13 Effect of a placed application of superphosphate on the relative yield of swedes *(Brassica napus)* grown on P deficient soils. Relative yield of the corresponding broadcast application = 100 (REITH [1972])

Soil group	No. of expts.	Rate of P (kg P/ha)	
		18	36
Old Red Sandstone	9	152	133
Acid igneous	9	138	122
Basic igneous	14	208	162
Slate and schist	10	169	154

increases in comparison with the broadcast application. Similar results have been reported by HOJMARK [1972]. On potassium deficient soils potassium placement is also often superior to broadcast application. On sites deficient in either phosphate or potassium, fertilizer application should be made in the spring when crop demand is high. Autumn application favours nutrient fixation because at this time the roots do not provide a nutrient sink.

6.2.5 Foliar application

Leaves and other aerial plant organs are very well able to take up nutrients in gaseous form (CO_2, O_2, SO_2) *via* the stomata. However, the uptake of nutrients in ionic form from solution is limited as the outer epidermal cells of the leaf are covered by the cuticle. This consists of wax films alternating with cutin lamellas. Cutin itself is a condensate of C_{18}-hydroxy fatty acids of hemihydrophilic nature (FRANKE [1967]). The cuticle is thus only partially permeable to water and dissolved solutes. Those nutrients that are taken up can help to meet the nutrient needs of the plant. Nutrient uptake by leaf tissue is more effective the longer the nutrient solution remains in the form of a fine film on the leaf surface. Thus on hot clear days when evaporation is high and water from the foliar spray can easily be evaporated, salts accumulate on the leaf surface without being absorbed. This causes leaf scorching and burning. Such detrimental effects can be avoided by using solutions of low concentration (about 2 to 5%) and spraying on cool, cloudy days or in the evening. In order to obtain thin surface films and thus provide a large surface contact, foliar spray solutions are often supplemented with agents which reduce water surface tension.

Basically the process of nutrient uptake by leaf cells is the same as that of nutrient absorption by plant root cells, the main step in the process being the transport through the biological membrane, the plasmalemma (see page 110). As transport through the plasmalemma is an active process, for most plant nutrients, the uptake rate is influenced by the physiological status of the leaf. In leaf tissues in contrast to the root this active uptake process is usually not the limiting step in ion uptake. The rate of uptake is controlled by the diffusion of plant nutrients from the water film on the leaf surface through the cuticle and cell wall material to the plasmalemma.

Foliar application of plant nutrients can be very efficient under certain conditions, but it should be remembered that in general leaves are only able to take up a relatively small quantity of nutrients in comparison with the plant's demand. This is particularly the case for macronutrients, which are required by crops in very high amounts. Foliar application of N, P and K is therefore not very common in practice. For nitrogen, the most common form of foliar application is urea, which is readily taken up and metabolized in the leaf tissue. According to FRANKE [1967] urea improves the permeability of the cuticle and thus favours diffusion conditions. MATHUR *et al.* [1968] reported that spraying urea on cotton resulted in significant yield responses and that foliar application was superior to soil application. On soils with a low N availability WALTER *et al.* [1973] obtained a yield increase and an improvement of grape quality by foliar application of urea. Such effects can be found, but the results must not be generalized. Under conditions of practical farming it is often difficult to distinguish between foliar uptake and root uptake, for much of the urea sprayed on leaves may fall on to the soil and find its way into the plant through the roots.

Foliar application is particularly useful under conditions where nutrient uptake from the soil is restricted. This is often the case for the heavy metals such as Fe, Mn, Zn and Cu. These nutrients are frequently fixed by soil particles and for this reason are scarcely available to plant roots. On such sites, foliar application in the form of inorganic salts or chelates is a valuable tool in combating nutrient deficiencies (TUKEY *et al.* [1962]). As micronutrients are only required in small quantities, a foliar spray applied once or twice and correctly timed, is adequate to meet the demand of the crop.

Nutrient sprays are particularly used for fruit trees. These crops are often deep rooting so that fertilizer applied to the soil surface may be of little use and more readily available to the cover crop. Thus COOKE [1972] reported that leaf spraying with urea was an effective means of applying nitrogen to apple trees in grass-sown orchards where the trees often suffer from nitrogen deficiency. Physiological disorders, such as 'bitter pit' in apples, which results from Ca deficiency, can also be alleviated to some extent by spraying the fruits with a solution of a Ca salt. Several applications must be made (SCHUMACHER and FRANKEN-HAUSER [1968]).

6.2.6 Nutrient ratios and recommendations

As already outlined in Chapter 5 (see page 267) the maximum effect of one particular plant nutrient can only be expected, if the supply of other plant nutrients is adequate. For this reason the ratio in which plant nutrients are applied in fertilizers is also important. This ratio depends on a number of factors including soil fertility status, crop species and crop management. If a soil is poor in one particular nutrient, as for example phosphate, fertilizers with relatively high P-contents should obviously be applied. For extreme deficiency in phosphate or potassium, the application of appropriate straight fertilizers is frequently recommended in order to raise soil fertility status to a satisfactory level. This is often the case where phosphate or potassium are fixed by soil minerals.

On soils of high fertility status, crop nutrient uptake ratios correspond very closely to crop nutrient requirements. Thus to some extent nutrient uptake ratios can be used to calculate fertilizer application rates. The ratio of the amounts of N, P and K taken up by cereals is in the order of 1:0.3:0.8; the corresponding ratio for sugar beet and potatoes is 1:0.3:1.8 (VON BOGUSLAWSKI and VON GIERKE [1961]). Hence for cereals, fertilizers containing nutrient ratios of about 1:0.5:1 are recommended, whereas sugar beet and potatoes require ratios with a higher proportion of potassium. The N, P and K uptake ratios for vegetative plant material such as grass, clover or lucerne are about 1:0.15:1.1. In clover and lucerne, N is mainly supplied by nitrogen fixation and for this reason only phosphate and potassium are generally applied in large amounts. The quantities of phosphate required by crops are higher than the amounts indicated by phosphate removal figures and the NPK uptake ratios because of the substantial quantity of fertilizer phosphate fixed in the soil. In long term field experiments KÖHNLEIN and KNAUER [1965] observed that the proportion of phosphate taken up by crops ranged from between 21 and 75% of the total phosphate applied. The extent of phosphorus fixation is very much dependent on soil phosphorus status, a lower proportion of applied phosphate usually being fixed by soils rich in phosphate (HUGHES and SEARLE [1964]).

In calculating nutrient ratios suitable for mineral fertilizer application, farm practice must also be taken into account. Crop rotation is important as the residues from one crop can considerably influence the amount of nutrient required by a following crop. Cereal straw, for example, contains about 17 kg N/ha, 3 kg P/ha and 30 kg K/ha. If this is ploughed into the field the following crop will have a useful source of K, but will need an additional N supply than normal, because part of the N application will have been utilized by the soil bacteria in decomposing the straw or even denitrified. Unharvested sugar beet leaves are a good source of plant nutrients, containing approximately 100 kg N/ha, 10 kg P/ha and 100 kg K/ha. These nutrients can largely be used by a following crop. On the other hand, sugar beet is a crop which has a very high nutrient requirement, and the roots and leaves of a sugar beet crop with a yield of 50 t roots/ha can remove as much as 260 kg N, 40 kg P and 360 kg K per ha from the soil. This places a high nutrient demand on the soil, particularly for K. If this has not been supplied to the sugar beet crop a succeeding crop may need more K than if it had followed a crop with a lower nutrient uptake.

On grazing pastures a considerable proportion of plant nutrients can be recycled directly by animals. On permanent pastures grazing animals can return as much as 75% to 80% of the phosphate and potassium taken up by the sward. The nutrient ratio of fertilizers applied to pastures should therefore contain low proportions of these nutrients (BERGMANN [1969]).

The nutrient ratio of fertilizers also depends on the degree of agricultural intensification. Where yield levels are high and intensive cropping is being carried out, the proportion of plant nutrients originating from the soil is generally small. This in particular is important for potassium. In extensive agricultural systems potassium is very largely provided by the soil. According to COOKE [1974] 'potassium fertilizers are increasingly needed when agriculture is intensified'. This is very well reflected in the nutrient ratios in fertilizers used in various regions of the world shown in Table 6.14. The relatively high phosphate consumption in Oceania results from the pasture dressing in New Zealand and Australia.

Table 6.14 Nutrient ratios in fertilizers used in 1972 in various regions of the world (FAO [1972])

	N	P_2O_5	K_2O
Western Europe	1	0.82	0.71
North America	1	0.61	0.53
Oceania	1	8.3	1.4
Latin America	1	0.70	0.47
Near East	1	0.42	0.03
Far East	1	0.33	0.20
Africa	1	0.77	0.44

For many years rule-of-thumb methods have been used in advising fertilizer usage, and it is only relatively recently that a quantitative approach has been attempted. The Ministry of Agriculture, Fisheries and Food Bulletin on Fertilizer Recommendation [1973] published in England has provided a very useful index method for recommending fertilizer application rates for a large number of temperate crops growing on different soils. The basis on which these recommendation are made are from numerous sources and years of advisory experience. This is coupled with soil analytical data. For any soil, each nutrient is given an index number representing the degree of nutrient availability. For P, K and Mg the index number from 0 to 9 is based on the estimation of the available soil nutrient by a suitable extractant. Standard methods are used. In the case of P, sodium bicarbonate at pH 8.5 is employed, whereas indices of K and Mg are obtained from M ammonium nitrate extracts. Table 6.15 shows the indices for these nutrients in relation to available levels in soil. 'Zero' is extremely low and '9' is very high. The critical levels usually lie between indices 1 and 2, and are in the order of about 15 ppm P, 120 ppm K and 50 ppm Mg. Below these values there is a strong possibility of nutrient deficiency. For N the index from 0 to 5 is based on the farming system and cropping history. In some cases

Table 6.15 Indices of P, K and Mg in relation to available soil nutrients (Ministry of Agriculture Fisheries and Food. Technical Bulletin No. 209. Fertilizer Recommendations. H.M.S.O. [1973])

Index	P Sodium bicarbonate pH 8.5 extract P (ppm in soil)	K Ammonium nitrate extract K (ppm in soil)	Mg Mg (ppm in soil)	Interpretation
0	0 – 9	0 – 60	0 – 25	Deficiency in arable crops expected
1	10 – 15	61 – 120	26 – 50	Possible deficiency in susceptible crops
2	16 – 25	121 – 240	51 – 100	
3	26 – 45	245 – 400	101 – 175	
8	201–280	2410–3600	1010–1500	Excessively high levels

Table 6.16 Nutrient requirements of sugar beet, potatoes and spring oats growing on sandy soils (kg/ha) (Ministry of Agriculture Fisheries and Food. Technical Bulletin No. 209. Fertilizer Recommendations. H.M.S.O. [1973])

Crop	N					P					K				Mg		
Nutrient Index	0	1	2	3	4	0	1	2	3	over 3	0	1	2	over 2	0	1	over 1
Sugar Beet	125	125	100	75	50	188	125	63	38	Nil	313	188	125	125	94	63	Nil
Maincrop Potatoes	225	188	150	100	75	313	250	219	188	125	313	250	250	188	75	38	Nil
Spring Oats	100	75	38	Nil	Nil	75	38	38	Nil	Nil	75	38	38	Nil	63	Nil	Nil

nitrogenous fertilizer requirement is further adjusted according to the average summer rainfall, soil depth, texture and the actual winter rainfall.

An example showing how the index system is applied to practical crop requirements is shown in Table 6.16. This gives the nutrient requirements of three crops growing on sandy soils. In addition to the figures given in Tables 6.15 and 6.16 the bulletin provides information advising which fertilizers to use, when to apply them and other factors pertaining to the management of each crop. This system is not the complete answer to all cropping problems. For example, the use of 'previous cropping' to obtain a nitrogen index is not entirely satisfactory. Soil testing using the N^{min} method as developed in Germany, however, may improve this situation (see p. 100).

A new approach for forecasting fertilizer requirements of vegetable crops growing on widely different soils has been developed by GREENWOOD et al. [1974]. These workers argue that of the more than 20 vegetable crops grown on widely different soils in the United Kingdom it is impracticable to carry out trials to cover more than a few possible combinations of crop and soil. They therefore developed an alternative 'short cut' method in which a model was first devised then calibrated against experimental data and used to predict response curves in different situations. Experiments were carried out to characterize the responses of 22 crops to N, P and K fertilizers so that the approach could be applied in practice. This modelling approach has proved to be extremely valuable in NPK fertilizer prediction for vegetable crops in the United Kingdom (GREENWOOD et al. [1980]). Such an approach may also well prove to be of value in predicting the fertilizer requirement of the agricultural crops.

6.3 General Aspects of Fertilizer Application

6.3.1 Fertilizer use and agricultural production

The application of science to agriculture has had an enormous impact on agricultural production. This can be seen very well from the data of Table 6.17 which compares present crop yields in Germany with those of nearly 100 years ago. Crop yields are now about three times greater than at the end of the last century. At that time 100 ha of farmland produced food for 129 people in one year. The same area now provides food for about 450 people. In other countries similar dramatic increases in crop production have also occurred. This increase in productivity is an important achievement of scientific research and an essential one, for without it famine would be common even in regions now producing a surplus of agricultural products.

Table 6.17 Mean crop yields in Germany at the present time compared with those before the introduction of mineral fertilization

	Yield in tonnes/ha 1878/88	1965/70
Wheat (grain)	1.3	3.8
Rye (grain	1.4	3.0
Barley (grain)	1.3	3.4
Oats (grain)	1.2	3.2
Potatoes (tubers)	8.2	27.0
Sugar beet (fresh roots)	22.0	43.4
Hay	3.1	6.7

Undoubtedly the spectacular rise in crop yields has resulted from a combination of factors. These include crop improvement by breeding for high-yielding cultivars, improved farming methods, the use of pesticides and herbicides and last, but not least, the application of fertilizers. These factors are all interrelated. In order to establish high crop yields, however, adequate amounts of plant nutrients must be available in the soil. This question has been discussed by GREENWOOD [1980] in a recent review. He points out that in the United Kingdom potential maximum cereal crop yields in the order of 20 tons dry matter/ha/year and containing not less than 1.5% N, 0.3% P and 1.5% K take up at least 300 kg N/ha, 60 kg P/ha and 300 kg K/ha. By comparison, however, most soils in the United Kingdom only release per year about 40 kg N/ha, 5 kg P/ha and 10–100 kg K/ha when continuously cropped with wheat. The differences to reach maximum potential have to be made up by fertilizer application. The high yields of modern agriculture are thus, to a considerable extent, due to the application of mineral fertilizers. This has also been very clearly shown in the findings of VIETS [1971] in the USA, who investigated the effect on the yields of a number of crops when the use of nitrogen and phosphate fertilizers was discontinued for a period of only one year. Figure 6.7 illustrates the severe yield reductions which ensued.

Fertilizer usage plays a major role in the universal need to increase food production to meet the demands of the growing world population. This is demonstrated in Figure 6.8 from an extensive FAO analysis (RICHARDS [1979]) of a large number of field trials carried out in developing countries. Fertilizer application resulted in marked crop yield increases, which for most crops was more than 100%. The extent to which fertilizers are used still differs considerably between various regions of the world (v. PETER [1980]). As can be seen from Figure 6.9 fertilizer consumption per ha and per capita is highest in the developed countries (UNIDO study quoted after v. PETER [1980]).

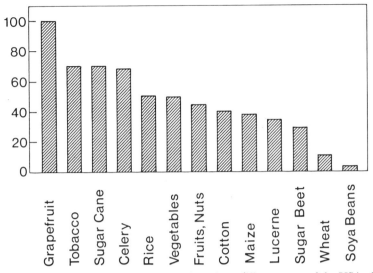

Fig.6.7 Estimated per cent reduction in crop yields from different parts of the USA, the first year with elimination of nitrogen and phosphate fertilizers (after VIETS [1971]).

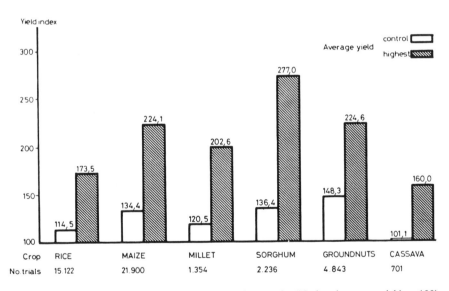

Fig.6.8 Crop response to fertilizers based on FAO/FP results (National average yield = 100) (RICHARDS [1979]).

In order to obtain satisfactory fertilizer responses new cultivars are often required. This is particularly the case for rice and wheat. Local cultivars are often tall plants and are susceptible to lodging, especially if fertilized with nitrogen.

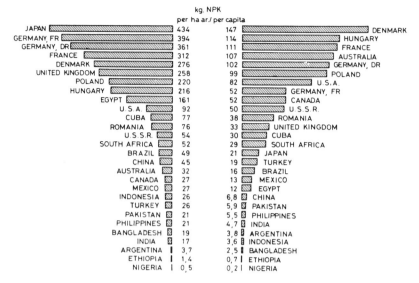

kg. NPK
per ha ar./ per capita

JAPAN	434	147		DENMARK
GERMANY, FR	394	114		HUNGARY
GERMANY, DR	361	111		FRANCE
FRANCE	312	107		AUSTRALIA
DENMARK	276	102		GERMANY, DR
UNITED KINGDOM	258	99		POLAND
POLAND	220	82		U.S.A.
HUNGARY	216	52		GERMANY, FR
EGYPT	161	52		CANADA
U.S.A.	92	50		U.S.S.R.
CUBA	77	38		ROMANIA
ROMANIA	76	33		UNITED KINGDOM
U.S.S.R.	54	30		CUBA
SOUTH AFRICA	52	29		SOUTH AFRICA
BRAZIL	49	21		JAPAN
CHINA	45	19		TURKEY
AUSTRALIA	32	16		BRAZIL
CANADA	27	13		MEXICO
MEXICO	27	12		EGYPT
INDONESIA	26	6,8		CHINA
TURKEY	26	5,9		PAKISTAN
PAKISTAN	21	5,5		PHILIPPINES
PHILIPPINES	21	4,7		INDIA
BANGLADESH	19	3,8		ARGENTINA
INDIA	17	3,6		INDONESIA
ARGENTINA	3,7	2,5		BANGLADESH
ETHIOPIA	1,4	0,7		ETHIOPIA
NIGERIA	0,5	0,2		NIGERIA

Fig.6.9 Fertilizer use intensity in selected countries (UNIDO [1976]).

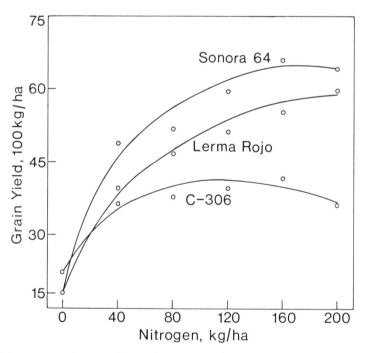

Fig.6.10 Response to nitrogen of one old and two modern wheat cultivars (after CHANDLER [1970]).

324

The newer dwarf cultivars are very resistant to lodging and high grain yields may be obtained when they are adequately supplied with plant nutrients. This is shown in the data of Figure 6.10 (CHANDLER [1970]). The typical tall local Indian wheat cultivar C–306 only responded to a low rate of nitrogen application and maximum grain yields were obtained at about 80 kg N/ha. In contrast the short stiff straw Mexican cultivars Sonora 64 and Lerma Rojo gave a much greater response to N and about twice the grain yields were obtained with a nitrogen application rate of 160 kg N/ha.

6.3.2 Fertilizer application and energy consumption

In the USA on an average size farm, one man produces enough food for about 50 people. This high degree of efficiency has only been achieved by the use of a considerable amount of energy mainly in the form of petrol and electricity. The application of fertilizers, herbicides and pesticides also involves an indirect consumption of energy as the production of these materials requires energy. According to LEWIS and TATCHELL [1979] the energy required for the production of 1 kg fertilizer plant nutrient is as follows:

$$N - 73 \text{ MJ}$$
$$P - 14 \text{ MJ}$$
$$K - 8 \text{ MJ}$$

The value obtained for N relates to modern production techniques. Older technologies consumed almost twice as much energy for the production of 1 kg fertilizer N. LEWIS and TATCHELL [1979] carried out a thorough investigation into the energy consumption of agricultural production under the conditions of UK agriculture. Their main results are reported in Table 6.18. From these data it is clear that the plant production has a positive energy balance since the energy output/input ratio is >1. The reverse is true for

Table 6.18 Energy output/input ratio of crop and animal products (data from LEWIS and TATCHELL [1979])

	Total	Increment obtained by fertilizer application
Wheat (winter)	2.2	3.3
Barley (spring)	2.0	3.2
Sugar	2.5	2.1[+)
Potatoes	1.3	2.0
Milk	0.40	0.41
Beef[++)]	0.21	0.22
Lamb[++)]	0.20	0.18

[+)] Low value because of poor weather
[++)] Total edible output

animal production. The table also shows that the application of mineral fertilizers improved the output/input ratio of crops. This finding is consistent with results of PIMENTEL et al. [1973] obtained for maize production in USA. It must be emphasized that the figures in Table 6.18 were calculated from data of only the edible plant parts *i.e.* grains or sugar or potato tubers. Other plant parts, which also contain energy, were not taken into account. The amount of energy present in cereal straw is usually higher than that contained in the grain which is considerable for 1 t of barley or wheat grain contains about 15 GJ of energy. Considerably higher ratios would thus have been obtained if these non edible parts had been taken into account.

A particularly low energy input is required for the cultivation of legumes as these crops require very little N fertilizer. Thus, according to GASSER [1977], over a cultivation period of 3 years lucerne requires only about 9 GJ/ha but yields about 320 GJ/ha. This is an output/input ratio about 35. Animal grazing especially on leguminous swards is also low in energy demand (LEACH [1976]).

In discussing energy demand for agricultural production it is important to understand that animal and plant production require only a small amount of energy in comparison with the total consumption of modern society. In the UK for example only about 4% of the total energy consumption is needed for agriculture. Of this 4%, about 1% is required for power machinery and 1% for the production of fertilizers (WHITE [1976]). This comparison clearly indicates that energy saving should not primarily be directed to agricultural production. Indeed GREENWOOD [1981] has shown that on a world scale only a minute fraction of present fossil energy consumption would be needed to manufacture all the fertilizer to grow enough food for everyone.

It should be emphasized that crop production is one of the few production processes with a positive energy balance. It now seems likely that in order to meet future energy needs this acquisition of energy by plants will play an increasingly important role. HALL [1977] cites 5 plant species, eucalyptus trees, hibiscus shrubs, Napier grass (a tropical fodder grass) sugar cane, and cassava, which are considered to be suitable for 'sun energy harvesting'. Recently species of *Euphorbiaceae* have also been considered as possible 'energy crops'. These plants contain latex which consists mainly of hydrocarbons and can easily be processed. A further advantage of these species is that they have a low water requirement and can grow in rather arid regions.

6.3.3 Fertilizer application and the environment

It is often argued that fertilizers pollute the environment. DAM KOFOED [1974] has cited three major aspects of fertilizer application which merit attention in relation to pollution problems. These are: pollution of drinking water, eutrophication of lakes and rivers, imbalanced quality of plant products.

6.3.3.1 Drinking water and fertilizers

The main constituent of fertilizers which has an undesirable effect on the quality of drinking water is nitrate. The presence of other plant nutrients, such as phosphate, potassium and magnesium can improve the quality of drinking water, as these ions are also directly essential for human and animal nutrition. Nitrate itself is not toxic, but nitrite originating from the reduction of nitrate induces methaemoglobinemia in infants. Nitrous acid may dissociate into OH^- and NO^+. The latter radical oxidizes the Fe^{II} of the haemoglobin to Fe^{III} which in this oxidized form is unable to adsorb O_2. According to COOKE [1972] there is some doubt as to the acceptable concentration of nitrate in drinking water. The World Health Organization Standard was 10 ppm NO_3-N. This has now been raised to a limit of 23 ppm NO_3-N in Europe and 45 ppm in the USA.

As nitrate fertilizers are being used in agriculture in increasing quantities there has been considerable concern that some fertilizer nitrates may be leached and carried into the deeper aquifers supplying drinking water. KOLENBRANDER [1972] reported extensive investigations into the quality of drinking water in the Netherlands over a forty year period. Crude water from about one third of the waterworks examined showed an increase in nitrate content of 0.57 ppm nitrate N since 1920. In the crude water of the remaining two-thirds of waterworks, no nitrate was detected. The frequency of distribution of the nitrate content in the unpurified tap-water was nearly the same for 1921 as 1966, whereas over the same period, fertilizer N application increased by about 150 kg N/ha/yr. From these results it would appear that even where the use of nitrogenous fertilizer has been extremely high fertilizer N has had no major influence on the nitrate content of drinking water.

It is not possible to generalize on the effects of fertilizer N on the nitrate content of ground water and drinking water. It is well known that the recovery of inorganic N fertilizers is incomplete and increasing rates of application have reduced average recovery. The extent to which leaching plays a role in this loss is not so clear. For arable crops 20–60% of applied N is taken up. The comparative figure for grass is 40–80%. Both these values vary depending on the soil and the season. According to the findings of PARKER [1972] under the climatic and agricultural conditions of the Mid-West USA, about 50% of the applied N was taken up by the crop in the first year. In this case only 5% was leached into the deeper soil layers, the remainder being lost by denitrification and fixation by microorganisms (Table 6.19). According to COOKE [1972] in Britain, soil leachates often contain about 10 ppm NO_3-N with somewhat higher values in spring or

Table 6.19 Fate of fertilizer nitrogen under the conditions of the Corn-Belt in the mid-West USA (Parker [1972])

Absorbed by the crop	50%
Fixed in organic form by microorganisms	30%
Denitrified	15%
Leached out	5%

autumn. Drinking water levels are considerably lower than this and well below the critical 23 ppm figure. Under conditions where NO_3-N levels are found to be high, fertilizer application rates, fertilizer timing, application techniques or even farm management practice should be amended, in order to avoid pollution. Adequate measures to prevent fertilizer loss by leaching are also in the farmer's interest particularly in view of high fertilizer costs. Soil nitrate analysis, *e.g.* the N^{min} method (see p. 100), can be used to adjust nitrogen application to crop demand and thus reduce nitrate pollution.

The level of nitrate concentration in ground water, aquifers and in surface water depends to a considerable extent on the mineralization of organic nitrogen compounds in the soil. The application of organic fertilizers (farmyard manure, green manure, slurries) in autumn or winter causes substantial nitrogen losses, which may thus affect nitrate content of ground water. It must be remembered that nitrate leaching also occurs in uncultivated soils, as the production of NO_3^- mediated by soil microorganisms is a natural process.

6.3.3.2 Eutrophication and fertilizers

Eutrophication or the promotion of the growth of plants, animals and microorganisms in lakes and rivers, is a natural process. If this is allowed to occur uninterrupted, it results in a progressively increasing deficiency of oxygen in the water. Thus organisms which live under anaerobic conditions are favoured more and more at the expense of aerobic organisms. Under these conditions organic material is not decomposed completely to H_2O and CO_2 but remains largely in a reduced form and accumulates. Besides this accumulation of organic compounds, metabolic end products of anaerobic microorganisms are produced, such as methane, ethylene, H_2S, butyric acid and other low molecular weight substances. These compounds are by and large toxic to aerobic living organisms. This is the main reason why the eutrophication of lakes and rivers has such a detrimental effect.

To understand the process of eutrophication the interrelated influences of the various kinds of organisms should be considered in more detail. The relationships between algae, photosynthetic bacteria and anaerobic bacteria living in lakes, where the circulation of water is mainly confined to the upper layer, is il-

328

lustrated in Figure 6.11 (STANIER *et al.* [1971]). In the upper layer algae and other photosynthetically active green plants are present. Photosynthetic activity ensures that this layer is aerobic and enriched with dissolved oxygen. The boundary between the aerobic water layer and the deeper anaerobic water zone favours the growth of photosynthetic bacteria, for at this depth the light intensity is still high enough to maintain photosynthesis but the medium is anaerobic, as required by all photosynthetic bacteria. These organisms, the purple sulphur and green bacteria, are fed by the metabolic end products of the anaerobic microorganisms, which are present below mainly in the muddy sediment of the lake. The photosynthetic bacteria use these end products, such as H_2S, butyric acid or other fatty acids as electron donors in photosynthesis and thus decompose the compounds, which are toxic to green plants. This narrow band of photosynthetic bacteria acts as a filter and keeps the upper layers of the water free from toxic substances. If the balance between these organisms is disturbed, increased quantities of the toxic substances may reach the surface of the lake, and affect

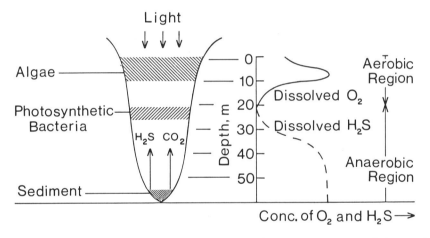

Fig.6.11 Oxygen and H_2S concentrations in a narrow deep water lake (meromictic lake) in relation to the growth of various organisms (after STANIER *et al.* [1971]).

the growth and activity of green plants. Photosynthetic oxygen production is reduced and the surface of the lake gradually becomes anaerobic and the life of aerobic organisms including fish is endangered.

Such a disturbance in the biological balance can be induced by too vigorous a growth of algae. When large amounts of dead algal material sediment, the anaerobic microorganisms at the bottom of the lake are provided with an abundant source of food. Large amounts of toxic substances are then produced. If these are in excess of the capacity of the photosynthetic bacteria, the filtering effect of these organisms is then reduced or lost and toxic substances are able to reach the upper layers of the lake.

Frequently phosphate is the limiting factor in the growth of algae in lakes and streams, and increasing contents of phosphate in the water often run parallel with the degree of eutrophication. The eutrophic threshold level below which algal growth is limited is considered to be in the region of .01 ppm phosphorus. The rise in the use of phosphatic fertilizers has sometimes been blamed for the increase in eutrophication. As already discussed on page 298, however, phosphate is very tenaciously held by soil particles and is leached from agricultural land into lakes and rivers at only a very low rate. Leaching is not affected by phosphate fertilization but is dependent on the solubility of naturally occurring phosphates in the subsoil. The greatest contribution of phosphate from agriculture to drainage waters appears to come from animal wastes which contain about 2–5 ppm P. By far the highest source of phosphorus, however, is not of agricultural origin at all. According to KOLENBRANDER [1972] the most important phosphate pollutant of lakes and streams is that of detergents and urban wastes. Soil phosphates contribute only to about 4 to 5% to the total phosphate leached into surface water. RYDEN et al. [1973] have provided a most useful detailed review on P in run-off and streams.

Nitrate is essential for algal growth. However as the critical level for growth (0.3 ppm N) is below the usual rainwater content (0.7 ppm N), the effects of NO_3^- leaching are not of major importance. Other plant nutrients do not limit the growth of aquatic plants to any extent.

6.3.3.3 Fertilizers – inorganic and organic

The quality of plant products can be considerably affected by plant nutrition (see Chapter 5), and the question is often asked whether any major differences in plant quality occur between plants supplied with inorganic or organic fertilizers. It is often believed by those who ought to know better, that for some reason inorganic fertilizers induce all manner of ills to man and beast, and should on no account be applied to the soil. Several points need to be clarified. It must first be remembered that even in organic fertilizers such as farmyard manure, slurries and green manure, most plant nutrients, including potassium magnesium and phosphate, are present in an inorganic form. Other nutrients, in particular nitrogen and sulphur, are converted to inorganic forms by soil microorganisms before the absorption by plant roots takes place. Thus, although plants may be supplied with organic fertilizers, they nevertheless take up inorganic nutrients derived from these organic materials. This is the basic reason why there are usually no major differences between a crop supplied with organic or with inorganic fertilizers. Inorganic and organic fertilizers do, however, differ in the availability of the plant nutrients they contain. Nutrients in inorganic fertilizers are directly available to plant roots, whereas the nutrients of organic materials and especially organic nitrogen are of low availability. Only about one-third of the N of farmyard manure applied to the soil is available to a crop in the first year (COOKE [1972]). This relatively slow release of nitrogen by organic fertilizers in comparison with inorganic N fertilizers can have some advantage in relation to crop quality (see page 366). The same effects, however, can be obtained using inorganic N fertilizers by using a timed or split application.

One severe drawback to the use of organic fertilizers (manure, green manure) is their dependence on environmental factors for the release of nitrogen. The conversion of the amino nitrogen and the heterocyclic nitrogen of organic substances *via* reduction to NH_4-N and its subsequent oxidation to NO_3-N is accomplished by a number of soil microorganisms (see page 341), whose metabolic activities are highly dependent on soil conditions. Low temperatures or drought reduce their activity and for this reason the rate of release of available nitrogen is decreased. When manure is ploughed into a soil in a dry spring scarcely any decomposition occurs. Very little nitrogen is thus available for the crop when it is most needed. If a wet summer or autumn follows this dry period, mineralization of organic nitrogen takes place very rapidly and provides nitrogen when it is no longer required by the crop. This may in part be leached and thus contribute to pollution. This is not a theoretical example but is what often happens in practical agriculture. In the case of sugar beet cultivation, a high rate of release of nitrogen from organic fertilizers late in the season may also badly impair crop quality (see page 275). This late release of nitrogen also explains the nitrate accumulation which often occurs in vegetable crops grown exclusively on organic N fertilizers. Here the findings of MAYNARD and BARKER [1972] are of interest. These workers showed that despite increased usage of inorganic N fertilizer, the nitrate contents of vegetables marketed in the USA at the present time do not differ in nitrate content from vegetables grown at the beginning of the century. Numerous examples, however, were cited by the authors to demonstrate the improvement of soil fertility brought about by fertilizer application over the same period. Increases in crop yields which have followed this improvement in fertility have already been discussed (see page 322).

Undoubtedly the application of organic materials increases the content of organic matter in the soil and thus has a beneficial effect on soil structure, water retention, rainfall penetration and other soil properties. These effects are particularly marked on sandy soils. The contribution of organic fertilizers to the content of humic substances in the soil, however, is often over-estimated. SCHMALFUSS and KOLBE [1963] found in an 80 year old field experiment, in which one treatment had been regularly supplied with farmyard manure, that of the total C of the manure applied, less than 1% was recovered in the humic substances in the soil. The humus content of soil appears to be much more dependent on particular crops grown and their rotation rather than the application of organic fertilizers (BRUIN and GROOTENHUIS [1968]). COOKE [1977] in discussing this question gives the following preferential sequence of crops and crop management treatments for increasing or maintaining the C content of soils: Clover/grass + FYM > Clover/grass grazing > Lucerne > Arable crops.

Inorganic fertilizers also increase the humus content of soils as they give rise to a higher production of plant residues and can also indirectly lead to a higher production of FYM. FRÜCHTENICHT et al. [1978] reported that the application of mineral fertilizers over a period of 100 years deepened the humus enriched top layer of an arable soil by a factor of 3 or 4. COOKE [1974] in referring to Rothamsted field experiments reported that 'no damage to productivity need result from continuous application of large amounts of fertilizers'. Some results of these experiments are shown in Table 6.20. The soil of this Broadbalk field from which the data were obtained is a silty clay loam which for the past 130 years has annually received the various treatments shown. Highest yields were obtained with the farmyard manure application, the NPK application and the farmyard manure + N application. Farmyard manure can thus to some extent replace the use of inorganic fertilizers. In practical farming terms, however, the complete substitution of inorganic fertilizers by farmyard manure is not a

Table 6.20 Yield of wheat and potatoes grown in rotation on Broadbalk field (Rothamsted England) (COOKE [1974])

Treatment	1973	1972	1971	1970
	Wheat, t/ha of grain			
None	2.4	3.4	2.5	2.3
PK	3.1	4.2	2.6	2.5
PK + 144 kg N/ha	3.9*	6.5	6.0	4.9
Farmyard manure	5.7	8.0	6.9	5.9
Farmyard manure + 96 kg N/ha	4.3	6.9	4.9	5.6
	Potatoes, t/ha of tubers			
None	13.5	10.8	7.8	12.6
PK	21.7	16.2	9.6	19.1
PK + 192 kg N/ha	49.2	38.8	46.6	41.8
Farmyard manure	47.1	40.2	36.2	43.8
Farmyard manure + 96 kg N/ha	48.8	41.4	49.4	49.1

Rates: Farmyard manure = 35 t/ha, PK = 73 kg P_2O_5, 110 kg K_2O, 16 kg Na and 11 kg Mg per ha

* Seriously lodged in 1973; yield with only 96 kg N/ha was better, 6.0 t/ha

feasible proposition as not enough manure is generally available to maintain the nutrient balance. In addition farming without mineral fertilizers may result not only in yield depressions but also affect animal fertility. This has been shown by the Haughley Experiment with dairy cows carried out in East Anglia in England (ALTHER [1972], BALFOUR [1975]).

Where organic farming is practiced there is inevitably a requirement for an input of nutrients into the system if yield levels are to be maintained. This nutrient input must ultimately originate from an inorganic source. This may be from animal feedstuffs or by the use of 'acceptable' fertilizers such as lime or rock phosphate. The only major nutrient that it is theoretically possible to maintain without inorganic fertilizer application is nitrogen. This could be totally supplied by fixation using leguminous plants. To achieve this, however, would involve the use of a large area of agricultural land with the main purpose of fixing molecular nitrogen.

Crop yields obtained at the end of the last century shown in Table 6.17 (page 322) were obtained under conditions where scarcely any inorganic fertilizer was available. Plant nutrients were recycled to a large extent and manures and wastes were used. In comparison with modern standards the yields obtained were miserably low. To completely eradicate the use of mineral fertilizers from present-day farming would inevitably mean a return to these low crop yields with all the accompanying undesirable consequences.

General Reading

ARNON, I.: Mineral Nutrition of Maize. International Potash Institute, Berne, 1975.

BANIN, A. and KAFKAFI, U. (ed.): Agrochemicals in Soils. Pergamon Press, Oxford, New York Sydney, Toronto, Paris, Frankfurt, 1980

BAULE, H. and FRICKER, C.: The Fertilizer Treatment of Forest Trees. BLV-Verlagsges. Munich, 1970.

FINCK, A.: (G) Fertilizer and Fertilizer Application. Verlag Chemie, Weinheim, New York, 1979

GREENWOOD, D.J.: Fertilizer use and food production: world scene. Fertilizer Research 2, 33–51 (1981)

GREENWOOD, D.J., CLEAVER, T.J., TURNER, M.K., HUNT, J., NIENDORF, K.B. and LOQUENS, S.M.H.: Comparison of the effects of nitrogen fertilizer on the yield, nitrogen content and quality of 21 different vegetables and agricultural crops. J. agric. Sci. 95, 471–485 (1980)

HERNANDO FERNANDEZ, V.: Fertilizers, Crop Quality and Economy, Elsevier Scientific Publishing Company, 1974.

HIGNETT, T.P.: Liquid fertilizer production and distribution. UNO, Second Interregional Fertilizer Symposium, Kiev, Ukraine, 1971; New Delhi, India, 1971.

INTERNATIONAL POTASH INSTITUTE: Transition from Extensive to Intensive Agriculture with Fertilizers. 4th Colloquium International Potash Institute, Berne (1969).

INTERNATIONAL POTASH INSTITUTE: Potassium in Tropical Crops and Soils. 10th Colloquium International Potash Institute, Berne (1973).

INTERNATIONAL POTASH INSTITUTE: Potassium Research-Review and Trends. Int. Potash Inst., Bern, 1978

KOLENBRANDER, G.J.: Does leaching of fertilizers affect the quality of ground water at the waterworks? Stikstof, *15*, 8–15 (1972).

LEWIS, D.A. and TATCHELL, J.A.: Energy in UK agriculture. J. Sci. Food Agric. *30*, 449–457 (1979)

OERTLI, J.J.: Controlled-release fertilizers. Fertilizer Research *1*, 103–123 (1980)

PETER, A. v.: Fertilizer requirements in developing countries. Proc. No. 188, The Fertilizer Society, London, 1980

SLACK, A.V.: Chemistry and Technology of Fertilizers. John Wiley and Sons, New York, London, Sydney, 1967.

SOCIETY of the SCIENCE of SOIL and MANURE, Japan: Proc. of the International Seminar on Soil Environment and Fertility Management in Intensive Agriculture. c/o National Institute of Agricultural Sciences Tokyo, 1977

TERMAN, G.L.: Volatilization losses of nitrogen as ammonia from surface-applied fertilizers, organic amendments and crop residues. Adv. Agron. *31*, 189–223 (1979)

WETSELAR, R. and FARQUHAR, G.D.: Nitrogen losses from tops of plants. Adv. Agron. *33*, 263–302 (1980)

Chapter 7

Nitrogen

7.1 Nitrogen in the Soil and its Availability

7.1.1 General aspects

Nitrogen is one of the most widely distributed elements in nature. The highest amount is present in a fixed form in the earth's crust in rocks and sediments. This is in contrast to the commonly held belief that the atmosphere is the largest reservoir of N_2. This ranks second. According to DELWICHE [1970] the atmosphere contains about 3.8×10^{15} tonnes of molecular N_2 whereas the amount of N present in the lithosphere is about 18×10^{15} tonnes. The soil accounts for only a minute fraction of lithospheric N, and of this soil N, only a very small proportion is directly available to plants. This occurs mainly in the form of NO_3^- or

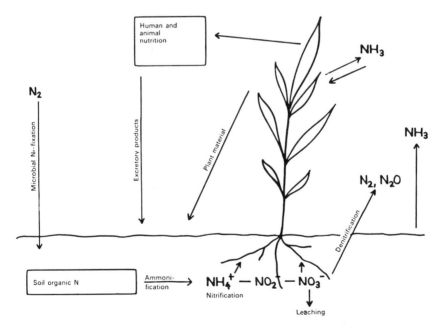

Fig.7.1 Nitrogen cycle in nature.

NH_4^+ ions. Nitrogen is a very mobile element circulating between the atmosphere, the soil and living organisms. Many factors and processes are involved in this N-turnover, some of which are physico-chemical, and others biological. The main outlines of the N cycle in nature are given in Figure 7.1.

7.1.2 Biological nitrogen fixation

The most important process by which N from the sterile inorganic molecular form in the atmosphere is fixed and converted to an organic form is termed nitrogen fixation. This is carried out by a number of different kinds of soil microorganisms. The biochemistry and importance of this process have already been discussed on page 173. Nitrogen may also be fixed chemically by the Haber-Bosch Process in which N_2 and H_2 react together under high temperature and pressure conditions to yield ammonia

$$N_2 + 3H_2 \rightleftarrows 2NH_3$$

This is the basis of ammonium fertilizer production. Although increasing amounts of atmospheric N are now being fixed by this and other chemical means, this amount is still very much less than the total quantity of N fixed naturally by microorganisms. According to CHATT [1976] total world biological N_2 fixation is in the order of 17.2×10^7 tonnes per annum, which is about four times that fixed by the chemical industry. This means that biological N_2 fixation contributes substantially to the supply of N to crops. The amount of N_2 fixed may differ considerably from one site to another. This very much depends on soil factors, such as soil pH, available P, K, the presence of heavy metals and the soil moisture regime. The content of inorganic nutrients in the soil is also of importance for the activity of N_2 fixing microorganisms. Table 7.1 shows the rates at which N is gained by biological fixation under different ecosystems (HAUCK [1971]). Fixation is rather low on arable land, but for pastures, forests and to a lesser extent for paddy, biological N fixation provides an important source of N. Nitrogen fixation in rivers and lakes also appears to be rather high.

Table 7.1 Nitrogen gains from biological N_2 fixation (HAUCK [1971])

Ecosystem	Range in reported values kg N/ha/year
Arable l and	7–28
Pasture (non-legume)	7–114
Pasture (grass–legume)	73–865
Forest	58–594
Paddy	13–99
Waters	70–250

Only procaryonts are capable of fixing (assimilating) molecular nitrogen. Eleven of the 47 bacteria families and six of the eight *Cyanophyceae* families are able to fix N_2 (WERNER [1980]). Some of these species are free living N_2 fixers; others live symbiotically. The most important free living N_2 fixing bacteria are members of the genera *Azotobacter, Beijerinckia, Spirillum* and *Enterobacter;* important N_2 fixers of the *Cyanophyceae* belong to the genera *Nostoc* and *Anabaena.* The quantities of N assimilated by these species are generally low and in the range of 5 to 10 kg N/ha. There are, however, exceptions and investigations especially of DÖBEREINER *et al.* [1972] have revealed that under tropical conditions amounts of 60 to 90 kg N/ha can be fixed per crop cycle. In some cases it is recognized that the free living bacteria are associated with plant roots. A well-known example of this kind is the association between the tropical grass *Paspalum notatum* and the bacteria *Azotobacter paspali.* This N_2 fixing bacteria occurs in the mucilage layer outside the root of the grass. *Paspalum* which is a C_4-plant species is believed to release abundant amounts of organic material from the roots, which serves as a nutrient source for the bacteria. This rather loose partnership between higher plant and bacteria cannot be referred to as a symbiotic relationship. It is simply an association. C_4 species appear especially able to form such bacterial associations. For maize *Spirillum lipoferum* is the most important N_2 fixer of this kind. Potential N_2 fixers for the C_3 crop plants are *Beijerinckia*-species and *Enterobacter* species for rice and *Bacillus maceraus* and *B. polymyxa* for wheat (NEYRA and DÖBEREINER [1977]).

The N_2 fixing efficiency of these bacteria depends much on environmental conditions. Most of the bacteria discussed above are sensitive to low pH conditions and to high O_2 concentrations. Under anaerobic conditions *Spirillum lipoferum* can reduce NO_2^-, so that this organism is also a potential denitrifier. Maximum N_2 fixing rates have been obtained at high soil temperatures ($33°C$). The potential N_2 fixing capacity of free living bacteria is thus highest in subtropical and tropical regions.

Cyanophyceae species play a major role in paddy soils. This nitrogen fixing blue-green algae *Anabaena azollae* lives in association with the aquatic fern *Azolla pinniata.* WATANABE *et al.* [1977] reported that by cultivation of this *Azolla-Anabaena* association in paddy, considerable amounts of N_2 can be trapped and subsequently used for the rice crop. In some cases where fertilizer N was not applied, up to 30 kg N/ha were estimated to be fixed by blue-green algae in one harvest. The same workers were also able to obtain 22 harvests of *Azolla* with a total amount of 465 kg N/ha fixed per year (WATANABE *et al.* [1980]).

As the level of soluble carbohydrates may often limit N_2 fixation in free living bacteria it seems possible that this may account for the evolution of some species of microorganisms which live in symbiosis with higher plants. In this symbiotic relationship, the microorganisms supply the fixed (reduced) nitrogen to the host plant which in turn provides soluble carbohydrates to the microorganisms. These symbiotic microorganisms include the *Rhizobium* species and some *Actinomyces*, such as *Actinomyces alni* and *Actinomyces elaeagni*. The efficiency of these organisms in N_2 fixation is considerable. DALY [1966] reported that under favourable conditions *Actinomyces alni* living in symbiosis with alder *(Alnus rugosa)* fixed about 150 kg N/ha per year. Such high rates of N_2 fixation can obviously have an important influence on the nitrogen economy of woodland soils associated with alder.

In agriculture the *Rhizobium* species which live symbiotically with legumes are the most important N_2 fixers. Good stands of clover and lucerne in which N_2 fixation is active can fix from 100–400 kg N/ha per year. According to STEWART [1967] there are about 12 000 known legume species which are host plants to *Rhizobium* bacteria. About 200 of these legume species are used as crop plants. This large number emphasizes the worldwide importance of legumes and their N_2 fixing potential. Six different *Rhizobium* species are known. These are listed together with their host plants in Table 7.2. There is a marked host specificity for *Rhizobium* species. If fixation is to be efficient it is important that a legume species is infected with the appropriate *Rhizobium* species. *Rhizobium trifolii* for example is capable of inducing nodulation on the roots of *Medicago* and *Vicia*, but the nodules are unable to bring about N_2 fixation (BJÄLFVE [1963]).

The infection of a host plant with *Rhizobium* bacteria starts with the penetration of the bacteria into a root hair cell. In the cell the bacteria are enclosed by a thread which grows into the cortical tissue of the root. Bacteria can then migrate from the thread into cells of the cortex. Nodulation can begin from this point on and involves the proliferation of the infected cells. In this process the bacteria is converted to a bacteroid which is about 40 times larger in volume than the original bacteria. The formation of bacteroids is closely associated with the

Table 7.2   Rhizobium species and their most important host plants

Species	Host plant
R. meliloti	Melilotus, Medicago
R. trifolii	Trifolium
R. leguminosarum	Pisum, Vicia
R. phaseoli	Phaseolus
R. japonicum	Glycine
R. lupinii	Lupinus

Phaseolus   Orithopus

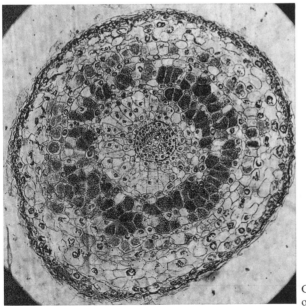

Cross section nodule
of alder

Plate 7.1 Nodulated roots of *Phaseolus vulgaris* (left) and *Orithopus sativa* (right). Below, transverse section through a young root nodule of *Alnus glutinosa*. (Photo: BECKING) Courtesy of: Bayerische Landesanstalt für Acker- und Pflanzenbau.

339

synthesis of the nitrogenase system and other enzymes required for the N_2 fixation process (see page 174). A useful review dealing with nodulation and infection of *Rhizobium* bacteria has been published by HÖLL [1975]. Plate 7.1 shows nodulated roots of *Phaseolus* and *Orithopus*.

The quantity of N_2 assimilated by *Rhizobium* bacteria depends to a large extent on nutritional conditions. Most *Rhizobium* species are sensitive to low pH conditions in the soil medium. Nodulation, size and number of nodules are favoured by Ca^{2+} (LOWTHER and LONERAGAN [1968]), whereas high concentrations (>1 mM) of nitrate, nitrite, NH_4^+ and urea restrict nodulation (RAGGIO and RAGGIO [1962], SUBBA-RAO and VASANTHA [1965]). More recent results suggest that these N compounds induce high NH_4^+ concentrations in the roots which block the gene responsible for the synthesis of nitrogenase (TUBB [1974], the most important enzyme system for N_2 fixation. It is generally known that N_2 fixation by *Rhizobium* is enhanced in host plants well supplied with phosphate and K (GUKOVA and TJULINA [1968], WU *et al.* [1969], MENGEL *et al.* [1974]). Cobalt and Molydenum are also essential elements for all N_2 fixing microorganisms (BOND [1970]).

Nodules are rich in soluble amino acids as compared with other plant organs The supply of amino acids from the nodules closely relates to the life cycle of the host plant. In the first few days after infection of the roots of young legume plants, the bacteria is completely dependent on the host plant, and the amino acids synthesized are used for the growth of the nodule. In the later stages, however, most of the amino acids synthesized are transported to the host plant. This transfer comes to an end rather abruptly on the termination of the flowering stage. Root nodules thus supply the plant directly with amino acids during the vegetative growing stage. The intensity of this supply of course depends to a large extent on the rate of photosynthesis and on the supply of root nodules with carbohydrates from the host plant (LINDSTROM *et al.* [1952], BACH *et al.* [1958]). BETHLENFALVAY and PHILLIPS [1978], FEIGENBAUM and MENGEL [1979].

In addition to biological fixation, some atmospheric N_2 is fixed by electrical discharge in the atmosphere (lightning) which results in the oxidation of N_2. The quantities gained in this way, however, are rather small and amount to only a few kg nitrate-N/ha/year under temperate climatic conditions. In the tropics the amount is higher although not usually in excess of about 10 kg N/ha/year.

7.1.3 Ammonification

Nitrogen fixation is only one of the major biological processes influencing the N cycle and N availability in the soil. In addition, proteolysis and ammonification, nitrification and denitrification are further processes which are controlled by microbial activity. Soil organic matter primarily contains N in the amino form (proteins) and to a lesser extent in the form of heterocyclic N compounds (N bases of nucleic acids). The release of amino N from organic matter is termed proteolysis and the reduction of amino N to NH_3 is called ammonification. These processes may be represented schematically as follows:

$$\text{Soil Organic N} \rightarrow RNH_2 + CO_2 + \text{Additional Products} + \text{energy}$$
$$RNH_2 + H_2O \rightarrow NH_3 + ROH + \text{energy}$$

In both processes energy is released and this is utilized by the heterotrophic microorganisms which bring about the reactions. These organisms require organic C as an energy source. According to BARBER [1971] the bulk of soil microflora is capable of bringing about the reactions described above. The mineralization of organic soil N is thus not generally limited by a lack of microorganisms, but it can be retarded by factors which depress their activity such as low temperatures and a deficiency or an excess of water. The NH_4^+ resulting from ammonification can easily be oxidized to NO_2^- and NO_3^- if O_2 is available and other environmental factors are conducive.

7.1.4 Nitrification

The biological oxidation of ammonia to nitrate is known as nitrification. This is a two-step process. Ammonia is first oxidized to NO_2^- which, in turn, is further oxidized to NO_3^-. The process is mediated by autotrophic bacteria, or in other words by bacteria which obtain energy from the oxidation of inorganic salts and use CO_2 as a source of C. Two very specialized groups of bacteria are involved, one in the oxidation of NH_4^+ to NO_2^- and the other in the oxidation of NO_2^- to NO_3^-. Several genera and species of ammonium and NO_2^- oxidizing autotrophs are known. Genera oxidizing ammonium include *Nitrosomonas*, *Nitrosolobus* and *Nitrosospira*. All have been isolated from a variety of soils including soils from the long term field experiments in Rothamsted, England and from acid tea soils from Bangladesh and Sri Lanka (WALKER [1976]). Interestingly *Nitrosomonas* was only found in soils which had received farmyard manure and other animal excreta whereas *Nitrosolobus* was ubiquitous. These observations strongly indicate that in many soils *Nitrosolobus* plays a much more significant part in nitrification than is generally recognized, and is more important than *Nitrosomonas* (BHUIJA and WALKER [1977]). Nitrite produced by the ammonium oxidizing autotrophs is rapidly oxidized to nitrate by *Nitrobacter* species. Both ammonium oxidizers and NO_2^- oxidizers are obligately aerobic. In waterlogged soils the oxidation of NH_4^+ is thus restricted. In addition, the nitrifying bacteria prefer more neutral to slightly acid pH conditions. Table 7.3 shows that low soil pH conditions substantially depress microbial NH_4^+ oxidation (MUNK [1958]).

Table 7.3 Rate of nitrification of NH_4^+ in relation to soil pH (20 mg NH_4-N added to the soil) (MUNK [1958])

Incubation duration in days	mg nitrate N formed/100 g soil pH 4.4	pH 6.0
14	1.78	8.0
21	2.30	12.0
35	4.72	21.4

The two step oxidation from NH_4^+ to NO_3^- takes place as follows:

$$2\ NH_4^+ \quad + 3\ O_2 \rightarrow 2\ HNO_2 + 2\ H^+ \quad + 2\ H_2O$$
$$2\ HNO_2 \quad + \quad O_2 \rightarrow 2\ NO_3^- \quad + 2\ H^+$$
$$\overline{\text{Net } 2\ NH_4^+ \quad + 4\ O_2 \rightarrow 2\ NO_3^- \quad + 4\ H^+ \quad + 2\ H_2O}$$

The net equation shows that nitrification is coupled with the release of H^+ and thus results in an acidification of the soil medium. The relationships of NH_4^+ oxidation, pH shift and NO_3^- formation are well demonstrated in an experiment of DUISBERG and BÜHRER [1954] the main results of which are presented in Figure 7.2. In the incubation period of 14 days nearly all the NH_4^+ was oxidized to NO_3^- with a concomitant drop in soil pH. After one week of incubation, a peak in the NO_2^- content occurred, which later disappeared due to the activity of the *Nitrobacter*. Generally NO_2^- does not accumulate in the soil, because the NO_2^- formed is readily oxidized by *Nitrobacter*. Both ammonium and nitrite oxidizers, obviously function 'in series'. Ammonia is thus rather rapidly converted to NO_3^-, provided that suitable conditions for nitrifying bacteria are present in the soil, as was the case in the example presented in Figure 7.2. The soil used was a fertile calcareous sandy loam with a pH of 7.8 and the experiment was carried out in the laboratory with optimum soil water and temperature conditions. In the field, nitrification often occurs at a lower rate, for as already mentioned, in soils of low pH and in waterlogged soils, nitrification is restricted or even completely inhibited. Under these conditions the soil may thus accumulate NH_4-N. Nitrification is also depressed in dry soils (SABEY [1969]).

Nitrifyers oxidize both NH_4^+ released by ammonification and NH_4^+ applied as fertilizer. Fertilizer NH_4^+ is thus also converted to nitrate. The rate at which this occurs of course depends on prevalent soil conditions (GASSER and IORDANOU [1967]). In practice it is often the case that a soil is treated with NH_4^+-N, but that crop uptake occurs mainly as NO_3^-.

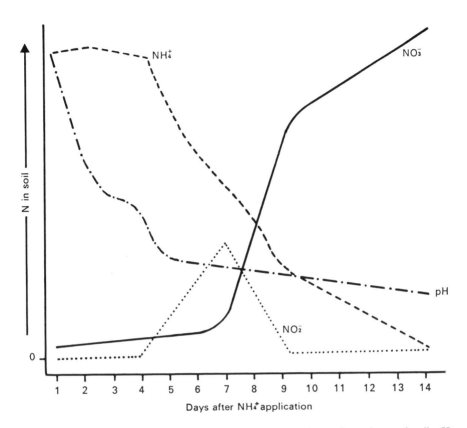

Fig.7.2 Relationship between microbial NH_4^+ oxidation, nitrate formation and soil pH (after DUISBERG and BUEHRER [1954]).

7.1.5 Denitrification

Many species of bacteria found in soils are capable of reducing nitrates and nitrites to nitrogenous gases (NO, N_2O, N_2) which are then released into the atmosphere. This dissimilatory reduction is known as denitrification, and may be represented according to the following reduction sequence

$$NO_3^- \rightarrow NO_2^- \rightarrow NO \rightarrow N_2O \rightarrow N_2$$

The denitrifying bacteria that bring about these reactions are essentially obligately aerobic except for the ability to utilize NO_3^- in the absence of oxygen (FOCHT [1978]). Nitrate acts in lieu of oxygen as a terminal acceptor of electrons produced during anaerobic respiration.

The amounts of N which can be lost from the soil system by denitrification can vary enormously. According to ALLISON [1966] these losses of gaseous N can range from about 5 to 50% of the total N applied. Even in aerated arable soils some N loss due to denitrification may occur because O_2 is often not uniformly distributed throughout the soil and some parts of the profile may be anaerobic (WOLDENDORP [1968]). Denitrification is promoted by high soil moisture conditions, neutral soil pH, high soil temperatures, a low rate of oxygen diffusion as well as the presence of soluble organic matter and nitrate.

Table 7.4 Nitrogen losses due to denitrification from various soil types under permanent grassland (according to DILZ and WOLDENDORP [1960])

Soil type	N-loss in % of applied N
Sand	11–25
Clay	16–31
Peat	19–40

Thus on well aerated sandy soils denitrification rates are generally lower than on clay soils (see Table 7.4). DILZ and WOLDENDORP [1960] found that denitrification losses are particularly high, when abundant living roots are present in the soil medium. It is supposed that root exudates stimulate the denitrifying bacteria and thus increase denitrification losses. This is supported by the findings of TROLLDENIER [1973], who observed in solution culture experiments with rice that increased microbial activity in the rhizosphere resulted in a lowered O_2 content of the root medium and thus improved conditions for denitrification. As already mentioned paddy soils are particularly susceptible to denitrification, as they are essentially anaerobic (PONNAMPARUMA [1965]).

Denitrification losses may be greater than generally assumed. In extensive field trials with barley measuring N transformations in soil plant systems KOWALENKO and CAMERON [1977] have concluded that unrecovered fertilizer N could largely be accounted for by denitrification. Using N-15 labelled fertilizer it was shown that the total recovery of fertilizer N in the crop and in the soil accounted in one year to 69% and in another year to 54% of the original application. The remaining unrecovered 31% and 46% respectively represented denitrification. Denitrification rates were at a maximum in Spring and early Summer and coincided with the maximum rates of N uptake by the crop. Applications of the nitrification inhibitor 'N serve' had little influence on denitrification losses. According to WERNER [1980] denitrification plays a major role in N turnover on a global scale. This is shown in Table 7.5 which provides data on N circulation between the atmosphere and the soil.

Generally the escape of gaseous N from the soil medium into the atmosphere is regarded as a nutrient loss and is therefore undesirable. On the other hand considerable amounts of NO_3^- are probably denitrified when draining into deeper parts of the soil profile so that the rate of transfer of NO_3^- to the ground water is lowered (KOLENBRANDER [1972]). Denitrification may thus have a very beneficial effect by preventing water pollution by NO_3^-.

Table 7.5 Global turnover between soil N and atmospheric N (data from WERNER [1980]), in 10^6 t/year

	Gain		Loss
Industrial production..........	46	Denitrification................	200–300
Biological fixation	100–200	NH_3-Volatilization	165
NO_3^-/NO_2^- precipitation	60		
NH_3-precipitation.............	140		

The possibility that nitrous oxide may act as an atmospheric pollutant has attracted considerable attention in recent years. The hypothesis has been advanced that nitrous oxide from denitrification in soils and natural waters is released into the atmosphere and then into the stratosphere, where it may lead to partial destruction of the ozone layer. This layer protects the earth from the biologically harmful ultra violet radiation from the sun. International concern has been expressed that the increasing use of N-fertilizers may increase N_2O levels in the atmosphere, by the denitrification of nitrate derived from these fertilizers and so induce the destruction of the ozone shield. The subject has been reviewed recently by BREMNER [1978] who concludes that there do not appear to be any valid claims that the increased use of N-fertilizers is destroying the ozone layer. An important point in favour of this view is the fact that no increase in atmospheric concentration of N_2O has been observed to parallel this striking recent increase in the use of N-fertilizers. One of the major difficulties in investigating atmospheric N_2O, namely a sensitive method of measurement, has recently been overcome, using gas chromatography. This advance should enable much more detailed investigations to be carried out in denitrification studies in the field.

7.1.6 Nitrification inhibitors

In order to avoid major NO_3^- losses as a result of denitrification or leaching nitrification inhibitors have been developed in recent years. The most important are listed below:
Nitrapyrin (2-chloro-6-[trichloromethyl] pyridine) = N-serve
ST (2-sulphanilamide thiazole)
Terrazole (5-ethoxy-3-trichloromethyl- 1, 2, 4 thiadizole)

KN₃ (potassium azide)
CS₂ (carbon disulphide)
Dicyandiamide (H₂N – C – NH – C ≡ N)
$$\quad\quad\quad\quad\quad\| $$
NH

Nitrapyrin is the most thoroughly investigated nitrification inhibitor (HUBER et al. [1977]). The inhibitors block the microbial oxidation of NH_4-N to NO_2^- and thus also the formation of nitrate. The loss of N by leaching or denitrification is therefore prevented. TOUCHTON et al. [1978] in studying the behaviour of nitrapyrin in different soils, found that the chemical is rather immobile in the soil and is especially bound to organic matter. The degradation of nitrapyrin depends on the degree to which it is adsorbed by soil colloids. Thus the degradation rate was higher in a sandy soil, low in organic matter, than in a clay loam rich in humus. Nitrapyrin degradation proceeds at a higher rate in soils of neutral pH than in more acid soils.

According to TOUCHTON et al. [1978] the half life period of nitrapyrin degradation is about 4 weeks, but this may differ depending on soil conditions and soil microbial activity. Soil accumulations of nitrapyrin and its principal metabolic product (6 chloro-picolinic acid) should be avoided, as both products can be taken up by plants and may be toxic to them. A typical nitrapyrin degradation curve is shown in Figure 7.3 from the work of TOUCHTON et al. [1978].

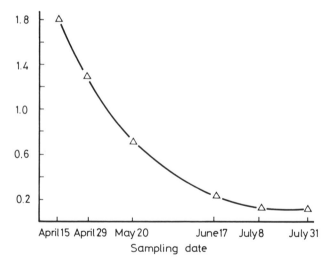

Fig. 7.3 Decline in soil nitrapyrin content following application. (after TOUCHTON et al. [1978]).

346

ASHWORTH et al. [1977] have reported that carbon disulphide (CS_2) is an efficient nitrification inhibitor. These workers found that this compound is superior to nitrapyrin as it is volatile and thus diffuses rapidly in the soil. Its inhibitory effect was faster than that of nitrapyrin. Similar encouraging results have been obtained by the application of trithiocarbonate (Na_2CS_3) which readily forms CS_2 in the soil according to the equation

$$Na_2CS_3 \rightarrow Na_2S + CS_2$$

Trithiocarbonate can be mixed with NH_3-N containing fertilizer solutions prior to soil application. Dicyandiamide is also known to be a nitrification inhibitor. In addition it also inhibits urease and thus blocks the degradation of urea (SOMMER and ROSSIG [1978]). Dicyandiamide may be produced in the soil during the degradation of calcium cyanamide (RATHSACK [1978]).

Nitrification inhibitors are mainly applied in autumn together with NH_4-N fertilizers. Numerous field experiments carried out in Indiana (USA) over a 5 year period have shown favourable results of nitrapyrin when applied together with NH_4-N or urea in autumn. This autumn applied N gave the same grain yields as a split N application (autumn and spring) without nitrapyrin. Nitrapyrin application not only reduced N losses but also resulted in a more uniform N supply to the plant roots and higher grain protein contents were obtained (HUBER et al. [1980]). Favourable effects of this kind have also been reported by HENDRICKSON et al. [1978a]), HUBER et al. [1977], and SOMMER and ROSSIG [1978]. On the other hand HENDRICKSON et al. [1978b] found that in sandy soils the nitrapyrin effect was only very brief. In an experiment with potatoes, applied NH_4-N was leached into deeper soil layers, and the contact between the nitrapyrin and the NH_4-N was poor. In this case the application of nitrapyrin depressed tuber yield.

7.1.7 Ammonium fixation

In contrast to NO_3^- which is rather mobile in the soil and hardly adsorbed by soil particles, NH_4^+ is strongly adsorbed to negatively charged clay minerals because of its cationic properties. In particular it can be bound rather selectively to 2:1 clay minerals, such as illites, vermiculites and montmorillonites. This process is called NH_4-fixation, and is analogous to K^+-fixation which is described in more detail on page 414. Ammonium and K^+ thus compete for the same selective binding sites. BARTLETT and SIMPSON [1967] reported, that the fixation of fertilizer K^+ was lowered by NH_4^+ application. According to the investigations of SIPPOLA et al. [1973] on Finnish soils, NH_4^+ is fixed in even larger quantities than K^+ by vermiculites. Because of this fixation, soils rich in 2:1 clay minerals often contain appreciable amounts of NH_4^+ in a fixed form which may range from 2000 to 3000 kg N/ha (SCHERER and MENGEL [1979]). In an analysis of a large number of soil samples BREMNER [1959] found that about 5–6% of the total N in the upper soil horizon was present in the form of fixed NH_4^+ whereas in the deeper part of the profile where the clay content was higher, this proportion of fixed NH_4^+ was as much as 20% and more.

It is generally held that so called fixed NH_4^+ cannot be exchanged by K^+ and is largely unavailable to plant roots. Recent results of KOWALENKO and CAMERON [1978] and MENGEL and SCHERER [1981], however, have cast doubt on this assumption. In experiments using N-15 KOWALENKO and CAMERON [1978] found that fertilizer NH_4^+ was fixed quickly after application but, at a later stage during the growing period, was taken up by the crop. In experiments of MENGEL and SCHERER [1981] as much as 100 to 300 kg N/ha of the fixed NH_4^+ were released during the growing period and entered the N cycle of the soil. The NH_4^+ release was especially high in the deeper soil layers (60 to 100 cm) and occurred during the main growing period. At the end of the growing period an increase in NH_4^+ fixation was observed. SCHERER [1980] found that loess soils especially showed a relatively high turnover of fixed NH_4^+, whereas the NH_4 turnover in soils of basaltic origin was negligible. VAN PRAAG et al. [1980] have also observed a high rate of release of 'fixed' NH_4^+ from loess soils. Clearly the clay mineral composition of the soil plays a major role in determining the extent of NH_4^+ fixation and release (see p. 414).

As a result of adsorption and fixation processes the mobility of NH_4^+ in the soil is essentially lower than that of NO_3^- (DAM KOFOED and KJELLERUP [1970]) and for this reason N is mainly leached out in the form of NO_3^- and only to a very small extent in the form of NH_4^+. This means that generally the NO_3^- content in drainage water is about 100 times higher than that of NH_4^+ (WILLIAMS [1970]). In the soil solution nitrate is also usually much higher in concentration than NH_4^+, except in acid soils.

7.1.8 Assimilation and release of inorganic nitrogen

Fertilizer N applied to a soil is also involved in the various N turnover reactions occurring in the soil medium. For example, urea applied to the soil is split into NH_4^+ and CO_2 by the enzyme urease (see page 367). The resulting NH_4^+ can be taken up by plants or microorganisms, adsorbed or fixed to soil particles, or oxidized to NO_3^-. Nitrate originating in this way or applied to the soil directly can be leached out, denitrified or absorbed by plants. GASSER et al. [1967] in experimenting with N-15 labelled $(NH_4)_2 SO_4$ applied to a sandy soil, found that an appreciable amount of fertilizer N was incorporated by microorganisms immediately after fertilizer application. In a later stage this was released and became available to the plant. Experiments of STANFORD *et al.* [1970] also show that fertilizer N is rather rapidly incorporated into the various fractions of organic soil N. Applied fertilizer N can therefore supply crops with both a direct source of N as well as an indirect source of N released from the mineralization of organic N compounds.

The amounts of N fixed by microbial immobilization of ammonium N have been reported by a number of authors. MYERS and PAUL [1971] for example found values in the range of 20 to 40 kg N/ha which were increased by about 7 to 15 kg N/ha by straw application. Precise data, however, are still lacking distinguishing between nitrogen immobilization and release as microbes as well as clay minerals may fix and release NH_4^+.

Nitrogen immobilization and the mineralization of organic N in the soil are opposite in effect. The net rate of release of inorganic N from these two processes is of outstanding importance for crop nutrition. Inhibiting microbial N assimilation by fumigation or irradiation thus improves N availability to higher plants (JENKINSON *et al.* [1972]). Generally the net release of inorganic N (NO_3^-, NH_4^+) is higher when the C/N ratio of the organic matter in the soil is low (QUASTEL [1965]). This means that the richer the organic matter is in N, the greater is the possibility that the N will be mineralized. This relationship is shown clearly in Figure 2.22 from incubation data of VAN DIJK [1968]. In soils with high C/N organic matter ratios, the rate of N mineralization was low and *vice versa*. According to VAN DIJK [1968] the C/N ratio considered along with the total N content of a soil provides an important means of assessing potential soil N mineralization. The fraction of N mineralized during the growing period is of importance in crop production. The amounts can vary considerably. In some soils only a few kg N/ha are released by mineralization but under optimum conditions as much as 100 kg N/ha and more can be produced. BLAND [1968] reported that for grass *(Lolium perenne)* and grass-clover swards about 70 to 100 kg N/ha were mineralized during one growing season in the climatic conditions of Western Scotland. On arable land in Central Europe average rates of 10 to 50 kg N/ha have been reported, as shown in Table 7.6 (VÖMEL [1965/66]). These results also show that per year about 0.5 to 1% of the total N in the upper soil layer was mineralized. To predict the rate of mineralization in a soil presents some difficulties, as the microbial decomposition of organic matter in the soil not only depends on the total organic matter and its C/N ratio but also to a large extent on soil moisture and soil temperature and thus also on climatic conditions. Highest rates of mineralization are observed under warm and moist conditions, whereas in dry and cold periods the decomposition of organic matter and thus also the release of inorganic N compounds is greatly retarded. The rate of mineralization can vary considerably between years. Thus a soil, which in one year may provide about 40 kg N/ha by mineralization, may well produce twice as much in another year. In most cases mineralization rates are calculated by difference. This does not take into account the release of NH_4^+ by clay minerals, and the rates thus obtained may give rise to errors.

Table 7.6 Total nitrogen in the upper soil layer (0–20 cm), C/N ratio and the rate of nitrogen mineralization (according to data of VÖMEL [1965/66])

Soil	C/N*	Total N* kg/ha	Mineralization kg/ha/year	Mineralized N in % of total N
Sand..............	12.5	1,590	9	0.57
Loam (alluvial)	8.7	4,650	43	0.93
Loam (loess)	9.4	2,850	11	0.39
Clay (basalt)	9.8	4,950	36	0.73

* Includes organic and inorganic nitrogen

7.1.9 Nitrogen of the soil solution

Because of the numerous processes which affect N turnover in the soil, the concentration of N dissolved in the soil solution can change considerably over short periods. This particularly applies to NO_3-N. Conditions favouring nitrification result in an increase in the NO_3^- content in the soil solution. Thus in spring when the temperature rises and aeration of the soil increases, the NO_3^- concentration in the soil solution is also raised (HARMSEN [1959]). When crop demand is high, however, NO_3^- is rapidly taken up by plant roots. (PAGE and TALIBUDEEN [1977]. WHITE and GREENHAM [1967] reported that in orchards under a grass cover, only low amounts of NO_3^- were found whereas in a similar fallow soil the NO_3^- content in the soil increased until summer, when the NO_3^- was leached into deeper soil layers by the summer rains. Nitrate levels in the soil solution can be as high as 20 to 30 mM after nitrogen fertilizer application. In fertile soils it normally ranges from 2 and 20 mM depending on the rate of mineralization and the uptake by plants. Usually the NO_3^- content of the soil solution is of major importance in plant nitrogen nutrition. In field experiments BARTHOLOMEW [1971] found that recovery of labelled N-15 fertilizer N by maize was closely related to the total amount of rainfall which fell during the experimental period, higher recoveries being found under lower rainfall conditions. This finding is consistent with observations that in dry periods NO_3^- accumulates in the upper soil layers (PAGE and TALIBUDEEN [1977]). At low levels of soil moisture, NO_3^- availability is reduced (MENGEL and CASPER [1980]).

7.2 Nitrogen in Physiology

7.2.1 General

Dry plant material contains about 2 to 4% N. This appears rather low in comparison with the C content which is in the order of about 40%. Nevertheless N is an indispensable elementary constituent of numerous organic compounds of general importance (amino acids, proteins, nucleic acids). Higher plants are major contributors to the large amount of N which is continuously being converted from the inorganic to the organic form. The most important inorganic sources involved in this conversion are NO_3^- and NH_4^+.

7.2.2 Uptake

Both NO_3^- and NH_4^+ forms can be taken up and metabolized by plants. Nitrate is often a preferential source for crop growth but much depends on plant species and other environmental factors discussed below. Arable crops mainly take up NO_3^- even when NH_4^+ fertilizers are applied, because of the microbial oxidation of the NH_4^+ in the soil. The rate of uptake of NO_3^- is generally high, and according to the investigations of ANSARI and BOWLING [1972] with decapitated sunflower plants, uptake occurs against an electrochemical gradient, indicating that NO_3^- is actively absorbed. Nitrate present in the root can readily be exchanged for NO_3^- of the soil solution. According to MORGAN et al. [1973] the efflux is a passive process whereas NO_3^- absorption is active. Further evidence of metabolic control of NO_3^- absorption has been provided by RAO and RAINS [1976]. Whether the uptake of NH_4^+ by plants is also an active process is still an open question.

A number of reports indicate that the uptake of both N-forms is temperature dependent, rates of uptake being depressed by lower temperatures (ZSOLDOS [1972], CLARKSON and WARNER [1979]). CLARKSON and WARNER [1979] conclude that when the two ions are supplied in equal concentrations to ryegrass NH_4^+ is absorbed more readily than NO_3^- at lower temperatures. The authors discuss the results in relation to the observation that under temperate European conditions most of the N uptake of a cereal crop is usually completed before the soil has reached an average temperature of 12°C (HAY [1976]). Clearly under such conditions the preferential form of supply should be NH_4– N. Why NH_4–N is taken up more rapidly especially at lower temperatures is not clear. CLARKSON and WARNER [1979] suggest that it may be attributable to physical changes in different parts of the cell membrane rather than to differences in temperature sensitivity of the two transport processes. There is some indication that NH_3 rather than NH_4^+ may be the form of uptake of ammonium–N. As NH_3 is a neutral molecule MOORE [1974] suggests that it can readily cross cell membranes.

A most important difference between NO_3^- uptake and NH_4-N uptake is in their sensitivity to pH. NH_4-N uptake takes place best in a neutral medium and it is depressed as the pH falls. The converse is true for NO_3^- absorption, a more rapid uptake occurring at low pH values (RAO and RAINS [1976]). These workers suggest that the reduction of NO_3^- uptake at high pH values may be due to the competitive effect of OH^- ions suppressing the NO_3^- uptake transport system.

Table 7.7   Uptake of labelled NO_3^- and NH_4^+ by young barley plants in relation to the pH of the root medium (according to MICHAEL *et al.* [1965])

pH	NH_4^+	NO_3^-
	in mg N/pot	
6.8	34.9	33.6
4.0	26.9	43.0

MICHAEL *et al.* [1965] studying the uptake of NH_4-N and NO_3^- by various plant species found in short term experiments that both N forms were absorbed at equal rates at a pH of 6.8. At pH 4.0, however, the uptake of NO_3^- was considerably higher than that of NH_4-N, as can be seen from Table 7.7. Ammonium-N uptake is also influenced by the carbohydrate status of plants. High carbohydrate levels in the plant favour the uptake of NH_4-N probably by enhancing NH_3 assimilation by the provision of C skeltons and energy (KIRKBY and HUGHES [1970], MICHAEL *et al.* [1970]). Nitrate uptake can be competitively depressed by NH_4-N, as shown by MINOTTI *et al.* [1969] and BLONDEL and BLANC [1974] using young wheat plants. NH_4-N uptake on the other hand is not affected by NO_3^- (MENGEL and VIRO [1978]).

Gaseous ammonia may also be absorbed by the upper plant parts *via* the stomata (see p. 304). This net uptake depends on the partial pressure of NH_3 in the atmosphere. FARQUHAR *et al.* [1980] reported that in *Phaseolus vulgaris* net NH_3 uptake was zero at the low atmospheric partial pressure of 2.5 nbar at 26°C. Increasing the partial pressures of NH_3 increased the net uptake and lowering the partial pressure resulted in a loss of NH_3 from the plant. The source of this released NH_3 is not yet clear. According to experiments of HOOKER *et al.* [1980] with wheat plants, NH_3 loss was higher at an advanced than at an earlier growth stage. These authors suggest therefore that the NH_3 release results from protein decomposition in senescent leaves. Since NH_3 release is highly temperature dependent, photorespiration may also be a potential source of NH_3 (see p. 156).

Ammonium-N in solution can be toxic to plant growth. The toxicity results mainly from ammonia (NH_3) which affects plant growth and metabolism at low concentration levels at which NH_4^+ is not harmful. The distribution of NH_4^+ and NH_3 in aqueous solutions is described by the equilibrium relationship:

$$NH_3 \text{ (aq)} \rightleftarrows NH_4^+ + OH^-$$
$$NH_3 \text{ (aq)} = NH_3 \text{ dissolved in water}$$

This equation shows that the NH_3 (aq) concentration depends very much on the pH of the medium so that the toxicity of NH_4-N is also controlled by pH (BENNETT [1974]). This relationship is illustrated in Figure 7.4 in which NH_4^+-N activity is plotted against pH. The incipient toxic concentration of NH_3 (aq) is about 0.15 mM and the lethal concentration about 6.0 mM. The combinations of pH and NH_4^+ activity which produce these levels are shown in the Figure. It is clear that the toxic effects of NH_4-N resulting from NH_3 (aq) are more likely to occur at higher pH levels. NH_3 (aq) particularly affects root growth. BENNETT and ADAMS [1970] reported that the roots of young cotton seedlings were

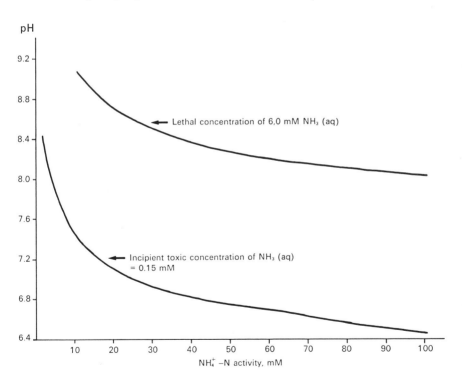

Fig. 7.4 Lethal concentration and incipient toxic concentration of NH_3 (aq) in relation to the pH and NH_4^+-N activity (after BENNETT [1974]).

353

injured by NH_3 (aq) concentrations as low as 0.2 mM. The germination of seeds can also be impaired by low NH_3 concentrations (BARKER et al. [1970]). The mechanism of NH_3 toxicity is not yet understood. BENNETT [1974] suggests that NH_3 (aq) can be toxic because it can traverse cell membranes. This view is supported by experimental data of HEBER et al. [1974], who showed that the outer chloroplast membrane was impermeable to NH_4^+ but allowed the diffusion of NH_3 (aq). This may explain the toxic effect of NH_4-N by the action of NH_3 (aq) in uncoupling photophosphorylation at the thylakoid membrane of the chloroplast (GIBBS and CALO [1959]). There is also evidence that NH_3 (aq) inhibits respiration (VINES and WEDDING [1960]). NH_4^+ can also be toxic to plant growth particularly in very acid media. Shoot and root growth are affected (MAYNARD and BARKER [1969]).

At acid to neutral pH values many plant species tolerate high levels of NH_4-N because the higher H^+ concentration depresses the NH_3 (aq) concentration. A number of crop species can therefore grow very well at NH_4-N levels of up to several mM provided that the pH is in the region of 4–6. This has been shown for a number of crops including wheat (BLONDEL and BLANC [1973], BRETELER and SMITH [1974]), sugar beet (BRETELER [1973]), and rice (DIJKSHOORN and ISMUNADJI [1972]). In the case of rice it was found that NH_4-N was a preferential source.

Highest N uptake rates were observed by BLONDEL and BLANC [1973] when both N forms, NH_4-N and NO_3-N, were present in the nutrient solution. This observation is consistent with earlier reports of DROUINEAU and BLANC [1961], who found that an addition of NH_4-N to NO_3-N cultures resulted in highest growth rates. Similar data were reported by COX and REISENAUER [1973] from dilute nutrient culture experiments. This beneficial effect of NH_4-N in combination with NO_3-N on growth needs to be tested using the precise flowing culture technique which has recently been developed and applied to NO_3^- uptake studies by CLEMENT et al. [1978]. Why NH_4-N should have this promoting effect on growth is not known. However, as the reduction of NO_3^- to NH_3 requires energy, it may be supposed that by supplying NH_4^+, energy is conserved and diverted to other metabolic processes including ion uptake and growth. It is also feasible that NH_4^+ at low concentrations may stimulate NO_3^- reduction. Possible reasons for the beneficial effect of low concentrations of NH_4-N have been discussed by KIRKBY [1968] and KIRKBY and HUGHES [1970].

Urea is generally converted into NH_4-N by urease in the soil (page 367). It can, however, be absorbed directly by plants although the rate of absorption appears to be low in comparison with that of NO_3^-. Table 7.8 shows that for sunflowers grown in water culture, higher dry matter yields were obtained in a 2 mM

NO_3^- than in a 8 mM urea treatment. The supply of urea not only resulted in a lower uptake of N, but also in a disturbance of the protein metabolism and a pronounced accumulation of aspargine occurred (KIRKBY and MENGEL [1970]). HENTSCHEL [1970] studying the uptake of NH_4-N and urea with labelled N also reported that urea was absorbed at a lower rate than NH_4-N by *Phaseolus vulgaris*. A number of recent reviews have dealt with the uptake of different forms of nitrogen and their effects on growth and metabolism (RAVEN and SMITH [1976], HAYNES and GOH [1978], KIRKBY [1981]).

Table 7.8 Influence of the form and level of nitrogen nutrition on the yield, nitrogen percentage and N-uptake by sunflower plants (KIRKBY and MENGEL [1970])

N-concentration of the nutrient sol. mM	Yield g DM/24 plants	N-content % in DM	Total N-uptake mg/24 plants
2 Nitrate	25.4	5.80	1,473
2 Urea	11.6	3.30	384
4 Urea	14.9	5.67	696
8 Urea	17.1	5.79	987

7.2.3 Nitrogen fractions

Nitrogen turnover in plants in characterized by three main steps, which are illustrated in Figure 7.5. The first step consists of the conversion of inorganic N into organic N compounds of low molecular weight. The details and the various processes involved in this step have already been discussed on page 168. In the second step, the synthesis of high molecular weight N compounds takes place. These compounds include proteins and nucleic acids. Low molecular weight organic N compounds and particularly amino acids serve as building blocks for these synthetic reactions. The third step represents the breakdown of the N containing macromolecules by hydrolyzing enzymes. These 3 steps in N turnover represent the pathways between the three main N fractions involved in N meta-

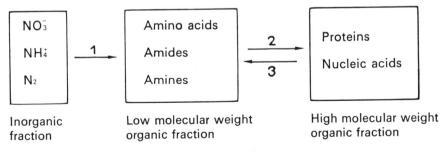

Fig.7.5 N-turnover between the three major N fractions in plants.

bolism: inorganic N, low molecular weight organic N compounds, and macro-molecular organic N compounds.

All three fractions are influenced by plant nutrition and in particular by the supply of N. Increasing the level of N nutrition results in an increase in all fractions but the extent to which this occurs differs between fractions. There is much experimental evidence to show that the content of soluble amino compounds (free amino acids, amines, amides) is considerably increased whilst the content of protein is only raised to a limited extent by high applications of fertilizer N. This finding is also shown in Table 7.9, which in addition also demonstrates that little difference was observed whether N was applied to the soil in the NO_3^- or NH_4-N form (MENGEL and HELAL [1970]). It can also be seen from Table 7.9 that the content of glutamate in particular responded to the increased N supply. Glutamate and glutamine are the first two amino acids synthesized during the process of NH_3 assimilation. Glutamate and aspartate as well as their amides also accumulate when high levels of inorganic N are applied to plants. Under such conditions inorganic N is obviously being assimilated at a higher rate than the amino acids are being used in protein synthesis. Heavy metal deficiencies (POSSINGHAM [1956]) or saline conditions (PLUENNEKE and JOHAM [1972]) can also result in an accumulation of soluble amino compounds in plant tissues. Plants suffering from K deficiency too often show increased contents of soluble amino acids and in some cases protein contents are enhanced (HSIAO et al. [1970]). According to KOCH and MENGEL [1974] such increases in protein contents under K deficiency conditions result from a depression in the growth rate.

In green plant material, protein N is by far the largest N fraction and amounts to about 80 to 85% of the total N. The N of the nucleic acids makes up about 10% and the soluble amino N about 5% of the total N present in plant material. Many crops are cultivated essentially to produce plant proteins. In vegetative plant material the proteins are mainly enzyme proteins, whereas in seeds and grains the major protein fraction is made up of storage proteins. In relation to

Table 7.9 Effect of N application on N fractions in upper parts of spring wheat at tillering stage (MENGEL and HELAL [1970]); relative values in brackets

N-rate, g N/pot	Protein N	Soluble amino N	Glutamate
		in Mol × 10^{-3}/100 g FM	
0.............................	30.5 (100)	0.358 (100)	0.033 (100)
0.6 as NH_4-N.....................	37.2 (122)	1.005 (283)	0.354 (1070)
0.6 as NO_3-N	39.2 (128)	1.398 (392)	0.450 (1360)

protein function it is necessary to distinguish between enzyme proteins, storage proteins and structural proteins, the latter mainly occurring in biological membranes. Nitrogen is also an essential constituent of various coenzymes. The protein content of vegetative plant organs as well as storage tissue may also be influenced by N supply. This question has already been discussed on page 240.

7.2.4 Translocation

Nitrogen taken up by plant roots is translocated in the xylem to the upper plant parts. The form in which N translocation occurs depends on the N uptake source and root metabolism. According to MARTIN [1970] nearly all the NH_4-N absorbed is assimilated in the root tissue and redistributed as amino acids. Nitrate-N can be translocated unaltered to shoots and leaves but this depends on the nitrate reduction potential of the roots (see p. 171). Nitrate and amino acids are thus the main forms in which N is translocated in the vascular system of higher plants. Generally in the xylem sap 70 to 80% of amino acids present are rich in N, with a N/C ratio greater than 0.4. It is believed that the function of these nitrogen-rich molecules (glutamine, asparagine) is to transport N with a minimum amount of C (PATE [1971]).

In N_2 fixing legumes the major N assimilation transport product may be asparagine as in the case for white lupin (ATKINS et al. [1975]). On the other hand for a number of legume species including soya bean, the ureides, allantoin and allantoic acid represent the bulk of N transported in the xylem after N_2 fixation (STREETER [1979]). Nitrate is universally absent in the phloem regardless of the form of N-nutrition, amino acids providing the means of N-transport in retranslocation.

Nitrogen translocation is an important process in plant life. Young leaves are supplied with amino acids until they have reached maturity (MILTHORPE and MOORBY [1969]). BURR et al. [1958] in studying the uptake and distribution of labelled NH_4-N in sugar cane plants found that the highest labelling occurred in the leaves with the highest growth rate. The oldest leaves showed the smallest import of labelled N. The intensity of N metabolism and particularly the rate of protein synthesis thus appears to control the import of N by different plant parts.

When the supply of N from the root medium is inadequate, N from older leaves is mobilized to feed the younger plant organs. For this reason, plants suffering from N deficiency first show deficiency symptoms in the older leaves. In such leaves protein has been hydrolyzed (proteolysis) and the resulting amino acids have been redistributed to the younger tips and leaves. Proteolysis results in a collapse of the chloroplasts and thus in a decline of the chlorophyll content. Hence yellowing of older leaves is a first symptom of inadequate N nutrition.

7.2.5 Nitrogen deficiency symptoms

Visual diagnosis of nutrient deficiency provides a valuable means of assessing the nutritional conditions of a crop. It is practiced successfully only by experts, as it requires much experience. Visual symptoms are only the consequence of metabolic disturbance, and different causes can lead to very similar syndromes. This is also the case for N deficiency. It is beyond the scope of this book to describe N deficiency symptoms in detail for different crops. Useful monographs giving exact descriptions and illustrated by coloured plates have been published by BEAR et al. [1949], BERGMANN and NEUBERT [1976], WALLACE [1961] and CHAPMAN [1966] for various crops and by BAULE and FRICKER [1970] for forest trees.

Nitrogen deficiency is characterized by a poor growth rate. The plants remain small, the stems have a spindly appearance, the leaves are small and the older ones often fall prematurely. Root growth is affected and in particular branching is restricted. The root/shoot ratio, however, is usually increased by N deficiency. As already pointed out, N deficiency results in the collapse of chloroplasts and also in a disturbance of chloroplast development (THOMSON and WEIER [1962]). Hence leaves deficient in N show chlorosis which is generally rather evenly distributed over the whole leaf. Necrosis of leaves or parts of the leaf occurs at a rather late and severe stage in the deficiency. In this respect N deficiency differs fundamentally from K and Mg deficiencies, where the symptoms also begin in the older leaves but where chlorotic and necrotic spots appear at a rather early stage. Deficiency symptoms of Fe, Ca, S are also similar to N deficiency being characterized by yellowish and pale leaves. In these deficiencies, however, the symptoms occur first in the younger leaves. These more general observations may be used to serve as a first means of distinguishing between these various nutrient deficiencies.

Plants suffering from N deficiency mature earlier, and the vegetative growth stage is often shortened. This early senescence probably relates to the effect of the N supply on the synthesis and translocation of cytokinins. According to investigations of WAGNER and MICHAEL [1971] the synthesis of cytokinins is depressed when N-nutrition is inadequate. As these phytohormones promote vigorous growth and the retention of the plant in a more juvenile stage, cytokinin deficiency may well result in senescence.

Nitrogen deficiency in cereals is characterized by poor tillering; the number of ears per unit area and also the number of grains per ear are reduced. The grains are small, but often relatively high in protein content, due to a decrease in the import of carbohydrate into the grains, during the later stages of grain filling.

7.3 Nitrogen Fertilizer Application and Crop Production

7.3.1 General

There is general agreement, that of all the nutrient amendments made to soils, N fertilizer application has had by far the most important effects in terms of increasing crop production. This is true for very different crops growing under the most widely varying conditions throughout the world. Numerous field experiments carried out in the past have shown that for many soils, N is the most important growth limiting factor.

7.3.2 Response to nitrogen application

Although crops usually respond to N fertilizers, this is not always the case. Response to N depends on soil conditions, the particular crop species and the plant nutrient supply in general. As far as soils are concerned, N response is generally poorer the higher the N content of the soil (WEHRMANN and SCHARPF [1979]). In the absence of a response, residual N and/or the rate of N release by microbial decomposition of soil organic matter is probably adequate to meet the demands of the crop. The relationship between fertilizer N response and soil organic matter was considered in field experiments by MÖLLE and JESSEN [1968]. These workers found that on sandy soils under the humid climatic conditions of Northern Denmark, N application rates of 90 to 135 kg N/ha for barley resulted in optimum economic returns. On peat soils, rich in organic N, however, rates of 45 kg N/ha were sufficient for optimum yields. High release rates of soil N may also be expected, if a grass sward is ploughed. The same is true for crops following a leguminous crop in the rotation. In both these examples N application is generally unneccessary. The cultivation of soils in the tropical rain zone also results in a high release of soil N in the first years of cropping. During this period the soils do not respond to N application (AGBLE[1973]). In following years, however, N application becomes increasingly important as the organic N of the soil is gradually exhausted. An extreme case of N release is reported from Israel, where a swamp was drained. The soils resulting from this treatment contained 20 to 80% organic matter. The mineralization of this organic matter was extremely high, and amounts in the order of 500 kg nitrate N/ha/year were accumulated in the upper soil layer. It is clear that under such conditions N treatment would have been superfluous (GISKIN and MAJDAN [1969]. Similar high rates of nitrification occur when the water table of peat soils is lowered. Such an example was reported by VAN DIEST [1977] from the low-moor peat soils in the Netherlands. In order to increase the nutrient holding capacity of these organic soils the water table was lowered from 25 to 75 cm below the soil surface. This resulted in N mineralization rates of about 1000 kg N/ha about half of which was taken up by the grass. The remaining N was leached or denitrified.

Organic soils make up only a small fraction of the world's cultivated soils. For this reason N responses can be expected from most soils provided that other growth factors are not limiting. One of the most important growth factors in this respect is water. Responses to N application are limited when water availability is restricted. This relationship has already been mentioned on page 271 (SHIMSHI [1969]). Table 7.10 from the data of LENKA and DASTANE [1970] also indicate that an optimum water regime gave rise to the highest N response for paddy

Table 7.10 Effect of land submergence on rice yield at two N application levels (LENKA and DASTANE [1970])

Irrigation treatment	Paddy grain yield, tonnes/ha	
	60 kg N/ha	120 kg N/ha
Saturation to field capacity	2.93	3.95
Saturation to 5 cm land submergence	3.94	5.40
10 to 5 cm land submergence	3.94	5.26

Table 7.11 Effect of increasing nitrogen rates in relation to phosphate and potassium dressings on grass yield (GARTNER [1969])

Fertilizer treatment kg (N P K)/ha			Yield tonnes DM/ha
N	P	K	
112	–	–	5.54
112	25	–	5.60
112	–	88	5.54
112	25	88	6.12
224	–	–	7.51
224	50	–	7.12
224	–	176	8.24
224	50	176	8.80
448	–	–	8.65
448	100	–	9.13
448	–	352	11.35
448	100	352	12.35

rice. Under arid conditions response to N fertilizer depends largely on annual rainfall and its distribution unless irrigation is practiced. The response to N also depends on how well the crop is supplied with other nutrients. This relationship has been established by a number of investigators. Table 7.11 shows an example of this kind (GARTNER [1969]). Without P and K applications the yield response to increasing N levels was smaller than when adequate amounts of P and K were applied. In addition these data also demonstrate that the response to the P and K application was greater with an abundant N supply.

As has already been mentioned in Chapter 6, high yielding crop cultivars in particular respond to N fertilizers. This not only is true for cereals and rice, but is also true for other crops including maize and sorghum. This is demonstrated in Figure 7.6 which shows N responses of different cultivars of sorghum.

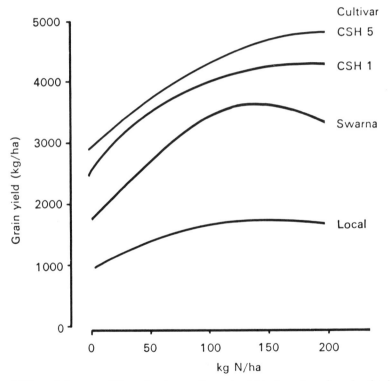

Fig. 7.6 Effect of the rate of N application on the grain yield of sorghum for a local cultivar and modern cultivars (after DE [1974]).

7.3.3 Nitrogen fertilizer application rates

The level of N that should be applied to a crop depends largely on the particular crop species and on the prevalent soil conditions. Generally the quantity of

N taken up by a good crop over the growth period serves as a guideline in assessing the appropriate rate of N application (kg N/ha). These quantities are listed for several crops in Table 6.2 (p. 296). When the rate of inorganic N release from soil organic matter is high, lower N application rates need to be applied. On the other hand, for poor soils low in N, the N application rate should be in excess of the total amount of N uptake.

Straw application to soils generally increases the immobilization of fertilizer N (TERMAN and BROWN [1968]). This often leads to a depression in crop yields (AMBERGER and AIGNER [1969]), although the effect can be overcome by an additional N application. Field trials of SCHMIDT and UNGER [1968] have shown that this should be in the order of about 1 kg N per 100 kg straw applied. In paddy soils incorporation of straw into the soil was not found to affect rice yields (WILLIAMS et al. [1972]).

Optimum rates of N application also depend on winter rainfall, as observed in field experiments, carried out over a number of years in the Netherlands (VAN DER PAAUW [1962]). In mild winters with heavy rainfall, considerable amounts of N are leached out of the soil. In order to maintain yield levels this loss must be compensated for by increased application of fertilizer N in spring.

In the long run, N removal from the soil be it as plant products, leaching or denitrification, must be balanced by an adequate return of N fertilizer. Very large amounts of N can be fixed by the *Rhizobium* legume associations. For this reason, forage legumes such as lucerne or clover are not usually treated with N (DOLL [1962]). Indeed N application may even depress yields, as fertilizer N inhibits N fixation and favours the growth of weeds. In grass legume associations, N application favours grasses which are able to compete with legumes for plant nutrients and other growth factors. Mixed grass clover swards should therefore not be treated with fertilizer N, if the proportion of legumes is adequate to meet the demands of the sward. When the proportion of legumes in the sward is very low, however, N fertilizer treatment is usually recommended. In Denmark DAM KOFOED and SØNDERGAARD KLAUSEN [1969] found that rates of 150 to 300 kg N/ha per year gave best results on grassland where the proportion of clover was very low or absent. Where conditions favour the growth of legumes, high forage yields can be obtained without N fertilizers. This is the case for large grassland areas of New Zealand (WALKER et al. [1954]).

Annual leguminous crops often respond to N fertilizer treatment. Fertilizing soya beans with N has thus become very common. Normally this is applied at the time of sowing in order to obtain a rapid growth of the young crop. BHANGOO and ALBRITTON [1972] found in field experiments, that rates of 112 kg N/ha increased soya bean yields by 10 to 15%. HULPOI et al. [1971] recommended 60 kg N/ha for this crop, grown on chernozem soils in Rumania. Broadbeans

(Vicia faba) and lentils also respond to low rates of N application (36 kg N/ha), as reported by HAMISSA [1974] and SCHERER and DANZEISEN [1980].

Excessive N application may be detrimental to crops. As already mentioned (see p. 275) a high level of N nutrition during the last months of sugar beet growth reduces the quality of the roots. For cereals lodging may result. In order to reduce susceptibility to lodging, it has become a common practice in Central Europe to apply chemicals, which shorten cereal straw length (see chapter 5.1.6).

Excess N can stimulate various fungal crop diseases (TROLLDENIER [1969]). Examples of this kind are brown rust *(Puccinia hordei)* on barley, brown leaf spot *(Helminthosporium oryzae)* on rice (HAK [1973]) and *Fusarium graminearum* on wheat (BUNESCU *et al.* [1972]). Disease may be especially severe, if the supply of K and P to the crop is low. On the other hand two diseases of maize *Pseudomonas syringae* (chocolate spot) and *Helminthosporium turcicum* (Northern corn leaf blight) appear to be reduced by high N application rates (KARLEN *et al.* [1973]).

7.3.4 Nitrogen fertilizers

The most common straight N fertilizers are listed in Table 7.12. For most N fertilizers NO_3^- and NH_4^+ are the N carriers. This is also the case for mixed and compound fertilizers. NH_4^+ is partially adsorbed on soil colloids

Table 7.12 Major nitrogen fertilizers

	Formula	% N
Ammonium sulphate	$(NH_4)_2SO_4$	21
Ammonium chloride	NH_4Cl	26
Ammonium nitrate	NH_4NO_3	35
Nitrochalk	$NH_4NO_3 + CaCO_3$	21
Ammonium nitrate sulphate	$NH_4NO_3 \cdot (NH_4)_2SO_4$	26
Potassium nitrate	KNO_3	14
Urea	$CO(NH_2)_2$	46
Calcium cyanamide	$CaCN_2$	21
Anhydrous ammonia	NH_3	82

and its uptake rate is usually therefore lower than that of NO_3^- under field conditions. For this reason most crops do not respond as quickly to NH_4^+ fertilizers as to NO_3^- application. Nitrate fertilizers are known to produce a rapid response in the plant. In most cases, however, the difference between both types of N fertilizers plays only a minor role. Thus HUPPERT and BUCHNER [1953] in evaluating numerous field experiments carried out in Germany, found that there were no major differences in yield response whether crops had been dressed with NO_3^- or NH_4-N. Only on more acid soils was NO_3^- superior to NH_4^+. WID-DOWSON *et al.* [1967] reported that $Ca(NO_3)_2$ gave larger grain yields of barley than $(NH_4)_2SO_4$ in three quarters of all the experiments carried out on light or medium textured soils in England. The yield differences, however, were not great. The question, of whether to apply NH_4- or NO_3-N depends on specific

percentage loss

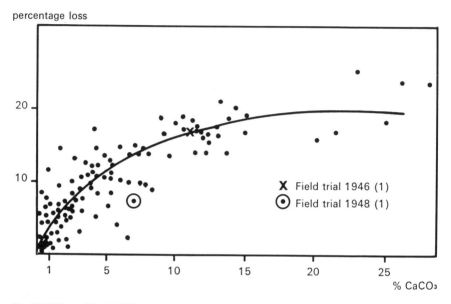

Fig. 7.7 Effect of the $CaCO_3$ content in the soil on the volatilization of NH_4–N (after LEHR and VAN WESEMAEL [1961]).

soil conditions. The risk of NH_3 loss by volatilization, for example, is considerably greater on high pH soils. Ammonium fertilizers are therefore not recommended on alkaline soils. According to LEHR and VAN WESEMAEL [1961] volatilization of NH_3 is correlated more with $CaCO_3$ content than with soil pH. This relationship is shown in Figure 7.7 from the results of 176 soil samples, gathered from all over the world. Urea application also leads to the loss of NH_3 by volatilization as urea is very rapidly converted to NH_3 particularly in alkaline soils. Considerable volatile losses of NH_3 may also occur after the application of urea even on acid soils. Losses are especially high if urea is surface-applied and drying conditions prevail. TERMAN [1979], who has treated the question of volatile losses of NH_3 in an extensive review paper, recommends that applied urea should be covered by a soil layer of at least 5 cm in depth.

The process of denitrification can also bring about a loss of N from the soil applied as N fertilizer. In anaerobic soils (reducing conditions – low redox potential) N is lost very readily in this way from NO_3^--fertilizers. This is especially true in paddy soils (PONNAMPERUMA [1978]). Here NH_4-N or urea are recommended as fertilizers. These N fertilizers should be worked well into the soil because oxidative conditions occur in the surface soil layer, which favour the oxidation of NH_4^+ to NO_3^- (see Figure 7.2). If NO_3^- is produced and leached into the deeper reductive soil layers it will be denitrified and thus lost (TORIYAMA [1973]).

Ammonium sulphate used to be a very important fertilizer, but its relative consumption has declined more and more in recent years. To some extent it has been replaced by urea which has a higher N content and is easily handled in solution form (see p. 312). Ammonium nitrate is an explosive salt and for this reason its direct use as fertilizer is prohibited in some countries. This rather high graded N fertilizer is now often used in the preparation of liquid fertilizers. Because of the risks of fires, however, NH_4NO_3 often is mixed with limestone. This mixture is safe and easy to handle and called nitrochalk. It is a well known straight N fertilizer, which due to its content of limestone prevents or delays acidification of the soil. Ammonium chloride is of only minor importance. According to COOKE [1972] it is suitable for paddy soils, where the use of $(NH_4)_2SO_4$ leads to the production of undesirable sulphide. Ammonium nitrate sulphate is a double salt of ammonium nitrate and ammonium sulphate made by neutralizing nitric and sulphuric acids with NH_3. The product is easy to handle and to store. Its consumption, however, has decreased in the recent years. Potassium nitrate contains 44% K_2O in addition to N. This fertilizer is often used as foliar spray. The same is true for urea, which is also used to a large extent in liquid fertilizers (see p. 312).

Calcium cyanamide contains N in the amide and in cyanide forms. This fertilizer has a darkish colour as it also contains some C, which is formed during the production process. Calcium cyanamide is soluble in water. As shown below it is converted in the soil to urea, which is again split into NH_3 and CO_2.

$$CaN - C \equiv N + 2\,H_2O \rightarrow H_2N - C = N + Ca\,(OH)_2$$
$$\text{Ca cyanamide} \qquad\qquad \text{Cyanamide}$$

$$H_2N - C \equiv N + H_2O \rightarrow H_2N - \overset{\overset{\displaystyle O}{\|}}{C} - NH_2$$
$$\text{Urea}$$

$$H_2N - \overset{\overset{\displaystyle O}{\displaystyle \|}}{C} - NH_2 + 2\,H_2O \rightarrow (NH_4)_2CO_3$$

$$(NH_4)_2CO_3 + 2\,H^+ \rightarrow 2\,NH_4^+ + CO_2 + H_2O$$

The conversion process needs water. For this reason the response of plants to calcium cyanamide application is delayed in dry soil conditions. During the conversion process in the soil intermediate toxic products can be formed. Generally calcium cyanamide is applied before sowing and worked well into the soil. The intermediate toxic substances are good weed killers and nitrification inhibitors. Cyanamide is a slow reacting N fertilizer. Dicyandiamide formed during the degradation of calcium cyanamide retards the ammonification of urea and also the oxidation of NH_4-N. The N effect of the fertilizer is thus delayed (RATHSACK [1978]). During the conversion process $Ca(OH)_2$ is also formed, which has a favourable effect on pH and soil structure in acidic soils.

The application of anhydrous NH_3 has already been discussed on page 312. The main drawback of this high graded N fertilizer is the special equipment required for its transport and application. Numerous field trials have shown that anhydrous NH_3 produces very much similar responses to solid N fertilizers (DAM KOFOED et al. [1967]). On heavier textured soils and under more continental climatic conditions, anhydrous NH_3 can also be applied in autumn without the risk of N loss by leaching (KORENSKY and NEUBERG [1968]). On these soils the risk of leaching losses only occur, if the NH_4^+ is oxidized to NO_3^- to any great extent. This microbial oxidation depends largely on the prevalent soil temperatures in autumn and winter. Thus under climatic conditions with mild winters and high rainfall the application of anhydrous NH_3 or other NH_4^+ fertilizers can lead to substantial N losses due to the leaching of NO_3^- (DAM KOFOED et al. [1967]). This loss of N during winter is probably the main reason why anhydrous NH_3 applied in autumn often results in lower yields than are obtained following a spring application (ROUSSEL et al. [1966]).

In the last decade slow-release nitrogen fertilizers have been developed with the object of reducing leaching losses which result from use of the more soluble fertilizers and to provide a more permanent source of available N. The most common slow release N fertilizers are urea formaldehyde polymers, isobutylidene diurea, crotonylidene diurea and sulphur coated urea or sulphur coated NH_4NO_3. The availability of the sulphur coated forms depends mainly on the physico-chemical conditions in the soil influencing solubility whereas the availability of urea formaldehyde and isobutylidene diurea is primarily controlled by the microbial activity in the soil. Soil conditions which stimulate microbiological activity in the soil tend also to enhance crop growth. The N

366

release from these fertilizers thus generally follows the N requirement of the crop.

In the decomposition of these slow N releasing organic fertilizers, urea is released by hydrolysis (Figure 7.8). This is then split by urease into NH_3 and CO_2. Ammonia can be further oxidized to NO_2^- and NO_3^- by nitrification (see p. 341). According to HADAS and KAFKAFI [1974] the rate of the microbial decomposition of urea formaldehyde is controlled by temperature. These authors found, that the rate constants for the overall process were several times higher at 24°C and 34°C as compared with a temperature of 14°C. At this lower temperature breakdown is particularly delayed during the first weeks after application. Nitrogen recovery as measured by the proportion of N taken up by the crop of the total N applied, is generally poor for these slow releasing N fertilizers as compared with the conventional water soluble N fertilizers (DAM KOFOED and LARSEN [1969], ALLEN et al. [1971]). STÄHLIN [1967] for example in testing a butylidene diurea on grassland, found that a rate of 500 kg N/ha provided for two years gave only poor yields in the 2nd year.

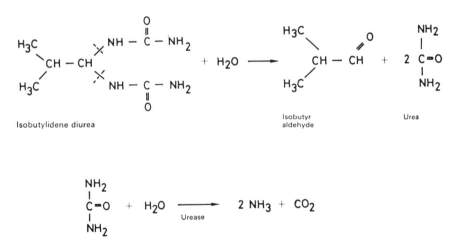

Fig. 7.8 Decomposition reactions of a slow-release N fertilizer (isobutylidene diurea).

A further disadvantage of the slow-release N fertilizers is their high cost per unit weight of N as compared with ordinary N fertilizers. There are, however, favourable reports in the literature regarding the application of slow release fertilizers. The topic has been recently considered by OERTLI [1980] in a review paper (see p. 303). At the present time slow-release N fertilizers are only a viable proposition for use in horticulture and for lawns. Here a high rate of N application can be given in one single dressing of these slow-acting materials without any risk to the plants. The same N level in the form of water soluble N materials would result in severe damage. This is the main advantage of these slow-release N fertilizers, that they may be applied in a single dressing.

General Reading

ALLISON, F.E.: Soil Organic Matter and its Role in Crop Production. Elsevier Sci. Publications, 1973

BARTHOLOMEW, W.V. and CLARK, F.E.: Soil Nitrogen. American Soc. of Agronomy, Inc., Madison, Wisconsin, USA 1965

BURESH, R.J., CASSELMAN, M.E. and PATRICK, W.H. jr.: Nitrogen fixation in flooded systems, a review. Adv. Agron. *33*, 150–192 (1980)

CLARK, F.E. and ROSSWALL, T. (Eds.): Terrestrial Nitrogen Cycles, Processes Ecosystem Strategies and Management Impacts, Ecol Bull. Stockholm 33, (1981)

DELWICHE, C.C. Ed.: Denitrification, Nitrification and Atmospheric Nitrous Oxide. Wiley, New York, London, Sydney, Toronto 1981

GREENWOOD, E.A.N.: Nitrogen stress in plants. Adv. Agron. *28*, 1–35 (1976)

HEWITT, E.J. and CUTTING, C.V. (Eds): Nitrogen Assimilation in Plants, Academic Press London, New York, San Francisco, 1979

INTERNATIONAL ATOMIC ENERGY AGENCY: Nitrogen-15 in Soil – Plant Studies, Vienna 1971

KIRKBY, E.A.: Nitrogen Nutrition of the Plant. The University of Leeds Press, Leeds 1970

NEYRA, C.A. and DÖBEREINER, J.: Nitrogen fixation in grasses. Adv. Agron. *29*, 1–38 (1977)

NIELSEN, D.R. and MacDONALD, J.G.: Nitrogen in the Environment. Vol. 1, Nitrogen Behaviour in Field Soil. Academic Press London, New York, San Francisco, 1978

NIELSEN, D.R. and MacDONALD, J.G.: Nitrogen in the Environment. Vol. 2, Soil Plant Nitrogen Relationship. Academic Press London, New York, San Francisco, 1978

PARSONS, J.W. and TINSLEY, J.: Nitrogenous Substances. In GIESEKING, J.E. (ed) Soil Components vol. 1, Organic Components p. 263–304, Springer-Verlag, 1975

SIMPSON, J.R. and FRENEY, J.R.: Fate of nitrogen under different cropping systems. In: LEECE, D.R. (ed.) Fertilizers and the Environment, p. 27–33. Austalian Institute of Agricultural Science. Sydney, 1974

WALKER, T.W.: The nitrogen cycle in grassland soils. J. Sci. Fd. Agric. *7*, 66–72 (1956)

Chapter 8

Sulphur

8.1 Soil Sulphur

Sulphur occurs in the soil in inorganic and organic forms. In most soils organically bound S provides the major S reservoir (REISENAUER *et al.* [1973], SCOTT and ANDERSON [1976]). In peat soils this can amount to almost 100% of the total S. Soil organic S can be divided into 2 fractions; carbon bonded S, and non carbon bonded S. The latter fraction is made up of phenolic and choline sulphates as well as lipids (FRENEY and STEVENSON [1966]). The carbon bonded S includes the S of amino acids although they appear to account for less than half of this fraction (WHITEHEAD [1964]). The C:N:S ratio in soil organic matter is approximately 125:10:1.2 (FRENEY [1961]). The inorganic forms of S in soil consist mainly of SO_4^{2-}. In arid regions soils may accumulate high amounts of salts such as $CaSO_4$, $MgSO_4$ and Na_2SO_4. Under humid conditions, however, SO_4^{2-} is present either in soil solution or is adsorbed on soil colloids. The SO_4^{2-} in soil solution is in equilibrium with the solid phase forms. The factors influencing the retention of SO_4^{2-} in soils have been considered in detail by REISENAUER *et al.* [1973]. The clay minerals are particularly important in this respect. Adsorption of SO_4^{2-} increases as the soil pH falls and is higher for kaolinitic than for 2:1 clay minerals. From the work of SCOTT [1976] on soils in North East Scotland, sulphate adsorption seems to depend more on active Fe than aluminium.

Under waterlogged conditions, inorganic S occurs in reduced forms such as FeS, FeS_2 (pyrites) and H_2S. The total S content of soils in temperate regions is in the range of 0.005 to 0.04% S (SIMON-SYLVESTRE [1969]). Total soil levels depend on the organic matter contents and also on climatic conditions. Under humid conditions high amounts of SO_4^{2-} are leached whereas in arid situations SO_4^{2-} accumulates in the upper soil layer. Soils of the temperate regions are generally higher in S the more organic matter they contain. Thus according to investigations of GRUNWALDT [1969] the S content of various soil types declines in the following sequence:

Calcareous organic soils > Peat > Marsh soils >
Grey brown podzolic soils > Podzols

The organic S fraction of the soil is rendered available to plants by microbial activity. In this process of mineralization H_2S is formed which under aerobic conditions readily undergoes autoxidation to SO_4^{2-}. In anaerobic media, however, H_2S is oxidized to elemental S by chemotrophic sulphur bacteria *(Beggiatoa, Thiothrix)*. The same bacteria can also oxidize S to H_2SO_4 under aerobic conditions. Elemental S is also oxidized by chemotrophic bacteria of the genus *Thiobacillus*. The overall process may be expressed in chemical terms as follows:

$$2H_2S + O_2 \rightarrow 2H_2O + 2S + 510 \text{ kJ}$$
$$2S + 3O_2 + 2H_2O \rightarrow 2H_2SO_4 + 1180 \text{ kJ}$$
$$\text{net: } 2H_2S + 4O_2 \rightarrow 2H_2SO_4 + 1690 \text{ kJ}$$

The oxidation of S thus results in the formation of H_2SO_4. A consequent increase in soil acidity thus occurs. The same process also accounts for the acidification resulting from the addition of elemental S to soils. This treatment is sometimes used to depress the pH of alkaline soils. In a similar way to the reactions described above FeS can be oxidized biologically and chemically to elemental S (SCHOEN and RYE [1971]) according to the equation:

$$FeS + H_2O + \tfrac{1}{2} O_2 \rightarrow Fe(OH)_2 + S$$

Under reducing soil conditions (waterlogged soils, paddy) H_2S is the most important end product of anaerobic S degradation. Organic suphides, such as methyl- and butyl sulphides are also formed, which like H_2S are both characterized by an unpleasant odour. Photosynthetic green and purple bacteria can oxidize H_2S to S by utilizing the H of the H_2S for photosynthetic electron transport. When this process is restricted H_2S may accumulate to toxic levels and thus impair plant growth. To some extent, the detrimental effect of H_2S can be alleviated by the addition of ferrous salts which form the sparingly soluble FeS (CONNELL and PATRICK [1969]). Sulphate reduction under anaerobic conditions is mainly brought about by bacteria of the genus *Desulfovibrio* (PONNAMPERUMA [1972]). These bacteria utilize the oxygen of the SO_4^{2-} as a terminal electron acceptor.

The processes of S conversion in soils are shown in Figure 8.1. Under reducing conditions H_2S is produced. Some H_2S can be released into the atmosphere and is thus lost from the soil system. Aerobic soil conditions shift the processes in favour of SO_4^{2-} formation. As this ion is relatively mobile in soils, some SO_4^{2-} may be lost by leaching. Sulphate is the form in which plants absorb S from the soil medium. In the plant itself a part of the absorbed sulphate is reduced and converted to an organic form (see page 180). Organic S present in the remnants of dead plant material in the soil is also involved in the S cycle as shown in Figure 8.1. A useful review of the S cycle in relation to soil and plant nutrition has been presented by WHITEHEAD [1964].

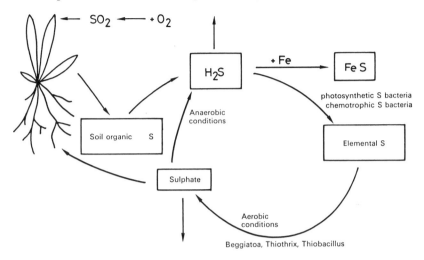

Fig. 8.1 Sulphur cycle in nature.

8.2 Sulphur in Physiology

8.2.1 Uptake and translocation

Plants mainly absorb S in the form of SO_4^{2-}. In the pH range to which roots are normally exposed, uptake is not very pH sensitive. HENDRIX [1967] found the highest uptake rate in bean plants at pH 6.5. Other plant nutrients scarcely affect the absorption of SO_4^{2-} by plant cells. Selenate, however, which is closely chemically related to SO_4^{2-}, depresses SO_4^{2-} uptake substantially (LEGGETT and EPSTEIN [1956]). This indicates that both ion species probably compete for the same carrier site. The actual uptake mechanism is not fully understood. NISSEN [1971] supposes that only a single uptake mechanism exists, the selectivity of which depends much on the prevailing SO_4^{2-} concentration in the nutrient solution. This still needs further elucidation (see p. 140). According to investigations of ANSARI and BOWLING [1972] with sunflowers, SO_4^{2-} is absorbed and translocated against an electrochemical gradient, which suggests that SO_4^{2-} uptake is an active process (see p. 125).

Sulphate is mainly translocated in an upward (acropetal) direction and the capability of higher plants to move S in a downward (basipetal) direction is relatively poor. In solution culture experiments with clover BOUMA [1967] found that as a result of interruption of the SO_4^{2-} supply (transfer into SO_4^{2-} free solution) S in the roots and petioles was translocated towards the younger leaves. The S of the older leaves, however, did not contribute to the S supply of younger tissues. This shows that translocation against the transpiration stream did not occur.

There is now a considerable body of evidence to show that plants can utilize atmospheric SO_2 as part of their S supply. FALLER et al. [1970], growing various plant species in growth chambers with defined SO_2 concentrations in the atmosphere as the sole S source, found that growth was reduced in the treatment where SO_2 was absent. The beneficial effect of SO_2 in alleviating S deficiency has also been reported by COWLING and LOCKYER [1976]. Once SO_2 is absorbed through the stomata it is distributed throughout the entire plant and has been detected in various S fractions such as protein S, amino acid S and sulphate S (DE CORMIS [1968]). The influence of the level of SO_2 nutrition on plant growth is shown in Table 8.1 (FALLER [1968]). The favourable effect on growth can be seen in the effects of low levels of SO_2 supplied to plants growing in a SO_4^{2-} free nutrient solution. At the highest SO_2 concentration supplied (1.5 mg SO_2/m^3), however, growth was depressed, and necrotic symptoms were observed in the leaves of maize and sunflowers (see p. 382).

Table 8.1 Effect of atmospheric SO_2 concentration on the growth of various plant species, grown in a sulphate free nutrient solution (data from FALLER [1968])

| | SO_2 concentration, mg SO_2/m^3 | | | | | Experimental period in days |
	0.0.	0.2	0.5	1.0	1.50	
			yield in g DM/plant			
Sunflowers	70	103	103	113	100	15
Maize	100	110	118	111	107	13
Tobacco	31	41	43	54	46	9

8.2.2 Metabolic functions of sulphur

The assimilation (reduction) of SO_4^{2-} has already been described on page 180. Normally, reduced S is rapidly incorporated into an organic molecule, the first stable organic S compound being cysteine. The SH (sulphydryl or thiol) group from cysteine can be transferred to phosphohomoserine to form cystathionine which breaks down to produce homocysteine. This compound in turn, can be converted to methionine by a CH_3 group transfer. According to WILSON et al. [1978] plants may also produce H_2S from SO_4^{2-} if very high amounts of sulphate are supplied.

Cysteine and methionine are the most important S containing amino acids in plants, where they both occur as free acids and as building blocks of proteins. One of the main functions of S in proteins or polypeptides is in the formation of disulphide bonds between polypeptide chains. The synthesis of the dipeptide cystine from two cysteine molecules illustrates the formation of a disulphide bond (S–S–bond) from two SH groups.

$$2 \times \text{Cysteine} \rightarrow \text{Cystine} + 2H$$

In an analogous way the formation of a disulphide bond can serve as a covalent cross linkage between two polypeptide chains or between two points on a single chain. It thus stabilizes the polypeptide structure (see Figure 8.2). The formation of disulphide bonds in polypeptides and proteins is an essential function of S in biochemistry, as these S-S bridges contribute to the conformation of enzyme proteins. Baking quality is also related to disulphide bridging as it is responsible for the polymerization of glutelin. The higher the degree of glutelin polymerization the better the baking quality (EWART [1978]). A further essential function of SH groups in metabolism is their direct participation in enzyme reactions, although not all free SH groups in enzymes are active.

As shown in the above equation cystine is formed by the oxidation (release of H) of two molecules of cysteine. The whole reaction serves as a redox system which can take up or release H atoms depending on prevailing metabolic conditions. Under reducing conditions (excess of H or reduced coenzymes) the equilibrium is shifted in favour of cysteine whereas under oxidizing conditions cystine is formed. The system thus functions as either an H donor or an H acceptor. The glutathione redoxsystem is analogous to the cysteine/cystine system. Glutathione is a tripeptide consisting of glutamyl (= residue of glutamic acid), cystei-

373

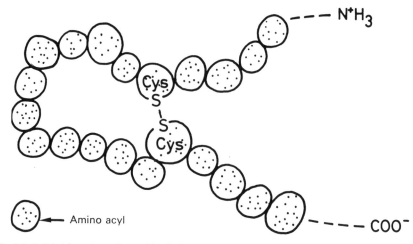

Fig.8.2 S–S bridge of a polypeptide chain.

nyl (= residue of cysteine) and glycine moieties (see formula on page 375). The reactive group of the system in the SH group of the cysteinyl moiety which forms an S-S bridge with the SH group of another glutathione molecule. Because of its higher water solubility, the glutathione redox system plays a more important role in metabolism than the cystine/cysteine redoxsystem. Reduced glutathione serves as a sulphydryl buffer which maintains the cysteine residues of proteins in a reduced form. The oxidized form of glutathione can be reduced by NADPH (see formula on the following page) ·

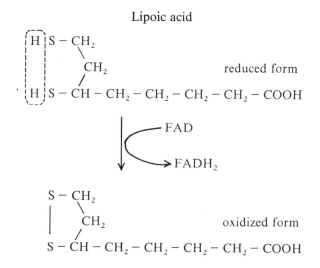

Lipoic acid

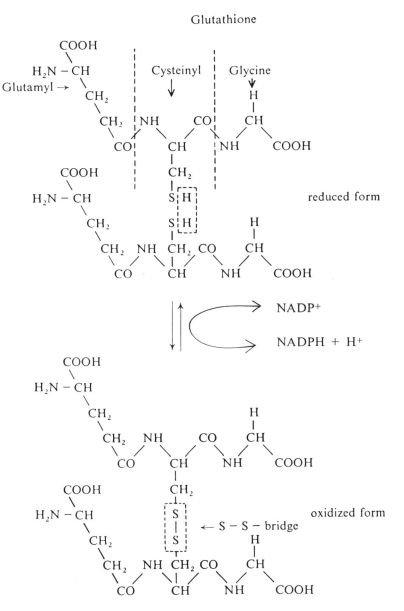

Glutathione

reduced form

NADP+

NADPH + H+

oxidized form

← S – S – bridge

The SH group of lipoic acid also participates in redox reactions in a similar way (see formula). Lipoic acid is a coenzyme which is involved in oxidative decarboxylation of α-keto acids.

An important group of S containing compounds are the ferredoxins (a type of non haem iron sulphur protein). These low molecular weight proteins contain a high proportion of cysteine units, and an equal number of S and Fe atoms in addition to the S contained is the cysteine and methionine units of the protein chain. The detailed spatial arrangement of the S and Fe atoms has not yet been worked out. However, it appears that these S and Fe atoms are linked together and that this combination is in turn linked to the protein chain *via* the S atoms of cysteine (see Figure 3.15 p. 146). This configuration confers a highly negative redox potential, the most negative known for a biological compound. The oxidized form is reduced by accepting an electron ejected from chlorophyll in the light reactions in photosynthesis. The reduced form is probably the ultimate source of reducing power for the reduction of CO_2 in the dark reactions of photosynthesis (see p. 152). It also serves an electron donor in sulphate reduction (p. 180), N_2 reduction (p. 172) and glutamate synthesis (p. 176).

Sulphur is a constituent of CoA and of the vitamins biotin and thiamine.

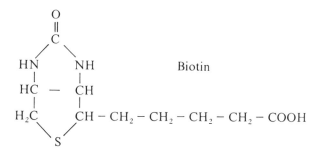

Biotin is associated with CO_2 fixation and decarboxylation reactions although it does not appear to be the prosthetic group of CO_2 fixing enzymes (ROBINSON [1973]).

Thiamine pyrophosphate

Sulphur is an essential element of the thiazole ring which is a component of the vitamin thiamine. Thiamine may occur as the free vitamin or as thiamine pyrophosphate. In contrast to animal tissues, plants contain thiamine very largely in the free vitamin form (ROBINSON [1973]). Little is known of the role of thiamine in plants. Thiamine pyrophosphate acts as a coenzyme in the decarboxylation of pyruvate to acetaldehyde and the oxidation of α-keto acids (LEHNINGER [1975], The basis of these reactions is the ability of the thiazole ring of thiamine pyrophosphate to bind and activate aldehyde groups.

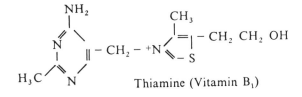

Thiamine (Vitamin B₁)

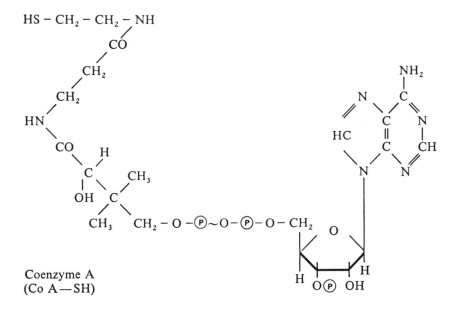

Coenzyme A
(Co A—SH)

In coenzyme A (CoA) the active site of the molecule is the SH group. It can react with organic acids according to the equation

377

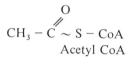

$$R - \overset{\overset{\displaystyle O}{\|}}{C} - \boxed{OH \quad H} S - CoA \rightarrow R - \overset{\overset{\displaystyle O}{\|}}{CO} \sim S \cdot CoA + H_2O$$

In this way the SH group becomes esterified with an acyl group of an organic acid. Coenzyme A thus serves as a carrier of acyl groups.

$$CH_3 - \overset{\overset{\displaystyle O}{\|}}{C} \sim S - CoA$$
$$\text{Acetyl CoA}$$

Acetyl CoA is formed when CoA reacts with acetic acid. This is an important example of an activated acid of this type and plays a very significant role in fatty acid and lipid metabolism.

Many plant species contain small amounts of volatile S compounds. In some plant groups these may be important. Sulphoxides $(R - \overset{\overset{\displaystyle O}{\|}}{S} - R)$ for example are responsible for both the lachrymatory factor in onions and the odour of garlic. The mustard oils which occur mainly in the *Cruciferae* are of particular agricultural significance. According to FOWDEN [1967] amino acids, such as glutamate, aspartate, alanine or serine are precursors of mustard oils. The main synthetic pathway is outlined below:

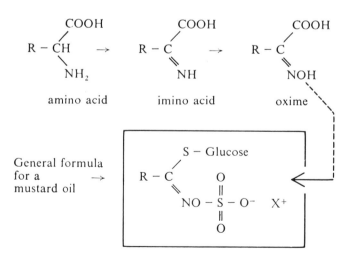

The general structure of a mustard oil given above shows that S occurs in two different forms. It is present as sulphate, and also as an S atom linking the glucose moiety with the rest of the molecule (S glycosidic bond). The cation X^+ is usually potassium. The correct chemical term for the mustard oils is mustard oil glucosides or glucosinolates. On hydrolysis glucosinolates yield isothiocyanates $(R - N = C = S)$, glucose and sulphate. The radical 'R' in the formula varies for different mustard oils:

$CH_2 = CH - CH_2 -$ Sinigrin *(Brassica nigra)*

$CH_2 -$ Glucotropaeolin *(Tropaeolum majus)*

$CH_2 - CH_2 -$ Gluconasturtiin *(Nasturtium officinale)*

$CH - CH_2 -$ Glucobarbarin *(Reseda luteola)*
               OH

$OH -$ $CH_2 -$ Glucosinalbin *(Sinapis alba)*

The plant species in which these glucosinolates mainly occur are cited in brackets. The high S contents generally found in the *Cruciferae* are largely attributable to these compounds.

The total S content in plant tissues is in the order of 0.2 to 0.5% S in the dry matter. ULRICH et al. [1967] studying S uptake and S content of lucerne *(Medicago sativa)* in solution culture found that in the range of inadequate S supply, raising the sulphate supply only increased the organic S content without increasing the sulphate content. As soon as the S demand of the plant was satisfied, however, the content of sulphate S increased whereas the content of organic S remained relatively constant. This relationship is shown in Figure 8.3 from the data of DELOCH [1960] for sunflowers. These results demonstrate that S taken up in excess of the demand of the plant for the synthesis of organic S compounds is stored as SO_4-S. In plant species capable of synthesizing mustard oils, organic S, rather than SO_4^{-2}, is the primary storage form. According to MARQUARD et al. [1968] the content of mustard oil in these plants depends very closely on the S supply. Plants well supplied with S are high in mustard oils. Increasing S application can enhance mustard oil concentration

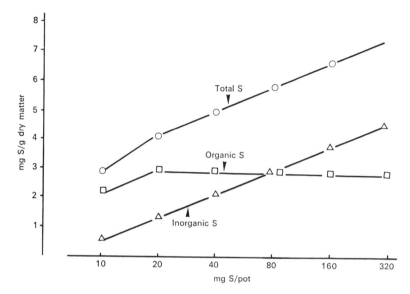

Fig.8.3 Influence of increasing levels of SO_4 nutrition on the total S, sulphate S and organic S of sunflower leaves (after DELOCH [1960]).

even after maximum growth has been attained. During senescence, proteins are hydrolyzed (proteolysis) and amino acid S released can often be oxidized to SO_4^{2-} (MOTHES [1939]). In this respect organic S differs fundamentally from organic N, which cannot be oxidized to NO_3^- in plant tissues.

With the exception of plant species containing S glycosides, the bulk of organic S consists of protein S in the form of cysteinyl- and methionyl-residues. As proteins have a defined composition, the N/S ratio of proteins varies only slightly and is in the order of 30/1 to 40/1 (DIJKSHOORN and VAN WIJK [1967]). Somewhat similar N/S ratios were found by RENDIG *et al.* [1976] in the protein of young maize plants. Chloroplast proteins and proteins associated with nucleic acids, however, have lower N/S ratios, as these proteins are comparatively rich in S (see Table 8.2).

Table 8.2 N/S ratio of various plant proteins (data from DIJKSHOORN and VAN WIJK [1967])

Protein	N/S ratio
Gliadin (grains)	33/1
Albumin (grains)	28/1
Globulin (grains)	67/1
Chloroplast proteins	15/1
Nucleoproteins	18/1

8.2.3 Sulphur deficiency and toxicity

As S is an essential constituent of proteins, S deficiency results in an inhibition in protein synthesis. The S containing amino acids (cysteine, methionine) which are essential building blocks of protein are deficient and thus proteins cannot by synthesized. For this reason non-S containing amino acids accumulate in S deficient plant tissues (LINSER et al. [1964]). COLEMAN [1957] observed that asparagine, glutamine and arginine are mainly accumulated. This finding is consistent with the results of EPPENDORFER [1968], who found an accumulation of amides in the soluble amino fraction of barley shoots suffering from an inadequate S supply. According to the findings of RENDIG et al. [1976] the accumulation of amide N in S deficient maize plants is associated with low levels of sugars. These low sugar contents result from the poor photosynthetic activity of chlorotic S deficient plants. From the foregoing discussion it is not surprising that in S deficient plants protein content is depressed. This holds not only for vegetative plant material, but also for cereal grains. Thus both EPPENDORFER [1968] and Coïc et al. [1963] have reported that the grains of S deficient barley and wheat contain less methionine and cysteine than found in cereals well supplied with S. The ratio 'organic N/organic S' is therefore considerably higher in S deficient plant tissues (70/1 to 80/1) as compared with normal plant tissues. This ratio can serve as a guide to indicate whether or not plants are adequately supplied with S. Another feature of S deficient tissues is the accumulation of NO_3-N. The influence of S deficiency on carbohydrate N and S compounds in plants is summarized in the results of ERGLE and EATON [1951] shown in Table 8.3.

In field crops sulphur deficiency and nitrogen deficiency are sometimes difficult to distinguish. In this instance leaf analysis can be invaluable. In S deficient plants the SO_4-S levels are very low whereas amide N and NO_3-N are accumu-

Table 8.3 The effect of sulphate concentration in the nutrient medium on the percentage dry weight of carbohydrates, nitrogen and sulphur compounds in the leaves of cotton (ERGLE and EATON [1951])

SO_4 in nutrient (ppm)	Fresh weight Plants (grams)	Sulphate S %	Organic S %	Total Sugar %	Nitrate N %	Soluble organic N %	Protein N %
0.1	13	0.003	0.11	0.0	1.39	2.23	0.96
1.0	50	0.003	0.12	0.0	1.37	2.21	1.28
10	237	0.009	0.17	1.5	0.06	1.19	2.56
50	350	0.10	0.26	3.1	0.00	0.51	3.25
200	345	0.36	0.25	3.4	0.10	0.45	3.20

lated. This contrasts markedly with N deficiency where soluble N levels are depressed and SO_4^{2-} levels are normal.

In plants suffering from S deficiency the rate of plant growth is reduced. Generally the growth of the shoots is more affected than root growth. Frequently the plants are rigid and brittle and the stems remain thin. In *Cruciferae* the lateral extension of the leaf lamina is restricted and the leaves are rather narrow. Chloroplast formation is affected and according to KYLIN [1953] decomposition of chloroplasts may even occur in severe cases. In contrast to N deficiency, chlorotic symptoms occur first in the younger, most recently formed leaves (MAYNARD [1979]). This shows that older plant tissues cannot contribute substantially to the S supply of younger leaves, which are obviously mainly dependent on S taken up by the roots. ULRICH et al. [1967] described the S deficiency symptoms of lucerne as follows: 'Sulphur deficiency symptoms appeared first at the top of the alfalfa plant. The leaves turned from a light green to a light yellow, often followed by pronounced yellowing. In time, all leaves on the plant became light-yellow to yellow in colour'. This development of S chlorosis observed in lucerne also holds true for many other plant species. In *Lolium multiflorum* shortened internodes were found in S deficient plants by ULRICH and HILTON [1968].

Plants are comparatively insensitive to high SO_4^{2-} concentrations in the nutrient medium. Only in cases where SO_4^{2-} concentrations are in the order of 50 mM as for example in some saline soils, is plant growth adversely affected. The symptoms, a reduction in growth rate and a dark green colour of the leaves, are not specific for S excess and are more typical of salt affected plants (see p. 229). Provided that SO_4^{2-} and Cl^- are given in isoosmotic concentrations, SO_4^{2-} is often more detrimental than Cl^- salinity (HENCKEL and SOLOVYOV [1968], MEIRI et al. [1971]).

The critical concentration of SO_2 in the atmosphere above which toxic effects in plants are observed is in the range of 0.5 to 0.7 mg SO_2-S/m³. High SO_2 concentrations result in necrotic symptoms in the leaves. The SO_2 concentration of the atmosphere is generally about 0.1 to 0.2 mg SO_2-S/m³. In industrial areas, however, concentrations several times higher than these normal levels have been registered. The causes of the SO_2 toxicity have been investigated by SILVIUS et al. [1975]. Sulphur dioxide absorbed by the leaves dissolves in the moist surfaces of the mesophyll cells in the stomatal cavities (see Figure 4.6, p. 200). The resulting sulphurous acid dissociates giving rise to H^+, HSO_3^- and SO_3^{2-}. Sulphate ions are produced by a free radical chain reaction and assimilated (see p. 180). From the findings of SILVIUS et al. [1975] it appears that a major reason for the toxic effect of SO_2 is that at high levels of exposure, SO_2 gas and the S anions (HSO_3^- and SO_3^{2-}) can accumulate and uncouple photophosphorylation (see p. 148).

Other detrimental effects including the disruption of chloroplast membranes can also result from SO_2 treatment (WELLBURN *et al.* [1972], PUCKETT *et al.* [1973]). In industrial regions, high levels of SO_2 in the atmosphere have resulted in the eradication of certain lichen species.

8.3 Sulphur in Crop Nutrition

8.3.1 Sulphur balance

Although the content of S in crop plants is of the same order as the P content, application of S does not generally play such an important role as P fertilization. This is due to the fact that SO_4^{2-} is not as strongly bound (fixed) to soil particles as phosphate and is thus more available to plant roots. In addition substantial amounts of S taken up by crops originate from the atmosphere or from fertilizers which contain S along with the major nutrient being applied *e.g.* ammonium sulphate or potassium sulphate. The quantities of S originating from the atmosphere depend on the distance from the sea, the rainfall and on the emission of SO_2 in smoke. Thus the atmosphere in highly industrialized areas generally contains more SO_2.

Some of the atmospheric SO_2 is dissolved in rain drops and in this form penetrates the soil, where it is oxidized to SO_4^{2-}. This process may contribute to soil acidification to a marked extent. The quantities of atmospheric S supplied to soils decreases with the distance from the sea (see p. 306). For this reason soils in maritime regions are also usually well supplied with S. DAM KOFOED and FOGH [1968] reported that in Denmark an average of 8 to 15 kg S/ha/yr is supplied to the soil by precipitation. According to RIEHM and QUELLMALZ [1959] at least the same amount of S in the form of SO_2 is absorbed directly by crops under conditions where high SO_2 concentrations are present in the atmosphere. These quantities are more than twice as high as the S requirement of most crop plants (see Table 6.2). These figures indicate the high contribution of atmospheric S to soils in maritime and industrial regions.

On the other hand large amounts of SO_4^{2-} can be leached when rainfall is high. This leached S often far exceeds the quantities taken up by crops. In long term lysimeter experiments PFAFF [1963] found that on medium textured soils about 130 kg S/ha/yr were leached. The S balance sheet from this investigation is presented in Table 8.4. It can be seen that the amounts of S supplied by rainfall and fertilizer were less than the quantities of S absorbed by crops and leached by rain. As the S content of the soil did not significantly decrease during the experimental period, PFAFF [1963] supposes that the S deficit of 41 kg S/ha/yr was covered by direct absorption from the atmosphere. As the experiments were carried out in an industrial area this seems a very reasonable assumption. In recent years atmospheric pollution by SO_2 in smoke has been much more strictly controlled than previously. The amount of S available to crop plants from the atmosphere has thus been reduced. From the results shown in Table 8.4 it would therefore appear that large regions of arable soils could well shift from a positive to a negative S balance. The situation is aggravated by the fact that the consumption of sulphate containing fertilizers is decreasing and particularly the use of ammonium sulphate and superphosphate.

Table 8.4 Sulphur balance sheet growing arable crops in an industrial area under Central European conditions (PFAFF [1963])

Supply to the Soil kg S/ha/yr		Loss from the Soil kg S/ha/yr	
Fertilizers............	62	Removal by crops	23
Precipitation	50	Leaching	130
	112		153

Deficit: 41 kg S/ha/yr

8.3.2 Sulphur application

In regions far from the sea and industry, inadequate S supply and S deficiency of crops are not uncommon. More than 40 years ago STOREY and LEACH [1933] observed S deficiency in tea plants in Malawi, and the deficiency became known as 'tea yellows'. Sulphur deficiency has now been widely recognized in many parts of the world including Africa, Australia, New Zealand and the U.S.A. Sulphur application to crops is thus becoming increasingly common.

Sulphur deficiency of groundnuts in the Savannah zone of Ghana has been reported by AGBLE [1974]. MCLACHLAN and DE MARCO [1968] obtained remarkable responses to sulphate dressings on pastures in Australia. WALKER and ADAMS [1958] carrying out field experiments on S deficient soils in New Zealand observed competition for S between grasses and clover. In the treatment without S nearly all the available SO_4^{2-} was taken up by grasses and N fixation by associated clover was negligible. Sulphur dressings of about 17 kg S/ha in combination with adequate N fertilizer resulted in remarkably good clover growth, and yields of dry matter and N recovered by the sward. The highest S treatment also resulted in extremely high N uptake by the herbage which was about three times higher than the N fertilizer rate applied. This experiment demonstrates the essential role of S in promoting growth and N fixation by leguminous plants.

384

The total S requirement of different crops depends on plant material production and also on the crop species. Crops with a high production of organic material such as sugar cane, maize and Bermuda grass have a high demand for S which is in the order of 30 to 40 kg S/ha/yr (see Table 6.2). A high S requirement is also characteristic of protein rich crops (lucerne, clover) and particularly of the *Cruciferae*. Thus the requirement of rape is about 3 times higher than that of cereals. *Cruciferae* need an appreciable amount of S for the synthesis of mustard oils. For this reason they respond most sensitively to an inadequate S supply. The S requirement of different crops is also reflected in the S content of their seeds and grains, as is shown in Table 8.5 (DELOCH [1960]).

Table 8.5 Sulphur content in grains and seeds of various crops (DELOCH [1960])

Gramineae		Leguminosae % S, DM		Cruciferae	
Barley	0.18	Broad beans ...	0.24	Rape	1.0
Oats	0.18	Bush beans	0.24	White mustard ..	1.4
Wheat	0.17	Peas	0.27	Oil radish	1.7
Maize	0.17	Soya	0.32	Black mustard ..	1.0

The most important S containing fertilizers are gypsum, superphosphate, ammonium sulphate, potassium sulphate, and sulphate of potash magnesia. Sulphur coated fertilizers (see p. 302) also contribute to the S supply of plants. Dressings of gypsum ($CaSO_4 \cdot 2H_2O$) are often used in cases where soils are absolutely deficient in S. McLACHLAN and DE MARCO [1968] reported that the efficiency of gypsum is higher when the granule size is small. The rates generally applied are in the range of 10 to 50 kg S/ha. In regions with high rainfall spring application is recommended in order to avoid leaching by winter rains.

General Reading

ANDERSON, J.W.: Sulphur in Biology. The Inst. of Biology's Studies in Biology, No. 101. Edward Arnold, London, 1978

BROGAN, T.C.: Sulphur in Forages. An Forás Taluntais, Dublin, 1978

DIJKSHOORN, W. and VAN WIJK, A.L.: The sulphur requirements of plants as evidenced by the sulphur-nitrogen ratio in the organic matter, a review of published data. Plant and Soil, *26*, 129–157 (1967)

EATON, F.M.: Sulfur, In: CHAPMAN, H.D. (ed.) Diagnostic Crieteria for Plants and Soils. p. 444–475. Univ. of California, Division of Agricultural Sciences, 1966

FRENEY, J.R. and NICOLSON, A.J.: Sulfur in Australia. Australian Acad. Sci. Canberra 1980

McLACHLAN, K.D.: Sulphur in Australasian Agriculture, Sydney University Press, 1975

NRIAGU, J.O. (Ed) Sulfur in the Environment. 2 vols., Wiley, 1978

RICHMOND, D.V.: Sulfur compounds, In: MILLER, L.P. (ed.). Phytochemistry, Vol. *3*, p. 41. Van Nostrad Reinhold, 1973

SVENSSON, B.H. and SÖDERLUND, G.H.: Nitrogen Phosphorus and Sulphur. Global Cycles. Scope Report 7, Ecol. Bull. 22 Stockholm, 1976

THOMPSON, J.F.: Sulfur metabolism in plants. Ann. Rev. Plant Physiol., *18*, 59–84 (1967)

WALKER, T.W.: The sulphur cycle in grassland soils. J. Br. Grassld. Soc., *12*, 10–18 (1957)

WHITEHEAD, D.C.: Soil and plant nutrition aspects of the sulphur cycle. Soils Fert., *29*, 1–9 (1964)

Chapter 9

Phosphorus

9.1 Soil Phosphorus

9.1.1 Phosphorus fractions and phosphate minerals

Phosphorus in soils occurs almost exclusively in the form of orthophosphate. The total content is in the range of 0.02 to 0.15% P. Quite a substantial amount of this P is associated with the soil organic matter (WILLIAMS [1959]) and in mineral soils the proportion of organic P lies between 20 to 80% of the total P. MANDAL [1975] reported that in rice soils of West Bengal organic P amounted on average to 35% of the total soil P. In virgin mineral soils the content of organic P depends much on soil age. This is illustrated in Figure 9.1. This shows

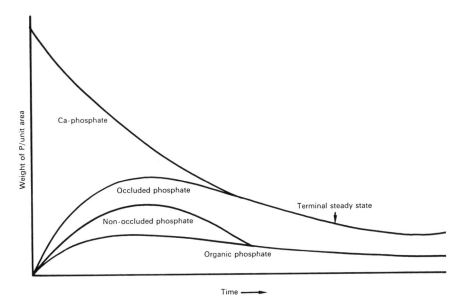

Fig. 9.1 Changes of soil phosphate fractions during pedogenesis (after WALKER and SYERS 1976]). Soils of different ages developed on the same parent material (chronosequence).

the distribution of soil P fractions in a chronosequence of soils developed in New Zealand (WALKER and SYERS [1976]). It can be seen that the proportion of organic P in the soil profile reaches a maximum and falls off slowly. For most mineral soils, apatites are believed to be the primary phosphate containing minerals from which the other P containing soil fractions are derived. In the diagram these derived P fractions are shown as 'non occluded inorganic phosphate' and 'occluded inorganic phosphate'. The non occluded fraction contains phosphate in solution, phosphate adsorbed to soil surfaces and some phosphate minerals. The occluded phosphate is held by Fe and Al minerals, often within a skin of Fe hydroxy compounds. Figure 9.1 also demonstrates that during pedogenesis an appreciable amount of phosphate is lost form the soil. This results largely from translocation of soluble P out of the soil profile. When one considers the time scale involved, however, it is clear that the annual rate of leaching of phosphate is extremely low (see p.298).

It is beyond the scope of this book to describe the various soil phosphate forms and the interrelationships between these forms. Considered simply from the viewpoint of plant nutrition three main soil phosphate fractions are important:

1. Phosphate in soil solution
2. Phosphate in the labile pool
3. Phosphate of the non-labile fraction.

These three fractions are represented schematically in Figure 9.2. The first fraction is clearly defined and is the phosphate dissolved in the soil solution. The second fraction is the solid phosphate which is held on surfaces so that it is in rapid equilibrium with soil solution phosphate. It can be determined by means of isotopic exchange and is called labile phosphate (see p.95). The third fraction is the insoluble phosphate. The phosphate in this fraction can be released only very slowly into the labile pool.

Many attempts have been undertaken to relate non-labile phosphate to specific soil minerals. Such investigations, however, are complicated by the fact that many soil phosphates contain impurities, which influence their solubility and hence their capability of exchanging phosphate ions with the soil solution. In many soils, apatites are the most important inorganic phosphates of the non-labile pool. In addition some Fe and Al phosphates as well as the organic soil P are also believed to exchange phosphate ions only very slowly and thus belong to the non-labile P fraction.

Some important soil phosphate minerals are presented in Table 9.1. Their solubilities are known in well defined systems. However, these data are of little use defining soil phosphate solubilities (LARSEN [1967]), because of the very

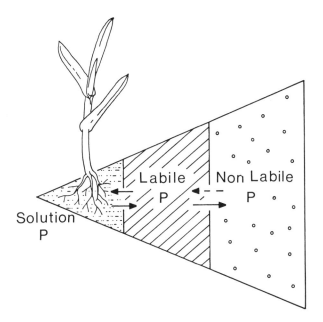

Fig.9.2 Schematic representation of the 3 important P soil fractions for plant nutrition.

Table 9.1   Important soil phosphate minerals

Hydroxyapatite	$Ca_5(PO_4)_3OH$
Fluorapatite	$Ca_5(PO_4)_3F$
Dicalciumphosphate	$CaHPO_4$
Tricalciumphosphate	$Ca_3(PO_4)_2$
Variscite	$AlH_2PO_4(OH)_2$
Strengite.................	$FeH_2PO_4(OH)_2$

complex nature of the soil system. Most phosphate minerals contain impurities, which may considerably influence their solubility. Thus hydroxyapatite with carbonate impurities has a far higher solubility than pure apatite (KHASAWNEH and DOLL [1978]). Strengite and variscite were held to be important soil phosphates. Evidence of LARSEN [1967] suggests, however, that they exist only under conditions where the pH is lower than 4.2 (strengite) or 3.1 (variscite). These two phosphate minerals therefore appear to be of minor importance for most agricultural soils. From these few comments it can be appreciated that the solubilities of phosphate minerals in the soil are not easy to predict. The part played by soil phosphate minerals in plant nutrition is thus much more complex than has often been supposed.

9.1.2 Phosphate adsorption, desorption and mineralization

The labile phosphate fraction consists mainly of phosphate adsorbed to the surface of clay minerals, hydrous oxides, carbonates and even apatites as well as Fe and Al phosphates. This fraction is in rapid equilibrium with the phosphate of the soil solution. The relationship between the quantity of phosphate adsorbed and the phosphate concentration of the equilibrated soil solution may be described approximately by a Langmuir type isotherm (see Fig. 2.4) (PARFITT [1978]). The steepness of the curve which is a measure of the phosphate buffer capacity or buffer power, and expresses the relationship between quantity (Q) and intensity (I) (see p. 71), can vary considerably for different soils. Generally sandy soils are characterized by a flat curve whereas for soils rich in clay minerals and sequioxides the curve is steeper.

An important factor influencing the slope of the curve is soil pH, since anions are adsorbed more strongly when the soil pH is low. As the soil pH is raised OH^- (HCO_3^-) ions are able to exchange with adsorbed phosphate and release it into the soil solution in a process known as desorption. The effect of pH on phosphate adsorption has recently been described in 'Andosols' by KAWAI [1980]. Allophanes are the major clay fraction in these soils and adsorb phos-

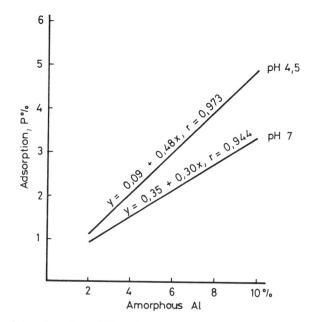

Fig. 9.3 Phosphate adsorption of 13 Andosols in relation to amorphous Al and pH (after KAWAI [1980]).

phate very strongly. Some of KAWAI's results are presented in Figure 9.3. The graph shows adsorbed P plotted against the percentage amorphous Al for 14 soils. It is obvious that the slope of the graph of phosphate adsorption was greater at pH 4.5 than at pH 7.0. In other words for a given increase in amorphous Al, P adsorption was greater at pH 4.5 than pH 7.0. The Figure further shows the linear relationship between phosphate adsorption and the amount of amorphous Al in these Andosols. In soils in which phosphate is the main adsorbed fraction, phosphate availability is increased by raising the soil pH. This has been shown in pot experiments by HAGEMANN and MÜLLER [1976]. Iron oxides adsorb phosphate more strongly than do layer silicate minerals. It is supposed that the phosphate thus adsorbed to iron oxide forms a crystalline structure. The non-specific adsorption of nitrate stabilizes phosphate adsorption on the surface of iron oxides.

Adsorption of phosphate to soil particles is frequently not an ideal adsorption process but rather a combination of adsorption and precipitation (LARSEN [1967]). Thus Ca carbonates adsorb phosphate which is then slowly converted into apatites (PARFITT [1978]). In this way some phosphate of the labile pool is continously being rendered immobile and so transferred to the non-labile phosphate fraction. This process of 'phosphate ageing' is especially rapid in calcareous soils as has been shown recently by KEERTHISINGHE and MENGEL [1979].

In addition to phosphate adsorption, the formation of precipitates of low solubility (Ca – Fe – and Al phosphates) may depress phosphate availability. The precipitation of Ca phosphates is promoted by high Ca^{2+} concentrations in the soil solution and by high pH conditions. A high soil pH can thus be associated with dramatically opposite effects on phosphate availability, since on the one hand the precipitation of Ca phosphate is favoured whereas on the other desorption of adsorbed phosphate is enhanced. In order to assess phosphate availability of soils it is thus pertinent to know which of these processes, Ca phosphate precipitation or phosphate desorption, is of greater importance. In general in soils rich in Al – and Fe oxides as well as in clay minerals phosphate desorption seems to be the more dominant process, whereas in poor sandy soils, in calcareous soils and especially in organic soils, phosphate precipitation plays a major role.

Under anaerobic conditions immobile phosphates can become soluble due to hydrolysis of Al – and Fe phosphates as well as a release of occluded phosphates (PONNAMPERUMA [1972]). This increase in soluble phosphate is often associated with an increase of the Fe^{2+} level in the soil solution indicating that the reduction of Fe^{3+} is associated with the release of phosphate.

The decomposition of organic matter is an additional process, which influences phosphate adsorption both directly and indirectly. Soil organic matter contains P so that the mineralization of organic matter releases phosphate into the soil solution. Phosphate liberated in this way is involved in the equilibrium between free and adsorbed phosphate ions. The microbial breakdown of organic soil matter is associated with an increased CO_2 production which possibly increases the solubility of soil phosphates.

Most of the organic soil phosphates are present in the form of the inositol phosphate ester, inositol hexaphosphate and to a lesser degree the di-tri- and tetraphosphates of inositol. Some of these organic phosphates are produced by higher plants, most, however, are synthesized by microorganisms (DALAL [1977]). Inositol phosphates are prone to adsorption and thus less available the higher the phosphate adsorption capacity of the soil.

(inorganic P)

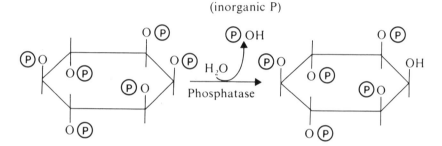

Inositol hexaphosphate   Inositol pentaphosphate

The ultimate process by which organic phosphates are rendered available is by cleavage of inorganic phosphate by means of a phosphatase reaction. The principle of this reaction is hydrolysis as shown in the above equation. The enzyme phosphatase is produced by the roots of higher plants as well as by numerous microorganisms (*Aspergillus, Penicillium, Mucor, Rhizopus, Bacillus, Pseudomonas*). According to SENTENAC et al. [1980] root cell walls are high in phosphatase activity. Phosphatases 'mineralize' phosphate of phytins, nucleic acids and phosphoglycerates. It has also been suggested that phosphatase acivity of the mycorrhiza may play a part in the ability of these organisms to mobilize soil P (DALAL [1977]). Microbial activity depends much on temperature and is highest in the range of 30 to 45°C. It is for this reason that organic phosphates are of greater importance to plant nutrition under tropical climatic conditions as compared with temperate conditions. DALAL [1977] in a useful review paper emphasises that the soil solution also contains appreciable amounts of organic phosphates which are only poorly available to plants and which are believed to be colloidal.

9.1.3 Phosphorus in solution and plant root interactions

The amount of phosphate present in the soil solution is very low in comparison with adsorbed phosphate. Adsorbed phosphate exceeds the phosphate of the soil solution by a factor of 10^2 to 10^3. The phosphate concentration of the soil solution itself is very dilute and in fertile arable soils is about 10^{-5} to 10^{-4} M (MENGEL et al. [1969], HOSSNER et al. [1973]). This is equivalent to about 0.3 to 3 ppm P. The most important P-containing ions in soil solution are HPO_4^{2-} and $H_2PO_4^-$. The ratio of these two ion species in soil solution is pH dependent. High H^+ concentrations shift the equilibrium to the more protonated form according to the equation:

$$HPO_4^{2-} + H^+ \rightleftarrows H_2PO_4^-$$

Figure 9.4 shows that at a pH 5, HPO_4^{2-} is almost absent whereas at pH 7 both phosphate species are present in fairly equal proportions.

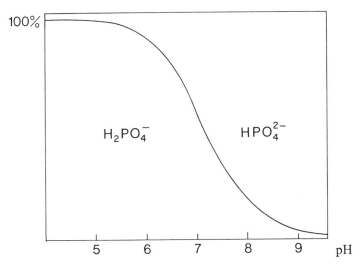

Fig.9.4 Ratio between $H_2PO_4^-$ and HPO_4^{2-} in relation to pH.

As plant roots push their way through the soil they come in contact with the phosphate of the soil solution. Provided that the roots have a high demand for P – and this is generally the case for growing plants – phosphate is absorbed by the roots at a high rate and the soil solution in the direct root vicinity is depleted of phosphate. This depletion creates a gradient between the phosphate concentration near the root surface and the phosphate concentration in the bulk soil (OLSEN and WATANABE [1970], the concentration gradient regulating the rate of phosphate diffusion towards the plant root (see p. 67). The importance of phosphate diffusion in supplying phosphate to plants has been demonstrated by BHAT and NYE [1974] in experiments showing that the degree of P depletion around onion roots corresponds fairly well with P diffusion calculations. Mass flow can also play a part in the transport of phosphate towards plant roots (see p. 67). Normally, however, its contribution is minimal since the phosphate concentration of the soil solution is so low (BOLE [1973]).

Experiments of SANDERS and TINKER [1973] have shown that root infection by endotrophic mycorrhizal fungi can stimulate plant growth by increasing the rate of phosphate uptake. An example of the dramatic effects that can be obtained is shown in Plate 9.1. Onion roots which were infected with an endotrophic mycorrhizal fungi took up phosphate at a considerably higher rate per unit length of root than non infected roots. Whether this effect is caused simply by the increased absorbing surface of the root-fungus association allowing an increase in soil exploration for soil phosphate, is not firmly established. CRESS et al. [1979] investigating the kinetics of P absorption in mycorrhizal and non mycorrhizal tomato roots have reported that a major factor contributing to the increased uptake by the mycorrhizal roots was an apparent greater affinity for P for the absorbing sites on the hyphae of the mycorrhiza. These results may explain the observations of COOPER and TINKER [1978] of only a poor correlation between P transport from hyphae and the number and length of hyphae involved. A site affinity mechanism appears to be a plausible explanation.

The influence of mycorrhizae on plant growth and phosphate uptake is particularly marked on soil where phosphate is limiting. The reason why mycorrhizal infection should be greater under P deficient conditions is not clear. JASPER et al. [1979] have suggested that a high carbohydrate level in the roots is an important prerequisite for good mycorrhizal infection. This is consistent with the observation that plants poorly supplied with P have higher root carbohydrate levels than plants adequately supplied with P. The inoculation of agricultural crops with appropriate endotrophic mycorrhizal fungi may well prove to be of agricultural importance in soils in which P is in short supply. According to BOWEN [1973] mycorrhizal hyphae are also able to grow well even under conditions of low soil water potential. This may be of particular importance for the mobilization of soil phosphate under dry soil conditions.

The influence of root exudates on the solubility of phosphate in the root vicinity has attracted considerable attention. It is now established that relatively large amounts of C assimilated in photosynthesis are transferred from the roots into the soil (see p. 82). BARBER and MARTIN [1976] for example found that 20% of the photosynthate of wheat seedlings was released into the soil and a significant fraction of the material consists of chelating acids. Such

Onion

a

b

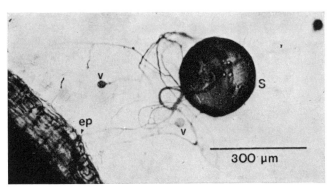

c

Plate 9.1 Root infection with endotrophic mycorrhizal fungi and phosphate uptake.

    a Response of onion growing on a P deficient soil to P fertilization and inoculation with endotrophic mycorrhizal fungi. Left, phosphate fertilizer. Centre, inoculation with endotrophic mycorrhizal fungi. Right, control.

    b Endomycorrhizal infection of onion by *Glomus mosseae..* The root cortex is full of hyphae, some of which bear vesicles (V). An external hypha (eh) is attached, entering the root at the point arrowed.

    c A germinated resting spore (S) of the endomycorrhizal fungus *Glomus macrocarpa.* One of the hyphae produced on germination has entered a nearby clover root (at point ep) to establish an internal infection. External vesicles (v) are seen.

    (Photos: SANDERS)

organic chelating agents could of course exchange with surface bonded phosphate thereby releasing phosphate for plant uptake. This seems a likely explanation of the findings of BREWSTER *et al.* [1976] who observed phosphorus depletion zones around rape roots very much deeper and wider than predicted from independent measurements on the plants and soils. MOGHIMI *et al.* [1978] have isolated 2 keto-gluconate from the rhizosphere of wheat roots in quantities that could solubilize considerable amounts of phosphate from hydroxyapatite. Such a chelate release from roots and root hairs could provide a very efficient means of solubilizing phosphate. The subject has recently been discussed by NYE [1977, 1979].

Another important influence of the roots on phosphorus availability is the effect in inducing pH changes in the rhizosphere. The pH at the root surface may be as much as one unit different from that of the bulk soil (see NYE [1977]). Such differences in pH are brought about by differential rates of uptake of cations and anions and associated with OH^- or H^+ effluxes. Here the form of N-nutrition plays an important role. In plants supplied with NO_3^- which is the usual form of N-nutrition in most agricultural soils, anion uptake exceeds cation uptake and OH^- or HCO_3^- is released from the roots (see p. 85). The rhizosphere pH is thus more alkaline than that of the bulk soil. On the other hand plants supplied with NH_4-N or molecular N_2 (symbiotic N_2 fixation) take up more cations than anions, release H^+ into the soil, and the rhizosphere is more acid (KIRKBY [1981]). These differences in behaviour may influence P uptake by plants since P solubility in the soil is highly pH dependent. In order to assess the effects of pH changes in the rhizocylinder on P uptake, the relationship between soluble P and pH must be known for a given soil. Soluble P usually, although not always, increases with a rise in soil pH from 4 to 6.5. For both calcareous and alkaline soils, however, soluble P invariably declines as the pH rises from 6.5 to 8.3. The effect of NH_4-nutrition in acidifying the rhizosphere and thus increasing P availability in alkaline and calcareous soils is therefore more clear cut than the alkaline influence of NO_3-nutrition on P availability in acid soils. A study investigating pH changes in the rhizosphere of soya bean roots induced by different forms of N-nutrition in relation to P uptake has been reported by RILEY and BARBER [1971] showing very clearly that with a decrease in pH, P uptake of the roots was increased.

A number of microorganisms are known which produce acids and chelating agents. These play a part in the solubilization of soil and fertilizer phosphates. Such microorganisms include: *Aspergillus niger*, strains of *Escherichia freundi*, some *Penicillium* species and *Pseudomonas* species (SUBRA RAO [1974]). Their significance on P uptake and crop growth is difficult to assess and requires further investigation.

9.2 Phosphorus in Physiology

9.2.1 Absorption and translocation

Plant roots are capable of absorbing phosphate from solutions of very low phosphate concentrations (LONERAGAN and ASHER [1967]). Generally the phosphate content of root cells and xylem sap is about 100 to 1000 fold higher than that of the soil solution. This shows that phosphate is taken up by plant cells against a very steep concentration gradient. The uptake is active. The relationship between plant metabolism and phosphate uptake has been studied by a number of authors who have mainly observed increased rates of phosphate uptake associated with higher metabolic activity. Thus HAI and LAUDELOUT [1966] reported that an increased partial pressure of O_2 in the nutrient solution resulted in a higher phosphate uptake rate in rice roots. WEIGL [1967] also found that P uptake by *Elodia canadensis* was higher in light than under dark conditions. These and other experimental data suggest that respiratory carbohydrate metabolism drives the active phosphate uptake process. It is supposed that this uptake is carrier mediated. Whether one or more carrier systems are involved still remains in question. The capability for active uptake of phosphate differs between plant species and may even differ between cultivars of the same species. BARBER and THOMAS [1972] for example found considerable differences in the rate of phosphate uptake by various maize cultivars. The authors suppose that the capability of plants in take up phosphate is fixed genetically. Similar findings in P efficiency have been reported for genotypes of other crops including sorghum (BROWN *et al.* [1977]). In agricultural practice P efficiency can be an asset when P is limiting. On the other hand BROWN *et al.* [1977] observed that these P efficient genotypes can also be a liability when they are subjected to Fe or Cu stress since the more efficient P utilization makes the plant more susceptible to Fe or Cu deficiency.

The rate of phosphate uptake is pH dependent. HENDRIX [1967] found that at pH 4, bean plants absorbed phosphate at a 10 fold higher rate than at a pH of 8.7. Similar observations have been made by HAI and LAUDELOUT [1966] who reported a maximum uptake rate by rice roots at pH 5.6. The rate of phosphate uptake declined rapidly with increasing pH. As this decrease followed the shift in the $HPO_4^{2-}/H_2PO_4^-$ ratio in the nutrient solution, HAI and LAUDELOUT [1966] suppose that only $H_2PO_4^-$ and not HPO_4^{2-} is absorbed actively. It is doubtful whether organic P compounds are taken up by plant roots to any great extent. According to investigations by ROUX [1968], P present in polyphosphates was only taken up by young barley plants after hydrolysis to the orthophosphate form.

Phosphate absorbed by plant cells rapidly becomes involved in metabolic processes. Thus JACKSON and HAGEN [1960] reported that after a period of only 10 min. following uptake, 80% of the phosphate absorbed was incorporated into organic compounds. The organic phosphates formed in this short time consisted mainly of hexose phosphates and uridine diphosphate. Phosphate is readily mobile in the plant and can be translocated in an upward or downward direction. Thus CLARKSON et al. [1968] found that phosphate taken up by basal root segments of barley plants was translocated to the root tip as well as to the upper plant parts. Young leaves are supplied not only by phosphate taken up by the roots, but also with phosphate originating from the older leaves (BOUMA [1967]). In the experiments of MORARD [1970] with buckwheat in culture solution, phosphate was translocated initially to the younger leaves. After some days, however, retranslocation occurred and the phosphate was partially transported to the older leaves. This downward movement occurs mainly in the phloem. MAIZEL et al. [1956] suggest that phosphorylcholine is the main P carrier in phloem transport. More recent data of HALL and BAKER [1972] show that inorganic P is also present in the phloem sap in substantial concentrations thus indicating that inorganic P plays a major role in phloem transport (see Table 4.5).

9.2.2 P fractions and metabolic functions

Phosphate in the plant occurs in inorganic form as orthophosphate and to a minor extent as pyrophosphate. The organic forms of phosphate are compounds in which the orthophosphate is esterified with hydroxyl groups of sugars and alcohols or bound by a pyrophosphate bond to another phosphate group. A typical example of a phosphate ester is fructose-6-phosphate.

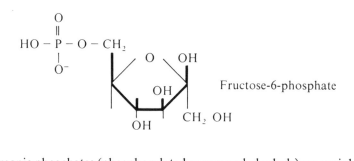

Fructose-6-phosphate

Such organic phosphates (phosphorylated sugars and alcohols) are mainly intermediary compounds of metabolism. Phosphate is also bound to lipophilic compounds particularly in phosphatidyl derivates (phospholipids). Lecithin is a typical example of this kind.

$$H_2C - O - CO - R$$
$$R^1 - CO - O - CH \qquad O$$
$$H_2C - O - P - O + CH_2 - CH_2 - N^+ (CH_3)_3$$
$$O^-$$

Phosphatidyl   Choline

Lecithin

As can be seen from the formula, P is bound in a diester linkage. Such compounds have a hydrophobic moiety in the fatty acid radical, and a hydrophylic moiety in the phosphate group. Compounds of this type, *e.g.* lecithin and phosphatidyl ethanolamine, are essential components of biological membranes (see p. 111).

The most important compound in which phosphate groups are linked by pyrophosphate bonds is adenosine triphosphate (ATP). The formula and some properties of this coenzyme have already been described on page 117. The pyrophosphate bond is an energy rich bond which on hydrolysis releases 30 kJ/Mol. The energy absorbed during photosynthesis, or released during respiration or anaerobic carbohydrate breakdown is utilized in the synthesis of the pyrophosphate bond in ATP. In this form the energy can be conveyed to various endergonic processes such as active ion uptake and the synthesis of various organic compounds. In these processes there is usually an initial phosphorylation reaction. This involves the transfer of the phosphoryl group from ATP to another compound, as shown in the following example:

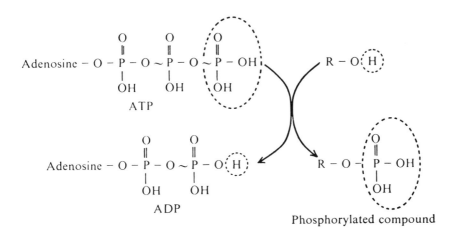

Phosphorylated compound

In this reaction the phosphorylated compound is loaded with energy (= priming reaction) and is thus enabled to participate in further metabolic processes.

It appears that the unique function of phosphate in metabolism is its formation of pyrophosphate bonds which allow energy transfer. Uridine triphosphate (UTP), cytidine triphosphate (CTP) and guanosine triphosphate (GTP) are analogous compounds to ATP. Uridine triphosphate is required for the synthesis of sucrose and callose, CTP for the synthesis of phospholipids, and GTP for the formation of cellulose. All these nucleotide triphosphates (ATP, UTP, GTP and CTP) are also involved in the synthesis of ribonucleic acids (RNA). For the synthesis of deoxyribonucleic acids (DNA) the 'deoxy form' of the nucleotide triphosphates is required. In the 'deoxy form' the ribose of the nucleotide is substituted by a deoxyribose. The structure of DNA and RNA is shown in Figure 9.5.

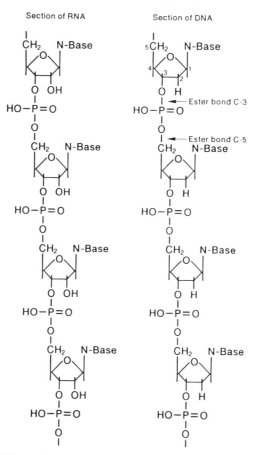

Fig. 9.5 Section of DNA and RNA, showing the phosphate ester bond at C-3 and C-5 of the ribose or deoxyribose respectively.

The phosphate group in nucleic acids bridges the ribose (RNA) or deoxyribose (DNA) with another ribose or deoxyribose by two ester bonds. DNA is the carrier of genetic information and the various forms of RNA function in protein synthesis. These few comments on organic phosphates indicate the universal and essential role of phosphate not only in plants but also in all other living organisms.

Another organic P compound is phytin. This occurs mainly in seeds. Phytic acid is the hexaphosphoric ester of inositol (see formula on p. 392). Phytin in plant seeds occurs as the Ca and Mg salts of phytic acid and is formed during seed formation. Immediately after pollination there is thus an increase in P transport towards the young developing seeds. Phosphorus in the phytin of seeds is regarded as a P reserve. During seed germination phytin P is mobilized and converted into other phosphate forms needed in the metabolism of young plants.

Most of the phosphate present in roots, stems and leaves is in inorganic form. The proportion of inorganic P of the total P is the highest in older leaves. Younger leaves contain relatively high quantities of organic P predominantly in the form of nucleic acids. In P deficient plant tissues the contents of inorganic P are particularly depressed whilst the organic P levels are little affected (MICHAEL [1939], HARTT [1972]). The main data of MICHAEL's investigation are shown in Table 9.2. It is obvious that in P deficient spinach leaves the content of inorganic P was drastically reduced whereas the contents of P in the phospholipids and in the nucleic acids were not affected. In oat grains a similar pattern of P content was observed with the exception of the phytin P. In vegetative plant organs inorganic P functions as the reserve form. In grains, however, this role is fulfilled by phytin. Similar observations have been made by BIELESKI [1968] who studied changes in the levels of P compounds in *Spirodela* after discontinuation of phosphate supply. When P deficiency was severe, the contents of phospholipids and

Table 9.2 Effect of P supply on the content of various P forms in spinach leaves and oat grains (MICHAEL [1939])

P supply	Phospholipid	Nucleic acid P in $^0/_{00}$	Phytin	Inorganic
		Oat grains		
Inadequate....................	0.22	2.1	0.05	0.5
Adequate	0.22	2.4	0.5	1.3
		Spinach leaves		
Inadequate....................	1.1	0.9	–	2.2
Adequate	1.1	0.9	–	18.0

RNA were also markedly depressed. BIELESKI's experiments also showed that the growth rate of P deficient plants was controlled by the rate at which phosphate was transported from the vacuole. As soon as this P reserve pool was depleted growth stopped.

9.2.3 Phosphorus deficiency

As already described on p. 211 the export of energy out of the chloroplast requires inorganic phosphate (WALKER [1980]). A primary effect of phosphate on autotrophic growth is thus the provision of chemical energy produced in the chloroplast. As numerous metabolic processes directly or indirectly depend on this energy supply, inadequate phosphate nutrition may affect various processes including protein synthesis and the synthesis of nucleic acids. Plants suffering from P deficiency are thus retarded in growth and the shoot/root dry matter ratio is usually low. In cereals tillering is affected. Fruit trees show reduced growth rates of new shoots, and frequently the development and the opening of buds is unsatisfactory. The formation of fruits and seeds is especially depressed in plants suffering from P deficiency. Thus not only low yields but also poor quality fruits and seeds are obtained from P deficient crops.

Generally the symptoms of P deficiency appear in the older leaves which are often of a darkish green colour. The stems of many annual plant species suffering from P deficiency are characterized by a reddish colouration originating from an enhanced formation of anthocyanins. The leaves of P deficient fruit trees are frequently tinged with brownish colour. Such leaves fall prematurely. According to BESFORD [1978] working with cucumber leaves, phosphatase activity can be used as a sensitive measure of P-status, a higher activity being found in the leaves poorly supplied with P.

The P contents of P deficient plants are generally low with about 0.1% P or less in the dry matter. Cereals and herbage adequately supplied with phosphate have P contents of about 0.3 to 0.4% P in the dry matter, during the vegetative growth stage. Generally the P content is higher in younger plants or plant organs. Thus the P content in mature straw of cereals is rather low (0.10 to 0.15% P in the dry matter), whereas in seeds and grains, P contents in the range of 0.4 to 0.5% P in the dry matter are found. This example shows that during grain and seed formation a considerable amount of P is translocated from leaves and stems towards the seeds or grains.

Extremely high phosphate levels in the root medium can depress growth. In solution culture experiments for example LONERAGAN and ASHER [1967] found that very high uptake rates of phosphate were associated with reduced growth rates in some plant species (Erodium, clover, silver grass). Such effects may well be dependent on phosphate retarding the uptake and translocation of some of the micronutrients including Zn, Fe and Cu.

9.3 Phosphorus in Crop Nutrition

9.3.1 Phosphorus availability and crop requirements

Since the early days of applying mineral fertilizers to soils, phosphate fertilization has always been important. Indeed vast areas of potentially good land are still agriculturally poor because of P deficiency. It must be remembered that in the soil phosphate can readily be rendered unavailable to plant roots, and that P is the most immobile of the major plant nutrients.

The term 'available phosphate' is often used to indicate a soil P fraction which can be utilized by plants. This term, however, is very vague and usually refers back to soil extraction methods which are often at variance from observations of crop response (see p. 92) (WERNER [1969]). From the discussion on soil phosphorus (p. 74) it is clear that generally phosphate availability to plants can be assessed by measuring the phosphate concentration in the soil solution and the ability of the soil to maintain the soil solution concentration (phosphate buffer capacity). Concentrations of about 10^{-4} M phosphate in the soil solution are considered as high and represent a high level of available soil phosphate. Phosphate concentrations of about 10^{-6} M in the soil solution are generally too low to supply crops adequately with P. Optimum soil solution phosphate concentrations probably differ for individual crops, cropping systems, and particular sites.

The quantity of P present in soil solution, even in soils with a fairly high level of available phosphate, is only in the range of 0.3 to 3 kg P/ha. As rapidly growing crops absorb phosphate quantities of about 1 kg P/ha per day, it is clear that the soil solution phosphate must be replenished several times per day by mobilization of phosphate from the labile pool. This labile phosphate is more or less identical with isotopically exchangeable phosphate (see p. 95). The quantity of this fraction present in the top soil layer (20 cm) is in the range of 150 to 500 kg P/ha. The rate of desorption is higher in soils with a higher P buffer capacity. For this reason such soils are better able to buffer the phosphate concentration of the soil solution during the growing season (WILLIAMS [1970]). According to experimantal data of OLSEN and WATANABE [1970] the P concentration of the soil solution and the phosphate buffer capacity are the most important parameters controlling the phosphate supply to plant roots. The optimum P concentration of the soil solution may thus be low if the phosphate buffer capacity is high and *vice versa*. This relationship has been confirmed by investigations of HOLFORD [1976] who calculated P fertilizer requirements in relation to the P-concentration of the soil solution and the phosphate buffer capacity.

Soils which are prone to strong phosphate fixation (adsorption to sesqui-oxides and clay minerals) often require extremely high phosphate fertilizer applications in order to alleviate the effects of fixation. Increasingly higher rates must be applied, the steeper the phosphate buffer curve. In these strongly phosphate fixing soils, pH correction is also recommended, since phosphate adsorption is especially high at low pH levels (see p. 390). If the quantity of available soil phosphate is in a normal range, the rate of phosphate application required should correspond to the amount of P removed by the crop. As some of the labile phosphate is rendered immobile (see p. 93), P application rates should be about 10 to 50% higher than the quantity of P taken up by the crop (see Table 6.2). The rates generally applied to arable crops range from 20 to 80 kg P/ha according to crop species and soil conditions. Crops with a high growth rate, producing large quantities of organic material, have a higher demand. This applies to maize, lucerne, intensive grass production, potatoes and sugar beet. In addition all intensive systems of arable cropping have a relatively high demand for phosphate. Phosphorus is particularly important for leguminous plants possibly by its influence on the activity of the *Rhizobium* bacteria. For mixed swards it is therefore important that soil P levels should be kept high in order to maintain the leguminous species. If the P supply to cereals is inadequate during the early stages of development, a reduction in the number of ears per unit area results and hence a depression in crop yield.

In fruit trees P deficiency results in an impairment in fruit setting. The development of the fruits is also restricted and often only small fruits of poor quality are harvested. In addition fruit maturation is delayed (PENNINGSFELD and KURZMANN [1966/67]). Ample phosphate supply to potatoes enhances the phosphate esterification of starch in potato tubers and thus improves starch quality (see p. 274).

9.3.2 Phosphatic fertilizers

The straight phosphate fertilizers which are used at the present time differ in chemical composition and solubility as can be seen from Table 9.3. Superphosphate is produced by the treatment of ground rock phosphate with sulphuric acid. The process yields a mixture of $Ca(H_2PO_4)_2$ and gypsum ($CaSO_4$). In the manufacture of triple superphosphate, phosphoric acid is used instead of sulphuric acid and the resulting product is Ca $(H_2PO_4)_2$. Mono and diammonium phosphates are made by adding NH_3 to phosphoric acid. Basic slags $(Ca_3(PO_4)_2 \cdot CaO + CaO \cdot SiO_2)$ are a by-product of the steel industry. In this process P originating from P containing ores is bound to CaO and silicates during smelting.

Table 9.3 Straight Phosphate Fertilizers

Name	Chemical composition	Solubility	Content of P_2O_5
Superphosphate	$Ca(H_2PO_4)_2 + CaSO_4$	water sol.	18–22
Triple superphosphate	$Ca(H_2PO_4)_2$	water sol.	46–47
Monoammonium phosphate	$NH_4H_2PO_4$	water sol.	48–50
Diammonium phosphate	$(NH_4)_2HPO_4$	water sol.	54
Basic slag (Thomas slag)	$Ca_3P_2O_8 \cdot CaO + CaO \cdot SiO_2$	citric acid sol.	10–22%
Sinterphosphate (Rhenania-type)	$CaNaPO_4 \cdot Ca_2SiO_4$	NH_4 citrate sol.	25–29%
Ground rock phosphate	Apatite	soluble in	29%
Fused Mg phosphate	Ca-Mg phosphate	citric acid	20%

For this reason basic slags also contain Ca as oxide and silicates. In addition Mg and some heavy metals (Fe, Zn, Cu) are also present. Sintered phosphate (Rhenania-type) is produced by a desintegration of rock phosphate with Na_2CO_3 and silica in a rotary kiln at about 1250 °C. The main constituents of this P fertilizer are $CaNaPO_4$ and Ca_2SiO_4 in a mixed crystalline structure. Other more recently developed fertilizers based on superphosphoric acid (polyphosphates) have already been considered on page 313.

Water soluble P fertilizers, basic slags, and sinter phosphate are suitable P fertilizers for most soil types. Rock phosphates differ widely in their fertilizer value depending on their origin. Hard crystalline apatites are very insoluble and thus almost useless as fertilizer materials. The softer rock phosphates from North Africa and elsewhere, however, may well be used as fertilizers under particular conditions. Numerous field experiments in Britain have provided evidence that rock phosphates yield satisfactory crop responses on acid soils, particularly when applied to grassland, swedes and kale (COOKE [1966]). The residual effects of rock phosphates have usually been less than those of P fertilizers with a higher solubility. VAN DER PAAUW [1965] carrying out field experiments on organic sandy soils in Holland reported that the value of Gafsa phosphate (soft rock phosphate) differed considerably and was lower on soils of high P fixing capacity. The P effect of this fertilizer depended on how much its application increased the water soluble phosphate in the soil. The rock phosphate was particularly effective on soils with a pH < 4.3. Similar results were reported by SCHÜLLER *et al.* [1975] from a long term field trial in Austria. On the acid soil (pH 5.5) rock phosphate application gave yields comparable with the superphosphate application. At the two other sites (pH 6.6 and 7.3) the yield of the rock phosphate treatment was about 20 to 40% lower than that of superphosphate.

Under tropical conditions, where soluble phosphates are easily leached from sandy acid soils the application of rock phosphates is useful. Experiments with sugar cane in Hawai showed that rock phosphate was as effective as superphosphate (AYRES and HAGIHARA [1961]). Favourable effects of rock phosphate on the growth of wheat, soya beans and maize have also been observed in India (MANDAL [1975]). MALOTH and PRASAD [1976] growing cowpeas *(Vigna sinensis)* on an alkali soil (pH 8.4) found that 200 kg P_2O_5/ha in the form of rock phosphate gave the same yield increase as 100 kg P_2O_5/ha in the form of superphosphate. On this particular soil, cereals did not respond to rock phosphate indicating that the effect of this fertilizer also depends on crop species. According to KHASAWNEH and DOLL [1978] who have treated the question of rock phosphate application in a useful review paper, differences in crop response are related to crop Ca^{2+} demand. Species with a high Ca^{2+} requirement promote the dissolution of rock phosphates as they represent a Ca^{2+} sink. In an analogous way soils with a high Ca^{2+} adsorption potential favour the dissolution of rock phosphates. Crops efficient in rock phosphate exploitation are: Lupins, buckwheat, clover, mustard, Swiss chard, rape and cabbage, whereas cotton, and most cereals are less efficient in the use of rock phosphate. The economic application of partially acidulated rock phosphates is also restricted to soils of low pH. The term 'partially acidulated' indicates that only a part of the total phosphate fertilizer is water soluble the rest being mainly apatite, which is only soluble, if the soil pH is low enough. Thus on soils with a slightly acid or neutral reaction, the apatite fraction of the partially acidulated fertilizer is hardly available to plants. TERMAN et al. [1964] report that the yield response of the partially acidulated materials corresponded to the percentage of soluble phosphate. Similar results were obtained by HAMMOND et al. [1980] in greenhouse experiments with maize. These authors found that on a silt loam soil with a pH range of 4.8 to 5.4, partially acidulated phosphate rocks were superior to non acidulated phosphate rocks, but inferior to superphosphate or triple superphosphate.

Although the solubility of phosphate in the various forms of compound fertilizers does not differ as much as that in straight phosphate fertilizers, there are differences in phosphate solubility and effectiviness. These especially become evident when phosphate containing compound fertilizers are applied to soils with a low phosphate status. From numerous field experiments carried out in India MAHAPATRA et al. [1973] concluded that the P-response was highest with superphosphate followed by ODDA nitrophosphate and least with PEC nitrophosphate. The abbreviations 'ODDA' and 'PEC' refer to different technological

406

processes by which these nitrophosphates are produced. For crops with a long growth period such as sugar cane, nitrophosphates were as good as superphosphate and in acid laterite soils the nitrophosphates were even superior to superphosphate.

The behaviour of fertilizer P in the soil also depends on fertilizer chemical composition. Water soluble phosphate fertilizers, *e.g.* superphosphate, reacts rapidly with Ca^{2+} which is present in abundant quantities in most soils. In this reaction the rather insoluble $Ca_3(PO_4)_2$ is formed.

$$Ca(H_2PO_4)_2 + 2\ Ca^{2+} \rightarrow Ca_3(PO_4)_2 + 4\ H^+$$

Tricalciumphosphate is also readily formed in calcareous soils:

$$Ca(H_2PO_4)_2 + 2\ CaCO_3 \rightarrow Ca_3(PO_4)_2 + 2\ H_2O + 2\ CO_2$$

In more acid soils the $H_2PO_4^-$ of the superphosphate is easily adsorbed by clay minerals. These reactions proceed more rapidly when the superphosphate is applied in a powdered form, as surface contact between the fertilizer and the soil is high. For this reason, superphosphate and most other water soluble fertilizer phosphates are applied in a granulated form.

The crystal structure of basic slags is complex. The material is metastable and its solubility rises as the surface contact between fertilizer and soil increases. Basic slags are therefore more soluble in powdered than in granulated form. The same applies to rock phosphates and sinter phosphate.

9.3.3 Phosphate application

As the mobility of phosphate in the soil profile is comparatively low, the uptake of fertilizer P depends much on root growth and the root morphology of the crop being considered. This was demonstrated in the results of PAGE and GERWITZ [1969] who examined crop uptake of labelled phosphates applied at different soil depths. It was found that lettuce mainly took up phosphate from the upper soil layer (0 to 18 cm), whereas carrots absorbed an appreciable proportion from the 30 to 40 cm depth zone. In this crop 10% of the total P uptake even originated from a soil depth deeper than 100 cm. From these results it can be seen that it is of importance to incorporate P fertilizers into the soil and this is especially the case when using low water soluble phosphates. For soils very low in available phosphate, placed phosphate fertilizer application is often superior to broadcast treatment. Placement of P fertilizer ensures that a higher concentration of fertilizer comes in contact with a more limited soil volume. The fertilizer is thus able to saturate the soil phosphate adsorption capacity to a greater degree. The phosphate concentration of the soil solution is thus higher in the placed zone. The beneficial effect of placed applications as compared with broadcast treatments has been reported by a number of authors (PRUMMEL [1957], LOCASCIO *et al.* [1960], RYAN [1962], REITH [1972]; see also p. 315).

With the exception of rock phosphates, which should be applied in Autumn, P fertilizers can be applied at any time of the year, provided the phosphate fixation capacity of the soil is not too high. When this is the case, water soluble phosphate materials should be applied preferentially in Spring. This reduces the fixation of the fertilizer P to a minimum as it allows the crop the best opportunity to compete with the soil for P utilization. In soils in which available phosphate levels are adequate, application of phosphate can be made every second year without running any risk of yield depressions (PRAUSSE [1968]). The rate of phosphate application, however, should be in the same order as the sum of the corresponding two single treatments. All P fertilizer treatments should take into account the relatively high P requirement of most crops in early growth stages. (see Table 2.12 on p. 80).

In most mineral soils mobility of phosphate is rather low so that fertilizer P is scarcely leached into the deeper soil layers (see p. 298). For this reason, there is no risk of P fertilizer loss by leaching at whatever time of the year phosphate is applied to mineral soils. For organic soils, however, movement of P fertilizer into deeper soil layers has been observed (MUNK [1972]).

General Reading

BLAIR, G.J. (Ed): Prospects for Improving Efficiency of Phosphorus Utilization. Reviews in Science 3. University of New England. Armidale, N.S.W. Australia, 1976

DALAL, R.C.: Soil organic phosphorus. Adv. Agron. *29*, 83–117 (1977)

KHASAWNEH, F.E. and DOLL, E.C.: The use of phosphate rock for direct applications to soils. Adv. Agron. *30*, 159–206 (1978)

KHASAWNEH, F.E., SAMPLE E.C. and KAMPRATH, E.J. (Eds): The Role of Phosphorus in Agriculture. Amer. Soc. Agron. Madison, 1980

LARSEN, S.: Soil phosphorus. Adv. in Agron., *19*, 151–206 (1967)

LOUGHMAN, B.C.: Metabolic factors and the utilization of phosphorus by plants. In: Phosphorus in the Environment: its Chemistry and Biochemistry. p. 155–174. CIBA Foundation Symposium 57, Elsevier/North Holland, 1978

MANDAL, S.C.: Phosphorus management of our soils. Need for a more rational approach. 40th Sess. Indian Soc. of Soil Sci., Bhubaneswar (1975)

PARFITT, R.L.: Anion adsorption by soils and soil material. Adv. Agron. *30*, 1–50 (1978)

TINKER, P.B.: Soil chemistry of phosphorus and mycorrhizal effects on plant growth In: Endomycorrhizas, SANDERS, F.E., MOSSE, B. and TINKER, P.B. (eds.), p. 353–371. Academic Press, London, New York (1975)

Williams E. G.: Factors affecting the availability of soil phosphate and efficiency of phosphate fertilizers. Anglo-Soviet Symposium on Agrochemical Research on the use of Mineral Fertilizers, Moscow 1970 (see Macaulay Institute Ann. Report, 1969/70. Macaulay Inst. for Soils, Craigiebuckler, Aberdeen, Scotland)

Chapter 10

Potassium

10.1 Soil Potassium

10.1.1 Potassium minerals and potassium release

The average K content of the earth's crust is in the order of about 2.3%. By far the greatest part of this K is bound in primary minerals or is present in the secondary clay minerals which largely make up the clay fraction of the soil of particle size less than 2 μm. For this reason soils rich in clay are also generally rich in K (ACQUAYE *et al.* [1967], GARDNER [1967], KAILA [1967]) and clay soils may often have in excess of 4% total K. The clay content of a soil is to some extent dependent on the soil parent material, but is also considerably affected by pedogenesis. Mature soils which have been subjected to strong weathering conditions are often low both in clay and K contents. Thus highly weathered sandy soils contrast markedly to young soils derived from volcanic material in which clay and K contents are generally high (GRAHAM and FOX [1971]).

In an extensive investigation comprising more than 1000 sites in Central Europe, LAVES [1978] found that soil K content was closely related to the content of illites and Al-chlorites and to a lesser degree to the content of smectites. Highest chlorite and illite contents associated with low levels of smectites were found in the brown soils of the montainous areas, whereas in the alluvial soils the situation was the reverse. Here smectites were dominant. The loess soils took on an intermediate position. Organic soils are frequently low in clay and K contents. The level of K in organic soils is in the region of 0.03% although the figure may vary somewhat between different classes of organic soils (BADEN [1965]).

The main source of K^+ for plants growing under natural conditions comes from the weathering of K containing minerals. The most important of these minerals are listed in Table 10.1. In the potash feldspars, K is located in the interstices of the Si, Al-O framework of the crystal lattice and held tightly by covalent bonds (RICH [1968]). The weathering of feldspars begins at the surface of the particle. Potassium is initially released by water and weak acids at a more rapid

Table 10.1 Potassium content of some primary and secondary clay minerals (SCHEFFER and SCHACHTSCHABEL [1976])

	content in % K_2O
Alkali feldspars.........	4–15
Ca-Na feldspars	0– 3
Muscovite (K mica).....	7–11
Biotite (Mg mica)	6–10
Illite	4– 7
Vermiculite	0– 2
Chlorite	0– 1
Montmorillonite........	0– 0.5

rate than other constituents. As weathering progresses, however, a Si-Al-O residue envelope is formed around the unweathered core. This layer reduces the rate of loss of K^+ from the mineral and thus protects it from further intensive degradation (RICH [1972]). Minerals of the mica type and also the secondary minerals of the 2:1 layer silicates differ fundamentally in structure from the feldspars. For this reason they also differ in their properties of releasing and binding K^+. The micas consist of unit layers each composed of two Si, Al-O tetrahedral sheets between which is an M-O, OH octahedral sheet, where M is usually an Al^{3+}, Fe^{2+}, Fe^{2+}, or Mg^{2+}. Potassium ions occupy the approximately hexagonal spaces between the unit layers and as a consequence the distance between unit layers is relatively small *e.g.* 1.0 nm in micas. The replacement of non hydrated interlayer K^+ by hydrated cation species such as Na^+, Mg^{2+} or Ca^{2+} expands the mineral with an increase in the distance between the unit layers, *e.g.* to 1.4 nm in vermiculite (see Figure 10.1).

Generally K^+ of the lattice is vulnerable to weathering and can diffuse out of the mineral in exchange for other cation species. High H^+ concentrations (NEWMAN [1969]) and low K^+ concentrations in the medium favour the net release of non exchangeable K^+ (interlayer K^+). This K^+ release according to v. REICHENBACH [1972] is an exchange process associated with diffusion in which K^+ adsorbed to i-positions of the interlayer zone is replaced by other cation species. If the replacing species is a large one (Na^+, Mg^{2+}, Ca^{2+}) then K^+ exchange results in an expansion of the clay mineral and the formation of wedge zones (see Figure 10.2). 'Frayed edge' or 'wedge' zone formation is typical of weathering micas and results from the dissolution of the silicate layer following the release of interlayer K^+ (RICH [1968]). The resulting widening gap between the two layers of the mineral favours the diffusion of the replaced K^+ out of the mineral. Thus JACKSON and DURING [1979] have shown that pretreatment of the soil with Ca^{2+} resulted in an expansion of the clay mineral and an increase in K^+ desorption. According to FARMER and WILSON [1970] this kind of weathering converts micas to the secondary 2.1 clay minerals, illite and vermiculite, the reaction sequence being as follows: Micas ($\sim 10\%$ K) $\rightarrow$ hydromicas (6–8% K) $\rightarrow$ illite (4–6% K) $\rightarrow$ transition minerals ($\sim 3\%$ K) $\rightarrow$ vermiculite or montmorillonite ($<2\%$ K) (SCHROEDER [1976]).

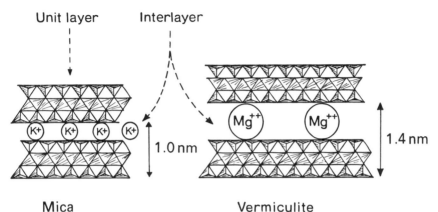

Fig. 10.1 Unit layer and interlayer of mica and vermiculite.

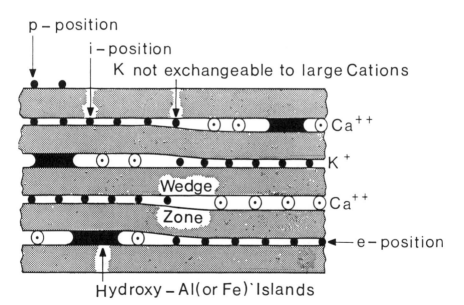

Fig. 10.2 Model of an expandible layer silicate with interlayers, wedge zone, p-, e- and i-positions (after RICH [1968]).

413

The rate of K^+ release by weathering not only depends on the K content of a particular mineral. It is also affected by even slight structural differences between minerals. Thus biotite a ferromagnesian mineral although generally lower in K content than muscovite, releases K at a faster rate because it is weathered more rapidly. The same is true for Ca feldspars which are degraded at a higher rate than K feldspars (DUTHION [1966]). According to RICH [1968] illite and other 2:1 minerals which contain mica like zones are the most important sources of K in soils.

10.1.2 Potassium fixation

As the depletion of K^+ from the interlayers of minerals continues, the rate of release becomes progressively slower. Interlayer sites become depleted of K^+ although they still retain a very high K^+ selectivity with respect to divalent ions (RAMAN and JACKSON [1964]). Addition of K^+ to such minerals results in a strong K^+ adsorption to these positions causing a contraction of the mineral (GRAHAM and LOPEZ [1969]). This process is called K^+ fixation. The contraction results in a reduction in the unit distance to about 1 nm. Zones of vermiculite structure in weathered biotite and muscovite characterized by a 1.4 nm layer distance thus regain the 1 nm spacing of mica when treated with K^+ (see Figure 10.1).

The degree to which K^+ fixation occurs depends on a number of factors including the charge density of the mineral, the extent of the wedge zone, the moisture content, the concentration of K^+ and the nature and concentration of competing cations in the surrounding medium. Fixation tends to be high when the negative charge per unit silicate layer ($=$ charge density) is high. When this occurs the positive K^+ ion is very strongly held by the negatively charged layers. If the wedge zone is confined to the edge of the particle only small amouns of K^+ can be fixed. However, if the zone penetrates deeply into the mineral, considerable amounts of K^+ can be withheld. Some minerals such as weathered micas, vermiculites and illites fix K^+ under both moist and dry conditions, whereas smectites only fix K^+ under dry conditions. For this reason fixation is frequently higher under dry than moist soil conditions (SCHROEDER [1955]). As the NH_4^+ is very similar to K^+ in ionic radius, this too can be fixed by expanded 2:1 clay minerals (BARTLETT and SIMPSON [1967]). Ammonium can also exchange for fixed K^+. The same holds true for H^+ (RICH and BLACK [1964]). Thus both ion species, NH_4^+ and H^+, can compete with K^+ for K fixing binding sites. This means that K^+ fixation is generally not so important in restricting K^+ availability to plants on acids soils (pH <4.5) as on limed agricultural soils. The fixing power of the 2:1 clay minerals usually follows the order vermiculite $>$ illite $>$ smectite.

Potassium fixation is of considerable importance in agricultural practice (see p. 431). The quanitites of fertilizer K^+ rendered unavailable in this way can be very high. Generally the K^+ fixation capactity is higher in the deeper soil layers because of the greater clay contents. Thus ARIFIN *et al.* [1973] found K^+ fixation levels as high as 1000 to 2000 mg K/100 g clay in the B horizon of important agricultural soils in the southern region of the USA.

10.1.3 Potassium adsorption and mobility

Soil clay content is not only of importance for K^+ release and fixation, it also considerably influences the mobility of K^+ in the soil. Potassium ions are adsorbed by clay minerals to binding sites which differ in selectivity. For the 2:1 clay minerals such as illites, vermiculites and weathered micas 3 different adsorption sites can be distinguished (Figure 10.2) (SCHOUWENBURG and SCHUFFELEN [1963]). These are as follows: sites at the planar surfaces (p-position), sites at the edges of the layers (e-position) and sites in interlayer space (i-position). The specificity of these three binding sites for K^+ differs considerably (BECKETT and NAFADY [1967]), EHLERS *et al.* [1967]). As has been already outlined on page 414, this specificity of K^+ binding in relation to other cations can be expressed in quantitative terms by the Gapon coefficient. This is higher the greater the specificity of the binding site for K^+. According to SCHUFFELEN [1971] the three different K^+ binding sites of illite have the following Gapon coefficients

p-position: 2.21 $(mM/l)^{-\frac{1}{2}}$
e-position: 102 $(mM/l)^{-\frac{1}{2}}$
i-position: infinite $(mM/l)^{-\frac{1}{2}}$

The Gapon coefficient may be calculated from molar (M) or milli molar (mM) concentrations. As numerical values can differ between the two forms of expression, units should always be stated. The coefficients shown above are based on mM concentrations and they refer to K/Mg exchange, thus comparing the specificity of the binding site for K^+ with that of Mg^{2+}. Values of the same order of magnitude have also been reported by DUTHION [1966] for K/Ca exchange. The considerable differences between the Gapon coefficient for the three K^+ binding sites demonstrate the immense distinction between sites for K^+ selectivity. The binding selectivities for K^+ by organic matter and clays of the kaolinite type are similar to the p-position sites (EHLERS *et al.* [1968]). Here the K bond is relatively weak so that K^+ absorbed may easily be replaced by other cations, and particularly by Ca^{2+} and Mg^{2+}. The i-position has the greatest specificity for K^+. These binding sites largely account for K^+ fixation in soils.

It is clear that the behaviour of K^+ in the soil is very much dependent on the clay content and types of clay minerals present. Potassium mobility and diffusion rates are generally low in soils rich in K^+ specific binding sites. The same is true for K^+ leaching (see p. 298). Under temperate climatic conditions this amounts only to about 8 kg K/ha/yr (VÖMEL [1965/66], COPPENET [1969]). On organic soils and sandy soils K^+ leaching rates may be considerably higher (DAM KOFOED and LINDHARD [1968], GISKIN and MAJDAN [1969]). Potassium application on these soils more prone to leaching should therefore be carried out in spring rather than in autumn, in order to prevent major K^+ loss by winter leaching. Soils rich in clay minerals of the kaolinite type are poor in K^+ specific binding sites. Such soils occur extensively in tropical regions. Problems associated with the inherently low K status of these soils are exacerbated by the excessive leaching resulting from the high tropical rainfall conditions.

10.1.4 Potassium fractions

Soil potassium can be divided in 3 fractions: Potassium as a structural element of soil minerals, K^+ adsorbed in exchangeable form to soil colloids such as clay minerals and organic matter, and K^+ present in the soil solution. In mineral soils most K occurs in the lattices of minerals and according to WIKLANDER [1954] and SCHEFFER et al. [1960] only 1 to 4% of the total K is present in adsorbed (exchangeable) form. Potassium in the soil solution makes up only a small percentage of the exchangeable fraction. The significance of these three fractions for the availability of K^+ to plant roots, however, is in the reverse order of their amounts in the soil, the K^+ in soil solution being by far the most important for plant supply (GRIMME et al. [1971]).

The main relationships between the three fractions are shown in Figure 10.3. Potassium released by weathering of minerals is dissolved in the soil solution. It can then be taken up directly by plant roots or be adsorbed by soil colloids. An equilibrium is thus set up between adsorbed K^+ and the free K^+ in soil solution. The K^+ level in the soil solution resulting from this equilibrium depends much on the selectivity of the adsorption sites. If these are specific for K^+, the concentration of K^+ in the soil solution tends to be low (REZK and AMER [1969]). If the binding sites are less specific for K^+, the K^+ concentration in the soil solution is generally higher (NEMÉTH et al. [1970]). The K^+ concentration of the soil solution very largely controls the K^+ diffusion rate towards the plant roots and therefore also the uptake of K^+ by plants (MENGEL and VON BRAUNSCHWEIG [1972]. DURING and DUGANZICH [1979], WANASURIA et al. [1981]). Besides the K^+ concentration of the soil solution, the K^+ buffer capacity of the soil is a further important factor determining K^+ availability (see page 73).

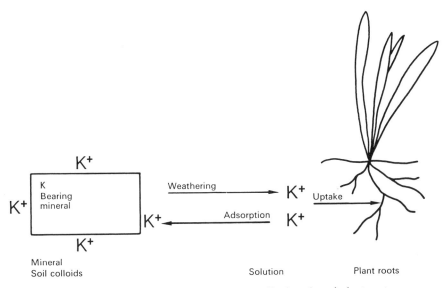

Fig.10.3 Potassium relationships in the soil between soil minerals and plant roots.

The more the exchangeable K^+ fraction is exhausted the greater is the contribution of the non exchangeable K^+ fraction to plant K^+ supply. (MENGEL and WIECHENS [1979]). The rate of release of non exchangeable K^+ can differ considerably between soils and thus often does not meet crop requirements (v. BOGUSLAWSKI and LACH [1971], GRIMME [1974]). Potassium release from the non exchangeable fraction is higher under moist than under dry soil conditions (MENGEL and WIECHENS [1979]). Grasses are better able to utilize the non exchangeable K^+ fraction than dicots, particularly legumes (BLASER and BRADY [1950], MALQUORI et al. [1975]). This is one important reason why grasses displace legumes in mixed swards under conditions of low K^+ availability (STEFFENS and MENGEL [1979]).

10.2 Potassium in Physiology

10.2.1 Uptake and translocation

Potassium is an essential element for all living organisms. In plant physiology it is the most important cation not only in regard to its content in plant tissues but also with respect to its physiological and biochemical functions. One main feature of K^+ is the high rate at which it is taken up by plant tissues. This high

417

uptake rate depends on an active uptake mechanism (see p. 125), and there is evidence that of all the essential mineral cation species, K^+ is the only one which can be transported against an electrochemical gradient into plant cells (SPANSWICK and WILLIAMS [1964], DUNLOP and BOWLING [1971], ANSARI and BOWLING [1972]). Recent experiments of CHEESEMAN and HANSON [1979] provide evidence that K^+ uptake is active at low K^+ concentrations in the nutrient solution and that the active uptake mechanism is inhibited by higher K^+ concentrations (see p. 128). Potassium uptake rates are also controlled by the internal K^+ concentration (GLASS [1976]) which in turn has an impact on cell turgor. According to ZIMMERMANN [1978] it is ultimately cell turgor which controls K^+ uptake. The results of GLASS and PERLEY [1980] are of interest in this context. These workers reported that 10 different barley cultivars differed markedly in their K^+ uptake rates and that there was a positive correlation between K^+ uptake rate and growth rate.

Potassium in the plant is very mobile. Its main transport direction is towards the meristematic tissues. Often K^+ from older plant organs is redistributed to younger tissues. This can be observed very clearly in an investigation of GREENWAY and PITMAN [1965] with young oat plants. The main results are shown in Table 10.2. It can be seen that the K^+ import into the oldest leaf was only slightly higher than the K^+ export. The exported K^+ was redistributed to the 2nd and youngest leaves. It is thus obvious that the younger leaves were supplied with K^+ originating from older tissues.

The reason why K^+ is preferentially transported to young meristematic tissues is not yet known, but relationships to protein synthesis, growth rate, and supply of cytokinins have been postulated (JACOBY et al. [1973]). These suggestions are supported by research data of COCUCCI and DALLA ROSA [1980] who found that the stimulating effect of IAA (indole acetic acid) on the elongation of maize coleoptiles is closely related to the release of H^+, the uptake of K^+, and the synthesis of proteins.

The bulk of K^+ is mainly taken up during the vegetative growth stage. For cereals this means that in the period from tillering to ear emergence, the rate of K uptake is particularly high. Under normal metabolic conditions hardly

Table 10.2 Turnover of potassium in oat plants at the third leaf stage (data of GREENWAY and PITMAN [1965])

Uptake in μM K/day	Oldest leaf	Second leaf	Youngest leaf
From the roots	1.9	2.7	2.0
From other plant organs.........................	−1.6	0.7	1.3

any net loss of K occurs from root tissue (JOHANSEN *et al.* [1970]). Even during the ripening stage of cereals the K^+ release by the roots to the root medium is very low and amounts to only about 1.5% of the total K in the plant (HAEDER [1971]). The high uptake rate of K^+ infers that it is a strong competitor in the uptake of other cation species (see p. 463). Their absorption rate is especially enhanced, when the K uptake is low (GRIMME *et al.* [1974]). On the other hand K uptake and retention in plant cells are also competitively affected by H^+, Ca^{2+}, Mg^{2+} and Na^+ (GÄRTEL [1955], ELZAM and HODGES [1967]).

A further typical feature of K^+ is its high concentration in the phloem sap. Indeed here it is the most abundant cation, amounting to about 80% of the total cation sum (HALL and BAKER [1972]). As the solutes of the phloem sap can be translocated both upwards (acropetal) and downwards (basipetal) in the plant, long-distance transport of K^+ can readily take place. Plant organs preferentially supplied with phloem sap such as young leaves, meristematic tissues and fleshy fruits (apples, grapes) are therefore high in K^+ (CASSAGNES *et al.* [1969]. The function of K^+ in phloem sap is not fully clear. According to a hypothetical scheme proposed by BEN ZIONI *et al.* [1971], K^+ in the phloem sap is the main counter ion of malate which is transported from the shoots to the root and respired. In the respiration process the anion equivalents of malate are transferred to HCO_3^- which are released from the roots into the nutrient medium. Nitrate ions can then be taken up in exchange and trans-located upwards in the xylem sap along with the K^+ ions originally acting as the counter ions for the downward movement of malate. Evidence of a K^+ recirculation mechanism of this kind has recently been reported for *Ricinus communis* by KIRKBY and ARMSTRONG [1980]. In this species a large fraction of the negative charge left over after NO_3^- reduction in the tops is effluxed as OH^- from the roots in exchange for the high excess anion over cation uptake. The same is possibly also true for many monocotyledons. In other species, however, as for example the tomato, the negative charge from NO_3^- reduction in the leaves is transferred to organic acid anions which are retained *in situ* in association with cations (KIRKBY and KNIGHT [1977]).

10.2.2 Water regime

Potassium is of utmost importance for the water status of plants. Uptake of water in cells and tissues is frequently the consequence of active K^+ uptake (LÄUCHLI and PFLÜGER [1978]). GREEN and MUIR [1978] reported that the expansion of cucumber cotyledons was closely related to their K^+ supply. ARNEKE [1980] found that the turgor (ψ_p) of young leaf cells of *Phaseolus vulgaris* was dependent of their K^+ content. In the low K^+ treatment the turgor was 5.05 bar which was significantly lower than the turgor of the high K^+ treatment which amounted to 7.17 bar. In the low K^+ treatment growth rate, cell size, and water content of the tissue were reduced. From the results of this experiment it was concluded that in young tissues K^+ is indispensable for obtaining optimum cell turgor which in turn is required for cell expansion. Turgor in young tissues appears to be the most sensitive parameter indicating K^+ nutritional status. Other K^+ related processes such as CO_2-assimilation, phosphorylation and protein synthesis are less sensitive in registering inadequate K^+ supply. Recent results of DELA GUARDIA and BENLLOCH [1980] also emphasize the essential role of K^+ for turgor and stem elongation of young sunflower plants. The results of these workers also showed that K^+ acts synergistically with gibberellic acid so that highest elongation rates were obtained when both K^+ and gibberellic acid were applied.

The lower water loss of plants well supplied with K^+ is due to a reduction in transpiration rate (BRAG [1972]) which not only depends on the osmotic potential of the mesophyll cells but is also controlled to a large extent by the opening and closing of stomata. Investigations of FISHER and HSIAO [1968] and HUMBLE and HSIAO [1969] have revealed that K^+ plays a significant role in stomatal opening and closing. Convincing evidence for this relationship has been provided by electron probe analysis studies of HUMBLE and RASCHKE [1971]. Using this technique it has been possible to measure the K^+ content of guard cells of open and closed stomata. Figure 10.4 shows the result of this experiment. It can be seen that the K^+ content in the open state is considerably higher than the K^+ content of guard cells from closed stomata. Under light conditions the guard cells produce abundant ATP in photosynthetic phosphorylation, thus supporting the active K^+ uptake mechanism with sufficient energy (HUMBLE and HSIAO [1970]). Potassium is therefore accumulated in the guard cells in considerable concentrations and the resulting high turgor pressure causes the opening of the stomata. Figure 10.4 also shows that the inorganic anions (Cl^-, $H_2PO_4^-$) do not accompany the K^+ uptake to any great extent. The major anion charge balancing the accumulated K^+ is malate. This is probably produced *via* the carboxylation of phosphoenol pyruvate (PEP) (see p. 135).

The mechanism of stomatal closure and opening depends entirely on the K^+ flux (PENNY and BOWLING [1974]). For this reason plants not adequately supplied with K^+ are impaired in stomatal activity (TERRY and ULRICH [1973]). It appears that in most plant species this opening/closing mechanism is absolutely dependent on the specific K^+ uptake process. Other univalent cations are thus generally unable to replace K^+ in this specific function (TROLLDENIER [1971]), except in a few plant species, *e.g. Kalanchoe marmorata* where Na^+ is effective. A review on stomatal action has been presented by RASCHKE [1975].

420

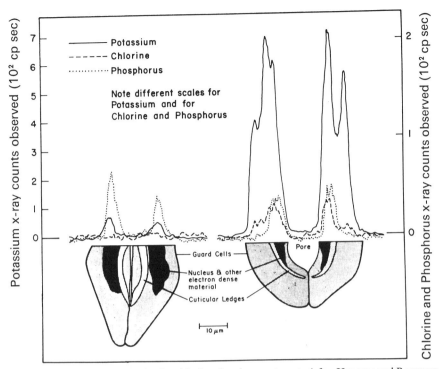

Fig. 10.4 Ion contents of guard cells with closed and open stomata (after HUMBLE and RASCHKE [1971]).

10.2.3 Photosynthesis and translocation of photosynthates

PEOPLES and KOCH [1979] have reported a clear effect of K^+ on the rate of CO_2 assimilation. Their investigations revealed that K^+ did not directly influence photosystem I or II, but rather promoted the *de novo* synthesis of the enzyme ribulose biphosphate carboxylase. Potassium also decreased the diffusive resistance for CO_2 in the mesophyll. Some of the most important data of this investigation are given in Table 10.3 showing that the increase in CO_2 assimilation was paralleled by an increase in photorespiration and a decrease in

Table 10.3 Effect of K^+ of CO_2-assimilation, photorespiration, and dark respiration (PEOPLES and KOCH [1979])

K^+ in leaves, % K i. DM	CO_2-assimil. mg/dm²/h	Photorespiration dpm/dm²/h	Dark respiration mg/dm²/h
1.28	11.9	4.00	7.56
1.98	21.7	5.87	3.34
3.84	34.0	8.96	3.06

421

dark respiration. These contrasting effects of K^+ on CO_2 assimilation on the one hand and dark respiration on the other have also been reported by JACKSON and VOLK [1968] and BARANKIEWICZ [1978].

Numerous authors have shown that K^+ enhances the translocation of photosynthates. This question has been recently treated by MENGEL [1980] in a review paper. The typical K^+ effect is shown in Table 10.4 from the data of HARTT [1969]. Potassium not only promotes the translocation of newly synthesized photosynthates but has also a beneficial effect on the mobilization of stored material. Thus KOCH and MENGEL [1977] as well as SEÇER [1978] found that in spring wheat K^+ increased the mobilization of proteins stored in leaves and stems and also promoted the translocation of the nitrogenous degradation compounds towards the grains. HARTT [1970] as well as MENGEL and VIRO [1974] have shown that the effect of K^+ on photosynthate translocation is not a consequence of a higher CO_2 assimilation rate. The mechanism by which K^+ increases the translocation rate has yet to be clearly established. MALEK and BAKER [1977] suppose that K^+ is directly involved in the process of phloem loading. In the phloem loading process K^+ is transported into the sieve cell as a counter ion to H^+ release (KOMOR et al. [1980]). This K^+ counter transport results in partial depolarization of the membrane which is believed to enhance ATPase activity and thus the phloem loading process (see Figure 3.9).

Potassium is known to have a beneficial effect on ATP synthesis (WATANABE and YOSHIDA [1970], HARTT [1972], PFLÜGER and MENGEL [1972]). As ATP is required for numerous synthetic reactions, K^+ may indirectly promote the synthesis of various organic compounds, such as proteins, sugars and polysaccharides.

Table 10.4 Translocation of C-14 labelled photosynthates in sugar cane with a low and high K supply (total label = 100%) (HARTT [1969])

| | % of total label | |
	+ K	– K
Fed blade	54.3	95.4
Sheath of fed leaf	14.2	3.9
Joint of fed leaf	9.7	0.6
Leaves and joints above fed leaf	1.9	0.1
Stalk below joint of fed leaf	20.1	0.04

10.2.4 Enzyme activation

The main function of K^+ in biochemistry is its activation of various enzyme systems (EVANS and SORGER [1966]). In most cases K^+ is the most efficient cation in effecting this activation. Figure 10.5 shows a typical example of an enzyme

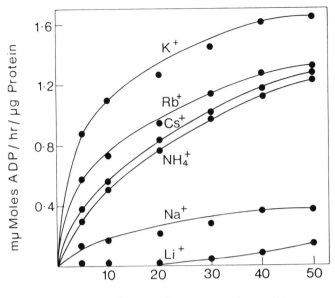

Fig. 10.5 Effect of univalent cation species on the activity of starch synthetase isolated from sweet corn (after Nitsos and Evans [1969]).

activated by univalent cations. The enzyme, a starch synthetase from sweet corn, was most strongly activated by K^+, followed by Rb^+, Cs^+ and NH_4^+. The activation by Na^+ was very poor and Li^+ had hardly any effect. With several enzymes, activation by NH_4^+ or Rb^+ is as efficient as the activation by K^+. This is of theoretical interest as the sizes of these three ion species are almost the same when hydrated. Activation thus seems to be related to the size of the activating ion. In whole plants, however, NH_4^+ and Rb^+ can not substitute for K^+ in activating enzymes, as they are toxic at the concentrations required (El-Sheikh and Ulrich [1970], Morard [1973]).

In vitro experiments have shown that maximum K^+ activation is obtained within a concentration range of 40 to 80 mMK. Whether this is also true for *in vivo* conditions is doubtful because *in vivo* metabolites may influence enzyme activity by allosteric effects. According to Suelter [1970] only low K^+ concentrations in the order of 2 mM are required for *in vivo* enzyme activation. This means that even under conditions of K^+ deficiency, enough K^+ is still available for maximum K^+ activation. Generally the K^+ concentration in the cytoplasm is in the range of 100 to 200 mM (Pierce and Higinbotham [1970]) and even in K^+ deficient tissues, localized K^+ concentrations as high as 50 mM are probably present. The importance of K^+ for enzyme activation is thus of more academic than practical interest. In growing plants there are more K+ sensitive processes such as water uptake and retention, phosphorylation, phloem transport, and the diffusion of CO_2 to the mesophyll. These processes are closely related to the K+ nutritional status of the plant and ultimately also to the control of growth and crop production.

The finding that low molecular weight compounds such as amino acids and sugars may accumulate in plants poorly supplied with K+ is probably not a direct consequence of impaired enzyme activity but due rather to an inadequate energy (ATP) supply. An energy shortage may induce a delay in protein synthesis which in turn may indirectly affect enzyme activity because of a lack in enzyme proteins. This has been shown for nitrate reductase by PFLÜGER and WIEDEMANN [1977] and for ribulose bisphosphate carboxylase by PEOPLES and KOCH [1979].

Severe K+ deficiency leads to the synthesis of toxic amines such as putrescine and agmatine (SMITH and SINCLAIR [1967]). According to SMITH and GARRAWAY [1964] agmatine is produced by the decarboxylation of arginine:

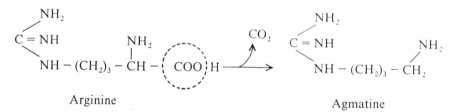

Arginine   Agmatine

Agmatine can then be converted to carbamylputrescine which is hydrolyzed to putrescine and carbamic acid:

Carbamylputrescine   Carbamic   Putrescine
                                            acid

These reactions are promoted when cellular pH levels are low (SMITH and SINCLAIR [1967]) as probably occur under K+ deficiency conditions. Accumulation of these toxic amines is especially high in the older leaves. Acid conditions in the plant due to K+ deficiency also induce the synthesis of proline (GORING and BUI HUY THIEN [1979]).

10.2.5 Replacement of potassium by sodium

The question of whether Na^+ can replace K^+ in physiological processes in the plant is not only of academic interest but also of practical importance in relation to fertilizer usage (see p. 432). In less specific processes such as raising cell turgor some replacement is possible. The extent to which substitution can occur, however, depends much on the uptake potential for Na^+. This differs considerably between plant species (MARSCHNER [1971]). Table 10.5 shows the Na^+ uptake potential of various crops. For the 'high' and 'medium Na species', the favourable effect of Na^+ is important on plant growth. This is particularly

Table 10.5 Uptake potential of various crops for sodium (data from MARSCHNER [1971])

High	Medium	Low	Very low
Fodder beet	Cabbage	Barley	Buckwheat
Sugar beet	Coconut	Flax	Maize
Mangold	Cotton	Millet	Rye
Spinach	Lupins	Rape	Soya
Swiss chard	Oats	Wheat	Swede
Table beet	Potato		
	Rubber		
	Turnips		

the case for the *Beta* species (EL-SHEIKH and ULRICH [1970]). In these species Na^+ contributes to the osmotic potential of the cell and thus has a positive effect on the water regime of plants. The beneficial effects of Na^+ on plant growth are particularly observable, when the K^+ supply is inadequate (HYLTON et al. [1967], AMIN and JOHAM [1968]). Table 10.6 shows such an example for rice (YOSHIDA and CASTANEDA [1969]). In the lower range of K^+ concentrations, Na^+ increased grain yields, whereas at the higher K^+ concentration Na^+ induced a slight yield depression. Under field conditions Na^+ deficiency of crop plants has not yet been observed. WOOLEY [1957], however, succeeded in inducing Na^+ deficiency symptoms in tomatoes under glasshouse conditions. According to BROWNELL and CROSSLAND [1972], Na^+ is an essential nutrient for some C4 plants. The effect of Na^+ on plant growth has been considered in papers by MARSCHNER [1971] and JENNINGS [1976].

Plants species and cultivars differ considerably in their ability to utilize K^+ (ASHER and OZANNE [1967, 1977]) and in recent years new crop cultivars have been developed which are highly efficient in K^+ utilization. This efficiency is defined in terms of weight of dry matter plant production per unit weight of K^+ absorbed. MAKMUR et al. [1978] screened 156 lines of tomato plants for K^+ efficiency. These workers observed that K^+ efficient lines were characterized by the capability of the plants to substitute Na^+ for K^+ to a high extent. GER-LOFF [1976] found in a number of *Phaseolus* cultivars that K^+ retranslocation in the plant is also important for K^+ efficiency.

Table 10.6 Effect of increasing potassium concentrations on the grain yield of rice, in the presence or absence of a high Na level in the nutrient solution (YOSHIDA and CASTANEDA [1969])

K-concentration	Grain yield, g/pot	
mM	– Na	+ 43 mM Na
0.025	4.6	11.0
0.050	6.9	19.9
0.125	26.4	46.6
0.250	63.3	67.3
1.25	67.5	75.9
2.50	90.8	87.6
5.00	103.6	92.6

10.2.6 Potassium deficiency

Potassium deficiency does not immediately result in visible symptoms. At first there is only a reduction in growth rate (hidden hunger), and only later do chlorosis and necrosis occur. These symptoms generally begin in the older leaves, due to the fact that these leaves supply the younger ones with K^+. According to investigations of PISSAREK [1973] with rape and of MORARD [1973] with sorghum, K^+ deficiency symptoms are first seen in the 2nd and 3rd oldest leaf and not in the oldest ones. In most plant species chlorosis and necrosis begins in the margins and tips of the leaves (maize, cereals, fruit trees) (Plate 10.1), but in some species such as clover irregularly distributed necrotic spots occur on the leaves (see Plate 10.2).

Plants suffering from K^+ deficiency show a decrease in turgor, and under water stress they easily become flaccid. Resistance to drought is therefore poor (PISSAREK [1973]) and the affected plants show increased susceptibility to frost damage, fungal attack, and saline conditions. In K^+ deficient plants often an abnormal development of tissues and cell organelles is observed. According to PISSAREK [1973] inadequate K^+ supply resulted in a reduced growth rate of the cambium in stems of rape *(Brassica napus)*. The formation of xylem and phloem tissue was restricted whereas the cortical tissue was affected only to a minor extent. Lignification of the vascular bundles is generally impaired by K^+ deficiency. This effect probably makes K^+ deficient crops more prone to lodging. K^+ deficiency also results in a collapse of chloroplasts (PISSAREK [1973]) and

426

Plate 10.1 K deficiency symptoms in older leaves of rape.
(Photo: PISSAREK)

Plate 10.2 K deficiency symptoms in white clover.

mitochondria (Kursanov and Vyskrebentzeva [1966]). Potassium deficiency symptoms of various plant species have been described in detail by Bussler [1964] and Ulrich and Ohki [1966].

10.3 Potassium in Crop Nutrition

10.3.1 Crop requirements and response

For thousands of years naturally occurring soil K was virtually the only K^+ source for plants so that soils low in available K^+ were infertile. Nowadays, inadequate soil K^+ levels are frequently corrected by the use of K fertilizers. In intensive cropping systems in particular, high application rates are employed. In order to maintain the fertility level of a soil, the amount of K^+ taken up by crops (kg K/ha) and that lost by leaching should at least be balanced by K fertilization. It is only in highly developed agricultural systems with top level yields, however, that the amount of K^+ returned to the soil is equal or in excess of that removed by crops. This means that in many cases soil K reserves are being depleted.

The quantities of K^+ removed from the soil by various crops are listed in Table 6.2. The table gives some indication of the rates at which K should be applied, the normal range being from about 40 to 250 kg K/ha/year. The quantity of K^+ removed from a soil depends very much on the yield level and also on the rate of K^+ leaching. The figures in Table 6.2 therefore provide only a rough working basis for fertilizer recommendations, as uptake is highly dependent on the K^+ availability. Where availability is poor, K^+ uptake by the crop from the soil is also low and unsatisfactory yields are obtained. Under such conditions fertilizer recommendations based on an average total K^+ uptake for a particular crop will not meet the needs of the crop nor raise the soil fertility status. The reverse situation occurs when soils are high in available K^+. Here fertilizer applications based on crop uptake can result in a higher K^+ uptake than is needed for maximum yield and hence also in a waste of fertilizer.

The level of available K^+ in the soil which may be considered optimum, cannot be expressed in general terms, since it depends on the crop as well as climate and soil conditions. v. Braunschweig [1978] carrying out numerous field trials in West Germany found that the lactate soluble K^+ level needed to be higher for soils rich in clay. Loué [1979] in evaluating more than 300 field trials carried out in France reported that K^+ application resulted in marked grain yield responses if the content of exchangeable K^+ was <80 ppm. On medium textured soils with levels of >160 ppm exchangeable K^+ only small increases in grain yield were obtained following K^+ fertilizer application.

428

Generally grasses and cereals respond less favourably to K^+ application than dicots, especially potatoes and legumes (VAN DER PAAUW [1958], SCHÖN et al. [1976]). These latter crops thus require higher levels of available soil K^+. For soils rich in non exchangeable K^+, this source may be utilized by crops to some degree (SINGH and BRAR [1977], GEORGE et al. [1979]). In the long term, however, these sources are also depleted and crop yields gradually decline (v. BOGUSLAWSKI and LACH [1971]).

In order to evaluate K^+ requirements of crops it is also important to consider the total length of the growing period. Tomatoes and sugar beet for example take up about the same amount of K^+ as sugar cane, per unit area per year. In the two former crops, however, the growth period is only about 120 days whereas in sugar cane the growth period may extend over the whole year (NELSON [1968]). This indicates that crops with the same total uptake may have a very different K demand (=uptake/unit time). Requirement also varies depending on the stage of growth, the highest uptake rate often being in the vegetative stage. In potatoes for example 50% of the total K^+ is absorbed in the first third of the growth period. In the cereals too, K^+ is particularly needed during vegetative growth, and K^+ application during the reproductive stage hardly affects grain yield (CHAPMAN and KEAY [1971]).

Another important factor in determining K^+ uptake by crops is the type of rooting system and its extent. This is well demonstrated in the competition which occurs between legumes and grasses for K^+ uptake. In the field when these species are growing together, K^+ uptake is considerably higher by grasses, and under low level K^+ conditions this can lead to the disappearacne of legumes from the sward. This competition was studied by LAMBERT and LINCK [1964] using intact root systems of lucerne and oats supplied with K-42. When whole root systems were used 91% of the labelled K^+ was found in oats and only 9% in the lucerne. However, when the K-42 was applied separately to intact root segments of lucerne and oats more labelled K appeared in the lucerne than in oats. These results indicate that root morphology (root length, number of root hairs) and probably also the individual K^+ uptake potential (K^+ absorbing power) of crop species appear to be important factors influencing competition between plant species for K^+.

The response to K^+ uptake by crops depends to a considerable extent on the level of N nutrition. Generally the better the crop is supplied with N the greater the yield increase due to K^+ (GARTNER [1969], HEATHCOTE [1972]. On the other hand applied N is only fully utilized for crop production when K supply is adequate.

In moving from an extensive to an intensive cropping system responses to K fertilizers are frequently not observed in the first years of application (ANDER-

SON [1973]). This is particularly true in more arid regions where little or no K^+ losses occur by leaching. Potassium reserves accumulated in the upper soil layers are often sufficient to supply crop needs in the first few years of intensive cropping. However, as soon as these reserves are exhausted because of the higher K^+ requirements of increased crop yields and continuous cropping, responses due to K^+ fertilization may be expected. The data of Table 10.7 from field experiments in East Africa show such an example where in the first two-year cycle the response to K fertilizer supply was poor or even negative whereas in the second two-year cycle a beneficial effect was observed for most crops (STEPHENS [1969]).

Table 10.7 Yield increases due to potassium fertilizer in the 1st and 2nd cycle of cropping (STEPHENS [1969])

	Yield increase in kg/ha	
	1st cycle	2nd cycle
Maize	– 30	138
Cotton	10	46
Sweet potatoes	1050	1800
Beans	13	12
Millet and Sorghum...	– 84	85

10.3.2 Deficient soils and fixation

Potassium deficiency occurs very commonly on a number of different soil types. It may appear where K^+ has been leached as for example on light sandy acid soils or on highly leached lateritic soils (ANDERSON [1973]). Organic soils and peats are also low in K. Occasionally, too, K is deficient on soils which have been heavily cropped and in soils which fix K^+ into a non replaceable form (ULRICH and OHKI [1966]). For these soil types, studies in continuous cropping without K^+ supplementation are of particular interest. On organic soils and sandy soils which are generally poor in K bearing minerals and hence in non exchangeable K^+, yield levels drop rapidly year by year as exchangeable K^+ is depleted. Finally very poor harvests are obtained. With soils richer in K bearing minerals, yields do not fall so rapidly. Moreover as environmental factors also cause yield fluctuations from year to year the slight yield depressions resulting from K^+ depletion are more difficult to observe. As pointed out on page 411, however, the K bearing minerals do not provide an inexhaustible K source and with time the rate of release of non exchangeable K^+ declines. In soils where K^+ originates mainly from 2 : 1 clay minerals the depletion of K^+ from these minerals enhances potential K^+ fixation. The more the mineral is depleted the higher becomes the fixation capacity. Eventually K^+ release becomes extremely low and drastic yield depressions occur. In order to obtain satisfactory yields from such soils high fertilizer rates are required because of the fixation of K^+ by the expanded clay minerals (see p. 414).

For soils in which vermiculite is the dominant clay mineral enormous amounts of K^+ may be fixed. In such a sandy clay loam soil from Michigan in the USA, DOLL and LUCAS [1973] reported that about 92% of the applied K^+ fertilizer was fixed. Tomato production was increased by applications of up to 1600 kg K/ha. Similar reports have been made in other parts of the USA as well as in the Danube valley in Germany (SCHÄFER and SIEBOLD [1972]).

Typical results of K^+ fertilizer applications to K^+ fixing soils are shown in Table 10.8. It can be seen that the response of maize was more spectacular than that of spring wheat (BURKART [1975]). The data of the table also indicate that in some cases rates as high as 300 kg K_2O/ha gave only slight responses and as much as 900 kg K_2O/ha were needed in order to obtain maximum grain yields.

Table 10.8 Effect of potassium fertilizer application on the grain yield on two K fixing sites (BURKART [1975])

K rate, kg K_2O/ha	Dornwag		Weng	
	Spring wheat 1972 t/ha	Maize 1973 t/ha	Maize 1972 t/ha	Spring wheat 1973 t/ha
0	3.27	2.48	5.34	4.83
300	3.96	3.88	5.63	4.62
600	6.16	5.04	8.66	5.07
900	4.48	5.48	9.37	5.21

10.3.3 Disease

Potassium not only influences crop production by enhancing growth and synthetic processes. It is also highly important in raising the disease resistance of many crop species. In maize for example stalk rot and lodging are usually more severe when soil K is low in relation to other nutrients (HOOKER [1966], KRÜGER [1976]). This beneficial effect of K^+ in preventing lodging is also true for other cereal crops (TROLLDENIER [1969]). In wheat too a lower incidence of powdery mildew caused by the fungus *Erysiphe graminis* has been observed in plots treated with additional potassium (GLYNNE [1959]). Some other crop diseases less frequent in plants well supplied with K^+ include: brown spot in rice caused by *Ophiobolus miyabeanus*, brown rust in barley infected with *Puccinia hordei* and *Fusarium* wilt in bananas resulting from *Fusarium oxysporum* (GOSS [1968]). According to the observations of BAULE [1969] forest trees adequately supplied with K^+ are also more resistant to fungal diseases. The nature of the action of K^+ in controlling the severity of plant diseases is still not understood. It may relate in part to the effect of K^+ in promoting the development of thicker outer walls in epidermal cells thus preventing disease attack (TROLLDENIER and ZEHLER [1976]). In addition as already indicated, plant metabolism is very much influenced by K^+. It is possible therefore that some plant diseases may be favoured by changes in metabolism associated with low plant K contents. The effect of K^+ on disease resistance in crop plants has been well reviewed by Goss [1968].

10.3.4 Fertilizers and application

Potassium is supplied to crops as a straight fertilizer or in the form of compounds. The most widely used and cheapest potash fertilizer is potassium chloride (KCl) which is known commercially as muriate of potash. The fertilizer contains about 50% K (60% K_2O). Besides this high grade form lower grade KCl fertilizer types (41% K and 33% K, or 58% K_2O and 40% K_2O) are also on the market. These forms contain substantial amounts of NaCl and are therefore suited to natrophilic crops (sugar beet, cabbage, oats). When added to the soil, KCl dissolves in soil solution giving K^+ and Cl^- ions. Potassium sulphate (K_2SO_4 sulphate of potash) contains a somewhat lower K content of about 43% K (52% K_2O) and is more expensive due to higher production costs. Potassium nitrate (KNO_3) 37% K (44% K_2O, 13% N), and potassium metaphosphate (KPO_3) 33% K (40% K_2O, 27% P) are both of relatively minor importance. Another K fertilizer is potassium magnesium sulphate (K_2SO_4, $MgSO_4$). This contains 18% K (22% K_2O) and 11% Mg (18% MgO) and is useful where Mg^{2+} is required in addition to K^+. Magnesium kainite ($MgSO_4 + KCl + NaCl$) is a low grade K fertilizer 10% K (12% K_2O), 3.6% Mg (6% MgO) and 18% Na (24% Na_2O). This is used mainly in Germany and the Netherlands for pasture dressing.

With the exceptions of potassium metaphosphate and potassium silicate all potash fertilizers are soluble in water. They are therefore very similar in availability so that differences between these fertilizers result from accompanying anions. In some cases the application of sulphur, magnesium, or sodium may be agronomically beneficial and an appropriate fertilizer should be chosen. Some crops are sensitive to high amounts of chloride. These chlorophobic species include tobacco, grapes, fruit trees, cotton, sugar cane, potatoes, tomatoes, strawberries, cucumber and onions. It is preferential to treat these crops with potassium sulphate. For potatoes, the use of sulphate rather than chloride generally results in higher starch contents (see Table 5.13). The effect of KCl as compared with K_2SO_4 on growth and yield of grapes *(Vitis vinifera)* was well demonstrated by EDELBAUER [1976] in a solution culture experiment. The most interesting data of this investigation are shown in Table 10.9. The depressive effect of chloride also had a negative influence on the sugar content of the juice whereas the acid content in the juice was hardly affected by the varying chloride/sulphate nutrition (EDELBAUER [1977]). HAEDER [1975] found that chloride affects the translocation of photosynthates from the upper plant parts to the tubers. This effect is shown in Table 10.10. In the 'chloride treatment' a relatively high accumulation of labelled photosynthates occurred in the stems whereas in the treatment 'Cl/SO$_4$' (half chloride, half sulphate) the negative effect of chloride on photosynthate translocation was alleviated to some degree.

Table 10.9 Effect of a varying chloride/sulphate nutrition on grape yield (EDELBAUER [1976])

Nutrient solution		Grape yield	Weight of	No. of
KCl, me/l	K_2SO_4, me/l	g/pot	cluster, g	clusters/pot
4.0	–	111	58.9	1.89
2.5	1.5	149	70.5	2.10
1.0	3.0	252	84.2	3.00
–	4.0	254	91.3	2.78

Table 10.10 Effect of chloride and sulphate nutrition on the relative distribution of labelled photosynthates in potato plants, total amount of labelled $C = 100\%$ (HAEDER [1975])

Plant organs	Treatment		
	Cl	Cl/SO$_4$	SO$_4$
Leaves	37	40	34
Stems	38	29	23
Tubers	21	27	39
Roots	4	4	4

Most field crops are not sensitive to chloride and for this reason are generally treated with muriate of potash. Oil palms and coconuts even appear to have a chloride requirement (VON UEXKÜLL [1972]). Potassium nitrate is mainly used for spraying on fruit trees and horticultural crops. Potassium metaphosphate and potassium silicates are used in cases where it is desirable that solubility should be low in order to prevent high concentrations in the root vicinity. Because of the high prices of these low soluble K fertilizers, they are only used occasionally for horticultural crops.

Potassium fertilizers are usually applied broadcast (REITH [1972]) and only in soils with a low level of available K^+ or with a high K fixation capacity is banded application recommended. Using this technique the K^+ fixation capacity of a restricted soil volume can be saturated and within this zone excess K^+ is available for uptake. In experiments with maize WELCH *et al.* [1966] observed that responses to banded K fertilizer were as much as 4 times greater than a broadcast treatment. It is also opportune to apply K fertilizers to K^+ fixing soils just before sowing the crop and also later as a top dressing in order to reduce the time of contact between fertilizer K^+ and the K^+ fixing minerals. The longer the time of contact the more fertilizer K^+ is fixed.

On fine textured soils the vertical movement of K^+ in the soil profile is restricted. This may affect the supply of fertilizer K^+ to the roots of some crop species. For example BUDIG [1970] found that grapes suffered from K^+ deficiency although the upper soil layer was rich in available K^+. However, the deeper soil layers (40 to 60 cm), from which the grape roots mainly drew their nutrients, were depleted of K^+. For such crops deep application of fertilizer K^+ is recommended.

High K^+ losses due to leaching occur only on sandy soils, organic soils and soils with kaolinite as the main clay mineral (see p. 298). These soils should be treated with fertilizer K^+ just before the crop is sown or planted in order to avoid excessive K^+ losses by leaching in rainy periods (winter rainfall, rainy season). For some crops split applications are even recommended under high leaching conditions.

General Reading

BUSSLER, W.: Comparative Examinations of Plants Suffering from Potash Deficiency. Verlag Chemie, Weinheim, 1964

DIEST, A. VAN: Factors affecting the availability of potassium in soils. In: Potassium Research – Review and Trends, p. 75–97, 11th Congr. Int. Potash Inst., Bern (1978)

EVANS, H.J. and SORGER, G.J.: Role of mineral elements with emphasis on the univalent cations. Ann. Rev. Plant Physiol., *17*, 47–77 (1966)

INTERNATIONAL POTASH INSTITUTE: Potassium in Biochemistry an Physiology. 8th Colloquium I.P.I., Berne, 1971

INTERNATIONAL POTASH INSTITUTE: Potassium in Soil. 9th Colloquium I.P.I., Berne, 1972

INTERNATIONAL POTASH INSTITUTE: Fertilizer Use and Plant Health, 12th Colloquium I.P.I., Berne, 1976

INTERNATIONAL POTASH INSTITUTE: Potassium Research – Review and Trends. 11th Congr. Int. Potash Inst., Bern (1978)

KILMER, V.J., YOUNTS, S.E. and BRADY, N.C. (eds.): The Role of Potassium in Agriculture. Amer. Soc. Agron., Madison, USA 1968

LÄUCHLI, A. and PFLÜGER, R.: Potassium transport through plant cell membranes and metabolic role of potassium in plants. In: Potassium Research – Review and Trends, p. 11–163. 11th Congr. Int. Potash Inst., Bern (1978)

MENGEL, K. and KIRKBY, E.A.: Potassium in crop production. Adv. Agron. *33*, 59–110 (1980)

SCHROEDER, D.: Structure and weathering of potassium containing minerals. *In:* Potassium Research – Review and Trends, p. 43–63. 11th Congr. Int. Potash Inst., Bern (1978)

SEKHON, G.S. (ed.): Potassium in Soils and Crops. Potash Research Institute of India, New Delhi, 1978

ULRICH, A. and OHKI, K.: Potassium, In: CHAPMAN, H.D. (ed.). Diagnostic Criteria for Plants and Soils. p. 362–393. Univ. of California, Division of Agricultural Sciences 1966

Chapter 11

Calcium

11.1 Soil Calcium

11.1.1 Calcium bearing minerals and weathering

The mean Ca content of the earth's crust amounts to about 3.64%. It is thus higher than that of most other plant nutrients (see Table 11.1). Calcium in the soil occurs in various primary minerals. These include the Ca bearing Al-Si-silicates such as feldspars and amphiboles, Ca phosphates, and Ca carbonates. The latter are particularly important in calcareous soils and are usually present as calcite ($CaCO_3$) or dolomite ($CaCO_3 \cdot MgCO_3$). The various forms of apatite occurring in soil include most known forms of Ca phosphates (see p. 389). The Ca content of different soil types varies widely depending mainly on parent material and the degree to which weathering and leaching have influenced soil development. Soils derived from limestone or chalk, and young marsh (polder) soils are usually rich in Ca with a high content of $CaCO_3$. The Ca content of such soils is often in the range of 10 to 20%. Even the surface layer of soils developed on limestone, however, can be low in Ca where leaching is excessive. Old soils, highly weathered and leached under humid conditions, are generally low in Ca. Two typical examples of such soils are the podzols of the temperate zone and

Table 11.1 Mean chemical composition of the earth crust to a depth of 16 km

Element	% weight	% volume	Element	% weight	% volume
O	46.46	91.77	H	0.14	0.06
Si..........	27.61	0.80	P..........	0.12	–
Al	8.07	0.76	C..........	0.09	0.01
Fe	5.06	0.68	Mn	0.09	–
Ca..........	3.64	1.48	S	0.06	–
Na..........	2.75	1.60	Cl..........	0.05	0.04
K..........	2.58	2.14	Br	0.04	–
Mg	2.07	0.56	F	0.03	–
Ti	0.62	–	All other elements......	0.52	0.10

the laterites of the humid tropics. In more arid conditions high Ca contents in the upper soil layer may occur in the form of an accumulation of gypsum ($CaSO_4 \cdot 2H_2O$).

Calcium bearing minerals play an important role in pedogenesis. Thus soils derived from Ca containing parent material such as basalt and dolerite generally contain higher amounts of secondary clay minerals. Soils developed from calcite, dolomite and chalk mainly belong to the rendzina group of soils. These shallow soils contain appreciable amounts of $CaCO_3$ and for this reason are alkaline in reaction. A high soil pH and the presence of Ca^{2+} favour the formation of Ca-humate complexes and account for the dark colour of this soil type.

The weathering of the primary Ca bearing minerals depends considerably on the formation of H^+ in the soil. Hydrogen ions and probably also chelating agents attack the Ca of the lattice structure of minerals and thus cause a dissolution of the mineral and a release of Ca^{2+}. These weathering processes along with the release of Ca^{2+} from exchange sites of soil colloids by H^+ account for the considerable amounts of Ca leached under humid climatic conditions. The rate of leaching of Ca^{2+} increases with the annual rainfall and with the content of Ca bearing minerals in the soil. Quantities of Ca leached under temperate conditions are in the range of 200 to 300 kg Ca/ha (see p. 298).

The weathering of carbonates is much dependent on the production of CO_2 in the soil. Calcite ($CaCO_3$) is a rather insoluble mineral, the solubility only being in the order of 10 to 15 mg Ca per litre (about 0.3 mM). In the presence of CO_2, however, $Ca(HCO_3)_2$ is formed which is much more water soluble.

$$CaCO_3 + CO_2 + H_2O \rightarrow Ca(HCO_3)_2$$

In soils containing free $CaCO_3$ the formation of $Ca(HCO_3)_2$ is thus an important means by which the leaching of Ca takes place. However, even in soils not containing $CaCO_3$, some $Ca(HCO_3)_2$ can be leached, as bicarbonate can also be produced from the dissociation of carbonic acid contained in rain water or from carbonic acid produced by the respiration of organic material in the soil. Hydrogen ions produced in the dissociation can release Ca^{2+} by weathering or by the exchange of 2 H^+ for 1 Ca^{2+} from clay colloids. This explanation to some extent accounts for the reason why applications of organic material to soils increases Ca leaching. During organic matter decomposition there is an increase in CO_2 release and hence also in carbonic acid formation in the soil.

In quantitative terms, however, NO_3^- formation appears to play a more important role than HCO_3^- in balancing Ca^{2+} and also Mg^{2+} in the leaching process in many soils (LARSEN and WIDDOWSON [1968]). Under natural conditions

NO_3^- originates largely from soil organic matter by the processes of mineralization and nitrification. Nitrification is an oxidative process:

$$2\,NH_4^+ + 4\,O_2 \rightarrow 2\,NO_3^- + 4\,H^+ + 2\,H_2O$$

Hydrogen ions produced by this means can release Ca^{2+} by exchange from soil colloids in exactly the same way as the release of Ca^{2+} induced by H^+ arising from the dissociation of carbonic acid. The rate of production of H^+ from nitrification, however, is usually considerably greater than that from carbonic acid dissociation. The process of nitrification therefore exerts a major influence on soil acidification and the leaching of Ca. Under conditions where nitrification can occur the application of NH_4-fertilizers has the same effect in increasing soil acidification and Ca leaching. Thus in general for every 100 kg $(NH_4)_2SO_4$ added to the soil about 45 kg Ca are removed in drainage water (RUSSELL [1973]).

Factors which influence the rate of nitrification can thus also affect the levels of NO_3^- and Ca^{2+} in soil solution. Thus WALKER [1946] observed almost equivalent increases in the levels of NO_3^- and the sum of Ca^{2+} and Mg^{2+} in the soil solution, when the soil temperature increased from winter to spring conditions. Similar findings reporting this equivalency in release have been made by LARSEN and WIDDOWSON [1968]. The gradual decrease in pH which occurs in all soils in humid regions is mainly due to the mineralization of organic N and to the formation of carbonic acid as described above. Some soils rich in organic S may also acidify as a result of the formation of H_2SO_4 (see p. 370). The main processes producing soil H^+ are shown in Figure 2.12.

Acidification of soils, however, is not only a question of N mineralization or NH_4^+-N application. Roots, themselves, are capable of excreting H^+ and thus may contribute to soil acidification. This occurs when plants take up NH_4-N or in the case of the legumes, during N_2 fixation. Generally with an increase of plant growth and production acidification also occurs in the soil. This has been shown by an experiment of MUNDEL and KRELL [1978] carried out over a 17 year period on an alluvial meadow soil with a low H^+ buffer power. During this period the pH of the soil fell from 7.0 to 5 or 4 in the soil of the high N treatments. Although N was applied as nitrochalk, a fertilizer which contains $CaCO_3$, and is thus alkaline, the soil pH and base saturation of the soil colloids decreased. This was related to the rate of fertilizer application as can be seen from Figure 11.1. Increasing the rate of N application decreased the pH of the soil. It is assumed that this fall in soil pH was mainly due to an enhanced nitrification of the applied NH_4^+.

In recent years soil acidification has increased on a global scale because of acid precipitation. The burning of fossil fuels leads to the formation of acids such as H_2SO_3, H_2SO_4, HNO_2, and HNO_3 which are returned from the

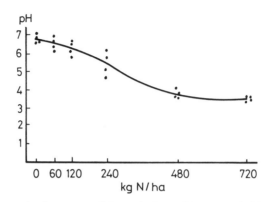

Fig.11.1 pH decrease in the upper soil layer during a 17 years period in relation to the N fertilizer rate (after MUNDEL and KRELL [1978]).

atmoshere to the earth in precipitation. 'Acid rains' with a pH as low as 2.4 have been recorded. On contact with the soil these acid rains rapidly break down soil minerals as well as depress soil pH and must therefore be considered as a serious ecological hazard.

During pedogenesis under humid climate conditions the leaching of Ca as nitrate and bicarbonate and thus soil acidification have contributed considerably to soil degradation. This detrimental process which gradually renders fertile soils more and more infertile is still continuing in many parts of the world. Acid soils not only possess a poor soil structure but are often low in Ca and Mg and contain high amounts of soluble Al and Mn, which are often toxic to crops (see p. 56).

In the history of man it is only relatively recently that this gradual soil degradation has been prevented by the application of alkaline materials to the soil. The application of limestone was mainly introduced in the last century and has maintained and even improved the fertility status of many cultivated soils. It appears that the application of alkaline material to soils is an essential means of maintaining the soil pH at an optimum level. Limestone is the most important material used for this purpose. The question of liming is discussed more thoroughly on page 454.

11.1.2 Calcium adsorption and soil solution

Besides the Ca bearing minerals a substantial amount of Ca^{2+} is adsorbed to organic and inorganic soil colloids. This exchangeable Ca^{2+} is of particular importance for soil structure. As already outlined on page 43 Ca^{2+} promotes the coagulation of soil colloids and thus improves soil structure and the stability of soil particles. For soils in which 2:1 clay minerals dominate, about 80% of the soil exchange capacity should be saturated with Ca^{2+} in order to maintain a satisfactory soil structure. For soils with kaolinite as the most important clay mineral a lower percentage of Ca^{2+} saturation in the order of about 20% is recommended (BROYER and STOUT [1959]). The adsorption sites of the inorganic soil colloids are not very selective for Ca^{2+}. As the electrostatic charge of Ca^{2+} is high due to its divalency and rather thin hydration shell, Ca^{2+} is relatively strongly adsorbed to different kinds of clay minerals in the soil. The adsorption bond of Ca^{2+} to organic colloids and especially to the humic acids is more specific. Thus in chernozems and calcareous peat soils, both of which soil types contain $CaCO_3$, the humic acids are mainly present in the form of Ca humate. Calcium adsorbed to soil colloids tends to equilibrate with the Ca^{2+} of the soil solution. According to the investigations of NEMETH et al. [1970] on a number of soil types, there is a fairly linear relationship between the exchangeable Ca^{2+} and the Ca^{2+} of the soil solution under equilibrium conditions (see Figure 11.2).

Most inorganic soils contain high enough levels of Ca^{2+} in soil solution and their exchange sites are well enough saturated with Ca^{2+}, to adequately meet

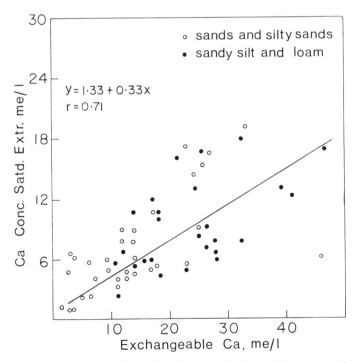

Fig. 11.2 Correlation between exchangeable Ca and soil solution Ca concentration for 72 different soils (after NEMETH et al. [1970]).

crop demands. It thus appears that liming is primarily a means of improving soil structure and pH. On acid peat soils, however, as are frequently used in horticulture, the natural Ca content can be so low that plants suffer from Ca deficiency. Here the application of Ca containing fertilizers is advisable.

11.1.3 Ecological aspects

Soils differ very widely in their pH and Ca contents. This is particularly the case in uncultivated soils. During evolution plant species have adapted to these varying pH and Ca conditions. For this reason remarkable differences in toleration occur between plant species and even varieties of a single species. In this respect plant species may be divided into *calcicoles* and *calcifuges*. The calcicoles are typical of the flora observed on calcareous soils whereas the calcifuge species grow on acidic soils poor in Ca. Fairly clear differences occur in Ca metabolism of these two groups. Many of the calcicole species contain high levels of intracellular Ca and high concentrations of malate, whereas the calcifuges are normally low in soluble Ca. Species and even cultivars may differ considerably in their capability to precipitate Ca^{2+}. It is supposed that this precipitation is mainly Ca oxalate. Other Ca containing crystals, the true nature of which have yet to be established, may also be formed (BANGERTH [1979]).

CLARKSON [1965] compared a calcicole and calcifuge species of *Agrostis* in their response to Ca^{2+}. Both species were grown at pH 4.5 in nutrient solution with increasing concentrations of Ca^{2+}. However, *Agrostis setacea* which is generally found on acid soils low in Ca, was little affected in growth by the additional Ca supply, whereas *Agrostis stolonifera* which is found on calcareous sites responded considerably to the higher Ca treatments. The same pattern was observed in Ca uptake as shown in Figure 11.3.

The level of Ca in the soil, however, is not the only factor of importance in the calcicole – calcifuge question, for calcareous and acid soils differ in other respects. Calcareous soils are higher in pH and carbonate content. They are richer in nutrients, the level of soluble heavy metals is usually lower and in addition the activity of the nitrifying and nitrogen fixing bacteria is higher. Thus as well as the effects of Ca levels *per se* all these other factors have a bearing on the ecology of plants growing on these soils. An example showing the significance of increased heavy metal solubility under acid conditions is shown from the work of RORISON [1960]. It was observed that the inability of the calcicole *Scabiosa columbaria* to grow under acid conditions originated largely from its intolerance of Al^{3+}. Plants grew poorly in soil at pH 4.8 but in nutrient solutions there was little difference in growth between pH 4.8 and 7.6. When Ca levels were increased without inducing a pH change, by addition of $CaSO_4$, no improvement in plant

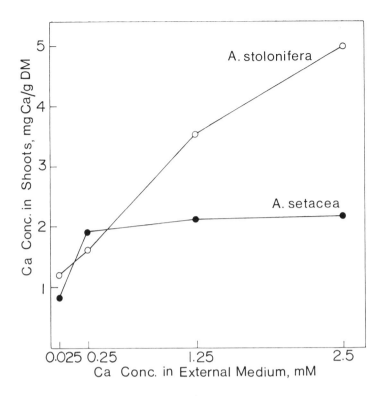

Fig.11.3 Ca concentration in the shoots of Agrostis species as a function of Ca in the external medium (after CLARKSON [1965]).

growth was observed. Addition of Al^{3+} to the low pH solution culture treatment, however, depressed growth in a similar way to the plants growing in soil at the same pH.

Another important aspect in the calcicole-calcifuge problem is the ability of different ecotypes to utilize Fe. HUTCHINSON [1967] tested 135 different plant species in their susceptibility to lime-induced chlorosis by high $CaCO_3$ levels in the soil. It was observed that plant species originating from acid soils were more susceptible than those from calcareous sites. Lime-induced chlorosis is a physiological disorder which is characterized by a light green to yellow colour of the youngest leaves and which results from a lack of 'active Fe' (see p. 484). HUTCHINSON [1967] too observed that the susceptibility of the ecotypes from acid soils to lime-induced chlorosis was not due to the lack of uptake of Fe by roots but rather in the inability of the roots to metabolize Fe. Lime-induced chlorosis can often be a severe problem in growing crops on calcareous soils (see p. 484). Ecological aspects of plant nutrition have been very well reviewed by

443

EPSTEIN [1972]. A useful volume dealing with ecological aspects of mineral nutrition has also been edited by RORISON [1969].

11.2 Calcium in Physiology

11.2.1 Uptake and translocation

Higher plants often contain Ca in appreciable amounts and generally in the order of about 5–30 mg Ca/g dm. These high Ca contents, however, mainly result from the high Ca levels in the soil solution rather than from the efficiency of the Ca uptake mechanism of root cells. Generally the Ca^{2+} concentration of the soil solution is about 10 times higher than that of K^+. The uptake rate of Ca^{2+}, however, is usually lower than that of K^+. This low Ca^{2+} uptake potential occurs because Ca^{2+} can be absorbed only by young root tips in which the cell walls of the endodermis are still unsuberized (CLARKSON and SANDERSON [1978]). The uptake of Ca^{2+} can also be competitively depressed by the presence of other cations such as K^+ and NH_4^+ which are rapidly taken up by roots (see p. 463).

The Ca content of plants is to a large extent genetically controlled and is little affected by the Ca supply in the root medium, provided that the Ca availability is adequate for normal plant growth. This has been very well demonstrated by LONERAGAN and SNOWBALL [1969], who compared the Ca contents of 18 different species grown in nutrient solution, with those grown in the field. As can be seen from Figure 11.4, there was little difference in the Ca content of a particular species whether the plants had been grown in soil or in solution culture.

The figure also shows the lower Ca contents found in monocotyledons than in dicotyledons. The uptake by both plant groups was investigated by the same workers using flowing nutrient solution in which very low but constant supplies of Ca^{2+} could be maintained. The results are shown in Table 11.2. Maximum growth rates of ryegrass were obtained at a much lower Ca concentration than for tomato (2,5 µM Ca^{2+} against 100 µM Ca^{2+}). The corresponding Ca contents were also much lower in the ryegrass (0.7% against 1.29%) thus indicating a higher demand by the tomato plant. Legumes and herbs were also shown to have a higher demand than the grasses. It is now generally held that the reason for this higher demand of dicotyledons for Ca^{2+} is causally connected with the higher cation exchange capacity of the roots as well as in other plant parts of dicotyledons. In plant tissues the CEC is largely made up of the free carboxylic groups of pectins (polygalacturonic acids) of the cell

444

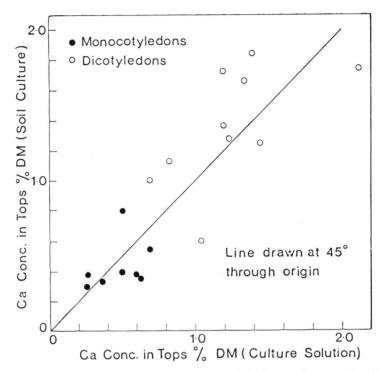

Fig. 11.4 Relation between the Ca content in the tops of 18 plant species grown in soil to the Ca content in the tops of the same plant species grown in culture solution (after LONERAGAN and SNOWBALL [1969]).

Table 11.2 The effect of calcium concentration in nutrient solution (μM) on relative growth rates of plants and calcium content in the shoots. (LONERAGAN *et al.* [1968] and LONERAGAN and SNOWBALL [1969])

Species	Ca supply in μM				
	0.8	2.5	10	100	1000
	Relative growth rate				
Ryegrass *(Lolium perenne)*	42	100	94	94	93
Tomato *(Lycopersicon esculentum)*	3	19	52	100	80
	mg/g DM				
Ryegrass *(Lolium perenne)*	0.6	0.7	1.5	3.7	10.8
Tomato *(Lycopersicon esculentum)*	2.1	1.3	3.0	12.9	24.0

wall system. In both uptake and transport it is now believed that extensive Ca movement is associated with the exchange sites (ISERMANN [1970], VAN DE GEIJN and PETIT [1979]). DREW and BIDDULPH [1971] also observed that after the uptake of the radioisotope Ca-45 by bean roots most of the label was in an exchangeable form independent of metabolism. Their findings are consistent with the report of RUSSELL and CLARKSON [1976] that Ca^{2+} is largely restricted from the protoplasm, with cytoplasmic activities being in the order of $10^{-3}-10^{-5}$ M (see CLARKSON and HANSON [1980]).

The uptake of Ca^{2+} by plant roots has been extensively studied by CLARKSON and co-workers in experiments investigating the ability of absorption and translocation of different parts of the root. The technique used has been to expose a small section of root from the intact plant to a radioactive tracer whilst supplying the rest of the plant root with the same bathing solution. Such experiments using Ca-45 have revealed that in contrast to potassium and phosphate, the transport of Ca (and Mg) is restricted to an area just behind the root tips. This difference in behaviour between nutrients has been explained in terms of root structure and particularly the development of the casparian strip (see Figure 4.5 p. 196). As roots age the endodermis becomes suberized although continuity of the symplast is maintained through the endodermal walls by plasmodesmata. CLARKSON argues that as the radial movement of Ca is prevented by the suberized endodermis, Ca^{2+} is not transported effectively by the symplast. The movement of Ca from the cortex to the stele is therefore restricted to the apoplastic or free space pathway which is only accessible in non suberized young roots. By constrast K^+ and phosphate transport occurs along the whole length of the root as movement takes place via the symplastic pathway. The main results of this work are discussed by RUSSELL and CLARKSON [1976].

From the above findings Ca uptake appears mainly to be a passive process. The same holds for the translocation of Ca^{2+} within the plant. Calcium in the xylem sap is translocated in an upward direction with the transpiration stream. Thus to a large extent the intensity of transpiration controls the upward translocation rate of Ca_2^+. This has been demonstrated in experiments of MICHAEL and MARSCHNER [1962] in which both oat plants and white mustard plants were exposed to different air humidities. When the air humidity was high (low transpiration conditions) there was a decrease in translocation of Ca^{2+} to the upper plant parts and also a depression in the rate of Ca^{2+} uptake. Similar observations have been reported by LAZAROFF and PITMAN [1966].

The movement of Ca^{2+} in the xylem vessels, however, can not be explained simply in terms of mass flow as Ca ions are absorbed by adjacent cells and also adsorbed to indiffusible anions in the xylem walls. According to BIDDULPH et al. [1961] the xylem cylinder of bean stems operates as an exchange column for Ca^{2+} and according to their investigations 'En masse flow in the vessels was inadequate for explaining the rapid deep-seated exchanges observed for this tracer' (Ca-45). This conclusion is supported by results of ISERMANN [1970], and

VAN DE GEIJN and PETIT [1979] who found that the adsorbed Ca^{2+} in the xylem tissue can be exchanged by other cation species and that such an exchange favours the upward translocation of Ca^{2+}.

The importance of exchange reactions in Ca^{2+} movement is particularly clear from studies on individual plant organs where the correlation between intensity of transpiration and uptake of Ca^{2+} is often much less close than for the plant as a whole. In leaves for example the influx of Ca sharply declines after leaf maturity even though a constant transpiration rate is maintained (KOONTZ and FOOTE [1966]). The same holds true for the influx of Ca^{2+} into fruit. In growing plants there is evidence that Ca^{2+} is translocated preferentially towards the shoot apex even though the transpiration rate here is much lower than in the older leaves. It now seems likely that this preferential movement is induced by the auxin indole acetic acid (IAA), which is synthesized in the shoot apex. It is believed that during growth an IAA stimulated proton efflux pump in the elongation zones of the shoot apex increases the formation of new cation exchange sites so that the growing tip becomes a centre for Ca accumulation. This relationship has been investigated by MARSCHNER and OSSENBERG-NEUHAUS [1977] using the IAA transport inhibitor 2, 3, 5 tri iodobenzoic acid (TIBA). Their results indicate a causal connection between TIBA-induced inhibition of IAA transport and the inhibitory effect of TIBA on Ca translocation into the shoot apex. BANGERTH [1979] suggests that the basipetal IAA transport forces Ca^{2+} to be translocated acropetally.

The rate of downward translocation of Ca^{2+} is very low due to the fact that Ca^{2+} is transported in only very small concentrations in the phloem (WIERSUM [1979]). RIOS and PEARSON [1964] observed that the downward transport of Ca in cotton plants was inadequate to support root growth in the Ca deficient nutrient solution portion of a split root medium. Once Ca is deposited in older leaves it cannot be mobilized to the growing tips. This has been convincingly shown by LONERAGAN and SNOWBALL [1969] using autoradiographs. Plants were not able to utilize Ca^{2+} from older leaves for the growth of meristematic tissues, even when Ca deficiency symptoms were observed in the growing tips. Another example demonstrating poor Ca transport in the phloem has been presented by MARSCHNER and RICHTER [1974]. These workers supplied root segments of intact young maize seedlings with labelled Ca^{2+}. It was found that this Ca was translocated exclusively to the upper plant organs and not to the root tips. Some data of this experiment are shown in Figure 11.5.

The reason why Ca^{2+} is present in the phloem sap in only very minute concentrations is not really known. VAN GOOR and WIERSMA [1973] claim that Ca^{2+} is precipitated as calcium phosphate in the phloem sap and cannot therefore be translocated. If this were the case, however, it might be expected that phosphate translocation should also be impaired. This has not been observed, nor has the accumulation of Ca phosphate in phloem tissue. MARSCHNER [1974] supposes that the extremely low levels of Ca^{2+} in the phloem sap result from an accumulation of Ca in the cells surrounding the phloem. He also suggests the possibility of Ca specific efflux pumps, located in the membranes of the sieve elements which could be responsible for removing Ca. EPSTEIN [1973] has proposed that the exclusion of Ca^{2+} from sieve tubes is part of a developmental process whereby sieve tube attain a relatively structureless condition and that this allows them to act in the conduction of a flowing solution.

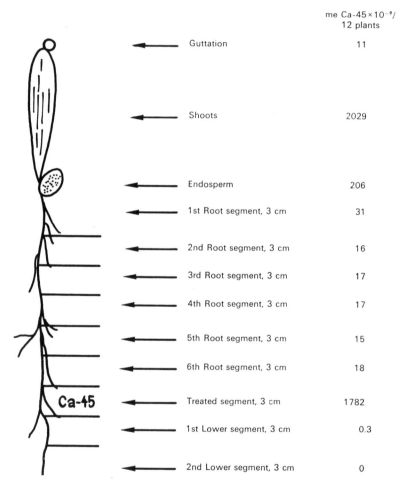

	me Ca-45×10⁻⁹/ 12 plants
Guttation	11
Shoots	2029
Endosperm	206
1st Root segment, 3 cm	31
2nd Root segment, 3 cm	16
3rd Root segment, 3 cm	17
4th Root segment, 3 cm	17
5th Root segment, 3 cm	15
6th Root segment, 3 cm	18
Treated segment, 3 cm	1782
1st Lower segment, 3 cm	0.3
2nd Lower segment, 3 cm	0

Fig.11.5 Distribution of Ca-45 in a maize seedling following application to a specific section of the root (after MARSCHNER and RICHTER [1974]).

As a result of the low Ca concentration in the phloem, all plant organs which are largely provided with nutrients by the phloem sap are rather low in Ca. On the other hand the K contents of these organs are relatively high, because K^+ is present in the phloem sap in abundant quantities. This relationship is particularly evident when the Ca and K contents of leaves are compared with those of fruits and storage tissues. The poor supply of Ca^{2+} to fruits and storage organs can result in Ca deficiency in these tissues (see p. 452).

11.2.2 Biochemical functions

The necessity of Ca^{2+} for plant growth can easily be demonstrated by interrupting Ca^{2+} supply to the roots. Their growth rate is immediately reduced and after some days the root tips become brown and gradually die. Calcium is required for cell elongation and cell division (BURSTRÖM [1968]), but the detailed reactions in which Ca^{2+} is involved in these processes are not yet known.

There is much evidence that Ca^{2+} is of fundamental importance for membrane permeability and the maintainance of cell integrity. The importance of this role of Ca in ion uptake has already been discussed (see p. 130). Micro electron probe studies of ROLAND and BESSOLES [1968] have revealed that Ca is located especially in the border zone between the cytoplasm and cell walls indicating high Ca contents in the plasmalemma. Calcium can be removed from membranes by treatment with EDTA. This treatment increases membrane permeability to such an extent that inorganic and organic compounds can diffuse out of the cell and considerable damage may result (VAN STEVENINCK [1965]). Impairment of membrane permeability by Ca deficiency, like the effect of EDTA, influences the retention of diffusible cellular compounds (DICKINSON [1967]). Membranes become leaky and as the deficiency progresses there is a general disintegration of membrane structure (MARINOS [1962]). In whole plants, the disorder occurs first in meristematic tissues such as root tips, growing points of the upper plant parts and storage organs. Brown melanin compounds resulting from polyphenol oxidation are associated with the deficient tissues. DEKOCK et al. [1975] claim that in tissues containing adequate amounts of Ca, this oxidation is inhibited by the chelation of the phenolic compounds by Ca.

The role of Ca^{2+} in membrane stability is not only of importance in ion uptake (see p. 130) but also in other metabolic processes. Typical features of senescence for example, are similar to these of Ca deficiency and can be retarded by Ca^{2+}. The features include a breakdown in the compartmentation of the cell and an increase in respiration following the leakage of endogenous respiratory substrates from the vacuole to the respiratory enzymes in the cytoplasm (BANGERTH et al. [1972]). POOVAIAH and LEOPOLD [1973] have demonstrated that senescence in maize leaves can be deferred by the addition of either Ca^{2+} or cytokinin and that the effects of these substances is additive. This role of Ca^{2+} in retarding senescence has also been clearly indicated in the more recent findings of POOVAIAH [1979]. Abscission of leaf blades of kidney bean caused by senescence of the pulvinar tissue was dramatically delayed by high Ca concentrations in the nutrient medium. Another aspect of the importance of Ca^{2+} in membrane stability has been discussed by MARSCHNER [1978]. He suggests that the low Ca content of storage organs induces a high membrane permeability and allows solute diffusion in these tissues. This is obviously of importance in fruits and storage organs which accumulate large amounts of sugars from the phloem.

Germination and the growth of pollen responds sensitively to inadequate Ca^{2+} supply (BREWBAKER and KWACK [1963], MASCARENHAS and MACHLIS [1964]). Calcium is also believed to be essential for the structure of the cell nucleus matrix (WUNDERLICH [1978]). Calcium may also activate enzymes and particularly those which are membrane bound (RENSING and CORNELIUS [1980]). A list of Ca activated enzymes has been published by WYN JONES and LUNT [1967].

Research within the last decade first in animal tissues and then more recently in plants has revealed the presence of Ca binding proteins and in particular calmodulin (Ca M). This protein interacts reversibly with Ca^{2+} to form a protein Ca^{2+} complex the activity of which is regulated by the cellular flux of Ca^{2+}. Calcium binding proteins act as potential receptors of Ca^{2+} mediating the effect of Ca^{2+} in cellular reactions. Calmodulin has been shown to play a central role in cellular regulation in animals and the same seems likely to be the case for plants. The subject which is currently receiving considerable attention has been reviewed recently by CHEUNG [1980].

11.2.3 Calcium forms and contents

Calcium occurs in plant tissues as free Ca^{2+}, as Ca^{2+} adsorbed to indiffusible ions such as carboxylic, phosphorylic and phenolic hydroxyl groups. It is also present in Ca oxalates, carbonates and phosphates. These compounds often occur as deposits in cell vacuoles. In seeds, Ca is present predominantly as the salt of the inositol hexaphosphoric acid (phytic acid). As already indicated Ca in the cell wall is associated with the free carboxylic groups of the pectins and saturates most of these sites.

The interrelationship between 'free' and 'bound' Ca is of importance in fruit ripening. This process may be considered as a special case of senescence and is associated with an increase in ethylene production. Ethylene synthesis is regulated by an enzyme system in the cell wall membrane complex (*i.e.* outside the cytoplasm). This production together with an increase in membrane permeability as a result of a fall in physiologically active Ca^{2+} may be considered as essential steps in fruit ripening. In addition fruit ripening requires the removal of Ca from the middle lamella. This is correlated with an increase in the activity of polygalacturonase, the enzyme responsible for dissolving the pectates of the middle lamella and softening the tissue. The involvement of Ca in ripening is shown in Table 11.3 which compares the Ca contents of two cultivars of tomato, a normal cultivar (Rutgers) and a non ripening mutant cultivar (rin) at three stages after anthesis. The table shows in the Normal Rutgers cultivar that during ripening the total Ca remained fairly constant but there was a marked shift from the bound to soluble fraction. In the case of the non ripening mutant rin the total Ca content increased dramatically as did the bound fraction. This finding is in accordance with the observations of LOUGHEED *et al.* [1979] that fruit ripening is depressed by Ca treatment and stimulated by Ca deficiency (FAUST and SHEAR [1969]). One may speculate that the low Ca concentration in phloem sap maintains the Ca^{2+} at a low level in fruits and storage organs so that maturation can take place.

Table 11.3 Calcium content in non ripening rin and Normal Rutgers pericarp tissue at different stages of fruit development (POOVAIAH [1979])

Days after anthesis	Soluble Ca, μg Ca in g DM		Bound Ca, μg Ca in g DM	
	rin	Rutgers	rin	Rutgers
40	299	349	530	562
50	412	602	667	246
60	492	622	1357	291

In plants which are poorly supplied with Ca a high proportion of the plant Ca ($>50\%$) may occur in the cell wall fraction or as oxalate (MOSTAFA and ULRICH [1976], ARMSTRONG and KIRKBY [1979]). Under such conditions essential functions of Ca^{2+} may be impaired such as in membrane stabilization. In a study of genotypes of tobacco BRUMAGAN and HIATT [1967] were thus able to show that differences in response to Ca deficiency were at least in part related to differences in oxalate formation.

11.2.4 Calcium deficiency and disorders

As already outlined above Ca deficiency is characterized by a reduction in growth of meristematic tissues. The deficiency can be first observed in the growing tips and youngest leaves. These become deformed and chlorotic and at a more advanced stage necrosis occurs at the leaf margins. The affected tissues become soft due to a dissolution of the cell walls. Brown substances occur which accumulate in intracellular spaces and also in the vascular tissue where they can affect the transport mechanism (BUSSLER [1963]).

Absolute Ca deficiency as described above occurs relatively seldom as most mineral soils are rich in available Ca. Indirect Ca deficiency resulting from an undersupply of Ca to fruit and storage tissues, however, is an often observed disorder. SHEAR [1975] cites a list of 35 such Ca related disorders in fruits and vegetables. In apple the disease is called bitter pit as the whole of the surface of the apple is pitted with small brown necrotic spots (Plate 11.1). In tomato the disease is known as blossom-end rot and is characterized by a cellular breakdown at the distal end of the fruit (Plate 11.1). A similar Ca deficiency disorder occurs in water melon. Ca deficiencies in vegetables, such as blackheart of celery, internal browning of *Brassica oleracea* (Brussels sprouts) blossom end rot of pepper and cavity spot of carrots have been recently described by MAYNARD [1979] in a useful review paper. All these tissues are mainly supplied with Ca^{2+} by the transpiration stream which translocates Ca^{2+} directly from the soil solution. If the xylem sap is low in Ca^{2+} or the rate of transpiration of the fruits is poor, as occurs under humid conditions, inadequate levels of Ca^{2+} may be supplied to the fruits and deficiency symptoms may result. Calcium translocation in the xylem sap may be depressed by NH_4-nutrition, soil water stress and high salt concentrations in the soil. These factors have therefore been found to favour the occurrence of blossom-end rot in tomatoes.

Calcium appears only to be transported from the soil solution to the upper plant parts *via* root tips (RUSSELL and CLARKSON [1976]). Any factor which prevents the growth of new roots (poor aeration, low temperatures etc.) may therefore be expected to prevent Ca uptake and thus induce deficiency. This may account for the observation that Ca related disorders often occur on soils adequately supplied with Ca, and that the weather appears to be a controlling factor (SCAIFE and CLARKSON [1978], BANGERTH [1979], KIRKBY [1979]).

The importance of maintaining an adequate level of Ca^{2+} in the xylem sap is very clear from the results of CHIU and BOULD [1976]. These workers observed that Ca stress during the fruiting stage of tomatoes caused serious blossom-end rot of fruits thus showing that Ca absorbed by the plants before fruiting was not subsequently available for fruit development. The results provide further evidence of the immobility of Ca in the phloem. In addition they also indicate that leaf analysis for Ca is not a reliable index for predicting Ca deficiency in fruits. The occurrence of the physiological disorders described above depends very much on the Ca levels in the fruits. In apples for example a close negative correlation has been found between the occurrence of bitter pit and Ca content (SHARPLES [1968]).

Plate 11.1 Upper part, bitter pit in apples, by courtesy of *U.S. Dep. of Agric.* Beltsville. (Photo: SHEAR)
Lower part, severe blossom end rot in tomato by courtesy of the *Macaulay Institute for Soil Research*, Aberdeen, Scotland.
(Photo: DEKOCK)

453

Fruits and storage tissues growing in the soil, such as peanuts, potatoes and celery bulbs are not supplied by the transpiration stream and for this reason Ca^{2+} must be absorbed directly from the soil medium. According to investigations of SKELTON and SHEAR [1971] growth and yield of fruits of peanuts *(Arachis hypogaea)* depend considerably on the Ca availability of the soil. Inadequate Ca supply to celery causes black heart. The role of Ca^{2+} in plant physiology and its importance for crop production have been reviewed by FOY [1974], by MARSCHNER [1974] and by BANGERTH [1979]. The importance of Ca in soil-plant relationships in tropical and subtropical conditions is considered by MALAVOLTA *et al.* [1979].

11.2.5 Strontium

Calcium and Sr are closely related chemically and in plants they show similar chemical behaviour. The uptake and distribution of both elements in plants are thus alike, but not identical (HUTCHIN and VAUGHAN [1968]). For example, in experiments with *Pisum sativum* MYTTENAERE [1964] found that Sr is deposited to a greater extent than Ca in cell walls. What is of major interest is that Sr^{2+} cannot substitute for Ca^{2+} in physiological processes. High Sr contents in plant tissues are toxic. Toxicity symptoms appear first in older leaves, which become brown and necrotic. The uptake of Sr^{2+} is restricted by Ca^{2+}. Liming can thus reduce the uptake of Sr (REISSIG [1962]). On the other hand plants low in Ca absorb Sr^{2+} at a higher rate (BALCAR *et al.* [1969]).

11.3 Liming and Calcium in Crop Nutrition

11.3.1 The pH effect and the calcium effect

The application of liming materials such as $CaCO_3$, CaO or $Ca(OH)_2$ to the soil has two effects. It supplies Ca^{2+} and it induces an increase in soil pH due to the alkaline reaction of these compounds. As already outlined on page 439 acidification of soils and Ca^{2+} loss by leaching run parallel under humid climate conditions. Thus the alkaline reaction of the liming material is needed for neutralizing soil H^+. In addition Ca^{2+} improves soil structure. In principle the pH increase brought about by liming material could also be induced by other compounds of alkaline nature, such as K_2CO_3 or Na_2CO_3. These compounds, however, are of no importance for the pH improvement of acid soils under practical conditions. The effects of soil pH on crop yields may differ considerably for various crops (see Table 2.10 p. 60). In a 50 years old field experiment carried out on a sandy soil in Germany, KÖHN [1976] found the following order of sensitivity to yield production in the 'no liming' treatment: fodder beets >barley >oats >wheat >potatoes. Rye in contrast gave the highest yields in the non limed plots.

On soils in which a pH increase is not desirable, but where Ca^{2+} is needed for amending soil structure, neutral Ca salts should be applied. Such soils are mainly salt affected soils, characterized by neutral to alkaline pH values and by an excess of Na^+. This is mainly adsorbed to soil colloids (see Table 2.4, p. 44). The application of neutral Ca salts results in a replacement of the adsorbed Na^+ by Ca^{2+}, thus increasing the Ca^{2+} saturation of soil colloids and inducing flocculation. The most important neutral Ca salt used for salt affected soils is gypsum ($CaSO_4 \cdot 2H_2O$). The quantities applied depend on the degree of salinization. Generally amounts of 15 to 40 t gypsum/ha are applied (RAIKOV [1971]). The effect of two treatments on a saline soil are shown in Figure 11.6 (RAIKOV [1971]). In one treatment gypsum was applied and in the other the saline soil was covered with a non saline soil layer. Crop yields obtained over a period of several years were compared with a control treatment, the relative yields of which are represented by '100' (line parallel to the x-axis in Figure 11.6). The treatment with gypsum resulted in considerable yield increases, in excess of those resulting from the more expensive 'soil covering treatment'. The gypsum treatment also improved soil structure, and the soil of the treated plots became darker in comparison with the control treatment. In addition the soil was easier to cultivate

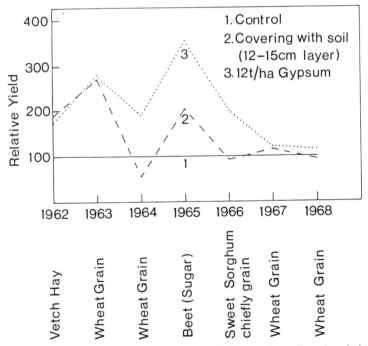

Fig. 11.6 Effect of various amelioration measures applied to a saline soil on the relative yields of various crops (after RAIKOV [1971]).

455

and did not compact crack or retain surface water. The application of gypsum is not referred to as liming but as the Ca^{2+} effect is similar to that of lime both treatments of liming and gypsum application are closely related.

11.3.2 Liming materials

Table 11.4 shows the most important liming materials. The carbonates are simply ground limestone or chalk. Burning Ca carbonate at 1100° results in thermal dissociation:

$$CaCO_3 \rightarrow CaO + CO_2$$

Table 11.4 Liming materials

Liming Material	Formula	Neutralizing value in CaO
Chalk or limestone........................	$CaCO_3$	50% CaO
Slaked lime	Ca (OH)$_2$	70% CaO
Burnt lime	CaO	85% CaO

'Burnt lime' is produced in this way. The Ca oxide formed (CaO) readily reacts with water thus forming Ca hydroxide (hydrated lime or slaked lime).

$$CaO + H_2O \rightarrow Ca(OH)_2$$

On contact with CO_2 this forms $CaCO_3$.

$$Ca(OH)_2 + CO_2 \rightarrow CaCO_3 + H_2O$$

Thus when hydrated lime is exposed to the atmosphere for a long period of time it is gradually converted to Ca carbonate by atmospheric CO_2.

Frequently liming materials also contain substantial amounts of Mg as well as Ca. Burnt magnesium lime for example consists mainly of CaO and MgO, and contains more than 5.5% Mg. Ground magnesium limestone is a mixture of $CaCO_3$ and $MgCO_3$ with an Mg content of 3% Mg and more. These Mg containing materials are particularly used for liming Mg deficient acid soils.

The value of liming material depends on their 'neutralizing value', which is expressed in terms of equivalents of CaO. 100 kg of $CaCO_3$ have the same neutralizing effect as 56 kg CaO. Thus the neutralizing value of 100 kg $CaCO_3$ is 56, whereas 100 kg Ca(OH)$_2$ has a neutralizing value of 76. As the neutralizing value is related to the quantity of carbonate or oxide present in the liming material $MgCO_3$ or MgO also contribute to the neutralizing efficiency. Generally all oxides, carbonates, and even silicates are alkaline in reaction. For this reason Ca silicates present in basic slags and sinter phosphates (see p. 405) have a neutralizing effect and are thus of some importance in controlling soil pH. In long-term field experiments SCHMITT and BRAUER [1969] found, that in plots supplied regularly with basic slag, the pH was only slightly depressed, whereas in plots treated with equivalent amounts of other P fertilizers the soil pH fell from 6.5 to 5.4 over a ten year period. Similar results have been obtained by ROSCOE [1960]. Some waste products are also used as liming materials. These are mainly carbonates. The waste product of sugar factories has a neutralizing value of about 20.

11.2.3 Lime application and reaction in the soil

As already mentioned above CaO reacts readily with H_2O, to form Ca hydroxide which directly neutralizes the free H^+ of the soil solution.

$$CaO \quad + H_2O \rightarrow Ca(OH)_2$$
$$\underline{Ca(OH)_2 + 2\ H^+ \rightarrow Ca^{2+} + 2\ H_2O}$$
$$Net:\ CaO \quad\ + 2\ H^+ \rightarrow Ca^{2+} + H_2O$$

Because of the high solubilities of CaO and $Ca(OH)_2$ both these compounds are quick acting in comparison with $CaCO_3$. Thus when a rapid change in soil pH is required or where soil reactions are slow, as in cold and wet soils, the application of CaO or slaked lime $(Ca[OH]_2)$ is recommended. $CaCO_3$ reacts more slowly. Under strong acid conditions it dissolves relatively quickly by neutralizing soil H^+.

$$CaCO_3 + 2\ H^+ \rightarrow Ca^{2+} + H_2O + CO_2$$

Under weak acid or even neutral conditions the presence of CO_2 favours the dissolution of $CaCO_3$ by forming Ca bicarbonate which in turn neutralizes soil H^+:

$$CaCO_3 \quad\ + CO_2 + H_2O \rightarrow Ca(HCO_3)_2$$
$$\underline{Ca(HCO_3)_2 + 2\ H^+ \quad\quad \rightarrow Ca^{2+} + 2\ CO_2 + 2\ H_2O}$$
$$Net:\ CaCO_3 \quad\ + 2\ H^+ \quad\quad \rightarrow Ca^{2+} + CO_2 + H_2O$$

Ca silicates present in basic slags and sinter phosphates are even slower in their neutralizing reaction than $CaCO_3$.

$$CaSiO_3 + 2\ H^+ \rightarrow Ca^{2+} + SiO_2 + H_2O$$

The rate of dissolution of liming materials also depends on particle size. Finely ground material reacts more rapidly than coarse material due to its larger surface area (BARROWS et al. [1968]).

Generally the application rates of liming materials are in the order of about 3 to 4 t CaO or 4 to 6 t $CaCO_3$/ha supplied over a 3 to 5 year cycle. The quantities required not only depend on soil pH (actual acidity), but also on the content of H^+ adsorbed to soil colloids (potential acidity). This relationship between the amount of limestone required in order to obtain given pH levels in different soils is shown in Figure 11.7 (PEECH [1961]). It is evident that in order to correct the pH of heavy acid soils (high cation exchange capacity = CEC) particularly large amounts of limestone must be applied.

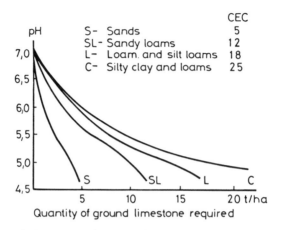

Fig 11.7   Relatonship between the quantity of lime stone required and the pH increase for various soil classes. (modified after PEECH [1961]).

Lime can be applied at any time in the year provided that soil moisture allows the soil to be worked. Lime should not be applied with NH_4^+ containing fertilizers, as the pH shift converts NH_4^+ to NH_3 which is partially lost by volatilization.

$$NH_4^+ + OH^- \underset{\longrightarrow}{\overset{\longleftarrow}{}} H_2O + NH_3$$

Soil classes and types differ in the optimum pH level at which they should be cultivated (see p.57). Generally as the clay content of a soil increases, the optimum pH also rises. According to SCHACHTSCHABEL [1967] soils rich in 2:1 clay minerals should be limed to a level, where some $CaCO_3$ is still present in the soil in order to maintain a good soil structure.

Raising the pH of acid soils is also a means of providing more suitable conditions for soil bacteria. This may influence various processes such as microbial N_2 fixation, denitrification of NO_3^- and mineralization of organic soil N. KUNTZE and BARTELS [1975] reported that too low a soil pH resulted in N deficiency of the herbage as a consequence of inhibited N mineralization of the organic matter in peat soils. A pH shift away from acid conditions is therefore frequently accompanied by an enhanced rate in the decomposition of soil organic matter by microorganisms. On sandy soils, organic matter plays an essential role in water retention. For this reason the pH of these soils should not be too high, in order to avoid excessive organic matter decomposition. Soil pH also has a pronounced influence on the availability of various soil nutrients (see page 58).

Liming not only plays a role in the amelioration of agricultural land it is also of importance for the recultivation of waste heaps. DAVISON and JEFFERIES [1966] in experimenting with substrate material from coal mine waste heaps found that liming in combination with mineral fertilizer application resulted in very high responses in the growth of *Agrostis tenuis*. The authors claim that the pH increase enhanced fixation of heavy metals which occur in excess in this waste material and which are phytotoxic under low pH conditions.

General Reading

BANGERTH, F.: Calcium-related physiological disorders of plants. Ann. Rev. Phytopathology *17*, 97–122 (1979)

BÜRSTRÖM, H.G.: Calcium and plant growth. Biol. Rev. *43*, 287–316 (1968)

CHAPMAN, H.D.: Calcium. In: CHAPMAN, H.D. (ed.): Diagnostic Criteria for Plants and Soils. p. 65–92. University of California, Division of Agricultural Sciences, 1966

FOY, C.D.: Effect of calcium availability on plant growth, In: CARSON, E.W. (ed.): The Plant Root and its Environment, p. 565–600. University Press of Virginia, Charlotteville, U.S.A., 1974

LONERAGAN, J.F., ROWLAND, I.C., ROBSON, A.D. and SNOWBALL, K.: The calcium nutrition of plants. Proc. 11th Int. Grasslands Congr. (Surfers Paradise Aust.), p. 358–367 (1970)

LONERAGAN, J.F. and SNOWBALL, K.: Calcium requirements of plants. Aust. J. Agric. Res. *20*, 465–478 (1969)

MARSCHNER, H.: Calcium nutrition of higher plants. Neth. J. Agric. Sci. *22*, 275–282 (1974)

MAYNARD, D.N.: Nutritional disorders of vegetable crops: A review. Journal of Plant Nutrition *1*, 1–23 (1979)

SHEAR, C.B. (ed.): International symposium on calcium nutrition of economic crops. *In:* Comm. in Soil Sci and Plant Analysis *10*, 1–501 (1979)

SIMON, E.W.: The symptoms of calcium deficiency in plants. New Phytol. *80*, 1–15 (1978)

WYN JONES, R.G. and LUNT, O.R.: The function of calcium in plants. Bot. Rev. *33*, 407–426 (1967)

Chapter 12

Magnesium

12.1 Soil Magnesium

The Mg content of most soils generally lies in the range of between 0.05% for sandy soils and 0.5% for clay soils. Higher levels are found in clay soils because Mg is present in relatively easily weatherable ferromagnesian minerals, such as biotite, serpentine, hornblende and olivine. In addition it occurs in secondary clay minerals including chlorite, vermiculite, illite and montmorillonite. Some soils contain Mg as $MgCO_3$ or dolomite ($CaCO_3 \cdot MgCO_3$). In arid or semi-arid regions soils may contain large amounts of Mg as $MgSO_4$.

The distribution of Mg in soils may be considered in the same way as the distribution of K (see p. 416), and divided into non exchangeable, exchangeable and water soluble forms. These three forms are in equilibrium. By far the largest fraction of soil Mg is in the non exchangeable form which includes all the Mg in the primary minerals and most of the Mg in the secondary clay minerals. Generally this fraction has not been considered of importance in the direct release of Mg to plants (SALMON and ARNOLD [1963]). More recent evidence suggests, however, that in some soils non exchangeable Mg may be more available than was previously believed. In soils containing high contents of expandable clay minerals both lattice and interlayer Mg may be available to plants (CHRISTENSON and DOLL [1973]), although the release rate of this Mg is low in comparison with crop demand. Exchangeable Mg is usually in the order of about 5% of the total Mg and this fraction along with the water soluble Mg is of greatest importance in the supply to plants. Exchangeable Mg normally constitutes from 4 to 20% of the cation exchange capacity. It is thus normally considerably lower than Ca which is in the order of 80% and higher than K which can be up to about 4% (see p.416). Magnesium in the soil solution like Ca^{2+} is present in fairly high concentrations and often between 2 to 5 mM, although the levels can vary considerably and values between 0.2 to 150 mM have been reported (see p.70). Some Mg occurs in soil in association with organic matter, but this fraction is usually small and less than 1% of the total soil Mg.

Magnesium like Ca^{2+} is relatively easily leached from the soil and amounts in the order of 2 to 30 kg Mg/ha/yr have been observed (see p. 298). The rate of removal depends considerably on the amount of Mg containing minerals in the soil, their rate of weathering, and the intensity of leaching, as well as on the Mg uptake by plants from the soil. In many soils the release of Mg^{2+} by weathering is able to balance removal by leaching. Frequently on sandy soils loss by leaching predominates. In such soils the subsoil often contains higher levels of Mg than in the upper part of the profile. In an observation of 63 uncultivated Swedish profiles WIKLANDER [1958] found an average Mg saturation of the exchange capacity in the upper soil layers (0–20 cm) of 17% (pH 5.4) whilst in the subsoil (40–50 cm) it was 29% (pH 5.8).

The level of Mg in soils depends to a large extent on soil type. Highly leached and weathered soils such as podzols and lateritic soils are generally low in Mg. On the other hand soils formed in depression sites, where leached nutrients may accumulate as in marsh soils or gleyed soils, tend to be high in Mg. The same applies to soils which are only lightly leached such as the solonchak and solonetz soils in which $MgSO_4$ usually occurs. Parent material too plays a role and generally soils developed on Mg rich rocks such as basalt, peridotite and dolomite are well supplied with Mg. In a study of 55 North German soils SCHROEDER and ZAHIROLESLAM [1963] found that the total Mg decreased from 0.5% in marsh soils to 0.05% in podzols in the following order: Marsh Soils > Brown Earth Silty Soils > Brown Earth Sandy Soils > Brown Podzolic Soils > Podzols. Soils formed on serpentine are very high in Mg. Such soils have a low Ca/Mg ratio on the exchange complex and even pure Ca deficiency may occur in the vegetation they support. The situation is complicated, however, in that high levels of toxic heavy metals especially Ni and Cr may be present. In addition the soils are often deficient in macronutrients. Serpentine soils have been discussed by KRAUSE [1958] and EPSTEIN [1972]. The behaviour of magnesium in soils as well as its role in plant nutrition have been considered recently by KIRKBY and MENGEL [1976].

12.2 Magnesium in Physiology

12.2.1 Uptake and translocation

Magnesium is generally taken up by plants in lower quantities than Ca^{2+} or K^+. The content of Mg in plant tissues is usually in the order of 0.5% of the dry matter. Cation competitive effects in uptake are of particular importance for Mg^{2+} as such effects frequently lead to Mg deficiency in the field. The competitive effect of NH_4^+ on Mg^{2+} uptake was observed by E. G. MULDER [1956]. The mechanism of the competition between NH_4^+ and Mg^{2+} is not yet clear. It probably depends on both the H^+ released during NH_4^+ incorporation, as well as on the direct effect of the NH_4^+ itself. D. MULDER [1950] reported that high levels of K^+ in the soil resulted in Mg deficiency in apple leaves. Many other authors have observed this antagonism both in water culture and field experiments. The data of GRIMME et al. [1974] also show that high Mg contents may occur in plants supplied with a low level of K nutrition. These higher Mg contents cannot be explained simply in terms of a 'concentration effect' resulting from a lower rate of growth but probably originate directly from enhanced Mg uptake at low levels of K-nutrition. This observation agrees well with the findings of LEGGETT and GILBERT [1969] who reported that the Mg uptake by soya beans was especially high when the nutrient solution was free of K^+. Similar observations have also been reported by HALL [1971] showing very much elevated Mg levels in Ca deficient tomato tissues. The level of Mg^{2+} in the nutrient medium is also of importance in relation to Mn uptake. LÖHNIS [1960] showed in a number of plant species that it is possible to prevent the appearance of Mn toxicity by increasing the level of Mg supply. Evidence of decreased Mn uptake by Mg has also been found by MAAS et al. [1969]. These antagonistic and synergistic ionic effects in Mg uptake appear to relate to ionic balance effects rather than to specific competitive effects for carriers (see p. 133).

Although high levels of K nutrition often depress total Mg uptake, increasing K supply affects the Mg content of different plant organs to a varying extent. As can be seen from Table 12.1 increasing K supply reduced the Mg content of to-

Table 12.1   Effect of an increasing K supply on the cation content of various organs of the tomato plant (VIRO [1973])

Treatment mM K/l nutrient solution	K	Na	Ca	Mg
		in % DM		
Leaves				
2	0.5	0.40	4.7	0.61
10	3.3	0.19	4.2	0.27
20	4.2	0.18	3.3	0.15
Roots				
2	0.2	0.36	3.9	0.33
10	2.2	0.25	3.2	0.31
20	2.4	0.13	3.3	0.26
Fruits				
2	1.6	0.10	0.09	0.07
10	2.5	0.07	0.08	0.08
20	2.7	0.06	0.07	0.09

mato leaves and roots considerably. The Mg content in the fruits, however, was somewhat increased by the higher levels of K in the nutrient solution. This observation was obviously not accidental as it was found at all six harvests of the tomatoes (VIRO [1973]). LINSER and HERWIG [1968] also reported that increased K supply resulted in higher Mg contents in the seeds of flax. Similar findings have been reported by ADDISCOTT [1974] for potatoes. It thus appears that K^+ promotes the translocation of Mg^{2+} towards fruits and storage tissues.

In contrast to Ca^{2+}, Mg^{2+} is very mobile in the phloem and can be translocated from older to younger leaves or to the apex (STEUCEK and KOONTZ [1970] SCHIMANSKY [1973]). The same is true of K^+. As fruit and storage tissues are highly dependent on the phloem for their mineral supply they are thus higher in K and Mg than in Ca (see Table 12.1).

12.2.2 Biochemical functions

In plant tissues a high proportion of the total Mg, often over 70%, is diffusible and associated with inorganic anions and organic acid anions such as malate and citrate. Magnesium is also associated with indiffusible anions including oxalate and pectate (KIRKBY and MENGEL [1967]). Cereal grains contain Mg as the salt of inositol hexaphosphoric acid (phytic acid). The most well known role of Mg is its occurrence at the centre of the chlorophyll molecule (see Figure 1.4). The fraction of the total plant Mg associated with chlorophyll, however, is relatively small and only in the order of 15 to 20% (NEALES [1956]). Even in plants deficient in Mg the amount does not exceed 30% (MICHAEL [1941]). Besides its function in the chlorophyll molecule Mg^{2+} is required in other physiological processes. One major role of Mg^{2+} is as a cofactor in almost all enzymes activating phosphorylation processes. Magnesium (Mg^{2+}) forms a bridge between the pyrophosphate structure of ATP or ADP and the enzyme molecule (Figure 1.1). According to BALKE and HODGES [1975] the activation of ATPase by Mg^{2+} is brought about this bridging function. In addition to phosphokinases some dehydrogenases as well as enolase are also activated by Mg^{2+}. In these enzymes, however, the Mg reaction is not specific and Mn^{2+} is often a more efficient activator.

A key reaction of Mg^{2+} is the activation of ribulose bisphosphate carboxylase. As has been already described on p. 149, light triggers the import of Mg^{2+} into the stroma of the chloroplast in exchange for H^+ thus providing optimum conditions for the carboxylase reaction. This relationship is illustrated in Figure 12.1 from WALKER [1974]. The favourable effect of Mg^{2+} on CO_2 assimilation and related processes such as sugar and starch production are probably the consequence of this activation of ribulose bisphosphate carboxylase.

464

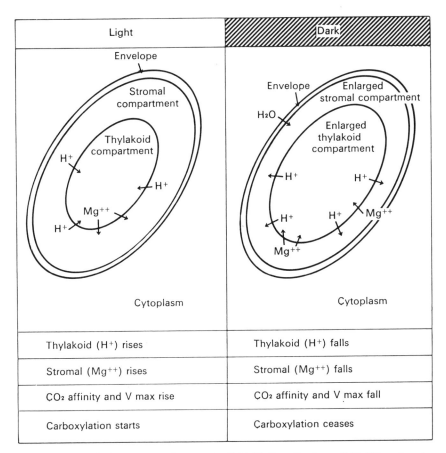

Fig.12.1 Hypothetical sequence of events in light-Mg^{2+} activation of RuBP carboxylase (after WALKER [1974]).

Generally when plants are Mg deficient the proportion of protein N decreases and that of non-protein N increases (HAEDER and MENGEL [1969]). From this it may be concluded that Mg deficiency inhibits protein synthesis. This does not result from the lack of synthesis of a particular amino acid, as for example is the case in S deficiency (see p. 381). The effect is probably caused by dissociation of the ribosomes into their sub-units in the absence of Mg^{2+} (Ts'o [1962], WATSON [1965]). Magnesium appears to stabilize the ribosomal particles in the configuration necessary for protein synthesis and is believed to have a similar stabilizing effect in the matrix of the nucleus. According to WUNDERLICH [1978] this is achieved by a bridging effect of Mg^{2+} on neighbouring indiffusible anions. The transfer of amino acyls from amino acyl tRNA to the polypeptide chain is also probably activated by Mg^{2+}.

12.2.3 Magnesium deficiency

Magnesium deficiency symptoms differ between plant species although some general characteristics are apparent. As already mentioned Mg^{2+} is mobile in the plant and deficiency always begins in the older and then moves to the younger leaves. Interveinal yellowing or chlorosis occurs and in extreme cases the areas become necrotic. Plate 12.1 shows Mg deficiency symptoms in a sugar beet leaf. This appearance is typical for a number of other dicotyledenous plants including grapes, field beans, bush beans, potatoes and tomatoes. In sugar beet the deficiency can often be mistaken for virus yellows. Another characteristic particularly of plants exposed to strong sunlight is their generally withered appearance, reminiscent of K deficiency, where the water content of the plant is disturbed (see p.426). Individual leaves suffering from Mg deficiency, however, are stiff and brittle and the intercostal veins are twisted. Mg deficient leaves often fall prematurely. In cereals and the monocots in general the appearance of Mg deficiency is different. As in the case of the dicots, the water and carbohydrate metabolism of the plant is also affected and deficiency begins in the older leaves. With the cereals, however, the base of the leaf first shows small dark green spots of chlorophyll accumulation which are apparent against the pale

Plate 12.1 Mg deficiency symptoms in a sugar beet leaf.

yellow background colour of the leaf. In more advanced stages of deficiency the leaves become more chlorotic and striped. Necrosis occurs particularly at the tips of the leaf. The symptoms are the same for wheat, oats, rye and also for maize in the early stages. As the plants age, however, the leaves of maize take on a more spotted appearance.

The effects of Mg deficiency on ultra structural changes have been investigated by a number of workers. Marked differences occur in chloroplast structure as might be expected. In *Phaseolus vulgaris* the grana are reduced in numbers, are irregular in shape and granal compartmentation is reduced or absent. In some cases starch grains are accumulated (THOMSON and WEIR [1962]). CHEVALIER and HUGUET [1975] studying the effect of Mg deficiency on the ultrastructure of chloroplasts of apple leaves found that inadequate Mg^{2+} supply resulted in a deformation of the lamellar structure. The mitochondria were also affected by Mg^{2+} deficiency, the cristae being underdeveloped. These symptoms of ultrastructure disorganization preceded visual Mg deficiency symptoms. *In vivo* concentrations of chlorophyll and thus also Mg concentrations are considerably higher in chloroplasts than in the cell as a whole (HEWITT and SMITH [1975]). It is therefore not surprising that chlorosis is often a first symptom of Mg deficiency.

In leaf tissue the threshold value for the occurrence of deficiency symptoms is in the region of about 2 mg Mg/g dry matter, although this is dependent on a number of factors including plant species. WARD and MILLER [1969] observed Mg deficiency symptoms in tomato leaves when the Mg content dropped below 3 mg Mg/g dry matter. Plants inadequately supplied with Mg^{2+} often show a delay of the reproductive phase. A detailed description of deficiency symptoms in many crops and the Mg levels in different plant species under varying conditions may be obtained from the data of EMBLETON [1966].

12.3 Magnesium in Crop Nutrition

12.3.1 Crop requirements and critical levels

The amounts of Mg taken up by some important crop plants is shown in Table 6.2. For arable crops the average uptake is in the region of about 10–25 kg Mg/ha/yr and generally the uptake of root crops is about double that of cereals. Sugar beet, potatoes, fruit and glasshouse crops are particularly prone to Mg-deficiency. In recent years the importance of Mg as a fertilizer has increased. Previously Mg was applied unwittingly as an impurity along with other fertilizers. The high purity of fertilizers used at the present day, however, means that this source of Mg application to the soil no longer exists. Increased crop yields resulting from higher applications of non-Mg containing fertilizers have also placed a greater demand on the soil for Mg. High levels of K^+ or NH_4^+ as already mentioned restrict Mg^{2+} uptake by plants. For these reasons Mg deficiency in crop plants is becoming more frequent and Mg applications are now common. Deficiencies occur particularly in highly leached humus acid soils or on sandy soils which have been given heavy dressings of lime. In some cases Mg deficiency occurs on soils high in K. The importance of ion antagonism in relation to Mg uptake has already been stressed. Clearly on acid soils it is possible to have a H^+ or even possibly an Al^{3+} competition for Mg^{2+} uptake, whereas Ca^{2+} competition may occur on highly limed soils. Figure 12.2 from STENUIT [1959] shows the relationship between soil pH and the intensity of Mg deficiency in oats grown in sandy soils. At a pH of about 5 the possibility of the occurrence of Mg deficiency is at a minimum. Lowering or raising pH depresses Mg uptake as

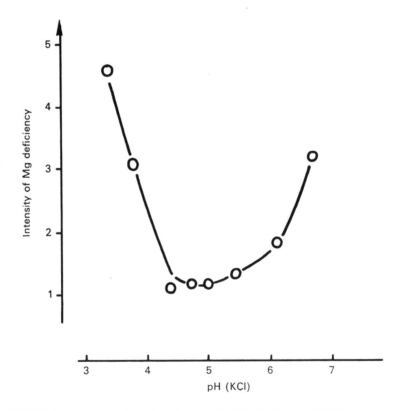

Fig. 12.2 Mg deficiency symptoms in oats and soil pH (after STENUIT [1959]).

a result of H^+ or Ca^{2+} competition. From this discussion it is clear that the presence and concentrations of H^+, K^+ and Ca^{2+} in the root environment can considerably influence the uptake of Mg^{2+} by crops. Magnesium availability also depends on soil moisture, as under dry conditions the Mg^{2+} flux towards the roots may be much impaired (GRIMME [1973]).

Numerous experiments have been carried out to investigate Mg relationships between plant and soil under Mg deficient conditions. PRINCE et al. [1947] concluded that, if Mg constitutes less than 6% of the exchange capacity, crops are likely to show response to Mg^{2+}. In experiments with sugar beet TINKER [1967] obtained responses in soils with cation exchange capacities of 5 to 10 me/100 g soil when they contained less than 0.2 me Mg/100 g soil (2 to 4% of the exchange capacity or 24 ppm exchangeable Mg). More recently reporting on the same crop from a survey of 60 field experiments DRAYCOTT and DURRANT [1971] have suggested a limit of 35 ppm exchangeable soil Mg^{2+} and 0.4 mg Mg/g dry matter of the leaf as critical levels at which no further yield increases result from Mg-fertilizer. In an advisory paper published in the UK agricultural advisory service Mg application is recommended for all crops growing on soils with less than 25 ppm exchangeable Mg and to susceptible crops when it is less than 50 ppm (N.A.A.S. [1968]). Above these levels Mg applications are only necessary when K levels are high, or when hypomagnesaemia may occur in animals or when glasshouse and fruit crops are being grown. These findings agree fairly well with the data reported in a review by DOLL and LUCAS [1973]. Best Mg fertilizer responses are generally found on light sandy soils. Thus DAM KOFOED and HOJMARK [1971] reported that on sandy soils in Denmark, fodder beet, swedes and potatoes all gave high yield responses to Mg application. The effect was less spectacular in cereals. ALTHERR and EVERS [1975] even found growth responses to Mg fertilization by spruce, grown on a bunter sandstone soil in

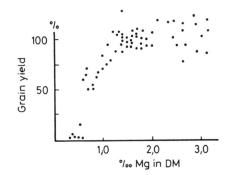

Fig. 12.3 Relationship between the relative grain yield of oats at maturation and the Mg content of the shoots at the onset of culm elongation (modified after PISSAREK [1979]).

Germany. Slight Mg deficiency in cereals during vegetative growth does not always result in a reduction in yield. Grain yield depressions do occur, however, when Mg deficiency symptoms are present on the flag leaves or ears (PISSAREK [1979]). The relationship between the Mg content in shoots of oats at the time of culm elongation and final grain yield are shown in Figure 12.3.

12.3.2 Magnesium fertilizers

The major Mg fertilizers used and their approximate Mg contents are shown in Table 12.2. Magnesium is supplied in most cases as carbonate, oxide or a sulphate. In general sulphate fertilizers are more rapidly effective than carbonate fertilizers but are also more expensive (JUNG and DRESSEL [1969]). Applications of dolomitic limestone are particularly useful on acid soils which need regular liming. Decomposition of the dolomite is also assisted by low soil pH. On more neutral soils $MgSO_4$ e.g. kieserite is more appropriate particularly on arable land where high levels of Mg are rapidly required.

The various forms of $MgSO_4$ differ considerably in solubility. Epsom salts $MgSO_4 \cdot 7 H_2O$ although more expensive is more soluble than kieserite ($MgSO_4 \cdot H_2O$). This has a practical significance, for, as has been pointed out by COOKE [1972], whilst 500 kg/ha $MgSO_4$ as kieserite applied to soil may be needed to prevent Mg deficiency in tomatoes, the trouble can be controlled by spraying 35 kg/ha of Epsom salt ($MgSO_4 \cdot 7 H_2O$) dissolved in 400 l water applied on a number of occasions over the growing season. Fertilizers containing only smaller percentages of Mg such as kainite, basic slags and some PK and NPK fertilizers, are useful in maintaining the Mg level of the soil. In cases, however, where Mg deficiency is suspected higher graded Mg fertilizers are prefered (see Table 12.2). Another Mg fertilizer not included in the sulphate or carbonate group is magnesium ammonium phosphate. This is a sparingly soluble salt used in horticulture particularly for young valuable plants sensitive to other forms of Mg treatment. The relative values of different Mg fertilizers as well as the use of

Table 12.2 Mineral Mg fertilizers

	% MgO
Magnesian limestone (Mg carbonate)	5–20
Ground burnt magnesian lime (Mg oxide)	10–33
Kieserite ($MgSO_4 \cdot H_2O$)	27
Epsom salts ($MgSO_4 \cdot 7 H_2O$)	16
Sulphate of potash magnesia ($K_2SO_4 \cdot MgSO_4$)	11
Magnesite ($MgCO_3$)	45

other Mg sources including farm yard manure, basic slags, and liming materials have been thoroughly discussed by COOKE [1972]. The rates of Mg application on sandy soils are in the range of 80 to 160 kg MgO/ha. These rates have resulted in substantial yield increases of various arable crops on sandy soils in Denmark (DAM KOFOED and HOJMARK [1971]). Potatoes in particular generally show a marked response to Mg treatment (JUNG and DRESSEL [1969]). Mg application is also important for pastures in relation to animal nutrition. Intensive grassland management frequently results in herbage with low contents of available Mg which does not meet the demand of milking cows so that animals suffer from grass tetany (hypomagnesaemia).

General Reading

EMBLETON, T.W.: Magnesium. In: H.D. CHAPMAN, Diagnostic Criteria for Plants and Soils. (ed.), p. 225–263. Univ. of California, Division of Agricultural Sciences, 1966

KIRKBY, E.A. and MENGEL, K.: The role of magnesium in plant nutrition. Z. Pflanzenern. Bodenk. 209–222 (1976)

SALMON, R.C.: Magnesium relationships in soils and plants. J.Sci. Food Agric., *14*, 605–610 (1963)

Chapter 13

Iron

13.1 Soil Iron

Iron makes up about 5% by weight of the earth's crust and is invariably present in all soils (see Table 11.1). The greatest part of soil Fe usually occurs in the crystal lattices of numerous minerals. The primary minerals in which Fe is present include the ferromagnesian silicates such as olivine, augite, hornblende and biotite. These minerals along with the biotite micas constitute the major Fe source in igneous rocks. Primary Fe oxides which occur in many soils include haematite (Fe_2O_3), ilmenite ($FeTiO_3$), and magnetite (Fe_3O_4). In sedimentary rocks Fe oxides and siderite ($FeCO_3$) are usually the most common primary Fe forms. Iron may also be present in secondary mineral lattices in soils and it is an essential element in a large group of clay minerals. As weathering proceeds, Fe originally present in the easily weatherable ferromagnesian primary minerals appears in illitic clay minerals. The high stability of primary Fe oxides means that during oxidative weathering Fe oxides accumulate as hydrous oxides in the clay fraction. Thus in soils at an advanced stage of oxidative weathering as is the case of lateritic soils, these oxides together with Al oxides and kaolinite predominate in the profile (OADES [1963]).

The content of soluble Fe in soils is extremely low in comparison with the total Fe content. Soluble inorganic forms include Fe^{3+}, $Fe(OH)_2{}^+$, $FeOH^{2+}$ and Fe^{2+}. In well aerated soils, however, Fe^{2+} contributes little to the total soluble inorganic Fe except under high soil pH conditions. Iron solubility is largely controlled by the solubility of the hydrous Fe (III) oxides. These give rise to Fe^{3+} and its hydrolysis species (LINDSAY [1972]):

$$Fe^{3+} + 3OH^- \rightleftharpoons Fe(OH)_3 \text{ (solid)}$$

The equilibrium is very much in favour of $Fe(OH)_3$ precipitation and is highly pH dependent, the activity of Fe^{3+} falling with increasing pH. At higher pH levels Fe^{3+} activity in solution decreases 1000 fold for each pH unit rise. The soluble Fe level reaches a minimum in the pH range between 6.5–8.0 (LINDSAY [1972]). Acid soils are thus relatively higher in soluble inorganic Fe than calcareous soils where levels can be extremely low. This may well contribute to Fe deficiency in crops growing on these soils.

When soils are waterlogged a reduction of Fe^{3+} to Fe^{2+} takes place accompanied by an increase in Fe solubility. Reduction is brought about by anaerobic metabolism of bacteria. This process of Fe reduction is of particular importance in paddy soils where rather high Fe^{2+} concentrations can result. This can often produce toxic effects in rice plants, known as 'bronzing.' In soils subjected to anaerobic conditions the ratio of activities of Fe^{3+}/Fe^{2+} can be an important parameter in relation to crop growth. This ratio can be assessed by measurement of the redox potential according to the equation

$$E = 0.77 + 0.059 \ \log \ \frac{^a Fe^{3+}}{^a Fe^{2+}}$$

Under anaerobic soil conditions reducing processes are favoured. Hydrous Fe oxides give rise to Fe^{2+} (PONNAMPERUMA [1972]) according to the equation

$$Fe(OH)_3 + e^- + 3H^+ \rightarrow Fe^{2+} + 3H_2O$$

From this equation it is evident that the reduction of Fe^{3+} to Fe^{2+} is associated with the consumption of H^+ and thus with an increase in pH. The reverse is the case as soil aeration is increased, a fall in pH being accompanied by the oxidation of Fe^{2+} to Fe^{3+}.

Differences in redox potential can often be observed in the same profile. In the deeper soil layers which are less well aerated, the fraction of Fe^{2+} of the total soluble Fe is frequently higher than in the upper horizons. The observations of WIKLANDER and HALLGREN [1949] for example showed that at a depth of 2 m over 90% of the soluble Fe was present as Fe^{2+}. The redox potential thus generally falls from the upper to the lower horizons.

An important feature of Fe both in soils and plants is the way it readily forms organic complexes or chelates. In excessively leached and poorly drained soils this property results in Fe being mobilized from the upper horizons and redeposited lower in the profile. In podzolic soils Fe appears to form Fe^{2+} complexes with polyphenols, simple aliphatic acids and fulvic acids from the acid litter layer. These complexes facilitate Fe movement, and may well be important in the supply of Fe to plant roots. A very useful review dealing with Fe compounds in soils is given by OADES [1963].

13.2 Iron in Physiology

13.2.1 Uptake and translocation

Iron may be absorbed by plant roots as Fe^{2+} or as Fe chelates. Fe^{3+} is only of minor importance because of the low solubility of Fe-III compounds at the pH of most soils. The availability of inorganic Fe to plant roots therefore appears to be dependent on the ability of the roots to lower the pH and to reduce Fe^{3+} to Fe^{2+} in the rhizosphere (MARSCHNER et al. [1974], BROWN [1978].

In contrast to inorganic Fe, Fe chelates are soluble and therefore available to the roots. However, the uptake rate of whole Fe chelate molecules is very low. For efficient utilization of chelated iron, separation between Fe and the organic ligand (chelate splitting) has to take place at the root surface when Fe chelates are supplied to plant roots at the normally low Fe levels required by plants (TIFFIN and BROWN [1961]). According to CHANEY et al. [1972] the reduction of Fe^{3+} is essential before Fe chelates can be split and Fe^{2+} absorbed by the roots. These authors suggest that Fe^{3+} reduction at the outer plasmalemma is mediated by a source of electrons from within the cells via a cytochrome or flavin compound. Only at high levels of Fe chelates in the nutrient medium were JEFFREYS and WALLACE [1968] able to detect appreciable quantities of Fe chelates in shoots.

Plants species differ in ability to utilize sparingly soluble inorganic Fe and Fe chelates for iron nutrition. So called Fe efficient plant species are able to lower the pH of the nutrient medium and to increase the reducing capacity of the root surface under iron stress conditions whereby Fe availability and absorption by the roots increase tremendously (MARSCHNER et al. [1974]). For sunflower plants it can be shown that these physiological changes of roots under iron stress are accompanied by typical morphological changes such as thickening of root tips due an enlargement of the cortex, additional division of rhizodermal cells and an intensified development of root hairs (RÖMHELD and MARSCHNER [1979]). These alterations in the root structure of Fe efficient plant species are associated with the development of transfer cells. Such cells which occur in the rhizodermis are highly specific for iron uptake and are involved in the increase in iron uptake during Fe stress (KRAMER et al. [1980]). Recent evidence of RÖMHELD and MARSCHNER [1981] indicates that iron stress reactions are rhythmic, and associated with marked fluctuations in the rate of Fe uptake. The physiological and morphological changes described above which accompany Fe stress, enhance the availability of sparingly soluble forms of Fe in the substrate. This temporary alleviation of Fe stress in the plant results in an increase in substrate pH (i.e. a net OH^- efflux replaces the net H^+ efflux) and a decrease in root reducing capacity, thus creating the conditions for the next sequence of Fe stress reactions. RÖMHELD and MARSCHNER [1981] hold the view that this rhythm in uptake and translocation of Fe is hormonally controlled, probably from the shoot apex. They suggest that the Fe nutritional status of the plant is transformed into a 'signal' which induces distinct biochemical and morphological changes within the roots causing a fine regulation of Fe supply to the plant. Auxins appear to be involved.

In contrast to Fe efficient plant species, Fe inefficient plant species – mainly the *Gramineae* – do not show morphological and physiological changes under Fe stress. These species are therefore unable to react to Fe stress by increasing Fe mobilization in the nutrient medium with a subsequent increase of Fe absorption by the roots.

The ample evidence that Fe uptake is metabolically controlled has been reviewed by MOORE [1972]. The results of TIFFIN [1966] for example show Fe concentrations in stem exudates of decapitated sunflower and soya bean plants, up to 30 times greater than in the ambient solutions. The uptake of Fe is considerably influenced by other cations. Competitive effects on iron uptake have been observed with Mn^{2+}, Cu^{2+}, Ca^{2+}, Mg^{2+}, K^+ and Zn^{2+} (LINGLE *et al.* [1963]). Such effects on absorption may partially account for the ability of heavy metals to induce Fe deficiency in a number of plant species (HEWITT [1963]). Heavy metals, in particular Cu and Zn are also known to displace Fe from chelate complexes forming corresponding heavy metal chelates. This may be important in limiting Fe uptake and utilization, either by reducing Fe chelate translocation to roots or within the plant itself by the effect of the heavy metal on centres of physiological activity for Fe. According to DEKOCK [1956] the detrimental effect of heavy metals on Fe uptake and transport in white mustard is greater the higher the relative stability of the heavy metal chelate. The extent of Fe deficiency symptoms caused by heavy metals thus followed a stability sequence:

$$Cu > Ni > Co > Zn > Cr > Mn$$

Iron is not readily mobile between different plant organs. Green plants deprived of Fe soon become chlorotic in the younger plant parts whilst older tissues remain green. Younger tissues are therefore dependent on a continuous Fe supply in the xylem or by a foliar application. The major form in which Fe is translocated in the xylem appears to be as ferric citrate (TIFFIN [1972]).

13.2.2 Biochemical functions

The tendency for Fe to form chelate complexes and its ability to undergo a valency change are the two important characteristics which underlie its numerous physiological effects.

$$Fe^{2+} \rightleftarrows Fe^{3+} + e^-$$

The most well known function of Fe is in enzyme systems in which haem or haemin function as prosthetic groups (see Figure 1.3). Here Fe plays a somewhat similar role to Mg in the porphyrin structure of chlorophyll. These haem enzyme systems include catalase, peroxidase, cytochrome oxidase as well as the various cytochromes. Catalase and peroxidase catalyse the following reactions

$$\text{catalase:} \quad H_2O_2 + H_2O_2 \rightarrow O_2 + 2H_2O$$

$$\text{peroxidase:} \quad AH_2 + H_2O_2 \rightarrow A + 2H_2O$$

The precise role of these enzymes in plant metabolism is still not understood. Much more is known of the function of cytochromes in electron transport and the involvement of cytochrome oxidase in the terminal step in the respiration chain. When Fe is deficient there is a reduction in the activity of all these enzymes although the effect is not so clear in the case of peroxidase (PRICE [1968]).

Although highly important in metabolism, the haem pigments constitute only about 0.1% of the total Fe in plant leaves (DEKOCK et al. [1960]). The remaining Fe is stored largely as a ferric phosphoprotein called phytoferritin. HYDE et al. [1963] have proposed that phytoferritin in leaves represents an Fe reserve used by developing plastids for photosynthetic needs. This is in agreement with BARTON [1970] who observed large quantities of phytoferritin in chloroplasts and confirms earlier evidence that chloroplasts are rich in Fe, containing as much as 80% of the total Fe in plants (NEISH [1939]). Another form of Fe occurring in the chloroplasts is ferredoxin. This is a nonhaem-iron protein which participates in oxido-reduction processes by transferring electrons. The significance of ferredoxin as a redox system in photosynthesis as well as in nitrite reduction, sulphate reduction and N_2 assimilation has already been described (see p.147 and Figure 3.16). Nonhaem-iron proteins are widely distributed in photosynthetic and nonphotosynthetic organisms.

In green plants there is often a good correlation between the level of Fe supply and the chlorophyll content, plants well supplied with Fe being high in chlorophyll (JACOBSON and OERTLI [1956], DEKOCK et al. [1960]). This relationship is shown in Table 13.1. It also illustrates the influence of Fe on the activity of catalase and peroxidase. Applying radioactive Fe-59 to tomato plants suffering from Fe chlorosis MACHOLD and SCHOLZ [1969] observed that the distribution of Fe-59 in the leaves corresponded exactly to the areas in which regreening occurred. This is shown in Plate 13.1. It is not surprising from this kind of evidence that the search for a possible function of Fe in the role of chlorophyll formation has received considerable attention. The metabolic pathway involved in chlorophyll formation is shown in Figure 13.1. The same pathway is also operative in the biosynthesis of haem (formula Figure 1.3). In Fe deficiency a decrease has been observed in the rate of condensation of glycine and succinyl

Plate 13.1 Uptake of Fe-59 by a chlorotic tomato leaf. The distribution of Fe-59 in the auto-radiograph (above) corresponds exactly to the area of the leaf in which regreening occurred (below).
(Photo: MACHOLD and SCHOLZ)

478

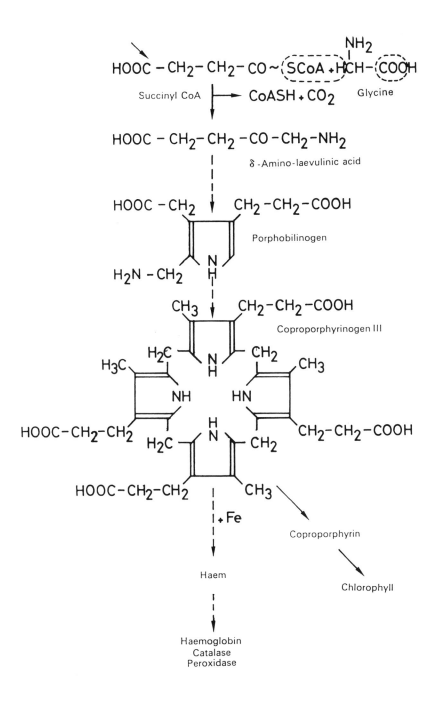

Fig. 13.1 Importance of iron in the synthesis of haem complexes.

CoA to form δ-amino-laevulinic acid (ALA) the precursor of porphyrins (BOGO-RAD [1960], MARSH et al. [1963]). According to MACHOLD and STEPHAN [1969] Fe is also necessary in the oxidation step from coproporphyrinogen to protopor-phyrinogen in chlorophyll synthesis. There is still considerable controversy as to whether Fe plays a direct role in chlorophyll formation. In a review of the func-tions of Fe in plants PRICE et al. [1972] suggest that Fe is not directly involved in the enzymic synthesis of porphyrins, and claims that the observed effects cited above are due to indirect causes. Recent results of TERRY [1980] indicate that Fe stress causes a failure in the formation of photosynthetic units.

Table 13.1 Effect of Fe supply on the Fe and chlorophyll contents and on enzyme activities in tomato leaves (MACHOLD [1968])

Treatment	Fe content, μg/g FW		Chlorophyll	Rel. enzyme activity	
	HCl soluble	Total	mg/g FW	Catalase	Peroxidase
Adequate Fe.......	10.3	18.5	3.52	100	100
Inadequate Fe	4.3	11.1	0.25	20	56

The possible involvement of Fe in protein metabolism has been suspected from the findings of a number of authors who have observed that in Fe deficien-cy the protein fraction decreases simultaneously with an increase in the level of soluble organic N compounds (BENNETT [1945], ILJIN [1951], POSSINGHAM [1956], PERUR et al. [1961]). In Fe deficient fruit tree leaves for example ILJIN [1951] found protein contents about half those of healthy leaves. From short term ex-periments on the alga Euglena gracilis it now seems likely that Fe is directly im-plicated in nucleic acid metabolism. PRICE et al. [1972] reported that in Fe defi-cient algae, the chloroplasts contained less than half the chloroplast RNA and chloroplast ribosomes of the non deficient controls. This was regarded as a di-rect consequence of a lack of Fe. The inhibiting requirement of Fe in N_2 fixation and NO_3-reduction appears to depend on the influence of non-haem iron prote-ins on electron transport (PRICE [1968]).

13.2.3 Iron deficiency and toxicity

The deficiencies of Fe and Mg are somewhat similar as both are character-ized by a failure in chlorophyll production. Iron deficiency, however, unlike Mg deficiency always begins in the younger leaves. In most species chlorosis is in-terveinal and a fine reticulate pattern can often be observed in the newly formed leaves, the darker green veins contrasting markedly against a lighter green or yellow background. The youngest leaves may often be completely white and totally devoid of chlorophyll. In the leaves of cereals the deficiency is shown by alternate yellow and green stripes along the length of the leaf. As high concentrations of Fe occur in chloroplasts it is not surprising that Fe deficiency causes marked changes in their ultrastructure. VESK et al. [1966] have observed both a reduction in the number and size of the grana.

A fairly well defined pattern of chemical composition is often shown in plants suffering from Fe chlorosis. In particular the P/Fe ratio is frequently higher than in comparative green tissues. As yet, however it is still a matter of speculation as to whether the high P/Fe ratio found in chlorotic tissues is the cause or the consequence of the chlorosis.

The net H^+ release from the roots of Fe efficient plant species suffering from Fe deficiency, is a reflection of a shift in ion uptake from the normal excess anion over cation uptake for NO_3^- nutrition (see p. 136), to an excess cation over anion uptake (VENKAT RAJU and MARSCHNER [1972]). This shift in cation-anion uptake results in an increase in organic anion accumulation within the plant (SCHERER [1978]). The concentration of citric acid in particular is often high in the roots of Fe deficient plants. DEKOCK and co-workers hold the view that the accumulation of this acid in chlorotic plant tissues is related to the relatively low levels of Fe^{2+} which are present in plants suffering from Fe chlorosis (DEKOCK et al. [1979]). Fe^{2+} is required for the activity of aconitase, the enzyme responsible for the conversion of the citric acid to aconitic acid. A low level of Fe^{2+} is thus associated with low aconitase activity and hence also with the accumulation of citric acid (DEKOCK and MORRISON [1958]). Other typical features of Fe deficient tissues include the accumulation of amino acids and nitrate. The accumulation of nitrate is especially indicative of a considerable disturbance in energy metabolism.

Iron toxicity is particularly a problem in flooded rice soils, since within a few weeks flooding may increase the level of soluble Fe from 0.1 ppm to 50–100 ppm Fe (PONNAMPERUMA [1978]). Iron toxicity in rice is known as 'bronzing'. In this disorder the leaves are first covered by tiny brown spots which develop into a uniform brown colour. This frequently occurs in rice leaves containing more than 300 ppm Fe (TANAKA and YOSHIDA [1970]). Iron toxicity is known in various rice growing areas and is especially frequent on heavy soils (TANAKA et al. [1973]) and is often associated with K^+ deficiency. TROLLDENIER [1973] reported that when K^+ nutrition is inadequate the capability of rice roots to oxidize Fe^{2+} to Fe^{3+} is impaired.

13.3 Iron in Crop Nutrition

13.3.1 Iron availability

The Fe content of green plant tissues is low in comparison with the macronutrients and generally in the order of about 100 ppm in the dry matter. In cereal grains, tubers and roots it is often considerably lower. Total soil Fe is thus always greatly in excess of crop requirements. According to LINDSAY [1974] most agricultural crops require less than 0.5 ppm in the soil in the plough layer whereas the total Fe level is about 2% or 20.000 ppm in the soil. Any problem of Fe supply to crops from soil is therefore always one of availability.

The solubility of inorganic Fe is highly dependent on soil pH. The influence of pH on the solubilities of Fe^{2+}, Fe^{3+} and total soluble Fe in equilibrium with Fe oxide is shown in Figure 13.2. LINDSAY [1974] has estimated that to enable mass flow to transport sufficient Fe to the roots, the total solubility must be at least 10^{-6} M. As can be seen in the Figure 13.2 this soluble inorganic Fe level is only achieved at pH 3, and by raising the pH to just over 4 only 1% of the Fe demand can be obtained. At normal soil pH levels therefore even allowing for the contribution of diffusion (O'CONNOR *et al.* [1971]) inorganic

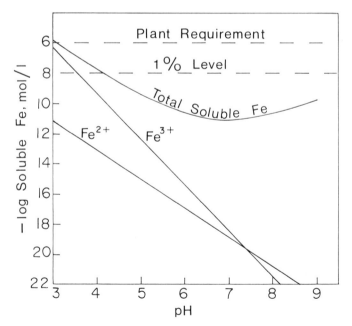

Fig. 13.2 Solubility of Fe in relation to the pH. The dotted lines indicate 100% and 1% plant requirement (after LINDSAY [1974]).

Fe levels are far below those required by plants. It appears therefore that for plants growing in soil the formation of soluble Fe organic complexes, mainly chelates, must play an important role in Fe supply. These compounds may originate as root exudates, from organic matter, as metabolic products of micro-organisms, or as Fe chelate fertilizers added to the soil. Soluble Fe organic complexes are known to occur in soils. WEBLEY and DUFF [1965] for example have shown that α-ketogluconic acid excreted from the rhizosphere can solubilize Fe which can then be taken up by plants. According to LINDSAY [1974] chelate concentrations as low as 10^{-8}–10^{-7} M are estimated as adequate when both diffusion and mass flow participate in the transport process.

Figure 13.3 shows a scheme, published by LINDSAY [1974], illustrating the role of chelates excreted by a root hair in solubilizing metal ions (M), *e.g.* Fe, of the solid soil phase. The complexed and thus soluble Fe diffuses to the root cells where it is absorbed. The significance of root exudates in the availability of Fe has been demonstrated by VENKAT RAJU and MARSCHNER [1972] and by MARSCHNER *et al.* [1974]. These workers observed a release of reducing

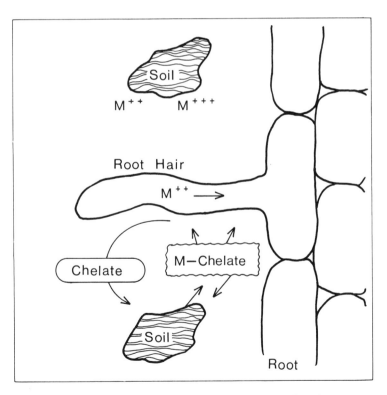

Fig. 13.3 Mobilization of soil metal ions by chelates (after LINDSAY [1974]).

substances from the roots of sunflower plants growing in culture solution under Fe stress conditions following the precepitation of Fe-III phosphate in the solution. This release was accompanied by a fall in pH in the culture medium brought about by an excess cation over anion uptake by the plants (VENKAT RAJU et al. [1972]). The fall in pH and the reducing effect of root exudates mobilized precipitated Fe by reducing it to Fe^{2+}. Iron availability was thus improved and regreening occurred in the plants.

The importance of root tips in the Fe nutrition of plants has been confirmed by recent investigations of CLARKSON and SANDERSON [1978]. This work has revealed that only root tips and not the basal parts of roots are capable of absorbing Fe. The contact zone between roots and soil of relevance to Fe uptake is thus very limited. According to these investigations the development of new root tips should also play an important role in determining the Fe uptake potential of plants.

Not all species are equally susceptible to Fe chlorosis. Iron deficiency is commonly observed in the calcifuge species such as *Azalea*, *Rhododendron*, and blueberry. The most important commercial crops affected are citrus, deciduous fruit trees and vines. Iron chlorosis has also been found in field beans, soya beans, maize, grain sorghum, legumes, rice and tomatoes.

13.3.2 Lime induced chlorosis

Iron chlorosis may result from an absolute Fe deficiency in the soil. Such cases may occur on degraded sandy soils, but are not frequent. Iron chlorosis on calcareous soils, however, often occurs. This lime induced chlorosis is not caused by absolute Fe deficiency. In most cases it does not even result as a consequence of too low an availability of Fe in the soil, but is rather a physiological disorder. Calcareous soils are characterized by high carbonate contents, by high Ca^{2+} concentrations in the soil solution and by a high pH level. All these soil factors have been cited as a cause of lime induced chlorosis, but it is now clear that none of them directly induces Fe chlorosis. The most important factor which brings about lime induced chlorosis is HCO_3^-. This ion affects iron uptake and translocation in the plant, as has been shown by RUTLAND [1971] for *Azalea* and by RUTLAND and BUKOVAC [1971] for *Chrysanthemum*. It is evident from Table 13.2 that the total uptake of Fe by *Azalea* was little depressed by HCO_3^- present in the nutrient solution. The translocation of Fe towards the younger leaves, however, was significantly affected. There is now evidence that Fe chlorosis frequently found on calcareous sites results primarily not because of low Fe availability in the soil, but because of a physiological disorder induced by excess HCO_3^- (MENGEL et al. [1979]). It is supposed that abundant HCO_3^- in the root medium results in Fe immobilization in the plant. This is demonstrated by the data in Table 13.3. The leaves analyzed were sampled from vines grown on a calcareous site known to produce Fe chlorosis in this crop. Total Fe did not differ between the chlorotic and green leaves. The major differences were found in the fraction of 0.5 N HCl soluble Fe. This fraction was clearly lower in Fe in the chlorotic leaves as compared with green leaves. Sequestrene application resulted in a substantial increase of this Fe fraction [sequestrene = Fe EDDHA = Fe-ethylene diamine (di o-hydroxyphenyl acetate)]. The critical level of about 48 ppm 0.5 N HCl soluble Fe in dry matter corresponds well with the critical level of HCl soluble Fe in tobacco leaves (47 ppm) found by JACOBSON [1945].

Table 13.2 Effect of HCO_3^- in the nutrient solution on the uptake and distribution of labelled Fe in *Azalea* (RUTLAND [1971])

	Young leaves cpm	Old leaves	Stems	Roots
without HCO_3^-.............................	420	70	75	1638
with HCO_3^-	272+	87	76	1438

+ significant difference at 5% level

Table 13.3 Fe solubility in green and chlorotic leaves of *Vitis vinifera* (MENGEL *et al.* [1979])

	H_2O ppm Fe in DM	0.5 N HCl	1.0 N HCl	Total Fe
Green leaves	4.8	48	24	107
Young chlorotic leaves	4.8	36	29	108
Old chlorotic leaves	4.8	36	28	108
Green leaves, treated with sequestrene .	7.2	58	33	139

Why HCO_3^- reduces Fe mobility in plants is not yet clear. It is feasible that a high uptake of HCO_3^- by plants may result in an increase in the pH of the plant tissues which in turn may lead to an immobilization of Fe. This supposition is consistent with the observation that Fe chlorosis is more likely to appear when plants are supplied with NO_3^- than with NH_4-N (MACHOLD [1967]) since nitrate nutrition is known for its alkaline effect on plant tissues and NH_3-nutrition for its acidifying effect (see p. 136). Increasing the level of nitrate nutrition can also favour the occurrence of Fe chlorosis (AKTAS and VAN EGMOND [1979]).

In calcareous soils HCO_3^- may accumulate due to the high pH level and the dissolution of carbonates according to the equation:

$$CaCO_3 + CO_2 + H_2O \rightarrow Ca^{2+} + 2\ HCO_3^-$$

The dissolution needs CO_2 which is produced by root and microbial respiration. If soil aeration and soil structure are satisfactory CO_2 may escape from the soil medium and HCO_3^- does not accumulate. Under high soil moisture conditions particularly in association with a poor soil structure, however, HCO_3^- may accumulate to concentrations as high as 400 to 500 ppm. Chlorosis is then likely to occur. This has been shown for fruit trees by BOXMA [1972] and for *Citrus* by KOVANCI et al. [1978]. These findings are consistent with the observation that Fe chlorosis is likely to be present under rainy weather conditions (GÄRTEL [1974]), when soil moisture is high and soil aeration poor.

Improving soil structure is therefore one of the most important measures in controlling Fe chlorosis. In vineyards, cultivation of deep rooting crops *(Brassica species)* between the vine rows reduces the hazard of chlorosis. Application of organic manures, however, is a doubtful means of correcting Fe chlorosis for although soil structure may be improved, enhanced CO_2 production in the soil may favour the formation of HCO_3^-. Lime induced Fe chlorosis is mostly controlled by foliar application of Fe chelates. Fe-EDDHA [= Ethylene diamine (o di o-hydroxyphenyl acetate)] has proved to be a suitable chelate for this purpose in contrast to Fe-EDTA (= Ethylene diamine tetra acetate) which is not stable enough (see p. 17). For successful control more than one application is often necessary.

Phosphate has been held to be the real inducer of Fe chlorosis on calcareous soils (GÄRTEL [1965], MILLER [1960]). KOVANCI et al. [1978] as well as MENGEL et al. [1979], however, were not able to find any relationship between the occurrence of chlorosis under field conditions and the level of available phosphate in the soil. MARSCHNER and SCHROPP [1977] in growing six different vine cultivars on calcareous soils in pot experiments, found that only one cultivar showed Fe chlorosis, when very high levels of phosphate were applied. It thus seems feasible that a phosphate excess may aggravate Fe chlorosis on calcareous soils. It should be borne in mind, however, that the level of soluble phosphate in calcareous soils is generally low and that these soils quickly render fertilizer phosphates insoluble.

Plate 13.2 shows Fe chlorosis in a vineyard. The light areas and stripes visible on the photograph are due to the chlorotic leaves. Even in forest trees *(Pinus silvestris)* lime induced chlorosis has been observed (ZECH [1970], CARTER [1980]). Cultivars of a given crop species may also differ considerably in their susceptibility to Fe-chlorosis. This has been shown for soya beans, maize and tomato (BROWN et al. [1972]) as well as for grapes (SAGLIO [1969]). BROWN [1963] reported that under Fe stress, chlorosis resistant cultivars of soya beans released more H^+ from the roots than susceptible cultivars. Analogous results have been found by MALISSIOVAS [1980] for two vine cultivars. H^+

excretion from the roots was greater in the Fe resistant cultivar. MENGEL and MALISSIOVAS [1981] hold the view that H^+ excretion results in the neutralization of HCO_3^- in the rhizosphere and thus controls Fe-chlorosis.

Plate 13.2 Iron chlorosis in a vineyard. White areas indicate the vines with Fe deficiency. (Photo: GÄRTEL)

Iron chlorosis sometimes occurs in practice as a result of high levels of heavy metals in the soil. The most well known example is that of Mn. High Mn:Fe ratios in the nutrient medium give rise to Fe deficiency symptoms. The effect does not appear to relate to uptake but to a disturbance in the enzyme activity of Fe, although the precise mechanism is not clear. It is suggested that Mn may compete for binding sites which are normally occupied by Fe. It was formerly accepted that Fe deficiency and Mn toxicity and *vice versa* could be identified in terms of the same disorder (SOMERS and SHIVE [1942]). More recent evidence suggests distinct differences (HEWITT [1963]); Fe deficiency begins with a somewhat uniform paling of the youngest leaves whereas in many species Mn toxicity starts with the appearance of chlorotic spots on the older leaves. In Mn deficiency the interveinal areas of the leaves become yellow whereas with Fe toxicity the whole leaf has an increased pigment content. Excess of other heavy metals in the soil including Cu, Cr, Ni and Zn may induce symptoms apparently identical with those of Fe deficiency. The relationship between heavy metal toxicity and induced Fe chlorosis has been reviewed thoroughly by HEWITT [1963] and by FOY *et al.* [1978].

487

13.3.3 Iron application

In the treatment of Fe chlorosis, the addition of inorganic Fe salts to the soil is mostly without effect for the Fe is rapidly made insoluble as oxides. Even foliar treatment with ferrous salts is not always satisfactory. Iron chelates are more effective and can be used as a fertilizer either as a soil additive or as a foliar spray. In soil applications, however, it is important to consider the stability of the chelate particularly in relation to the soil pH. At higher soil pH levels, soil Ca^{2+} present in higher concentration can displace Fe^{3+} from less stable chelates giving rise to a Ca-chelate and precipitated Fe-oxide thus rendering the Fe unavailable. Differences in the stability of chelates are reflected in plant responses. The results of LINDSAY et al. [1967] showing the yield response of sorghum to various Fe chelates correcting Fe deficiency in a calcareous soil are presented in Figure 13.4. Fe EDDHA [ethylenediamine (di o-hydroxyphenaylacetic acid)] the chelate which gave the highest response is stable throughout the pH range 4–10, whereas the stability of Fe DTPA (di ethyltriamine pentacetic acid) and

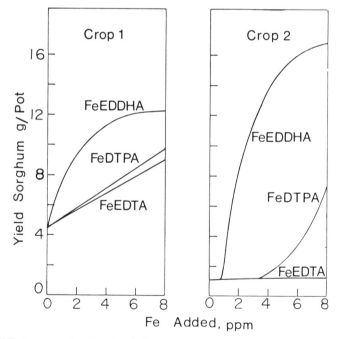

Fig.13.4 Effectiveness of various Fe chelates in correcting Fe deficiency in a calcarious soil for two croppings of sorghum (after LINDSAY [1974]).

EDTA   = Ethylene diamine tetraacetic acid
DTPA   = Diethylene triamine pentaacetic acid
EDDHA = Ethylene diamine (di o-hydroxyphenylacetic acid)

488

Fe EDTA (ethylene diamine tetraacetic acid) falls above pH 7 and 6 respectively so that correspondingly lower sorghum yields were obtained.

Unfortunately the most stable chelates still tend to be too expensive for commercial use. In citrus, applications of about 10–20 g Fe in chelated form per tree have proved satisfactory. The different forms of Fe used and methods of application used to combat Fe chlorosis, have been reviewed by MURPHY and WALSH [1972]. The application of other fertilizers can sometimes indirectly influence the Fe supply to plants. Acid fertilizers and particularly NH_4-fertilizers can depress chlorosis symptoms. This may result from the lower pH around the root zone (LUCAS and KNEZEK [1972]).

General Reading

In addition to the general literature given below the following references are of interest.

LINDSAY, W.L.: Role of chelation in micronutrient availability, In: E.W. CARSON, (ed.): The Plant Root and its Environment, p. 507–524. University Press of Virginia, Charlotesville, 1974

OADES, J.M.: The nature and distribution of iron compounds in soils. Soils and Fertilizers, 26, 69–80 (1963)

PRICE, C.A.: Iron compounds and plant nutrition. Ann. Rev. Plant Physiol., 19, 239–248 (1968)

PRICE, C.A.: Molecular Approaches to Plant Physiology. McGraw Hill, p. 244–249, 1970

WALLACE, A. et al.: Iron deficiency in plants and its correction. In Commun. in Soil Sci. and Plant Analysis 1, 1–127 (1976)

WALLIHAN, E.F.: Iron, In: H.D. CHAPMAN, (ed.). Diagnostic Criteria for Plants and Soils, p. 203–217. University of California, Division of Agricultural Sciences, 1966

ZHIZNEVSKAYA, G.Ya.: Iron in plant nutrition. Agrochemica, 17, 46–68, (1972)

Chapter 14

Manganese

14.1 Soil Manganese

Manganese occurs in various primary rocks and particularly in ferro-magnesian materials. The Mn released from these rocks by weathering forms a number of secondary minerals the most prominent being pyrolusite (MnO_2) and manganite [MnO (OH)]. Manganese and Fe oxides often occur together in nodules and iron-pans. Total Mn levels may differ considerably between soils. According to SWAINE [1955] Mn contents between 200 and 3000 ppm are most common. The most important Mn soil fractions are Mn^{2+} and the Mn oxides in which Mn is present in trivalent or tetravalent form. Divalent Mn is adsorbed to clay minerals and organic matter and is also the most important Mn form in soil solution. The relationships between the Mn^{2+} and the Mn oxides are presented in Figure 14.1. This so-called Mn cycle in the soil (DION and MANN [1946]) shows that the equilibrium between the various Mn forms is governed by oxidation – reduction processes. The most important fraction in plant nutrition is Mn^{2+}. In addition, easily-reducible Mn contributes to plant supply. These combined fractions, Mn^{2+} and easily-reducible Mn, are called 'active Mn'. As the level of Mn^{2+} in the soil depends on oxidation-reduction reactions, all factors influencing these processes have an impact on Mn availability. These factors include soil pH, organic matter content, microbial activity and soil moisture. Under waterlogged conditions as for example in paddy soils, reducing processes dominate and thus provide a high level of Mn availability which may even result in Mn toxicity (TANAKA and YOSHIDA [1970]). After submergence and almost parallel with the disappearance of O_2, the level of soluble Mn^{2+} rises. In acid soils high in active Mn the concentration of Mn^{2+} may easily attain toxic levels, while in calcareous or sodic soils the Mn level does not rise much after flooding. On these soils Mn deficiency can even occur in rice under submergence conditions (RANDHAWA et al. [1978]). The effect of anaerobic soil conditions (flooding) and of liming on Mn availability as reflected in Mn content of lucerne grown on the soil is shown in Table 14.1 (GRAVEN et al. [1965]).

491

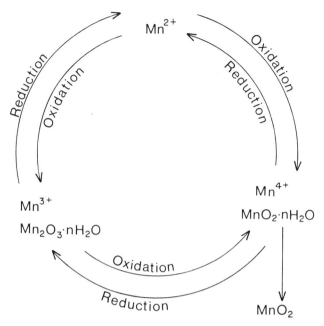

Fig.14.1 Mn oxidation-reduction cycle in the soil (after Dɪᴏɴ and Mᴀɴɴ [1946]).

Table 14.1 Effect of liming and a 3 day period of flooding on dry matter yield and Mn contents in lucerne (Gʀᴀᴠᴇɴ *et al.* [1965])

Treatment g CaCO₃/pot	Flooding	g, DM pot	Mn content ppm Mn in DM
0	−	3.1	426
0	+	1.2	6067
20	−	5.7	99
20	+	3.0	954

Manganese availability is also higher in acid soils due to the higher solubility of Mn compounds under low pH conditions. Lɪɴᴅsᴀʏ [1972] stresses that the soluble Mn^{2+} decreases 100 fold for each unit increase in pH. Under high soil pH conditions Mn availability can thus be inadequate to meet plant demand. According to the investigations of Pᴀɢᴇ [1962] an increase in pH also enhances the production of Mn soil organic matter complexes which also render Mn less available. In addition, the microbial activity which influences Mn oxidation is pH dependent and has an optimum at about pH 7 (Jᴏɴᴇs [1957]). Killing off these Mn oxidizing microorganisms, as for example by steam sterilization, results in an increase in Mn availability (Rᴏʟʟ-Hᴀɴsᴇɴ [1952]). From the above

492

discussion it is clear that soils of high pH with large organic matter reserves are particularly prone to Mn deficiency. It is understandable that liming depresses Mn availability (GISIGER and HASLER [1949], COTTENIE and KIEKENS [1974]), whereas the application of physiologically acid fertilizers, as for example, $(NH_4)_2SO_4$ has a beneficial effect on Mn uptake by plants (KÜHN [1962]). Divalent Mn dissolved in the soil solution is of direct importance in plant nutrition. This dissolved Mn^{2+} is in equilibrium with Mn^{2+} adsorbed to clay minerals and organic matter. According to GEERING et al. [1969], the Mn^{2+} level of the soil solution of acid and neutral soils is in the range of 10^{-6} to 10^{-4} M. These workers suggest that in soil solution Mn is present largely as organic complexes. On the other hand LINDSAY [1974] found that the affinity of Mn^{2+} for synthetic chelates is comparatively low and complexed Mn can easily be replaced by Zn^{2+} and Ca^{2+}. The levels of Mn in soil solution are considerably higher than those of Cu and Zn. Under very dry conditions Mn salts in the soil can be irreversibly dehydrated and thus become less available. Drying, however, may also result in the splitting of Mn double salts. In this process Mn^{2+} is released. Manganese in the divalent form is fairly mobile in the soil and can easily be leached. This happens particularly on acid podzolic soils.

The formation of Mn oxides in soils appears to regulate the levels of Co in soil solution and hence Co availability to plants. According to MCKENZIE [1975] one of the most important properties of soil Co is its association with Mn oxide minerals.

14.2 Manganese in Physiology

14.2.1 Uptake and translocation

As observed by COLLANDER [1941] about 40 years ago, the rate of Mn uptake differs considerably between plant species. Generally, however, uptake rates are lower than for other divalent cation species (Ca^{2+}, Mg^{2+}). There is ample evidence that Mn uptake is metabolically mediated (MOORE [1972]). In a similar way to other divalent cation species, Mn^{2+} participates in cation competition. Magnesium in particular depresses Mn uptake (LÖHNIS [1960], MAAS et al. [1969]). Liming also reduces uptake not only by the direct effect of Ca^{2+} in the soil solution, but also as a result of the pH increase.

In its chemical behaviour, Mn shows properties of both the alkali earth cations such as Mg^{2+} and Ca^{2+} and the heavy metals (Zn, Fe). It is therefore not surprising that these ion species affect uptake and translocation of Mn in the plant (HEWITT [1948]). On the other hand Mn^{2+} may also depress the uptake of other cation species. Figure 14.2 shows such an example, where increasing Mn

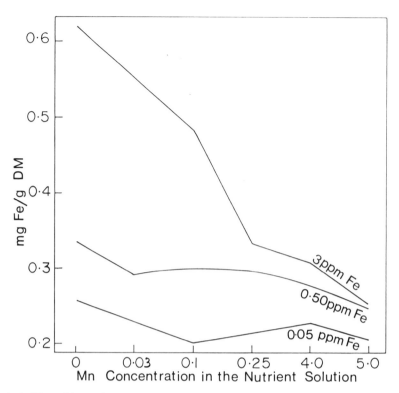

Fig. 14.2 Effect of increasing Mn concentration in the nutrient solution on the Fe content in soya bean plants supplied with three different Fe-levels (after SOMERS and SHIVE [1942]).

supply reduced the Fe content of soya bean plants (SOMERS and SHIVE [1942]). The reduction was particularly marked where a high Fe level (3 ppm) was applied.

SIDERIS and YOUNG [1949] found that plants supplied with NH_4^--N took up lower amounts of Mn^{2+} than NO_3^- fed plants. This result, however, can probably be accounted for by the more general effects of different N sources on cation-anion balance during the uptake process (see p. 136) rather than by a specific competition between NH_4^+ and Mn^{2+} for uptake. According to WITTWER and TEUBNER [1959], Mn is relatively immobile in the plant. It is still not clear whether it can be translocated in the phloem to any extent. TIFFIN [1972] studied the translocation of a number of heavy metals in tomatoes. In electrophoretic examinations of exudates it was found that Mn migrated towards the cathode. It thus appears that Mn is mainly transported as Mn^{2+} and not as an organic complex. Somewhere similar observations have been made in

494

ryegrass extracts by BREMNER and KNIGHT [1970]. Manganese is preferentially translocated to meristematic tissues. Young plant organs are thus generally rich in Mn (AMBERGER [1973]. In solution culture experiments WILLIAMS and VLAMIS [1957] found that the addition of Si improved the distribution of Mn in barley plants.

14.2.2 Biochemical functions

In its biochemical functions Mn^{2+} resembles Mg^{2+}. Both ion species bridge ATP with the enzyme complex (phosphokinases and phosphotransferases). According to LEHNINGER [1975], however, the bridge formed by Mn^{2+} differs slightly from that formed by Mg^{2+}. Decarboxylases and dehydrogenases of the TCA cycle are also activated by Mn^{2+}, although it appears that in most cases Mn^{2+} is not specific for these enzymes and can be substituted by Mg^{2+}. In other reactions there is a specific Mn requirement. Manganese brings about the oxidation of IAA by activating IAA oxidases (MUMFORD et al. [1962]). This finding agrees well with the results of TAYLOR et al. [1968] who observed abnormally high IAA activity in the leaves of Mn deficient cotton plants. The precise mechanism by which Mn activates the oxidases is still not clear, although it is probable that the valency change Mn^{3+} to Mn^{2+} is involved in these oxidative processes.

Manganese is also in some way involved in the oxidation-reduction processes in the photosynthetic electron transport system. According to BISHOP [1971] Mn is essential in photosystem II (see p. 145) where it participates in photolysis (ANDERSON and PYLIOTIS [1969]). When Mn is deficient, the structure of chloroplasts is markedly impaired even when other organelles show no visible alteration (POSSINGHAM et al. [1964]). Two separate Mn fractions were isolated by CHENIAE and MARTIN [1970] in chloroplasts; one was loosely and the other firmly bound to the membrane. It appeared that the loosely bound fraction was associated with O_2 evolution whereas the firmly bound Mn fraction was an essential part of the as yet unknown electron donor in photosystem II. There is an indirect relationship between the influence of Mn on photosynthesis and on NO_2^- reduction (HEWITT [1970]). Inhibition of NO_2^- reduction may also possibly exert a feedback control on NO_3^- reductase activity. Under conditions where the rate of NO_2^- reduction is low it might well be expected that NO_3^- reductase activity should be depressed. An accumulation of NO_3^- should thus result as sometimes occurs in Mn deficient plants.

14.2.3 Deficiency and toxicity

Chloroplasts are the most sensitive of all cell organelles to Mn deficiency (HOMANN [1967]). In whole plants BUSSLER [1958] reported that tissues suffering from Mn deficiency have a small cell volume, cell walls dominate and the interepidermal tissue is shrunken. Manganese deficiency resembles Mg deficiency, as in both cases interveinal chlorosis occurs in the leaves. In contrast to Mg deficiency, however, Mn deficiency symptoms are first visible in the younger leaves, whereas in Mg deficiency the older leaves are first affected. Manganese deficiency symptoms in the dicots are often characterized by small yellow spots on the leaves. In this respect this syndrome differs from that of Fe deficiency where the whole young leaf becomes chlorotic. A typical example of Mn deficiency is presented in the lower part of Plate 14.1, showing Mn deficiency in sugar beet. The deficiency is in an advanced stage and only the veinal areas are still green. In monocots and particularly in oats, Mn deficiency symptoms appear at the basal part of the leaves (FINCK [1956]) as greenish grey spots and stripes. Oats in particular are prone to Mn deficiency during the tillering stage. The disease is known as 'grey speck'. The turgor of the affected plants is reduced and at an advanced stage of disease the upper part of the leaf breaks over near the middle (see Plate 14.1).

The Mn status of plants is reflected in their Mn contents. The critical deficiency level for most plant species is in the range of 15 to 25 ppm Mn in the dry matter of upper plant parts. Figure 14.3 shows a clear relationship between the intensity of Mn deficiency and the Mn content in the foliage of sugar beet (FARLEY and DRAYCOTT 1973).

High levels of Mn can be toxic to plants. In the case of soya bean this occurs when the Mn concentration is in excess of about 160 ppm in the mature foliage (OHKI [1977]). Toxicity symptoms are generally characterized by brown spots particularly in the older leaves and an uneven distribution of chlorophyll (BUSSLER [1958]). The brown spots have been found to consist of precipitates of Mn oxides. Manganese toxicity is considered by MORGAN et al. [1966] to be an expression of auxin deficiency caused in turn by a high IAA oxidase activity. This view is consistent with the findings of HORST and MARSCHNER [1978] of a lower auxin activity in Mn toxic tissue. The lower auxin activity impaired the IAA stimulated proton efflux pump thereby inhibiting cell wall expansion and the formation of new negatively charged sites. The authors were able to demonstrate that the CEC of Mn toxic tissue was lower than that of normal tissue and that the movement of Ca to growing points was restricted under conditions of Mn toxicity (see p. 447)

Plate 14.1 Upper part, 'grey speck' in oats. (Photo: VON PAPEN)
Lower part, Mn deficiency in sugar beet. (Photo: DRAYCOTT)

Manganese toxicity can be counteracted by Si (VLAMIS and WILLIAMS [1967]). The effect appears to result from a depression in Mn uptake in rice (VORM and VAN DIEST [1979]). In beans Si induces a more uniform Mn distribution within the leaf (HORST and MARSCHNER [1978b]). Excess Mn may also induce Fe deficiency (FOY et al. [1978]).

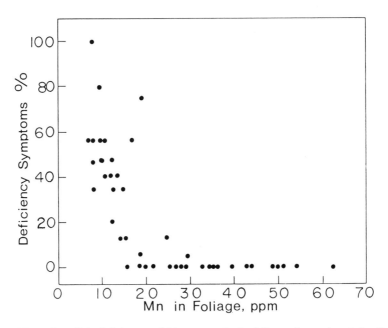

Fig. 14.3 Intensity of Mn deficiency and Mn content in the foliage of sugar beet (after FARLEY and DRAYCOTT [1973]).

14.3 Manganese in Crop Nutrition

Most soils contain adequate levels of available Mn so that Mn applications are unnecessary. The total amount of Mn taken up by arable crops is low and ranges from between 500 to 1000 g Mn/ha (SCHACHTSCHABEL [1955]). Calcareous peat soils (organic soils, high in pH) are particularly low in available Mn and it is on these soils that Mn deficiency often occurs in crops. Application of Mn salts to the soil, *e.g.* $MnSO_4$, is usually of no use in alleviating deficiency, because the applied Mn^{2+} is rapidly oxidized. When such soils are treated with Mn fertilizers, banded placement rather than broadcast application should be carried out. RANDALL and SCHULTE [1971] found that 5.6 kg/ha of banded Mn as sulphate was equivalent to 67.2 kg/ha of broadcast Mn. Generally for soil application $MnSO_4$ is superior to Mn chelates, although foliar application of Mn is frequently recommended on these calcareous organic soils. DRAYCOTT and FARLEY [1973] in comparing soil application of Mn silicate and Mn oxides with Mn foliar sprays found that the soil application did not prevent Mn deficiency in sugar beet whereas Mn foliar application corrected the deficiency and increased sugar yields. Spraying 1 to 5 kg Mn/ha is sufficient to offset deficiency in most crops. According to OZAKI [1955] $MnSO_4$ is considered to be the most effective inorganic carrier of Mn in foliar spray solutions. Of the organic Mn carriers, Mn-EDTA appears to give the best response.

Some podzolic soils are particularly liable to be low in available Mn. This group of soils however, differs from the organic soils already discussed, in that podzols are inherently low in Mn. This low Mn status mainly results from high leaching. Manganese deficiency on these sites is frequently aggravated by liming (ZHIZNEVSKAYA [1958]) because of the resulting pH increase. As Mn^{2+} applied to these soils is not so rapidly oxidized as in the calcareous organic soils, Mn soil applications are well able to correct the deficiency. Rates of about 30 kg Mn/ha as $MnSO_4$ are generally applied. In severe cases, however, levels as high as 100 to 200 kg Mn/ha are recommended (HENKENS [1965]). In addition to the soil types mentioned above alluvial soils and marsh soils derived from calcareous materials are also prone to Mn deficiency. The uptake of Mn by crops can be depressed by high levels of available Fe, Cu or Zn.

The incidence and severity of Mn deficiency appears to depend on seasonal conditions. The deficiency is often worse in cold wet seasons possibly as a result of a reduction in root metabolic activity affecting Mn uptake. Such effects may also account for the increased prevalence of Mn deficiency often observed where good growing conditions follow a cold or dry period (BATEY [1971]).

Soil analysis is not very reliable in diagnozing available soil Mn status in relation to crop response. According to BROWMAN et al. [1969] who compared a number of the standard methods, NH_4-acetate extraction with a correction for pH gave the most satisfactory results. Similar observations were made by FARLEY and DRAYCOTT [1976]. Ammonium acetate extractable Mn correlated best with Mn deficiency, plant Mn, and response to treatment. The most

Table 14.2 Sugar beet response to Mn in relation to NH_4-acetate extractable soil Mn, and Mn in the dried foliage (FARLEY and DRAYCOTT [1976])

Ammonium acetate extractable soil Mn ppm	Plants with symptoms %	Mn in dried foliage ppm	Response
< 1.2	100–50	< 20	large
1.2–1.8	49–25	20–30	small
> 1.8	< 25	> 30	none

important results of this study are shown in Table 14.2. The Mn contents of a large number of crops differing in Mn status is provided in the accumulated data of LABANAUSKAS [1966].

Crops differ in their susceptibility to Mn deficiency. Two of the most well known deficiency diseases in arable crops are grey speck in oats *(Avena sativa)* and marsh spot in peas *(Pisum sativum)*. Other sensitive crops are: apple, cherry, citrus, raspberry, and sugar beet.

On acid soils high in Mn availability, plants can take up considerable amounts of Mn so that levels in the order of 1000 ppm Mn in the dry matter are not uncommon. LÖHNIS [1960] found Mn contents in *Vaccinium myrtillus* higher than 2000 ppm in the dry matter. On such soils Mn toxicity in crops is often observed and is aggravated by reducing conditions in the soil. There is now considerable interest in screening crop genotypes for resistance to Mn toxicity. This is particularly true for some tropical crops when growing conditions are commonly acid and available Mn levels high. FOY [1976] recommends that for Mn screening, soils should be high in total Mn within the pH range of 5.0 to 5.5. Here Mn will be soluble in toxic concentration but Al toxicity will be minimal or absent. Manganese tolerant species and cultivars commonly take up Mn at a lower rate (BROWN *et al.* [1972]).

General Reading of Chapters 14–20 see p. 571

Chapter 15

Zinc

15.1 Soil Zinc

The average Zn content of the lithosphere is about 80 ppm (GOLDSCHMIDT [1954]). In soils it is usually present in the range of 10–300 ppm occurring in a number of different minerals. The ionic radius of Zn^{2+} is very similar to that of Fe^{2+} and Mg^{2+}. To some extent therefore Zn^{2+} may substitute for these ions by isomorphous replacement in mineral structures, in particular in the ferro-magnesian minerals augite, hornblende and biotite. The occurrence of Zn in these minerals makes up the bulk of Zn in many soils. In addition Zn forms a number of salts including ZnS, sphalerite (ZnFe)S, zincite ZnO, and smithsonite $ZnCO_3$. Apart from ZnS, however, which may be present under reducing conditions, most of these salts are too soluble to persist in soils for any length of time (LINDSAY [1972]). The two Zn-silicates $ZnSiO_3$ and Zn_2SiO_4 (willemite) also occur in some soils.

As well as in the occurrence in minerals, Zn may be found on exchange sites of clay minerals and organic matter or adsorbed on solid surfaces. The element may be adsorbed as Zn^{2+}, $ZnOH^+$ or $ZnCl^+$ and may also become non-extractable possibly by entering holes normally occupied by Al^{3+} in the octahedral layer. According to GRIMME [1968] the intensity of Zn adsorption by goethite increases as the pH rises and for this reason the mobility of Zn is particularly restricted in neutral and alkaline soils. The level of Zn in soil solution is very low. HODGSON et al. [1966] reported values of between about 3×10^{-8} to 3×10^{-6} M. Zn solubility is especially low on soils of high pH and particularly when $CaCO_3$ is present.

Zn interacts with soil organic matter, and both soluble and insoluble Zn organic complexes are formed. According to HODGSON et al. [1966], on average, 60% of the soluble Zn in soil occurs in soluble Zn organic complexes. STEVEN-SON and ARDAKANI [1972] in a review of micronutrient organic matter reactions concluded that soluble Zn organic complexes are mainly associated with amino, organic and fulvic acids whilst insoluble organic complexes are derived from humic acids.

The level of Zn in soils is very much related to the parent material. Soils originating from basic igneous rocks are high in Zn. In contrast soils derived from more siliceous parent materials are particularly low. Occasionally very high levels of Zn may occur in soils which have been affected by mineral wastes.

15.2 Zinc in Physiology

15.2.1 Uptake and translocation

The levels of Zn in plant material are low and as shown in Table 15.1 are generally in the order of up to 100 ppm in the dry matter. The Zn requirement of plants is correspondingly small. CARROLL and LONERAGAN [1969] obtained maximum or near maximum yields of 8 different plant species in flowing water culture experiments with Zn concentrations in the range of 0.01×10^{-6} M to 2.5×10^{-6} M. Maximum yields of plants were obtained with an uptake of between 10–30 ng atoms of Zn per gram of fresh root material per day. The results are considerably lower than those found in earlier investigations using static water cultures (SCHMID et al. [1965]). In this latter investigation higher values may well have resulted because of the difficulty in avoiding root depletion effects. The availability and uptake of Zn and other micronutrients has been considered by LONERAGAN [1975] in an excellent review paper.

There is considerable disagreement in the literature as to whether Zn uptake is active or passive. This has been discussed in some detail by MOORE [1972]. He holds the view that on balance the evidence suggests that Zn uptake is metabolically controlled. LINDSAY [1972] has also pointed out that much of the controversy arises because early workers did not differentiate between passive exchange adsorption and active accumulation in cells. In plant roots 90% of the total Zn may occur on exchange sites or adsorbed to surfaces of the cell

Table 15.1 Zinc content of various crops ppm DM (BOEHLE and LINDSAY [1969])

	Deficient	Low	Sufficient	High
Apple Leaves	0–15	16–20	21– 50	>51
Citrus Leaves	0–15	16–25	26– 80	81–200
Lucerne Tops	0–15	16–20	21– 70	>71
Maize Leaves	0–10	11–20	21– 70	71–150
Soya Bean Tops	0–10	11–20	21– 70	71–150
Tomato Leaves	0–10	11–20	21–120	>120

walls in the cortex. Conclusions of passive Zn uptake from short term experiments must therefore be regarded with suspicion. SCHMID et al. [1965] using barley roots observed a steady state uptake rate for Zn typical of metabolic uptake. Zn uptake was considerably reduced by low temperature and metabolic inhibitors. The same observation was made in sugar cane leaf (BOWEN [1969]). In addition both experiments showed that Cu strongly inhibits Zn uptake. It seems possible that these two ions compete for the same carrier site. Similar competitive effects of Fe and Mn on Zn uptake have been reported in rice seedlings (GIORDANO et al. [1974]). In addition these workers showed that severe retardation of Zn absorption is brought about by various metabolic inhibitors. Depressing effects on Zn uptake by the alkaline earths ($Mg^{2+} > Ca^{2+} = Sr^{2+} = Ba^{2+}$) over a wide concentration range have also been observed in wheat plants (CHAUDHRY and LONERAGAN [1972]).

The form in which Zn is translocated from the roots to the upper plant parts is not known. However, Zn has been detected in xylem exudates of decapitated tomato and soya bean plants in considerably higher concentrations than in the bathing solution of the roots (TIFFIN [1967], AMBLER et al. [1970]). Electrophoretic evidence indicates that Zn is not bound to stable ligands as is the case with Cu^{2+}, Ni^{2+} and Fe^{3+}. In tomato exudates TIFFIN [1967] observed that Zn is slightly cathodic and concluded that it is not translocated as citrate, as zinc citrate complexes are anodic. The mobility of Zn in plants is not great. Zinc accumulates in root tissues especially when Zn supply is high. In older leaves Zn can become very immobile (RINNE and LANGSTON [1960]). The rate of Zn mobility to younger tissues is particularly depressed in Zn deficient plants (LONERAGAN [1975]).

The interaction between Zn and P has been studied by many workers, and high levels of P supply are well known to induce Zn-deficiency. Leaving aside the soil-plant relationship which is discussed later, it has been shown that excess phosphate results in a metabolic disorder and may lead to Zn deficiency symptoms. Thus MARSCHNER and SCHROPP [1977] found that high phosphate rates to vine grown in pot experiments using a calcareous soil induced Zn deficiency symptoms in the leaves. In addition growth depression and low Zn concentrations were observed in the younger leaves. In parallel solution culture experiments these workers were not able to induce Zn deficiency, although the Zn concentrations in the leaves of the vine plants were lower than the Zn concentration found in the leaves with Zn deficiency symptoms. It is suggested that phosphate may affect the physiological Zn availability in plant tissues. The old idea that Zn becomes ineffective in metabolism because it precipitates as $Zn_3(PO_4)_2 . 4H_2O$ can now largely be ignored. The solubility of the compound is such that this is too high to cause Zn deficiency unless it becomes physically separated from the plant sap. The literature on Zn/P relationships in plants has been well reviewed by OLSEN [1972].

An interaction between Zn and Fe has been observed by WARNOCK [1970]. Phosphorus induced Zn-deficient maize plants were found to accumulate high levels of Fe, and to a lesser extent Mn. Interference of excess Fe was suggested as a contributory factor in the physiological malnutrition of Zn-deficient plants.

15.2.2 Biochemical functions

In its function in some enzyme systems, Zn^{2+} resembles Mn^{2+} and Mg^{2+} in that it brings about the binding and conformation between enzyme and substrate. A number of enzymes including enolase are thus activated in more or less the same way by Mn^{2+}, Mg^{2+} or Zn^{2+}. Until relatively recently the only authenticated enzyme specifically activated by Zn^{2+} was carbonic anhydrase. This enzyme catalyses the reaction

$$H_2O + CO_2 \rightleftarrows H^+ + HCO_3^-$$

This enzyme has been shown to be localized in the chloroplasts (JACOBSON et al. [1975]). These workers suppose that it functions in mediating short term transient pH effects thus acting as a buffer. It is suggested that because of the highly concentrated nature of the enzyme in the stroma it is able to protect proteins from denaturation from local pH changes associated with H^+ pumps (see p. 152) and the incorporation of CO_2 into ribulose 1.5 bisphosphate. In the last few years other Zn metallo-enzymes have been recognized. These include a number of dehydrogenases in particular glutamic acid dehydrogenase, lactic acid dehydrogenase, alcohol dehydrogenase as well as proteinases and peptidases (VALLEE and WACKER [1970]).

Zn is closely involved in the N-metabolism of the plant. PRICE et al. [1972] cite a number of references indicating that the earliest possible causal event of Zn deficiency is a sharp decrease in the levels of RNA and the ribosome content of cells. This reduction in RNA synthesis leads to an inhibition of protein formation whilst glucose, nonprotein N and DNA are relatively increased (PRICE [1962]). PRASKE and PLOCKE [1971] have observed in *Euglena gracilis* that the cytoplasmic ribosomes which usually contain substantial amounts of Zn become extremely unstable with Zn deficiency. This finding may well relate to the reduction in RNA synthesis. Zn is required in the synthesis of tryptophan (TSUI [1948]). As tryptophan is also a precursor of indole acetic acid the formation of this growth substance is also indirectly influenced by Zn.

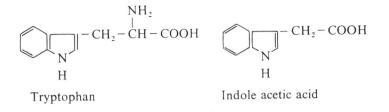

Tryptophan   Indole acetic acid

In Zn deficient tomato plants Tsui [1948] observed low rates of stem elongation, low auxin activities and low tryptophan contents. More recently Salami and Kenefick [1970] have confirmed this work growing maize in nutrient solution. These workers found that Zn deficiency symptoms could be eliminated by additions of either Zn or tryptophan to the nutrient medium thus providing indirect evidence of the necessity of Zn for the synthesis of optimum tryptophan levels. In complete contrast to these results Takaki and Kushizaki [1970] who also worked with maize found higher levels of tryptophan in Zn deficient plants and concluded that Zn is required in the synthesis of indole acetic acid from tryptophan. As has been pointed out be Price [1970], a causal relationship between Zn, tryptophan and indole acetic acid has yet to be established.

According to Jyung *et al.* [1975] Zn has a possible role in plant metabolism involved in starch formation. These authors compared the behaviour of two cultivars of navy bean *(Phaseolus vulgaris)* grown under Zn deficient conditions, one susceptible to Zn deficiency and the other not. It was found that the starch content, the activity of the enzyme starch synthetase, and the number starch grains were all more depressed in the susceptible cultivar. The study proved a very close inverse relationship between the degree of Zn deficiency and starch formation. Whether this effect on starch formation is a primary result of Zn deficiency still remains an open question.

Zinc along with Cu has been shown to be a constituent of the enzyme superoxide dismutase. This enzyme brings about the decomposition of O_2^- radicals which can be produced from molecular O_2. It thus protects aerobic organisms from attack by O_2^- radicals (see p. 517).

15.2.3 Zinc deficiency

Plants suffering from Zn-deficiency often show chlorosis in the interveinal areas of the leaf. These areas are pale green, yellow, or even white. In the monocots and particularly in maize, chlorotic bands form on either side of the midrib of the leaf. In fruit trees leaf development is adversely affected. Unevenly distributed clusters or rosettes of small stiff leaves are formed at the ends of the

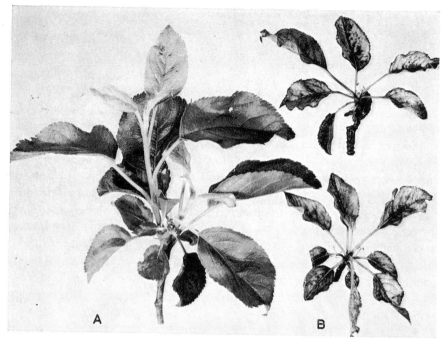

Plate 15.1 Zn deficiency of apple trees (little leaf):
  A: Normal shoot
  B: Zn deficient shoots. Note rosetting, upward curling and waviness of leaf margins, and interveinal chlorosis. (Photo: BOULD)

young shoots. Frequently the shoots die off and the leaves fall prematurely. In apple trees the disease occurs in the early part of the year and is known as rosette or little-leaf. This deficiency is shown in Plate 15.1. Not only is leaf development restricted. Fewer buds are formed and of those that are, many remain closed. Crop yields are consequently drastically reduced. The bark of Zn deficient trees too is characteristically affected and is rough and brittle (BOULD *et al.* [1949]. Symptoms of Zn deficiency in vegetable crops are more species-related than are deficiency symptoms of other plant nutrients. In most cases, however, Zn deficiency is characterized by short internodes and chlorotic areas in older leaves. Sometimes chlorosis also appears in younger leaves (MAYNARD [1979]). Zn deficiency is closely related to the inhibition of RNA synthesis. The deficiency prevents the normal development of chloroplast grana and vacuoles are developed in them (THOMSON and WEIER [1962], JYUNG *et al.* [1975]). The level of Zn in Zn-deficient plants is low as shown in Table 15.1 and usually in the range of about 0–15 ppm in the dry matter (BOEHLE and LINDSAY [1969]).

15.2.4 Zinc toxicity and tolerance

Zn toxicity may occur in areas particularly in the neighbourhood of Zn ore deposits and spoil heaps. Some plant species, however, are Zn tolerant and are able to grow in soils abnormally high in Zn. ANTONOVICS *et al.* [1971], for example, quote Zn levels of between 600 to 7800 ppm in the dry matter of tolerant plant species growing in calamine soils.

BRADSHAW [1952] working in North Wales, a region that was formerly extensively mined for minerals, showed that populations of the grass *Agrostis tenuis* had evolved which were tolerant to the Zn and Pb contaminated soils of the area. Much valuable information into the mechanism of heavy metal tolerance has stemmed from this observation, for the use of tolerant and non-tolerant plant strains has provided a very useful means of investigating Zn and other heavy metal toxicities. Zinc tolerant races of *Agrostis tenuis* take up more Zn into the roots than non-tolerant plants (ANTONOVICS *et al.* [1971]). Part of the Zn tolerance mechanism is dependent on the ability of the tolerant strains to bind Zn in the cell walls (TURNER [1969]). In experiments with Zn-65 PETER-SEN [1969] observed that Zn is especially associated with the pectate fraction in tolerant ecotypes. There is considerable evidence, however, that cell wall binding in the roots is not the only mechanism by which high concentrations of Zn are restricted from active metabolic sites. Some plants species and ecotypes are able to tolerate very high levels of Zn in the leaves and other upper plant parts. For example CARLES *et al.* [1969] reported very high levels of Zn (1000 ppm) in the leaves of the Zn tolerant species *Armeria helleri*. This observation is consistent with the results of WAINWRIGHT and WOOLHOUSE [1975] who found almost equal levels of Zn in Zn tolerant and Zn susceptible *Agrostis tenuis* plants growing in water culture high in Zn. The susceptible plants, however, had lost 50% of their chlorophyll, whereas the tolerant plants were not affected.

There is some biochemical evidence to account for the fact that leaves are able to contain high Zn contents without suffering toxic effects. In a study of a Zn tolerant cultivar of *Phaseolus vulgaris*, RATHORE *et al.* [1972] observed no enhanced Zn accumulation in cell walls but very high levels in the cytoplasm. It appears that mitochondria are in some way involved in Zn inactivation. This is strongly suggested from the results of TURNER and MARSHALL [1972] who observed a positive linear relationship between the degree of Zn tolerance of *Agrostis tenuis* and the capacity of mitochondrial preparations from the plants to bind Zn. WYN-JONES *et al.* [1971] have also observed that oxygen uptake by mitochondria from Zn tolerant *Agrostis tenuis* was inhibited by Zn to a lesser extent than by mitochondria extracted from the susceptible ecotypes.

According to DENAEYER-DE SMET [1970] some plant species tolerate high

Zn levels in the soil due to their low uptake ability for Zn. Physiological mechanisms of heavy metal tolerance in plants are discussed in a very useful paper by WAINWRIGHT and WOOLHOUSE [1975].

Zinc toxicity results in a reduction in root growth and leaf expansion which is followed by chlorosis. In soya beans RAUSER [1973] observed that a red-brown pigment, probably a phenolic substance, is distributed throughout the plant. High levels of Zn in the nutrient medium depress the uptake of P and Fe (ADRIANO et al. [1971]).

15.3 Zinc in Crop Nutrition

15.3.1 Crop requirement and availability

Zn deficiency is one of the commonest micronutrient deficiencies and it is becoming increasingly significant in crop production. The susceptibility of crop plants to Zn deficiency varies considerably depending on species and even cultivars. The cereals such as oats, barley, wheat, and rye as well as the grasses are rather insensitive. Other crops such as potatoes, tomatoes, sugar beet, and lucerne are only moderately sensitive whilst some crops including maize, hops, flax, and field beans are highly susceptible to Zn deficiency (VIETS et al. [1954]). This final group along with fruit trees, citrus and grapes may be regarded as test crops for Zn availability.

In most soils the total Zn content by far exceeds crop requirement and availability is the important limiting factor. Some highly leached acid soils, however, are very poor in Zn with total values of 10–30 ppm. Soil solution concentrations and labile Zn level in particular are often low, and Zn deficiency may result from the inherently low Zn content of the soil.

Zn mobility in soils is important in relation to Zn availability. ELGAWHARY et al. [1970] calculated the fractions of Zn taken up by maize due to mass flow and diffusion (see p.65). Mass flow was determined as described by BARBER [1962] as the product of soil solution concentration and the water transpired by the plant. Diffusion was calculated as the difference between total uptake and mass flow. The results of ELGAWHARY et al. [1970] showed that 95% of the total Zn is moved by diffusion. Diffusion gradients may therefore occur, and root depletion zones similar to those of phosphate have been demonstrated using autoradiographs (BARBER et al. [1963]). As plant species differ in their Zn requirements, LINDSAY [1972] has suggested that this may be one factor explaining differences in sensitivity to Zn deficiency, for plants growing in identical environments. Factors which limit the rate of diffusion of Zn to plant roots must

508

also reduce Zn availability. This is probably the most important reason why Zn deficiency often occurs on compacted soils or where root growth is restricted as in container grown plants.

The concentration of water soluble Zn in soil solution falls with increasing pH. Liming thus depresses Zn uptake, as has been observed in ryegrass by COTTENIE and KIEKENS [1974]. From the practical viewpoint this is of importance as Zn deficiency occurs more usually on naturally high pH soils or on highly limed soils. Calcareous soils are particularly prone to Zn-deficiency. TANAKA and YOSHIDA [1970] in surveying the most important rice growing areas of Asia found that Zn deficiency of rice only occurs on soils with high pH and in particular on calcareous soils of high pH. The availability of Zn is reduced by flooding because of the formation of sulphides and carbonates under anaerobic conditions (YOSHIDA et al. [1971]). It appears that Zn deficiency in flooded rice soils results from the combined effect of high pH, high HCO_3^- levels, sulphide production and impeded internal drainage. The deficiency is often accompanied by visible symptoms of Fe toxicity.

In an analogous way to Fe (see Figure 13.3) the availability of Zn also depends on the content of chelating agents in the soil, which can be exuded by plant roots or result from the decomposition of organic matter (LINDSAY [1974]). This is probably the reason, why many workers have established a high correlation between available Zn and soil organic matter (FOLLETT and LINDSAY [1970]), and why Zn deficiency frequently occurs on sites where the organic surface soil has been removed. According to LINDSAY [1974] various metallic ions compete for the binding sites of chelating agents. The Zn^{2+} of the Zn EDTA complex is completely replaced by Ca^{2+} at higher pH values. This replacement of Zn^{2+} by Ca^{2+} may well account for the low Zn availability on high pH calcareous soils. The close relationship between chelating effects and Zn availability is also reflected in an investigation of HAQ and MILLER [1972]. These workers found a significant correlation between the Zn content of young maize shoots sampled on 85 sites in Ontario and the Zn extracted from these soils by chelating agents (Ethylene-diamine-tetraacetate = EDTA and Diethylene-triamine-pentaacetate = DTPA). On the other hand organic matter may restrict Zn availability. Some organic soils particularly peats and humic gley soils are deficient in Zn (LUCAS and KNEZEK [1972]). A low total Zn level may be an important contributory factor but availability factors also play a role. In practice high available phosphate levels in soil are well known to reduce Zn availability. It was formerly held that this occurred because the formation of zinc phosphate $Zn_3(PO_4)_2 4H_2O$ in the soil reduced the Zn concentration in the soil solution to deficiency levels. However this was not observed in experiments testing the solubility of this compound under various conditions (JURINAK and INOUYE

[1962]). These workers found that even when the solubility was at a minimum it was over 100 times greater than the Zn concentration required for maximum growth as determined by CARROLL and LONERAGEN [1969]. It seems likely therefore that the physiological effects of Zn/P interactions in the plants as discussed previously are more important in limiting Zn availability than Zn/P soil relationships.

Zinc deficiency may relate to climatic conditions. In some areas cool temperatures and wet spring seasons bring about the onset of this deficiency (LUCAS and KNEZEK [1972]). This may be dependent to some extent on restricted root development in cool soils or a depression in the microbiological release of Zn from organic matter caused by low temperatures.

15.3.2 Zinc application

Zn uptake by crops is usually less than 0.5 kg/ha/yr. In practice Zn deficiency is easy to correct either by spraying or by soil application with Zn fertilizers. Applications are usually in the range of about 4 kg/ha of Zn and this is effective for 3 to 8 years. $ZnSO_4$ is the most commonly used fertilizer largely because of its high solubility. On acid sandy soils it may be preferable to spray the crop or use a less readily available Zn source because $ZnSO_4$ is very easily leached. The same applies to alkaline soils which fix Zn very strongly. Under such conditions Zn chelates are often used. With the intensification of agricultural production in tropical and subtropical zones the occurrence of Zn deficiency has increased. DE [1974] found enormous grain yield increases of pearl millet by an application of $ZnSO_4$/ha on sandy soils in India. The effect of Zn application on the grain yield of wheat on two locations in Egypt is shown in Table 15.2. On the alluvial soil the Zn response was only modest and the foliar application was as efficient as the soil application. For the calcareous soil, the soil application of Zn resulted in a marked increase in grain yield (SERRY et al. [1974]). RANDHA-WA et al. [1978] hold the view that many rice growing areas are deficient in Zn and merit Zn application. Rates of 50 to 100 kg $ZnSO_4$/ha are recommended.

Table 15.2 Effect of Zn application on the grain yield of wheat (SERRY et al. [1974])

Treatments	Alluvial Soil	Calcareous soil
	tonnes/ha	
NPK	4.21	1.49
NPK + Zn foliar spray...........................	4.67	1.54
NPK + 24 kg $ZnSO_4$/ha soil appl.	4.68	1.86
NPK + 48 kg $ZnSO_4$/ha soil appl.	4.62	2.09

Zinc application together with gypsum has often proved to be especially beneficial (TAKKAR and SINGH [1978]). It is of particular interest that rice is prone to Zn deficiency under cold weather conditions. Generally soil Zn application is superior to a foliar spray. A detailed discussion of Zn fertilizers and their use is given by GIORDANO and MORTVEDT [1972] and by LINDSAY [1972].

Chapter 16

Copper

16.1 Soil Copper

Copper occurs in the soil almost exclusively in divalent form. The largest fraction of Cu is usually present in the crystal lattices of primary and secondary minerals. In addition Cu occurs in organic compounds, is present as an exchangeable cation on soil colloids and is a constituent of the soil solution. In a fractionation study of Cu in British soils, MCLAREN and CRAWFORD [1973] found total Cu levels in the range of about 5–50 ppm, a high proportion of which was present in occluded or lattice form. The Cu concentration of the soil solution is usually very low being in the range of 1×10^{-8} to 60×10^{-8} M. HODGSON et al. [1966] observed that more than 98% of soil solution Cu is complexed with organic matter. Copper is, in fact, more strongly bound to organic matter than are other micronutrient cations (e.g. Zn^{2+}, Mn^{2+}), and Cu organic complexes play an important role in regulating Cu mobility and availability in the soil.

In comparison with other cations Cu is held very tightly on inorganic exchange sites (GRIMME [1968]) and this exchangeable form is not readily available to plants. However, cation exchange for Cu^{2+} and $CuOH^+$ can take place and H^+ appears to be the most effective ion in this respect. At least as the soil pH is increased by liming Cu availability generally declines. The Cu concentration in soil solution in chalk soils is particularly low. According to LINDSAY [1972] the level of Cu in soil solution decreases with increasing pH due to stronger Cu adsorption. The equilibrium concentration of Cu maintained by sparingly soluble Cu salts such as carbonates and oxides is higher than the normal levels of Cu in the soil solution. The presence of carbonates or oxides in the soil therefore plays no part in restricting Cu availability. The Cu concentration in the soil solution is governed by copper adsorption to soil particles.

As Cu is strongly bound to soils it is very immobile. Copper added to the soil as a result of the use of Cu containing sprays or fertilizers is thus largely restricted to the upper soil horizons (DELAS [1963]). The Cu content of many soils therefore decreases down the profile. Copper displacement from soils can be brought about either by strong acids or the use of organic compounds which form Cu complexes. The significance of these complexing reagents can be appreciated by the fact that KCN is capable of extracting more than 50% of the total soil Cu whereas non-complexing reagents extract only very small quantities. BERINGER [1963] investigated the effects of a number of complexing reagents on Cu availability. Applying $CuSO_4$ to a humic sandy soil poor in Cu resulted in an almost total adsorption of Cu after two hours. When the same soil was treated with different Cu chelates, however, only a small proportion of the added Cu was adsorbed. The extent of copper adsorption decreased as the stability constants of the applied chelates increased (Table 16.1.).

Table 16.1 Cu adsorption of various Cu compounds by a humic sandy soil, low in Cu (BERINGER [1963])

Cu compound	Stability constant (log K)	Adsorption in % of the total Cu applied
$CuSO_4$	−	99.4
Cu-nitrilo triacetate	12.1	44.5
Cu-ethylene diamine tetraacetate	18.3	7.3
Cu-diaminocylohexan-N, N′-tetraacetate	21.3	5.3

As Cu deficiency occurs primarily on humus rich soils which bind Cu^{2+} very strongly, it may be supposed that certain defined organic forms are more readily able to render Cu unavailable. This has been confirmed by neutron activation studies of organically bound Cu in soil solution by MERCER and RICHMOND [1970]. These workers showed that Cu availability in organic soils depended not only on the concentration in soil solution but also on the form in which the Cu occurred. Copper complexes in the soil solution of molecular weight <1000 were much more available to plants than Cu complexes with a molecular weight in excess of 5000.

16.2 Copper in Physiology

16.2.1 Uptake and translocation

Copper is taken up by the plant in only very small quantities. The Cu content of most plants is generally between 2–20 ppm in the dry plant material. It is thus about one-tenth of the Mn content. Copper uptake appears to be a metabolically mediated process and there is evidence that Cu strongly inhibits the uptake of Zn and *vice versa* (SCHMID *et al.* [1965], BOWEN [1969]). This apart, however, the uptake of Cu is largely independent of competitive effects and relates primarily to the levels of available Cu in the soil. Using excised roots from different plant species KELLER and DEUEL [1958] established that Cu is able to displace most other ions from root exchange sites and is very strongly bound in the root free space. This observation may well account for the finding that roots are frequently higher in Cu content than other plant tissues (RUSS [1958], HILL [1973]).

Copper is not readily mobile in the plant although it can be translocated from older to younger leaves. Results of LONERAGAN [1975] show that the movement of Cu is strongly dependent on the Cu status of the plant. In wheat plants well supplied with Cu, movement from the leaves to the grains can readily occur, but in deficient plants Cu is relatively immobile. In a number of plant species TIFFEN [1972] showed that Cu is present in xylem exudates in anionic Cu complex form. Several anionic forms of Cu have also been observed in ryegrass (BREMNER and KNIGHT [1970]). As Cu has a strong affinity for the N atom of amino acids, TIFFIN [1972] suggests that it is quite likely that these compounds act as Cu carriers in plant fluids.

16.2.2 Biochemical functions

Relatively high concentrations of Cu occur in chloroplasts. NEISH [1939] found that about 70% of the total Cu in the leaf was bound in these organelles. In this respect Cu is similar to iron. Copper is a contituent of the chloroplast protein plastocyanin which forms part of the electron transport chain linking the two photochemical systems of photosynthesis (BISHOP [1966], BOARDMAN [1975]). Additional evidence suggests that Cu may play a part in the synthesis or the stability of chlorophyll and other plant pigments although the mechanism is not clear.

Several Cu containing enzymes are known that catalyze reactions that reduce both atoms of molecular oxygen. These oxidases include cytochrome oxidase as well as a number of other enzymes including ascorbic acid oxidase, polyphenol oxidase and laccase. The reactions brought about by ascorbic acid oxidase and polyphenol oxidases (tyrosinase), involve both a reduction of oxygen and a hydroxylation. This is illustrated below from the review of GUNSALUS *et al.* [1975]. Dopamine is the amine of di-hydroxyphenylalanine. The enzyme dopamine-β-hydroxylase which catalyzes the reaction is ascorbic acid oxidase.

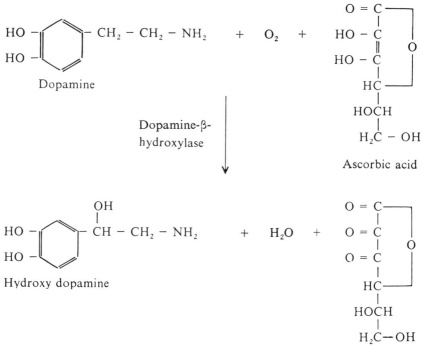

Dopamine   + O$_2$ +   Ascorbic acid

Dopamine-β-hydroxylase

Hydroxy dopamine   + H$_2$O +   Dehydroascorbic acid

In phenol oxidation reactions, monophenols and diphenols are involved according to the following reaction sequence:

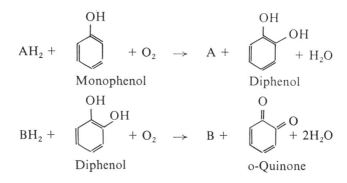

AH_2 + Monophenol + O$_2$ → A + Diphenol + H$_2$O

BH_2 + Diphenol + O$_2$ → B + o-Quinone + 2H$_2$O

It is characteristic of this type of reaction that O$_2$ is split into its atomic components; one O atom is used in the hydroxylation reaction and the other for the production of H$_2$O. In this reaction the monophenol molecule is oxidized to a diphenol which in turn is oxidized to an o-quinone compound. Accumulation of these o-quinones may give rise to polymerisation whereby dark brown melanin compounds are formed. This occurs when fruit and potatoes are cut open and the tissues exposed to the oxygen of the atmosphere.

Recent experimental data suggest that the desaturation and the hydroxylation of fatty acid is also catalyzed by Cu containing enzymes (WAHLE and DAVIES [1977]). Thus the desaturation of stearic acid by Δ9-desaturase which results in the production of oleic acid requires Cu and O_2. It is believed that Cu mediates in these oxidation reactions by undergoing cyclic oxidation associated with electron transfer.

$$Cu^{2+} \rightleftharpoons Cu^+ - e^-$$

In the oxidized proteins it is supposed that the Cu atoms are present as a $Cu^{2+} - Cu^{2+}$ pair thus enabling the transfer of two electrons to one molecule of oxygen.

An interesting development has taken place concerning the role of Cu and Zn in biochemistry. Both these elements have been found to be present in the enzyme superoxide dismutase which occurs ubiquitously in all aerobic organisms (McCORD et al. [1971], FRIDOVICH [1975]). The molecular weight of the enzyme is about 32 000 and it contains 2 Cu atoms and 2 Zn atoms. The reaction it catalyzes is the dismutation of superoxide radicals.

$$O_2^- + O_2^- + 2 H^+ \rightarrow O_2 + H_2O_2$$

The superoxide radical which can be readily produced from molecular O_2, is a highly reactive free radical form of oxygen and extremely detrimental to cells. The presence of superoxide dismutase thus enables organisms to survive in the presence of molecular O_2. It is now believed that obligately anaerobic organisms cannot withstand molecular O_2 because of the absence of superoxide dismutase.

It seems possible that besides its already well established roles Cu has other functions in plant metabolism. Numerous indications of this occur in the literature. Copper appears to participate both in protein and carbohydrate metabolism. In Cu deficient plants protein synthesis is disturbed and there is a build up of soluble amino-N compounds (POSSINGHAM [1956]). This can be explained both by the function of Cu as a cofactor in enzyme synthesis, as well as by the possible effect of Cu on DNA and RNA synthesis. In young growing organs, where protein synthesis is most active, lower levels of DNA have been observed in Cu deficient tissues (OZOLINA and LAPINA [1965]).

Observations of HALLSWORTH et al. [1960] suggest that there is a specific requirement for Cu in symbiotic N_2 fixation. At low levels of Cu nutrition nodulation of *Trifolium subterraneum* was considerably depressed, although as yet no mechanism for this has been identified. It is supposed that Cu may be involved in leghaemoglobin synthesis (HALLSWORTH et al. [1960]). Another possiblity is that Cu deficiency depresses the activity of the terminal oxidase (cytochrome oxidase) in the nodules which in turn results in an increase in the O_2 tension in nodular cells unfavourable for N_2 fixation (CARTWRIGHT and HALLSWORTH [1970]).

16.2.3 Copper deficiency and toxicity

Copper deficiency is well known in a number of different crop plants. In cereal crops the deficiency shows first in the leaf tips at tillering although in severe cases it may appear even earlier. The tips become white and the leaves are narrow and twisted. The growth of the internodes is depressed (BROWN et al. [1958]). As growth progresses the deficiency becomes more severe and in extreme cases ear or panicle formation is absent (see Plate 16.1). A typical feature of the deficiency in cereals is the bushy habit of the plants with white twisted tips and a reduction in panicle formation. When the deficiency is less pronounced panicle formation may occur but the ears are not fully developed and may be partially blind (SCHARRER and SCHAUMLÖFFEL [1960]). This symptom is associated with the role of Cu in pollen grain viability. In Cu deficient trees the development of 'pendula' forms may occur (OLDENKAMP and SMILDE [1966]). It is believed that this deficiency symptom relates especially to the role of Cu in polyphenol oxidase acitivity and hence the synthesis of lignins. According to RAHIMI and BUSSLER [1973] lignification is inhibited in Cu deficient tissue and this is associated with inadequate development in xylem vessels. This function of Cu explains the close relationship in cereals between Cu nutritional status and haulm stability. It also clarifies the interaction between Cu and N fertilizer application in relation to lodging. (VETTER and TEICHMANN [1968]). The characteristic behaviour of Cu deficiency affecting newly developing tissues, appears to be dependent on the low mobility of Cu in deficient plants (LONERAGAN [1975]). A detailed survey of symptoms of Cu deficiency in a number of crop plants is given by REUTHER and LABANAUSKAS [1966] and CALDWELL [1971].

For most plant species high amounts of Cu in the nutrient medium are toxic to growth. The effect appears to relate in part to the ability of Cu to displace other metal ions and particularly Fe from physiologically important centres. Chlorosis is thus a commonly observed symptom of Cu toxicity, superficially resembling Fe deficiency (DANIELS et al. [1972]).

The inhibition of root growth is one of the most rapid responses to toxic Cu levels. WAINWRIGHT and WOOLHOUSE [1975] compared the effects of increasing Cu concentrations in a nutrient culture on the plasmalemma of the roots of a non-tolerant and a Cu-tolerant race of Agrostis tenuis. Damage to the plasma-

Plate 16.1 Cu deficiency in oats, left normal, right, deficient
(Photo: MENGEL)

lemma as measured by K+ leakage was considerably higher in the non tolerant race. It was concluded that as the effect of excess Cu was to damage membrane structure, part of the Cu tolerance behaviour operates through an exclusion mechanism in the plasmalemma. Calcium plays an essential role in maintaining membrane structure (see p. 129). The findings of WALLACE *et al.* [1966] that high levels of Ca alleviate Cu toxicity thus also supports the view that excess Cu exerts a detrimental influence on membrane structure.

In an investigation of the flora of high Cu bearing soils in Zaire, DUVIGNEAUD and DENAYER-DE SMET [1959] observed that some plant species were capable of accumulating Cu to levels of the order of 1000 ppm in the dry matter. Why such plants show no signs of Cu toxicity let alone are able to grow on these soils at all is not yet clear. Some species do accumulate a high proportion of Cu in the roots so that it may be supposed that in part exclusion of uptake is operative. Large amounts of Cu may therefore be bound to the negatively charged sites of the pectic substances (COO⁻ groups) in the cell walls in the root cortex. In other species, however, there is no doubt that anywhere from 2 to 50 times the normal values of Cu are found in leaves. In these plants the toxic

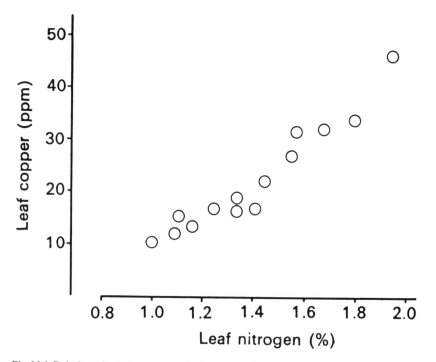

Fig. 16.1 Relationship between N and Cu content in the leaves of the Rhodesian copper flower, *Becium homblei* (after REILLY [1969]).

behaviour of excess Cu is in some way prevented. The results of REILLY [1969] presented in Figure 16.1 perhaps give an indication of how this may occur. The Figure shows that in the leaves of *Becium homblei*, the Rhodesian copper flower and a Cu tolerant plant, that there is a remarkably high correlation ($r = 0.84$) between the values for Cu and the total N. These results provide no physiological evidence of any relationship between Cu and N. Nevertheless, as pointed out by REILLY [1969] there is evidence that Cu may form coordinate compounds with NH_2 groups characteristic of amino acids and proteins. Such observations have been made by TIFFIN [1972]. These findings might offer an explanation as to why some plants are Cu tolerant, for if Cu in the plant is complexed, it is likely that the access of Cu^{2+} to physiologically active centres is restricted even though the plant may have a very high Cu level.

16.3   Copper in Crop Nutrition

16.3.1 Crop requirement and availability

As the total Cu content of plant material is normally less than 10 ppm the Cu requirement of crop plants is correspondingly small. Most soils contain adequate levels of available Cu to meet this demand. Soils in which Cu deficiency occurs are either inherently low in Cu or more usually are poor in available Cu. The Cu inherently low group includes soils which are excessively leached, such as the sandy podzolic soils and soils developed on parent material poor in copper. Included in the second category where availability limits plant uptake are organic and peaty soils, calcareous soils and some soils high in clay content. Copper deficiency is common on newly reclaimed peats and for this reason the deficiency has been called 'reclamation disease'.

Crop plants differ in their sensitivity to Cu deficiency. In general, the most responsive crops to Cu fertilizers are oats, spinach, wheat, and lucerne. In the medium range are cabbage, cauliflower, sugar beet and maize, whilst beans, grass, potatoes, and soya beans show a low response. The influence of Cu fertilization on oats, one of the most sensitive crops, is shown in Table 16.2 from the results of SCHARRER and SCHAUMLÖFFEL [1960]. These findings from a glasshouse experiment clearly show that Cu deficiency decreases grain yield in favour of the formation of vegetative plant material. The study of Cu deficiency in the field is often more complex than under glasshouse conditions. In an extensive survey of Cu deficiency on chalk rendzina soils DAVIES *et al.* [1971] observed that deficiency symptoms in barley and wheat were aggravated when these crops followed a

Table 16.2 Effect of Cu application on the yield of oats, grown on a Cu deficient soil (SCHARRER and SCHAUMLÖFFEL [1960])

Cu application, mg Cu/kg soil	Straw, g/pot	Grains, g/pot
None	72.6	29.6
1.2	57.0	56.7
8.3	58.4	57.7

Brassica crop. Blackening symptoms were observed in wheat and the deficiency symptoms were accentuated by warm wet summer conditions.

Fertilizer application can also lead to the onset of Cu deficiency, and particularly where high levels of N are applied (REUTHER and LABANAUSKAS [1966]). The prolonged use of phosphatic fertilizers has also been cited as a cause of Cu deficiency in some soils (BINGHAM [1963]). According to DEKOCK et al. [1971] applications of phosphate to peat soils low in Cu availability may induce Cu deficiency in plants by bringing about a more effective utilization of N in the synthesis of plant protein which may bind the Cu. Applications of Zn fertilizers have also been shown to aggravate Cu deficiency in soils with marginal Cu levels (CHAUDHRY and LONERAGAN [1970]).

16.3.2 Copper application

In the assessment of available soil Cu both inorganic and chelating extractants have been used. Extracting with N HNO_3, HENKENS [1965] recommends a minimum of 4 ppm Cu as a measure for the adequate growth of cereal crops. Using the chelating reagent DTPA (diethyl triaminepentacetate) which is more sensitive than EDTA, FOLLETT and LINDSAY [1970] suggest a figure of 0.2 ppm as being the critical Cu level for this extractant. Extraction of soil Cu by chelates, including DTPA do not always give reliable results. Thus HAQ and MILLER [1972] found only a poor correlation between the Cu content of maize plants and the amount of Cu extracted from the soil by a number of different chelating agents.

Another approach to estimate the Cu-status of plants is that of determining the activity of a Cu containing enzyme in the plant. The activity of ascorbic acid oxidase in citrus leaves has been shown to correlate very well with Cu levels in the culture medium (BAR AKIVA et al. [1969]). The Cu content in leaves of wheat and barley has also been used in the diagnosis of Cu deficiency. DAVIES et al. [1971] tentatively suggest that Cu levels less than 2 ppm are indicative of deficiency whilst levels over 3 ppm may be adequate. The Cu content of grains is a reliable index of the Cu nutritional status of cereals. This is shown in Figure 16.2 where the percentage of blind oat grains is plotted against the Cu content of the grains. The critical content is about 2.5 to 3.0 ppm Cu in the dry matter (Russ [1958]).

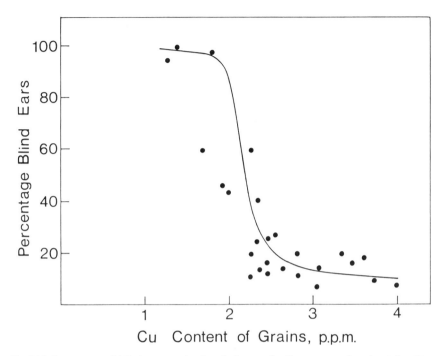

Fig. 16.2 Percentage of blind oats grains in relation to the Cu content of grains (after Russ [1958]).

When it is considered that an average cereal crop removes only about 20–30 g Cu/ha, it is clear that the amount of Cu which is necessary to apply is small. However, as already mentioned, Cu is strongly bound to the soil and for this reason the amount of Cu fertilizer applied must exceed the crop uptake considerably. Both inorganic and organic Cu fertilizers are used to alleviate Cu deficiency (CALDWELL [1971], MURPHY and WALSH [1972]). Most frequently $CuSO_4$ is applied to the soil. A single application of about 1–10 kg Cu/ha is usually adequate on mineral soils whereas somewhat higher levels are needed for organic soils (REUTHER and LABANAUSKAS [1966]). There are, however, a number of problems associated with $CuSO_4$. When the salt is applied to the soil a large proportion of the Cu^{2+} ions are rapidly brought into solution and are immobilized by strong adsorption to exchange sites. In addition toxic residual effects can result on some soils. Where low or medium responsive vegetable or field crops are being grown, a total application not in excess of 22 kg Cu/ha has been recommended (Murphy and Walsh [1972]). Some of the residual effects of soil application have been alleviated either by the use of Cu metal dusts which release Cu at a slower rate (Kühn and Schaumlöffel [1961]) or more usually by the use of Cu chelates. Foliar applications of Cu are usually made using $CuSO_4$, Cu oxychloride, Cu oxide or Cu chelates. Again the sulphate form is less satisfactory because of scorching of the foliage. Seed dressings with Cu salts have been tried, although the results have been variable (Murphy and Walsh [1972]).

Cu toxicity in plants does not frequently occur in practice because Cu is very strongly bound to soil particles. Toxicity can appear on soils affected by Cu ores or in soils which have been treated over a period of years with Cu salts. In some soils in France on which vines have been cultivated the prolonged use of Bordeaux Mixture has had such an effect (Delas [1963]). Copper toxicity appears to occur most severely on acid soils where Cu is not so strongly bound (Drouineau and Mazoyer [1962]), and is thus more available for plants. Copper toxicity problems can become acute particularly where Cu containing wastes are applied to soils regularly. Such soils can be very severely affected because of the low rate at which Cu is leached into the deeper soil layers. This question has been recently treated by Dam Kofoed [1980]. Pig manure and sludges, especially those of industrial origin may be very high in Cu (see Table 16.3). Frequent application of these materials may result in toxic Cu levels in the soil. Crops differ in their susceptibility to copper toxicity. Legumes are supposed to be especially sensitive. Cu enriched plant material can also be a hazard to animals. Ruminants and especially sheep are more suceptible to fodder rich in Cu than pigs or poultry. A concentration of 50 ppm Cu in the dry matter is considered as upper limit for forage.

Table 16.3   Cu concentrations of organic manures and wastes (Dam Kofoed [1980])

	ppm Cu in fresh weight	dry weight
Cattle manure	9	34
Pig manure	21	86
Poultry manure	30	69
Slurry, pig	18	265
Slurry, cattle	4	43
Sludge, household	46	113
Sludge, industry	353	1477

Chapter 17

Molybdenum

17.1 Soil Molybdenum

The total Mo content of most agricultural soils lies between 0.6–3.5 ppm (Swaine [1955]) with an average total Mo content of 2.0 ppm and an average available content about 0.2 ppm (Cheng and Ouellette [1973]). Values can, however, vary widely depending on the parent material. According to Massumi [1967], who investigated soils from various regions in Northern Germany, oxalate soluble Mo was highest in marsh soils and lowest in podzolic soils. The range of oxalate soluble Mo for the various soil types was as follows:

Marsh	0.17	to 1.4 ppm
Greybrown podzolic soils	0.1	to 0.5 ppm
Peat soils	0.1	to 0.5 ppm
Podzolic soils	0.09	to 0.36 ppm

In contrast to the heavy metals already discussed, Mo largely occurs in the soil as an oxycomplex (MoO_4^{2-}). This property clearly distinguishes Mo from the other heavy metal nutrients and molybdate more resembles phosphate or sulphate in its behaviour in the soil. Molybdate is adsorbed by sequioxides and clay minerals in an analogous way to phosphate. Adsorption in most cases is thus that of ligand exchange. It is thus rather specific and the molybdate anion is strongly bound (Hingston et al. [1972]). Of all plant nutrient anions molybdate ranks second after phosphate in its strength of adsorptive binding (Parfitt [1978]). Molybdate adsorption isotherms parallel those of phosphate and can be described approximately by the Langmuir equation. Typical Mo adsorption curves are shown in Figure 17.1 from the work of Barrow [1970]. As is generally applicable to all anion adsorption processes, the strength of Mo adsorption decreases with increasing pH. According to investigations of Reisenauer et al. [1962] maximum Mo adsorption is obtained at pH 4. This pH dependence of Mo adsorption has practical consequences as Mo deficiency can often be controlled by liming. Adsorbed Mo can be replaced by other anions. In this respect phosphate and OH^- appear to be especially effective as replacing anions (Parfitt [1978]).

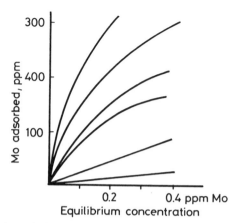

Fig.17.1 Mo adsorption of six soils differing in pH and Mo adsorption capacity (after BARROW [1970])

From the above discussion it is understandable that the Mo content of the soil solution may vary considerably. Concentrations in the order of a 2×10^{-8} to 8×10^{-8} M have been reported (LAVY and BARBER [1964]). The fraction of Mo in the soil solution of the total soil Mo may also be very different between soils. In some Californian soils for example it has been established that $^2/_3$ of the total Mo is water soluble whereas in Mo deficient soils in Florida the water soluble Mo made up less than 1% of the total Mo (WIKLANDER [1958]). In addition to Mo adsorbed on soil colloids and the Mo in soil solution, the element also occurs in nonexchangeable form in a number of mineral structures. These include MoS_2, present in soils under reducing conditions, Ca-molybdate, and hydrated Mo oxides. Molybdenum may also be associated with Fe oxide minerals in adsorbed, occluded or semicrystalline forms as is the case in the sesquioxide fraction in acid soils (REISENAUER *et al.* [1962], TAYLOR and GILES [1970]). On iron-stone soils of low pH, Mo may be so strongly fixed that Mo deficiency may occur (SCHLICHTING [1960]).

A fraction of soil Mo is present in organic form. With the breakdown of organic matter this is frequently converted to a plant available form. MITCHELL [1954] reports that even on acid soils plants can take up adequate levels of Mo when the breakdown of organic matter releases enough Mo.

17.2   Molybdenum in Physiology

Mo is absorbed as molybdate by plants. Uptake can be reduced by competitive effects of SO_4^{2-} (STOUT *et al.* [1951], REISENAUER [1963]). On the other hand phosphate ions enhanced Mo uptake into the tops in short-term experiments (STOUT et al. [1951]). Although there is no direct evidence that Mo is taken up actively the ionic interactions described above are suggestive of metabolically controlled uptake (MOORE [1972]). The form in which Mo is translocated is unknown. TIFFIN [1972] has suggested that it may possibly move in the xylem as MoO_4^{2-}, as Mo-S amino acid complex or as a molybdate complex with sugars or other polyhydroxy compounds. According to HEWITT and AGARWALA [1952], Mo is located primarily in the phloem and vascular parenchyma. It is only moderately mobile in the plant.

The Mo content of plant material is usually low and less than 1 ppm in the dry matter. Some typical results of the contents of a number of plant species are shown in Table 17.1. Contents are normally low because of the extremely small levels of MoO_4^{2-} in the soil solution. In contrast to other micronutrients, however, Mo can be taken up in much higher amounts by plants without normally resulting in toxic effects. AGARWALA and HEWITT [1954] found for example that

Table 17.1   Mo content of different plants in ppm Mo in the dry matter (JOHNSON [1966])

Lucerne leaves	0.34	Sugar beet tops	0.72
Phaseolus bean tops	0.40	Tomato leaves healthy	0.68
Spinach leaves	1.60	Tomato leaves deficient	0.13

Mo contents in plant material may vary by a factor of 100. Cotton plants supplied with excess Mo accumulated levels of up to 1500 ppm Mo in their leaves (JOHAM [1953]). The same kind of observation was made for *Phaseolus* beans by WIDDOWSON [1966]. Occasionally toxicity has been reported at very high levels of Mo supply. In tomato leaves an intense golden yellow colour was found when the Mo content was to the range of 1000 to 2000 ppm (JOHNSON [1966]). The physiological requirement for Mo is very low and less than 1 ppm in the dry matter (STOUT and MEAGHER [1948]).

Molybdenum is an essential component of two major enzymes in plants, nitrogenase and nitrate reductase, the effective mechanism of both of which probably depends on valency change (see p. 170). Nitrogenase consists of two enzyme protein complexes the bigger of which contains Fe and Mo in a ratio of about 9:1 (see Figure 3.26). According to BERGERSEN [1971] the basic mechanism of N_2 fixation by nitrogenase, and thus the Mo function too, is the same for free living N_2 fixing bacteria as for N_2 fixing microorganisms living in symbiosis with higher plants. The essentiality of Mo for *Actinomyces alni* of alder *(Alnus glutinosa)* was established by BECKING [1961]. In the absence of Mo, alder seedlings developed N deficiency. When Mo was supplied, N uptake was enhanced and Mo accumulated in the root nodules at the site of N_2 fixation (Table 17.2). Similar results have been reported by MULDER [1948] who found that the Mo content in the nodules of *Pisum* was about 10 times higher than that of the leaves.

Nitrate reductase is the most well studied Mo containing enzyme. It was isolated from soya beans by EVANS and NASON [1953] and it catalyzes the reduction of NO_3^- to NO_2^- (see p. 169). The activity of the enzyme in cauliflower is en-

Table 17.2 Mo contents in various plant parts of young alder (BECKING [1961])

	Leaves	Stems	Roots	Nodules
	ppm Mo in the dry matter			
No Mo application	0.01	0.14	0.24	2.00
Mo application.....................	0.27	1.89	2.62	17.3

hanced by increasing levels of Mo supply (CANDELA *et al.* [1957]). NICHOLAS and NASON [1955] also observed that removal of Mo from the enzyme by cyanide dialysis resulted in a loss of activity of the enzyme which could only be reactivated by Mo addition. Mo deficiency in plants thus leads to a decrease in the activity of nitrate reductase. For plants supplied with NO_3-N this results in an accumulation of NO_3^- in plant tissues and a consequent decrease in the levels of soluble amino compounds (POSSINGHAM [1956]). MULDER [1948] suggests that Mo is also essential for microbial denitrification.

The uptake of Mo in plants per unit of dry matter production is greater in the presence of NO_3-N than NH_4-N (GIORDANO *et al.* [1966]). It is likely that plants grown exclusively with NH_4^+-N do not require Mo. Thus HEWITT and GUNDRY [1970] showed that under sterile conditions cauliflowers grown with NH_4-N and without Mo did not develop Mo deficiency symptoms, whereas under non sterile conditions Mo deficiency appeared. Most experiments comparing different forms of N in relation to Mo requirement have been conducted under non sterile conditions. It may well be therefore that the Mo requirement reported in earlier investigations in plants supplied with NH_4-N may have resulted from the Mo demand for the reduction of NO_3^- taken up after nitrification of NH_4^+ in the nutrient medium. It will be of interest to see whether the results of HEWITT and GUNDRY [1970] are repeated in other plant species.

As the most important function of Mo in plant metabolism is in NO_3^- reduction, Mo deficiency resembles N deficiency (HAGSTROM and BERGER [1965]),

Plate 17.1 Mo deficiency in cauliflower. Lower part, beginning of the deficiency in young plants (Photo: BRANDENBURGER)

old leaves becoming chlorotic first. In contrast to N deficiency however, necrotic symptoms very quickly appear at the leaf margins because of nitrate accumulation (MAYNARD [1979]). Molybdenum deficient plants are restricted in growth, their leaves become pale and eventually wither. Flower formation may be restricted (HEWITT et al. [1954]). The similarity to N deficiency is particularly applicable to the *Leguminosae* in which Mo deficiency may restrict N nutrition by affecting both NO_3^- reduction and N_2 fixation. In clover stands Mo deficiency often occurs very unevenly giving rise to a yellow chequered appearance against a dark green background of normal plants.

Molybdenum deficiency frequently appears first in the middle and older leaves. They appear yellow to a yellowish green and the leaf margins roll in on themselves. Leaves are also often small and covered by necrotic spots. Molybdenum deficiency has probably been most frequently observed in the *Cruciferae* and in particular in cauliflower. Interveinal chlorotic markings occur on the leaves which often have a grey-green limp appearance. The middle lamella of the cell wall is not completely formed. This can be observed at a very early stage in leaf development BUSSLER [1970]. In extreme deficiency the leaf lamina is not formed and probably only the leaf rib is present. This appears rather like a whip and for this reason the deficiency is called 'Whiptail'. Plate 17.1 shows a typical example of 'whiptail' in cauliflower. In citrus a yellow spotting on the leaves is a characteristic symptom.

17.3 Molybdenum in Crop Nutrition

Most soils contain enough Mo in available form to adequately meet the needs of crop plants. In some areas, however, particularly on acid soils (pH <5.5), Mo deficiency can arise because of high Mo fixation in the soil. Thus in the USA the geographic pattern of Mo deficiency mainly follows the regions of acid sandy soils, although the effect may be masked by the common use of lime (KUBOTA and ALLAWAY [1972]). Highly podzolised soils frequently show Mo deficiency as the total Mo content is low, and the element is largely unavailable because of the low soil pH. Molybdenum deficiency symptoms are commonly observed on soils derived from quartzic material, sandy pebbly alluviums, sandy loams and on soils with high anion exchange capacities (CHENG and OUELLETTE [1973]). Soils with secondary iron oxide accumulations such as the ironstone soils of Australia and Holland are also often Mo deficient as they fix Mo very strongly. Molybdenum deficiency may occasionally appear on peat soils. This is most likely brought about by the retention of Mo by insoluble humic acid from the peat. Humic acid probably reduces the MoO_4^{2-} to Mo^{5+} which becomes fixed in this cationic form (SZALAY and SZILAGYI [1968]). In some freely drained calcareous and serpentine derived soils an absolute deficiency of Mo can occur. In general the critical level for Mo deficiency is about 0.1 ppm available Mo in the soil.

Individual crop plants differ considerably in their requirement for Mo. The *Cruciferae* and particularly cauliflower and cabbage have a high Mo demand. The same also applies to the legumes because of the requirement of the root nodule bacteria. In a survey of 21 states in the USA lucerne was found to be the most common crop species showing Mo deficiency, followed by cauliflower, broccoli, soya beans, clover and citrus (BERGER [1962]). In general the monocots are not very sensitive to Mo deficiency. Plants which are Mo deficient usually have Mo levels lower than 0.2 ppm in the dry matter (JAMES *et al.* [1968]). Thus in Mo deficient cauliflower leaves, Mo contents of 0.1 ppm in the dry matter were found by MASSUMI [1967], whereas in the leaves well supplied with Mo the content amounted to about 0.5 to 0.8 ppm Mo.

As Mo deficiency occurs under acid conditions, where excess amounts of Mn^{2+} and Al^{3+} are taken up, the deficiency is frequently accompanied by toxic effects of Mn and Al. The typical whiptail Mo deficiency symptom of cauliflower, however, can not be induced by Mn toxicity (AGARWALA and HEWITT [1954]).

Most frequently liming is enough to prevent Mo deficiency. In some cases, however, it is only by the application of Mo salts that it is possible to increase yields and plant Mo content (HAGSTROM and BERGER [1965]). Molybdenum application is always preferable to liming when an increase in soil pH is not necessarily desirable. On the other hand great caution must be taken with Mo fertilization as this can result in high Mo levels in fodder which are toxic to animals. Ruminants in particular are susceptible to high Mo levels in the fodder. A Mo content of 5 ppm in the dry matter is regarded as the provisional threshold level for toxic herbage (CHENG and QUELLETTE [1973]). The disease molybdenosis generally begins with a diarrhoea (GRAUPE [1966]). Excess Mo in the diet appears to interfere with normal Cu absorption and utilization and gives rise to an induced Cu deficiency in animals (THOMSON *et al.* [1972]). In Britain the disease in cattle is known as teart and occurs on high pH soils rich in Mo.

As can be seen from Table 17.3, plant species differ in their response to Mo application. High application rates are likely to result in toxic Mo levels in clover (GRAUPE [1966]). Table 17.4 shows the recommended amounts and the frequency of application for a number of crops (BERGMANN [1960]). Molybdenum deficiency can be corrected by applications of Na molybdate, NH_4 molybdate, soluble molybdenum trioxide and molybdenized superphosphate. In some cases seed treatment may be carried out prior to planting with a 1% solution of molyb-

Table 17.3 Effect of Mo application on the Mo content of various plant species (GRAUPE [1966])

Mo-application rate	None	4 kg Na$_2$MoO$_4$/ha
	ppm Mo in the dry matter	
Medicago sativa	0.03	1.58
Trifolium repens	0.02	13.0
Trifolium pratense...........................	0.14	28.6
Lolium multiflorum...........................	0.08	2.19
Bromus mollis	0.03	2.65
Taraxacum officinale	0.31	37.4

Table 17.4 Frequency and rate of Mo application on Mo deficient soils (BERGMANN [1960])

	g Na-molybdate/ha	Frequency
Pastures and fodder plants	150– 200	each 4th to 6th year
Arable crops, vegetables and fruits	150– 200	each year
Cauliflower	500–2000	each year

date, or dusting with NH$_4$ molybdate at the rate of 100 g per ha. Foliar application of 0.5% NH$_4$ molybdate solution to vegetables may also be recommended. Molybdenosis is commonly associated with alkaline organic soils as well as young soils derived from volcanic ash. In the USA problem areas characteristically occur on poorly drained neutral or alkaline soils formed on granitic alluvium narrow floodplains and alluvial pans of small streams (KUBOTA and ALLAWAY [1972]). Soils with more than 100 ppm total Mo are considered suspect.

Chapter 18

Boron

18.1 Soil Boron

The total B content of soils is in the range of 20 to 200 ppm. Most soil B is unavailable to plants, the available (hot water soluble) B fraction ranging from 0.4 to 5 ppm (GUPTA [1979]). Boron is present in various minerals of which tourmaline (3–4% B) is the most important. In these minerals B may substitute for Si in the tetrahedral structures. Soluble B in the soil consists mainly of boric acid B (OH)$_3$. Under soil pH conditions this acid is not deprotonated (dissociated) and thus in contrast to all other essential plant nutrients B is mainly present in a non ionized form in soil solution. This may be the main reason why B can be leached so easily from the soil. GUPTA and CUTCLIFFE [1978] thus reported that more than 60% of applied B was not recovered in the upper layer of a podzolic soil five months after application. In contrast to humid areas B may accumulate in arid regions to toxic levels in the upper soil layer (KANWAR and SHAH SINGH [1961], KICK [1963]).

According to PARFITT [1978] boric acid does not act as a proton donor but rather as a Lewis acid accepting OH$^-$.

$$B(OH)_3 + H_2O \rightarrow B(OH)_4^- + H^+ \qquad pK = 9.0$$

The high pK value indicates that the formation of the anion [B(OH)$_4^-$] is only of significance in the upper pH range. The B(OH)$_4^-$ thus formed is adsorbed by sesquioxides and clay minerals, illites being more effective in B adsorption than kaolinites and smectites. The pH dependence of the formation of the B(OH)$_4^-$ anion may be the reason why B adsorption increases with rising soil pH. This effect of pH on borate adsorption is in marked contrast to the effect of pH on the adsorption of other anion species where adsorption is depressed as soil pH is increased. Maximum B adsorption has been found at pH 9 (HINGSTON *et al.* [1972]). Boron adsorption is a ligand exchange (see p. 34) in which the OH$^-$ of the adsorbing surface may be replaced by B(OH)$_4^-$. In addition borate ions may react with the surface hydroxyls forming a borate-diol complex as suggested by SIMS and BINGHAM [1968].

$$- \overset{|}{\underset{|}{Si}} - OH \quad H \, O \\ \overset{|}{\underset{|}{O}} \qquad\qquad B - OH \; \rightleftharpoons \; \\ - \overset{|}{\underset{|}{Al}} - OH \quad H \, O$$

$$- \overset{|}{\underset{|}{Si}} - O \\ \qquad\qquad\qquad\; B - OH + 2\,H_2O \\ - \overset{|}{\underset{|}{Al}} - O$$

Boron may also be held by organic matter since the carboxylic acids of humic colloids may condense with boric acid. RUSSELL [1973] suggests that as this bond is probably stronger than the borate sesquioxide bond under acid or neutral conditions, humic colloids most likely form the principal reservoir for B in many agricultural soils.

The increase in borate adsorption with rising soil pH accounts for the lower B availability in soils of high pH, and the fact that overliming can induce B deficiency in crops. The lower rates of B leaching from neutral and alkaline soils are also a consequence of B adsorption.

18.2 Boron in Physiology

18.2.1 Uptake and translocation

Boron is probably taken up by plants as the undisociated boric acid although the process is not well understood. There is still controversy as to the extent to which the uptake process is passive or active. TANAKA [1967] reported that part of B accumulated by sunflower roots was passively adsorbed forming a borate complex with polysaccharides in the free space. This suggestion was mainly based on the stoichiometry found between B uptake and H^+ release. Other workers have also reported that B uptake is a non metabolic process (OERTLI [1963], BINGHAM et al. [1970]). In an investigation into the uptake of B by excised barley roots BOWEN and NISSEN [1976] have characterized the fractions of the free space B. A high fraction of the total B was found to be present in the water free space or reversibly bound in the cell walls as borate polysaccharide complexes. According to these workers there is a component of B uptake under metabolic control but this can only be detected experimentally after B reversibly accumulated in the free space has been removed. It would seem that the active component is probably relatively small. Uptake thus mainly follows water flow through the roots.

Boron is relatively immobile in plants and frequently the B content increases from the lower to the upper plant parts (CRIPPS [1956], WILKINSON [1957]). According to the findings of MICHAEL et al. [1969] in tobacco, the rate of transpiration has a decisive influence on the upward transport of B in the plant, which suggests that B is mainly translocated in the xylem. This accounts for the accumulation of B in leaf tips and margins (JONES [1970]). Accumulation of B can in some circumstances lead to toxic effects and some plant species are adapted to secrete B in guttation droplets (OERTLI [1962]). The movement of B along with the transpiration stream also explains the fact that B deficiency always begins at the growing points. This behaviour is similar to that of Ca. Like Ca too B is virtually absent from the phloem sap. High concentrations of B occur in certain plant organs such as anthers, stigma, and ovary, where levels may be twice as high as in stems. These differences are demonstrated in the data of SYWOROTKIN [1958] presented in Table 18.1 showing the B contents in various parts of the opium poppy.

Table 18.1 B content of various plant parts of the opium poppy (SYWOROTKIN [1958])

Plant organ	B, ppm in DM	Plant organ	B, ppm in DM
Capsule of seeds	69	Culm	17
Upper leaves	45	Roots	20
Medium leaves	34	Seeds	21

18.2.2 Meristematic growth and assimilate transport

A common feature in B deficiency is the disturbance in the development of meristematic tissues, whether these are root tips, tips of upper plant parts or tissues of the cambium. Thus GUPTA [1979] holds the view that a continuous supply of B is required for maintenance of meristematic activity. The reason for this B requirement is not yet known, but it has been shown that B is required for the synthesis of N-bases such as uracil (ALBERT [1968]). Additions of both uracil and orotic acid, an intermediate in uracil biosynthesis, were found to alleviate B deficiency symptoms. (BIRNBAUM et al. [1977]). This finding strongly suggests that B is involved in uracil synthesis. Uracil is an essential component of RNA and if it is absent RNA containing assemblies such as ribosomes cannot be formed, thus affecting protein synthesis. Ribonucleic acid synthesis, ribose formation, and the synthesis of proteins are most important processes in meristematic tissues. If they are disturbed by a lack of boron the entire process of meristematic growth is impaired. This interpretation is consistent with the finding of HUNDT *et al.* [1970] who showed that phosphate incorporation into nucleic acid was affected in B deficient sunflowers (see Table 18.2).

A further essential consequence results from a deficiency of uracil. This N-base is also the precursor of uridine diphosphate glucose (UDPG) which is an essential coenzyme in the formation of sucrose which is the most important sugar transport form (see p. 216). If its synthesis is inhibited translocation of assimilates is also affected. This is exactly what has often been observed in B deficient plants. Assimilates formed in the leaves are only poorly translocated to other plant parts. In addition B deficiency also results in enhanced callose production so that callose plugs are formed which are likely to block the sieve plate pores (van den VENTER and CURRIER [1977]). Whether this enhanced callose production is in some way related to inhibited sucrose synthesis is not yet clear. However, blocked sieve plate pores have a detrimental effect on phloem transport.

Table 18.2 Influence of B on DNA phosphate, RNA phosphate and protein of sunflower plants, suffering from moderate B deficiency (HUNDT *et al.* [1970])

B in the nutrient solution, ppm	Leaves	Roots
DNA phosphate in % of total phosphate		
0	0.2	0.5
1	1.4	1.8
RNA phosphate in % of total phosphate		
0	1.4	3.6
1	6.4	13.0
Protein N mg/pot		
0	627	713
1	1267	1468

POLLARD *et al.* [1977] have suggested that B has a direct effect on influencing the confirmation and activity of specific membrane components of the cell. This view is supported by the rapid recovery of metabolism-linked ion transport observed by this workers when B was added to deficient roots. Associated with the recovery in transport was a recovery in the activity of membrane bound K^+ stimulated ATPase (see CLARKSON and HANSON [1980]). POLLARD *et al.* [1977] suggest that a possible mechanism for membrane control by B is the reaction of B with polyhydroxy compounds thus influencing the activity and integrity of the membrane (see GUPTA [1979]).

18.2.3 Nucleic acids and phytohormones

A decrease in RNA content was claimed to be the first symptom in B deficient tomato roots following a cessation in growth (JOHNSON and ALBERT [1967]). The effect of deficiency could be prevented by additions of the bases thymine, guanine and cytosine. From these findings it was concluded that B plays a role in N base utilization and hence in RNA metabolism. The involvement of B in RNA synthesis has been demonstrated more recently. Using P-32 ROBERTSON and LOUGHMAN [1974] showed that B deficiency greatly reduces the rate of incorporation of P into the nucleotides (Figure 18.1). The disturbing effect of B deficiency on nucleic acid metabolism and protein synthesis is demonstrated very well in the results of HUNDT *et al.* [1970] in a study on N-metabolism of sunflowers in relation to B supply. In plants poorly supplied with B, NO_3-N accumulated in the roots, leaves and stems showing that NO_3^- reduction and amino acid synthesis were inhibited. When only a low level of B was resupplied to moderately B deficient plants, there was a rapid response to P-32 uptake and incorporation into

−B− = boron deficient; −B+ = boron deficient resupplied with boron after 90 minutes; +B+ = non-deficient

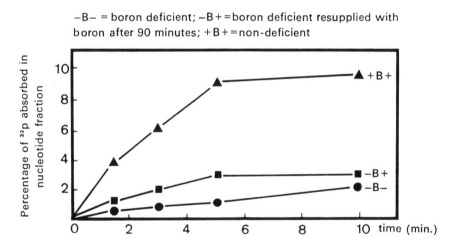

Fig. 18.1 Incorporation of absorbed phosphate into the nucleotide fraction in relation to the level of B nutrition (after ROBERTSON and LOUGHMAN [1974]).

DNA or RNA, and enhanced protein synthesis (Table 18.2). The role of B and other plant nutrients in protein synthesis has been very well reviewed by AMBERGER [1975].

When B is deficient, the synthesis of cytokinins is depressed (WAGNER and MICHAEL [1971]). On the other hand there is a good deal of evidence in the literature that auxins accumulate in B deficient tissues. COKE and WHITTINGTON [1968] suggest that necrosis in the growing points of B deficient plants is caused by auxin accumulation. They hold the view that B protects the IAA oxidase system by complexing with inhibitors of IAA oxidase. A possible relationship between B deficiency and auxin metabolism has also been postulated by CRISP *et al.* [1976] who observed that the onset of the necrotic disorder in lettuce known as 'Tipburn' had a close temporal association with a marked B deficient mediated increase in auxin activity. SHKOLNIK [1974] in a paper reviewing the role of B in plants proposes that the accumulation of excess auxins and phenols is the primary cause of necrosis in plants associated with B deficiency. The possible roles for B in auxin metabolism, protein synthesis and phosphate utilization have been discussed by PRICE *et al.* [1972].

The ability of B to form polyhydroxy compounds makes its biochemical study both complex and elusive. Further study of the interesting observation that B is not essential for animals, fungi and certain algae (DEAR and ARNOFF [1968]) may perhaps provide an indication of its essential nature in higher plants.

18.2.4 Boron deficiency

Boron deficiency first appears as abnormal or retarded growth of the apical growing points. The youngest leaves are misshapen, wrinkled and are often thicker and of a darkish blue-green colour. Irregular chlorosis between the intercostal veins may occur. The leaves and stems become brittle indicating a disturbance in transpiration. As the deficiency progresses the terminal growing point dies and the whole plant is reduced and flower and fruit formation is restricted or inhibited. The typical dying off symptom of the terminal growing point as a result of B deficiency is shown for the tomato plant in Plate 18.1 from the work of BROWN (1979). This author also found that B deficiency is associated with an increase in ascorbate oxidase activity in the leaves. The two tomato cultivars investigated by BROWN (1979) differed significantly in their sensitivity to boron stress. Boron plays a particular role in the germination of pollen tubes. Thus plants inadequately supplied with B show a disturbance in pollen germination and fruit formation is impaired. In some plant species the affected growth of pollen results in parthenogenesis. This is true for grapes and parthenocarpic fruits may result. The fruits developed remain very small and are of poor quality (GÄRTEL [1974]). Plate 18.1 shows a mature bunch of grapes from a B deficient vine. Boron deficiency also affects root development, and in B free nutrient solutions root growth is inhibited (BUSSLER [1960]). Roots appear slimly and are thickened, and the tips are necrotic.

The most well known B deficiency symptoms are crown and heart rot in sugar beet. The symptoms begin with anatomical changes at the apical growing points. The youngest leaves are curled and stunted and turn brown or black.

Plate 18.1 Boron deficiency. Upper part. B deficiency in tomatoes, the plant in the middle showing typical symptoms at the growing point. (Photo: BROWN). Lower part: Grape bunch with B deficient fruits (Photo: GÄRTEL).

Eventually the inner leaves are affected and the main growing point dies. Older leaves are brittle and chlorotic. The crown of the beet begins to rot and infection then sets in, and the whole plant becomes affected. As might be expected the healthy part of the beet is low in sugar. In turnips and swedes, B deficiency results in glassy like roots which are hollow and cracked. The appearance of

539

cracked stems is also an indication of B deficiency in celery. The development of scaly surfaces and the formation of internal and external cork like material is typical of the features associated with B deficiency in many plants including tomatoes, cauliflower, citrus and apple. These typical corky like deficiency symptoms possibly relate to the association of B with pectic materials in cell walls. In this respect B and Ca have certain features in common. Bitter pit which occurs in Ca deficient apples can sometimes be effectively reduced by B sprays particularly if they are applied when the trees are in blossom (DUNLAP and THOMPSON [1959]). In a valuable review paper GUPTA [1979] has described B deficiency symptoms of the major crops.

18.3 Boron in Crop Nutrition

18.3.1 Availability and boron application

Boron is of interest in crop production both from the viewpoint of its effects in deficiency and excess. According to REISENAUER et al. [1973] deficiencies of B occur in a wider range of crops and climatic conditions than deficiencies of any other micronutrient element. Boron is also probably more important than any other micronutrients in obtaining quality high crop yields.

The soils on which B deficiency occurs include those which are inherently low in B such as soils derived from acid igneous rocks, and podzolised soils. Sandy acid soils in particular need regular treatment with B fertilizers as borate is very easily lost in leaching. The same treatment is also required when acid soils are limed, as excess amounts of lime can induce this deficiency (WALSH and GOLDEN [1952]).

Boron availability decreases with increasing soil pH. Inadequate B availability has thus frequently been observed on calcareous soils. This relationship is shown in Table 18.3. Raising the soil pH and soil Ca carbonate levels con-

Table 18.3 Effect of soil pH and carbonate on the proportion of sugar beet infected by crown and heart rot (data of SCHEFFER and WELTE [1955])

pH	Carbonate, %	Percentage of sugar beet		
		Healthy	Infected	Dead
6.7	0.1	100	0	0
7.0	0.1	99	1.0	0
7.5	0.3	46	40	14
8.1	14.4	0	25	75

siderably increased the occurrence of B deficient sugar beet (SCHEFFER and WELTE [1955]). High clay soil contents also impair B availability, probably due to borate adsorption. Uptake of B by plants correlates well with hot water soluble B extracts of soils. At less than 1 ppm water soluble B, soils may not supply sufficient B to support plant growth, whilst values above 5.0 ppm B may be toxic (REISENAUER et al. [1973]). A review of the extraction techniques used to determine available B in soils has been published by FARRAR [1975].

Boron availability is also related to seasonal behaviour. Deficiency appears to be more prevalent in a dry summer following a wet winter or spring. The effect is most pronounced when good growing conditions in spring are followed by a long dry spell (BATEY [1971]). Probably B mobility in the soil medium is much impaired in dry seasonal periods.

The most well known B fertilizer is borax ($Na_2B_4O_7 \cdot 10\,H_2O$). Besides this other B containing materials e.g. borated superphosphate are also used. Boric acid (H_3BO_3) is frequently applied as leaf spray, particularly when the soil is potentially capable of fixing high amounts of boron. One problem of B application is the very narrow range of concentrations in the soil at which neither deficiency nor toxicity occur. If too much B is applied, and this may occur with uneven spreading, the crop may be damaged. One means used to avoid excess B levels is the use of boro-silicate glass frits. These are of sintered glass with a large surface area and provide a slow release of B into the soil solution. Band or foliar applied B is often more efficient in correcting B deficiency than broadcast application. FOROUGHI et al. [1973] were able to control B deficiency in bitter oranges by soil application of borax in quantities of 50 to 200 g B per tree and by foliar application of 15 to 60 mg B/tree in the form of solobur (see Table 18.4). This correction of B deficiency improved fruit quality considerably.

Table 18.4   B-fertilizers, their chemical formulae and their B content (after GUPTA 1979)

Boron source	Chemical formula	B (%)
Borax	$Na_2B_4O_7 \cdot 10H_2O$	11
Boric acid	H_3BO_3	17
Boron frits (contained in a moderately soluble glass)	$Na_2B_4 \cdot XH_2O$	10–17
Sodium tetraborate		
Borate-46, Agribor, Tronabor	$Na_2B_4O_7 \cdot 5H_2O$	14
Borate-65	$Na_2B_4O_7$	20
Sodium pentaborate	$Na_2B_{10}O_{16} \cdot 10H_2O$	18
Solubor (partially dehydrated)	$Na_2B_4O_7 \cdot 5H_2O + Na_2B_{10}O_{16} \cdot 10H_2O$	20–21

The fertilizer rate for sugar beet is in the order of 1.0 to 2.0 kg B/ha (about 10 to 20 kg borax/ha). Turnips have a higher B requirement than sugar beet and are frequently treated at higher rates. Because of the risk of B toxicity, however, the rates applied should not be too high. Generally only the crop of a rotation, which has the highest B requirement, is treated with B. For arable crops this is usually sugar beet. The quantities of B taken up by crops during a season are low. For sugar beet this quantity amounts to about 350 to 400 g B/ha (HENKENS [1965]). Thus the rates generally applied are several times higher than crop uptake. The most important straight B fertilizers are shown in Table 18.4

18.3.2 Crop requirement

Crops differ in their sensitivity to B deficiency. The most sensitive crops are sugar beet, mangels and celery. Various *Brassica* crops such as turnips, cauliflower, cabbage and brussels sprouts also have a high B requirement. Of the fruit trees, apples and pears, are known to be particularly sensitive to B deficiency (BRADFORD [1966]). GÄRTEL [1974] claims that B deficiency of grapes is one of the most severe non-parasitic disease in vine growing. Fruit formation is impaired (see p.539) and yield depressions as high as 80% may occur compared with plants adequately supplied with B.

Some legumes also have a high B requirement. OUELLETTE and LACHANCE [1954] reported that in Canada a considerable extent of the lucerne crop suffered from B deficiency. The degree of B deficiency correlated negatively with the B level in the plant, and lucerne plants with less than 15 ppm B were regarded as inadequately supplied. This figure compares well with the critical level of 10 to 25 ppm B in the dry matter reported by MARTIN and MATOCHA [1973] for the same crop. The critical B content for blades of sugar beet is in the same range. Non deficient blades show contents as high as 35 to 200 ppm B in the dry matter (ULRICH and HILLS [1973]). GÄRTEL [1974] reported that the stigmae of grapes well supplied with B contains 50 to 60 ppm B in the dry matter, compared with 8 to 20 ppm in stigmae of B deficient plants. In the B deficient plants fertilization is impaired.

In general, dicots have a higher B requirement and B content than monocots (SHIVE [1941]). For this reason B deficiency of cereals is less common. SYWOROT-KIN [1958] distinguishes between three plant groups with regard to B content and B requirement: Monocots, dicots and dicot species with a latex system such as dandelion, poppy and some *Euphorbiaceae*. This distinction is explained by the proportion of meristematic tissue and thus B requiring tissue typical for these three plant groups. The dicots contain appreciable amounts of cambium as well as meristematic growing points whereas in the *Euphorbiaceae*, there is also additionally a latex system requiring B. These differences reflect the mean B contents of the three plant groups (see Table 18.5).

Table 18.5 Boron content of various plant groups (SYWOROTKIN [1958]), (B in ppm DM)

Monocots		Dicots		Dicots with a latex system	
Barley	2.3	Peas	22	Dandelion	80
Wheat	3.3	Beets	49	*Euphorbia*	93
Maize	5.0	Lettuce	70	Poppy	94

18.3.3 Boron toxicity

As B is toxic to many plant species at levels only slightly above that required for normal growth, toxicity effects may occasionally arise by excessive use of B fertilizers or on soils with high B contents such as those derived from marine sediments. The toxicity is, however, more usually associated with arid and semi arid regions where B levels are frequently high in the soil. The B status of irrigation water is particularly important in these regions. REISENAUER *et al.* [1973] cite the observations of the University of California Agricultural Extension Service [1969] which found that at 1 ppm in the water sensitive crops may show visible injury and at 10 ppm even the tolerant crops may be affected. According to REISENAUER *et al.* [1973] toxicity in crop plants is likely to occur when the level of hot water soluble B in the soil exceeds 5 ppm B, whereas soil levels of <1 ppm B are generally not high enough for optimum plant growth. Boron toxicity may also be caused by industrial pollution as has been reported by JUDEL [1977]. Coniferous trees were found to be particularly affected and the polluted needles of *Picea* species had B contents as high as 960 ppm B in the dry matter. The B contents of grasses showing severe toxicity symptoms were in the range of 270 to 570 ppm B. Soils polluted with B can be corrected by irrigation with B free water. Boron availability and thus the uptake of excess B can also be depressed by liming (JUDEL [1977]).

Some of the most sensitive crops to B toxicity are peach, grapes, kidney beans and figs. Semi-tolerant plants include barley, peas, maize, potato, lucerne, tobacco, and tomato whilst the most tolerant crops are turnips, sugar beet, and cotton. Toxic effects of B result in leaf tip yellowing followed by progressive necrosis. This begins at the tip and margins and finally spreads between the lateral veins towards the midrib. The leaves take on a scorched appearance and drop prematurely. These effects have been described in detail for a number of plant species (BRADFORD [1966]).

Chapter 19

Further Elements of Importance

In the previous chapters all elements which have been considered, with the possible exception of Na, are essential plant nutrients. Without any one of these essential elements the plant would be unable to complete its life cycle. All these elements too play a part in plant metabolism although as in the case of some of the micronutrients the essential roles are as yet ill defined.

In addition to these nutrients are a group of elements which can have a beneficial effect on plant growth. Two well known examples of this type are Si and Co. Under certain conditions both these elements can stimulate plant growth and are essential for some plant species. In this chapter the essential element Cl has also been included.

19.1 Chlorine

In nature Cl^- is widely distributed and subject to rapid recycling. Chloride in the soil is not adsorbed by minerals and is one of the most mobile ions, being easily lost by leaching under freely drained conditions. Accumulation can occur, however, in a number of situations. Soils high in Cl^- include those affected by the sea or treated with irrigation water containing Cl^-, and poorly drained soils receiving run off from other areas. Lightly leached soils can also contain high concentrations of Cl^-.

Most plant species take up Cl^- very rapidly and in considerable amounts. The uptake rate depends primarily on the concentration in the nutrient or soil solution, SCHMALFUSS and REINICKE [1960]. There is considerable evidence that uptake is metabolically controlled. Chloride uptake is sensitive to both to variations in temperature and metabolic inhibitors (ELZAM and EPSTEIN [1965]). According to GERSON and POOLE [1972] uptake also occurs against an electrochemical gradient. In the movement of Cl^- into plant tissues the plasmalemma is fairly permeable. When Cl^- concentrations in the outer medium are high the tonoplast rather than the plasmalemma becomes a limiting barrier to Cl^- movement (CRAM [1973]). Chloride can thus be accumulated in the cytoplasm under conditions of high uptake. In its transport through the cortex to the central cylinder there is evidence that the symplastic pathway presents the main route (STELZER et al. [1975]). In green tissues Cl^- uptake is enhanced by illumination (BARBER [1968], MACDONALD et al. [1975]) as ATP formed during photosynthetic phosphorylation provides an energy source for active uptake. Competitive effects in uptake between Cl^- and NO_3^-, and Cl^- and SO_4^{2-} are well known in the literature (DE WIT et al. [1963]). In practical terms this may affect crop quality. In potatoes for example MURAKA et al. [1973] showed that an application of Cl^- decreased both total N and NO_3^--N in the tops although protein N was not affected. Chloride is not only taken up by roots it may also be absorbed by aerial plant parts as chloride or chlorine gas (JOHNSON et al. [1957]). The quantities of Cl^- in the atmosphere and rain water are considerably influenced by the distance from the sea, falling off rapidly moving inland (see p. 306).

It is now well established that Cl^- is essential for higher plants. The physiological requirement is very low and in the order of a few ppm. In comparison most plants contain high amounts of Cl^- generally in the range of 2 to 20 mg Cl/g dry matter. However, concentrations can be much higher particularly in the halophytes. The function of Cl^- in plants is still obscure. A number of workers have shown that in isolated chloroplasts Cl^- is an essential cofactor in photosynthesis. These in vitro experiments have indicated that Cl^- is required for photosynthetic O_2 evolution at photosystem II (BOVE et al. [1963], KELLEY and IZAWA [1978]). This role of Cl^- in intact plants has been questioned by TERRY [1977] who showed that even for a growth reduction of 60% in Cl^- deficient sugar beet leaves, CO_2 uptake was not affected whether expressed on the basis of leaf area or chlorophyll.

Besides its possible role in photosynthesis chloride fulfills other functions in the plant. These mainly relate to the high mobility of the Cl^- and the fact that the ion is tolerated over a wide concentration range. Chloride may also act as a counter-ion in rapid K^- fluxes and contribute to turgor. In this respect Cl^- can replace NO_3^- which is also a mobile anion or act in place of malate (see p. 133). CLARKSON and HANSON [1980] have drawn attention to the virtue of the biochemical inertness of Cl^-, as this enables it to fill osmotic and cation neutralization roles which may have biochemical or biophysical consequences of importance. A number of chlorinated organic compounds occur in plants but these are not believed to be of any great significance in metabolism (MILLER and FLEMION [1973]). Plants which take up large amounts of Cl^- usually have a high water content since the Cl^- is an important osmoticum.

Deficiency symptoms have been observed by a number of workers using different crops (BROYER et al. [1954], ULRICH and OHKI [1956]). Wilting is a common feature and it appears that transpiration is affected. In addition the plants are often chlorotic. In sugar beet leaf growth is slowed down due to a lower rate of cell multiplication. Leaf area is reduced and partial chlorosis occurs. According to JOHNSON *et al.* [1957] the critical Cl level for deficiency in non halophytic plants is about 70 to 100 ppm Cl$^-$ in the dry matter.

Plate 19.1 Chloride toxicity in leaves of maple.   (Photo: WALTER)

Soils considered low in Cl^- are below 2 ppm (JAMES et al. [1970]). In practice Cl^- deficiency very seldom occurs because the presence of Cl^- in the atmosphere or in rain water is more than enough to meet the 4 to 10 kg/ha/year demand by crops (REISENAUER et al. [1973]). Indeed even under laboratory conditions it is difficult to induce Cl^- deficiency because of atmospheric contamination (JOHNSON et al. [1957]).

The effect of excess Cl^- in plants is a more serious problem. Crops growing on salt affected soils often show symptoms of Cl toxicity. These include burning of leaf tips or margins, bronzing, premature yellowing and abscission of leaves (EATON [1966]). An example of Cl toxicity in maple is shown in Plate 19.1 from the work of WALTER et al. [1974]. These symptoms arose following salt application to the road and roadside made to prevent snow lying in winter. Plant species differ in their sensitivity to Cl^-. Sugar beet, barley, maize, spinach and tomato are highly tolerant whilst tobacco, beans, citrus, potatoes, lettuce and some legumes are very prone to toxicity. This latter group of chlorophobic crops should be treated with sulphate rather than chloride based fertilizers. Reduction in yield and quality in crops is associated with tissue levels of 0.5–2% Cl for sensitive crops and 4% or more in the dry matter of tolerant plant species (REISENAUER et al. [1973]).

The role of Cl^- in the nutrition of coconut and oil palm has taken on a greater significance in recent years. The works of von UEXKÜLL [1972] and DANIEL and OCHS [1975] have shown that growth responses following Cl^- application may be obtained both in coconut and oil palm. As yet, however, no new specific role for Cl^- has been identified in these species.

19.2   Silicon

Silicon is the second most abundant element in the lithosphere after oxygen and occurs in almost all minerals. The accessibility of Si to plants depends largely on how rapidly weathering takes place bringing Si into soil solution. In minerals highly resistant to weathering such as quartz it is completely unavailable. Soluble Si is present as monomeric $Si(OH)_4$ in a wide pH range (2 to 9) and is in equilibrium with amorphous SiO_2 with an equilibrated concentration of about 2 mM (PONNAMPERUMA [1972]). At pH > 9, $Si(OH)_4$ is deprotonated (JONES and HANDRECK [1965]). Monosilicic acid in the soil solution is mainly controlled by pH dependent adsorption reactions on sesquioxides. Adsorption decreases at either side of a maximum at pH 9.5. Aluminium oxides are more effective than iron oxides in adsorption although the actual mechanism is still not clear (JONES and HANDRECK [1967]). Acid soils thus tend to contain higher concentrations of Si in soil solution and liming has been found to decrease the uptake of Si by a number of crop plants (GROSSE-BRAUCKMANN [1956]). An assessment of the available Si in the soil has been obtained from the ratio of easily extractable Si to the free or easily extractable sesquioxides. The higher the ratios of Si/Al or Si/Fe the greater was found to be the uptake of Si by rice (see JONES and HANDRECK [1967]).

It is known that below a pH of 9 silicon is taken up by plants in the form of the uncharged monosilicic acid (JONES and HANDRECK [1965]) although there is no universal agreement on the mechanism of uptake. In experiments with oats JONES and HANDRECK [1965] concluded that uptake was passive as the observed levels in the plant closely agreed with calculated levels derived from data of soil solution concentrations and water uptake by transpiration. In other species relatively low in Si, as for example *Trifolium incarnatum* (crimson clover), they suggested that plants must have some mechanism by which monosilicic acid was excluded at the root surface or within the roots. Evidence of a metabolically mediated uptake has been found by BARBER and SHONE [1966]. A 2 to 3 times greater entry of silicic acid into barley roots was observed than could be accounted for by transpiration. The process appeared to require metabolic energy as it was sensitive to metabolic inhibitors and variations in temperature. Accumulations of Si in the sap of rice plants several hundred fold greater than in the outer solution are also indicative of metabolic uptake (OKUDA and TAKAHASHI [1965]). From these contrasting observations it seems likely that interspecies differences may well be important in relation to Si uptake.

The prevalent form of Si present in plants is silica gel occurring in the form of hydrated amorphous silica SiO_2nH_2O or polymerized silicic acid. In the rice plant this makes up 90 to 95% of the total silicon (YOSHIDA et al. [1962]). Other forms of Si include silicic acid and colloidal silicic acid. Silicon in the xylem sap has been shown to be present as monosilicic acid (JONES and HANDRECK [1967]).

The distribution of Si in plants is very much dependent on plant species. In plants low in Si such as tomato, radish, and chinese cabbage there may be little difference between tops and roots (OKUDA and TAKAHASHI [1965]). In other cases such as in crimson clover, the root may accumulate much higher levels of silicon. For plants high in Si such as rice and oats more than 90% of Si may be in the tops.

Once the silica gel has solidified and deposited it becomes immobile in the plant (YOSHIDA et al. [1962]). In oats it has been reported that the outer epidermal cells are impregnated with silica which is intimately associated with the cell wall constituents (JONES and HANDRECK [1967]). Electron microscopic studies by YOSHIDA and co-workers on the epidermal cells of the leaf blade of rice showed a layer of silica combined with cellulose overlain by a layer of silica below the cuticle. These workers stressed the importance of the double silica layer, in limiting unnecessary water loss and preventing penetration by fungal hyphae. Dicots showed no accumulation of silica in epidermal sites.

Plant species can be divided in Si accumulators with a Si content of about 2% in the dry matter and non Si accumulators having a Si content of about 0.25% in the dry matter. Si accumulators mainly include the *Gramineae* and *Cyperaceae*. Most dicots, such as radish, chinese cabbage and onions are non Si accumulators. In these species Si supply does not result in a growth response (TAKAHASHI and MIYAKE [1977]). Tomatoes were not thought to respond to Si supply but recent solution culture experiments of TAKAHASHI and MIYAKE [1977], revealed a clear Si response of this species. First symptoms of insufficient Si supply appeared at the first bud flowering stage. The growth of the meristem tissue at the top was depressed and the young leaves near the top showed deformations. In other plant species Si deficiency leads to a 'weeping willow' habit of growth, withering of leaves, and wilting symptoms. This latter feature undoubtedly relates to the higher transpiration rate of plants low in Si. The appearance of necrotic spots on the leaves of grasses and cereals has been observed by several authors investigating Si deficiency. This effect, however, is probably caused by Mn and Fe toxicity as these and other mineral nutrients concentrate in the aerial parts of plants where Si concentrations are low (VLAMIS and WILLIAMS [1967]). From all these observations it would appear that Si is necessary for the development of many plant species and appears to be essential for plants with normally high Si contents such as rice, grasses and horsetails (LEVIN and REIMANN [1969]).

The most important crop which responds to Si is rice. As shown in Figure 19.1 from an investigation of PARK [1970] a significant relationship occurs between the Si content in the rice straw and the yield of brown rice. Silicon especially promotes the reproductive organs of rice, as was found by OKUDA and TAKAHASHI [1966] in a solution culture experiment with lowland rice. Data of this investigation shown in Table 19.1, clearly indicate that Si had a particularly beneficial effect on the grain weight. In addition, however, other grain yield components such as number of panicles, number of spikelets per panicle, and the percentage of fully ripened grains were favourably influenced by Si.

The search for a metabolic role of Si to justify its essential nature in some higher plants has been undertaken by many workers. ENGEL [1953] found that 20% of the total Si in rye straw was present in the cellulose framework and also identified the presence of a silicon galactose complex. Whether such a complex or similar compounds are of significance in metabolism is still not clear. Hy-

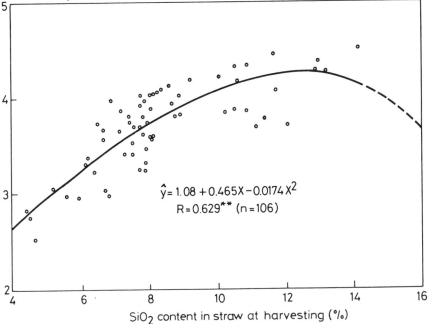

$$\hat{y} = 1.08 + 0.465X - 0.0174X^2$$
$$R = 0.629^{**} \ (n = 106)$$

Fig. 19.1 Relationship between brown rice yield and SiO_2 content in straw at the harvesting stage (after PARK [1979]).

Table 19.1 The effect of Si supply on the growth and grain yield of lowland rice (OKUDA and TAKAHASHI [1965])

	Top length (cm)	Number of panicles/pot	Number of spikelets/panicle	Percentage of fully ripened grains	Weight of mature grains (g/pot)
−Si.............	85	9.5	49.3	55	5.25
+Si.............	94.5	11.6	63.2	76	10.83

droxyl groups of silicic acid like those in phosphoric and boric acids can condense with sugars, alcohols and organic acids. The chemical similarities between Si, P and B means that an indication of the role of Si may be obtained by observing the way in which it replaces or interferes in the functioning of phosphorus or boron. Possible P – Si interactions have been examined and some similarities do exist. GANSSMANN [1962] for example observed that addition of silicate in water culture solutions depressed phosphate uptake. On the other hand Si was not able to replace P to the slightest extent in alleviating P deficiency. The two elements also behave differently in respect to metabolic inhibitors in uptake (OKUDA and TAKAHASHI [1965]). Comparisons between Si and B are more difficult as the precise functions of B in plant metabolism are almost as little understood as those of Si. There is evidence, however, that high Si/B ratios in the culture medium may restrict the growth and the uptake of B by marine diatoms (LEWIN [1966]). A relatively new approach to the problem of silicate metabolism has been provided by the use of germanic acid. This acts as a specific inhibitor of silicic acid metabolism, and affects only organisms with a Si requirement (WERNER [1967]). As yet, however, it has still not been possible to detail specific metabolic functions to Si in higher plants.

Silica containing fertilizers can increase the availability of soil phosphate (FISHER [1929]). Experiments on barley at Rothamsted in England quoted by RUSSELL [1973] show a dressing of 450 kg/ha sodium silicate applied annually is still increasing phosphate uptake in the no phosphate plots after a century of use. The mechanism by which the silicate is effective, is probably dependent on an increase in phosphate availability resulting from exchange of silicate for phosphate adsorbed to sesquioxides (GANSSMANN [1962]). The silica fertilizers include soluble silicates, sinterphosphates and Ca silicate slags. Occasionally they are used in soils low in silica to improve crop yields and crop quality. On paddy rice soils, silicate slags are sometimes employed to increase soil pH and soluble silica (RUSSELL [1973]). In the cereals and in rice in particular, Si is especially important in strengening the upright habit of the crop, decreasing excess water loss and protecting plants against fungal attack. Increases in yield and sugar contents of sugar cane have also been claimed using silica fertilizers on soil low in silica (AYRES [1966]).

19.3 Cobalt

The Co concentration in the dry matter of plants grown in soil normally lies between 0.02 to 0.5 ppm. In soils the content is usually much higher and levels from 1 to 40 ppm are common although many values in excess of 40 ppm have been reported (SWAINE [1955], VANSELOW [1966]). Co occurs in all igneous rocks in concentrations from 1 ppm to several hundred ppm, the level of Co closely following the distribution of Mg in the ferromagnesian minerals (MITCHELL [1964]). In the ultrabasic rocks such as dunite, perioditite and serpentine where the content of Mg rich ferromagnesian minerals is high, levels from 100 to 300 ppm Co may be present. On the other hand acidic rocks including granites containing high contents of Fe rich ferromagnesian minerals are low in Co with levels from 1–10 ppm. The distribution in the sedimentary rocks is much dependent on their mode of formation. In the argillaceous rocks such as shales the Co content may be relatively high and from 20–40 ppm, whereas sandstones and limestones are usually poor in Co with contents below 5 ppm. In the soil Co occurs primarily in the crystal lattices of ferromagnesian minerals and as such is unavailable to plants (MITCHELL [1972]). After release from these minerals by weathering, Co^{2+} is held largely in exchangeable form or as organo mineral complexes. Exchangeable Co^{2+} is very firmly bound and like Cu^{2+} the concentration in the soil solution is extremely low. The rate of weathering is more rapid in poorly drained conditions. This is reflected in a higher available Co content than in freely drained soils derived from similar parent materials, even though the total soil Co level may be lower in the poorly drained sites (MITCHELL [1964]). Cobalt can be rendered unavailable by adsorption on the surfaces of Mn oxides. In some Australian soils TAYLOR and MCKENZIE [1966] reported an average of 79 per cent of total soil Co associated with Mn oxide minerals. Similar results have been reported in Ireland from soils on which 'pine' the cobalt deficiency disease of sheep has been observed (FLEMING [1977]).

Plants may take up Co through the leaf, however, Co taken up in this way is practically immobile (GUSTAFSON and SCHLESSINGER [1956]). Cobalt taken up by the roots primarily follows the transpiration stream so that there is an enrichment of Co at the leaf margins and tips (LANGSTON [1956]).

Co behaves like other heavy metals. In a similar way to Fe, Mn, Zn and Cu it tends to form chelate compounds. It can also displace other ions from physiologically important binding sites and can thus decrease the uptake and mode of action of other heavy metals. NICHOLAS and THOMAS [1954] observed that excess Co nutrition induced Fe deficiency. HEWITT [1953] also reported that the toxic effects of excess Co resembled Mn deficiency. Both these observations indicate that the toxic effects of excess Co relate to the effect of Co in displacing other heavy metals from physiologically important centres. The effects of Co toxicity in plants result in leaves which are chlorotic and necrotic, and which frequently wither completely.

A few plant species are less sensitive to Co toxicity. In some cases Co is accumulated at levels over 100 times that of other plants growing in the same soil. The swamp black gum *(Nyssa sylvatica)* which grows in the south-eastern U.S.A. can have Co contents approaching 1000 ppm in the dry matter. This species acts as a very good guide to Co availability and values in the leaf of less than 5 ppm are indicative of Co deficiency in ruminants feeding on herbage from the same environment (VANSELOW [1966]). Other plant species in which Co accumulates serve to indicate the presence of cobaltiferous ores. One such species found in the Sharba region of Zaire and occurring only in areas rich in Co is *Crotolaria cobalticola* (Fleur du Cobalt). Values from 500 to 800 ppm Co have been observed in the dry matter of this species (DUVIGNEAUD and DENAEYER-DE SMET [1959]):

It is now well established that Co is essential for microorganisms fixing molecular N_2. Cobalt is thus required in the nodules of both legumes and alder (REISENAUER [1960], KLIEWER and EVANS [1962]), as well as in N_2 fixing algae (HOLM-HANSEN *et al.* [1954]). Enhanced N_2 fixation has been found to occur in nodulated lucerne plants supplied with cobalt (POWRIE [1964]). The drastic effect of a Co deficient nutrient medium on the growth of soya bean is shown in Plate 19.2. Cobalt is the metal component of vitamin B_{12}. In a somewhat similar way to Fe in haemin, Co is chelated to 4 N atoms at the centre of a porphyrin structure (Figure 19.2). This Co complex provides a prosthetic group which is associated with a nucleotide in the B_{12} coenzyme. This has been termed the cobamide coenzyme (KLIEWER and EVANS [1963]). How this coenzyme is effective in N_2 fixation is still not completely understood. The findings of KLIEWER and EVANS [1963] presented in Table 19.2, however, show the pronounced effect of increasing Co levels in the nutrient medium in raising the fresh weight yields, N-uptake and B_{12} coenzyme content of the symbiotic N fixing bacteria *Rhizobium meliloti*. The Co requirement for N_2 fixation is extremely low, WILSON and REISENAUER [1967] found that for lucerne 10 ppb Co in the nutrient solution was adequate. This is about $1/300$ of the Mo requirement on an atomic basis.

Table 19.2 Effect of Co on the growth and yield of N and B_{12} coenzyme in *Rhizobium meliloti* (KLIEWER and EVANS [1963])

Co concentration in medium μg/l	Fresh weight of cells mg/flask	Total N mg/flask	B_{12} coenzyme content n moles/g fresh weight
0.00	547	118	<1.00
0.02	790	188	12.9
2.00	1034	272	45.0

One pathway in which Co appears to be essential is in the transformation of propionate to succinyl coenzyme. This occurs in nodule bacteroids and cultured *Rhizobium* cells. Several steps are involved in the conversion:

Propionate → Propionyl Co A → Methyl malonyl Co A → Succinyl Co A
The succinyl Co A produced reacts with glycine to form aminolaevulic acid (ALA) which is then converted to haem by a number of further steps (see p.479). It seems likely that this is the mechanism by which propionate is incorporated into the haem moiety of leghaemoglobin (EVANS and RUSSELL [1971]). In the absence of Co the process does not take place as the formation of succinyl Co A

Plate 19.2 The effect of the addition of 0.1 μg of Co/l in the nutrient solution on the growth of
soya bean in symbiosis with *Rhizobium japonicum* .
(Photo: AHMED and EVANS)
By courtesy of *Plenum Publishing Co. Ltd.)*.

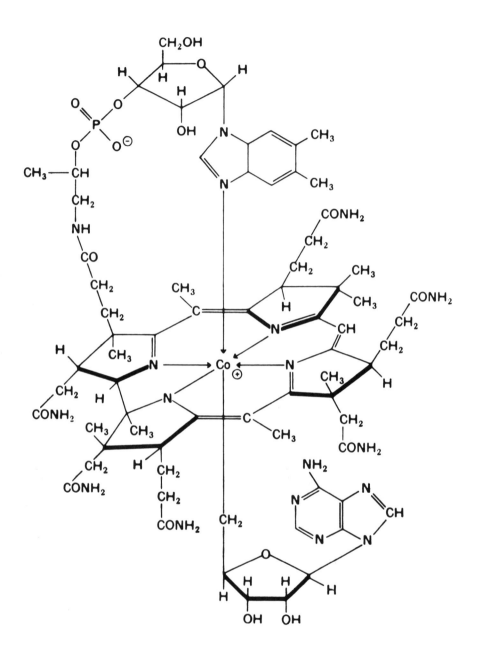

Fig.19.2 Structure of the cobamide coenzyme.

is blocked. Cobalt appears to be essential for the activity of the enzyme methyl malonyl Co A mutase which catalyzes the conversion of methyl malonyl Co A to succinyl Co A. Cobalt deficiency thus inhibits the formation of leghaemoglobin and hence N_2 fixation. The propionate pathway may also serve another function by supplying the TCA cycle with succinyl Co A. This may be important for in the N_2 fixation process as oxoglutarate is continuously being drained off from the cycle to form glutamate (see p. 175).

Another role of Co in *Rhizobium* is in activating the nucleotide reductase system. When Co is deficient a development of abnormally elongated *Rhizobium* cells occurs and symptoms suggesting a lesion in the cell division process are apparent. Co appears to be necessary in order that sufficient B_{12} coenzyme is synthesized to allow the normal functioning of the nucleotide reductase system (EVANS and RUSSELL [1971]).

It is still in question whether in addition to its requirement in symbiotic N_2 fixation, Co is essential for higher plants. Evidence supporting a Co requirement for higher plants was put forward by HALLSWORTH and co-workers, who reported a significant increase in the dry weight yields of non nodulated subterranean clover plants resulting from the addition of very low concentration of Co to the nutrient medium (HALLSWORTH et al. [1965], WILSON and HALLSWORTH [1965]). A similar response of wheat to Co was observed by WILSON and NICHOLAS [1967] who also confirmed the earlier work with non nodulated subterranean clover. In addition these workers reported Co deficiency symptoms in both plant species as shown by chlorosis in the younger leaves. Cobalt complexes of low molecular weight were also detected in plants grown aseptically thus indicating the incorporation of Co into the metabolism. Similar observations have been made by FRIES [1962] who detected vitamin B_{12} in peas, wheat and lupins cultured under aseptic conditions. The work of WILSON and NICHOLAS [1967] is the first report of Co deficiency in higher plants. More evidence, however, is still required before Co can be classified as an essential element.

Cobalt is also of importance in animal nutrition. It is well established that Co is a metal component of Vitamin B_{12} which is essential in N-metabolism in the ruminant. Inadequate levels of Co in the herbage can lead to Co deficiency symptoms in ruminants characterized by a lack of appetite, lack of growth, and poor reproductive ability. The critical Co level of the diet of ruminants is about 0.08 ppm in the dry matter of the herbage (UNDERWOOD [1971]). Ruminants with a diet based on forage grasses and cereal grains usually require Co supplementation as grasses are often low in Co. Considerably higher levels are usually found in legumes. This is shown in Table 19.3 from a comparative study between grasses and legumes growing on many sites from widely differing soil types in the U.S.A. (KUBOTA and ALLAWAY [1972]).

Table 19.3 Comparison of Co concentrations of common forage plants grown on widely different soils (KUBOTA and ALLAWAY [1972])

	Plant species	Co concentration µg/g dry matter
Legumes	Lucerne	0.18
	Alsike clover	0.27
	Red clover	0.15
Grasses	Brome grass	0.04
	Cocksfoot	0.08
	Timothy	0.04

Cobalt deficiency occurs in highly leached sandy soils, soils derived from acid igneous rocks or in highly calcareous or peaty soils. It is favoured if the soil pH is neutral to alkaline (MITCHELL [1972]). Various extractants have been used to determine readily soluble or available Co. These include 2.5% acetic acid (pH 2.5), neutral N ammonium acetate, or 0.05 M EDTA. Acetic acid extracts of normal agricultural soils give Co levels from 0.05–2 ppm. Where values are less than 0.1 ppm Co deficiency may be suspected. The deficiency can be controlled by administration of a Co salt to the soil at the rate of 1 or 2 kg/ha. If the soil contains large amounts of manganese minerals capable of immobilizing cobalt, higher quantities are required (McKENZIE [1975]).

19.4 Vanadium

Vanadium is widely distributed in biological materials and there are many reports that low concentrations can have a favourable effect on the growth of microorganisms, animals and higher plants (ARNON and WESSEL [1953], PRATT [1966]). It is claimed to be essential for the green alga *Scenedesmus obliquus* (ARNON and WESSEL [1953] although its role is unknown. Some evidence suggests that V may partially substitute for Mo in N_2 fixation in microorganisms but the evidence for the substitution in symbiotic N_2 fixation is not conclusive (STEWART [1966]).

In the higher plants there is no evidence as yet that V is an essential element for any plant species. WELCH and HUFFMAN [1973] grew lettuce and tomato in nutrient solution much lower in V concentration than than required by *Scenedesmus obliquus*. No evidence of V deficiency was observed and these workers claimed that if V is essential for plants adequate levels in plant tissues are less than 2 ng per g dry weight. This concentration is considerably below the normal values found in plant material which average about 1 ppm.

In excess amounts V can be toxic and this has been observed in water culture experiments (WARRINGTON [1955]). Neither deficiency nor toxicity, however, are of any significance under field conditions.

Chapter 20

Elements with More Toxic Effects

There is no clear division between elements which are toxic to plants and those which have a beneficial or even essential effect. The effect of any element on the plant depends not only on its chemical properties but also on its concentration and the presence and concentrations of other elements. The physiological age and species of the plant concerned as well as other environmental factors are also of importance. Some elements such as Fe, Mn, Cu, B, Zn are essential at low concentrations but are toxic at higher levels. The toxic effects of these elements have already been discussed in the appropriate chapter for each nutrient. In the case of the heavy metals Pb and Cd, toxicity is induced by the mimicking of lighter essential elements in uptake and biochemical behaviour.

20.1   Iodine

Iodine and Bromine are typical of most of the elements described above. Neither have been shown to be essential to plants but both are reputed to produce stimulating effects on plant growth at low concentrations. Toxic effects are produced at higher concentrations. For I, the stimulating effect has been observed at I levels in the order of 0.1 ppm in soil and nutrient solution whereas toxic effects occur in excess of about 0.5–1.0 ppm (MARTIN [1966]). This latter concentration is considerably higher than normal soluble soil I levels so that I toxicity has not been reported on agricultural soils.

The toxic effects of high I levels begins in the older leaves. In tomato they become chlorotic and absciss, whilst the younger leaves remain a very dark green colour. Growth is severely restricted and the leaves curl back and necrosis occurs at the tip and edges. In severe cases the plant dies. Iodide toxicity has been found where the level in the plant is in excess of 8 ppm. Normal levels in healthy plants range from 0–0.5 ppm. High levels of Cl^- can reduce the toxic effects of I^- which suggests that there is a competitive effect between both elements (LEWIS and POWERS [1941]). Iodine is required in animal nutrition, as it is an essential element of the hormone thyroxine.

$$\text{HO} - \langle\!\!\!\!\!\!\bigcirc\!\!\!\!\!\!\rangle - \text{O} - \langle\!\!\!\!\!\!\bigcirc\!\!\!\!\!\!\rangle - \text{CH}_2 - \underset{\underset{\overset{+}{\text{NH}_3}}{|}}{\text{CH}} - \text{COO}^-$$

thyroxine

20.2 Bromine

Bromine is taken up by plants as Br^-. In general the ion is not so toxic as I^- and indeed it has been used in many physiological studies in ion uptake. Normally the levels of Br^- in soils are very low so that Br^- toxicity does not occur naturally. In recent years, however, with the use of Br^- containing soil fumigants such as methyl bromide, toxic effects have been reported in a number of sensitive plants such as carnations, chrysanthemums, potato, spinach, and sugar beet (MARTIN [1966]). Symptoms of Br^- toxicity resemble excess salt effects and leaves often become chlorotic followed by expanding leaf tip necrosis and edge necrosis. Poor seed germination may also result. Some plant species are insensitive to Br toxicity. These include carrot, tobacco and tomato. These species can accumulate over 2000 ppm Br^- without showing any adverse effects. Normal Br^- levels for plants growing in soil, however, are usually much lower and in the range of 0–260 ppm (MARTIN [1966]), concentrations at the lower end of the scale being more frequent.

To a certain extent Br^- can substitute for part of the Cl^- requirement of plants (BROYER et al. [1954]). OZANNE et al. [1957] observed that part of this effect resulted from the displacement of Cl^- from non effective sites such as in the root to more essential positions. These workers also observed that typical Cl^- deficiency symptoms could be alleviated by the addition of Br^-.

20.3 Fluorine

Fluorine generally occurs in plant material in the range of 2–20 ppm in the dry matter, although some plant species are capable of accumulating much higher amounts. The poisonous South African shrub *Dichapetalum cymosum* for example can accumulate as much as 200 ppm. In this species F is present as fluoroacetate. This is toxic to animals for on ingestion it is converted to fluorocitrate. This competitively inhibits the enzyme aconitase responsible for the conversion of citrate to isocitrate in the TCA cycle. Commercial tea has also been shown to

560

have levels of F as high as 400 ppm (MITCHELL and EDMAN [1945]) and also to contain fluoroacetate. Very large amounts, however, must be ingested in order to induce toxicity.

High levels of F are usually toxic to plants. Respiration can be both stimulated and inhibited. According to MILLER and MILLER [1974] fumigation of soya beans with HF at first stimulates respiration and this is followed by respiratory inhibition. It is well known that of the respiratory enzymes enolase in particular is very sensitive even to low F levels. The reason for the primary stimulating effect on respiration, however, is not so clear. According to LEE et al. [1965] glucose 6 phosphate dehydrogenase, catalase, peroxidase and cytochrome oxidase activities in soya beans are all increased by fluoride treatment. This may well contribute to the observed primary respiratory stimulation. Fluoride inhibits inorganic pyrophosphatase and hence the oxidation of free fatty acids (LEHNINGER [1975]).

Fluorine toxicity is only found under field conditions in industrially polluted regions where hydrofluoric acid occurs. Exposure of plants to even a few ppb hydrofluoric acid over a period of several months gives rise to foliar toxicity effects in many crops. Symptoms differ between plant species but two basic types occur. These are marginal necrosis sometimes called burnt tip, and interveinal chlorosis (BREWER [1966]). Most plant species show marginal chlorosis and damage with interveinal chlorosis as an earlier symptom of a less acute form of toxicity. A few species including maize, however, only show the chlorosis effect. Some crops are more sensitive than others to hydrofluoric acid toxicity and these include grapes and fruit trees. Generally crops which accumulate high levels of F are less sensitive. Toxicity symptoms have been discussed in detail by BREWER [1966].

The total F content of a soil is usually unrelated to F availability. The form taken up by plants is soluble fluoride, and the predominant factors controlling the level of this ion in soil solution are the soil pH and the amount of soil Ca and P (HURD-KARRER [1950]). When the soil pH is high or when soil Ca or P are present in large amounts, soil fluorine is fixed as calcium fluoride (CaF_2) or aluminium silicofluoride [$Al_2(SiF_6)_2$]. Even when soluble fluoride levels are high as in acid soil conditions, however, soil F^- is not readily taken up by plant roots. This low uptake potential of F^- was demonstrated by VENKATESWARLU et al. [1965] who compared the uptake of F^- and Cl^- by barley roots. When the concentration of the two ions at the root surface were identical a 100 fold higher uptake of Cl^- resulted. These effects of poor availability in the soil and low uptake potential account for the normally minute levels of F^- in plants and the infrequency of F toxicity caused by excess uptake from the soil. The subject of fluoride and plant life has been reviewed by WEINSTEIN [1977].

20.4 Aluminium

More than 15% of the earth's crust is made up of Al_2O_3. Aluminium is thus an important constituent of the soil, and along with Si is the major element making up the lattices of primary and secondary clay minerals. The solubility of Al in the soil is too low in neutral and alkaline soils to be toxic to plant growth. Indeed there is some evidence that low levels of Al can have a beneficial effect on plant growth although the mechanism is not clear (Foy [1974]). Higher plants usually contain in the order of about 200 ppm Al in the dry matter. In tea the levels may be as high as 2000–5000 ppm and according to Chenery [1955] Al is necessary for the normal growth of the tea bush.

On acid soils with pH values below 5.5 the solubility of Al increases sharply and more than half the cation exchange sites may be occupied by Al (Evans and Kamprath [1970]). Under such conditions Al toxicity in plants is likely to occur. In cultivated naturally acid soils in particular, soil acidity often increases down the profile so that the rooting depth of the plant is restricted and water and nutrients of the subsoil cannot be exploited. The first observable effect of Al on plants is a limitation in root growth (Clarkson and Sanderson [1969]). Root tips and lateral roots become thickened and turn brown (Foy et al. [1978]). Frequently phosphate uptake and phosphate translocation to the upper plant parts are affected. The toxicity in the tops is therefore often characterized by symptoms similar to those of P deficiency such as dark green leaves, stunted plant growth and purpling of the stems (Foy [1974]). In the plant cell Al may interfere with the phosphate metabolism by the formation of stable Al-phosphate complexes. Aluminium is known to bind strongly to the phosphate groups of nucleic acids which may result in an inhibition of cell division (Morimura et al. [1978]). Aluminium also affects the activities of phosphokinases and ATPases.

Aluminium toxicity is frequently accompanied by high levels of Fe and Mn and low concentrations of Ca and Mg in the plant tissues. This is to be expected as Al toxicity is associated with acid soil conditions where the availability of both Fe and Mn is high and where the levels of Ca and Mg are often

Table 20.1 Effect of liming on 3 wheat cultivars grown on an Al toxic soil (Foy *et al.* [1965])

CaCO₃ added, ppm	Soil pH	Yield of tops, g dry matter/pot		
		Atlas 66	Monon	Thatcher
0	4.2	1.50	0.49	0.23
1500	5.1	4.23	3.66	3.71
3000	5.8	4.25	4.66	4.76
4500	6.7	3.67	3.95	3.99
6000	7.2	3.16	2.99	2.81

low because of leaching (PLANT [1956]). The detrimental effect of acid soils on plant growth is often due to high soluble Al levels rather than to high H^+ concentrations. The application of lime is the most effective means of controlling Al toxicity in acid soils. Plant species and even cultivars of the same species differ considerably in their tolerance of excess soluble or excess exchangeable Al. In Table 20.1 such an example is shown comparing the yields of three wheat cultivars growing on an Al toxic soil (FOY et al. [1965]). The high soil Al in this experiment had much less effect on 'Atlas 66' than on the other two cultivars, 'Monon' and 'Thatcher'. The data of the table also show that liming alleviates Al toxicity and that at a pH of 5.8 the toxicity disappeared and maximum yields were obtained. On a world scale, acid soils constitute a major restriction to increasing crop yields because of Al and Mn toxicity. Screening genetic material for Al and Mn tolerance is therefore of extreme importance and the subject is receiving considerable attention (see KONZAK et al. [1976]).

One reason for cultivar differences in response to Al relates to the varying ability of plants to modify the pH of the soil root interface. Thus FOY et al. [1967] observed that Al sensitive wheat and barley cultivars decreased the pH in the growth media more than did the Al tolerant cultivars. The plant-induced lowering of the pH increases Al solubility and hence potential toxicity. The same effect is seen with NH_4 nutrition. Cation uptake exceeds anion uptake and an associated root excretion of H^+ occurs lowering of the pH in the root environment. The effect of Al on growth depression is thus considerably greater with NH_4 than with NO_3 nutrition (BARTLETT and RIEGO [1972]).

In some Al tolerant wheat cultivars the tolerance mechanism is related to the fact that these cultivars can also take up NO_3^- at high rates in the presence of NH_4^+. Aluminium tolerance can also be dependent on an Al exclusion mechanism. This has been shown by HENNING [1975] who experimented with the Al tolerant wheat cultivar 'Atlas' and the Al sensitive cultivar 'Brevor'. The tolerant cultivar required about 100–200 times as much Al in the medium as did the Al-sensitive 'Brevor' before Al penetrated the plasmalemma of meristematic root cells. Once inside the cell Al was equally harmful to both cultivars. This example shows that the plasmalemma may exclude Al, and that in this respect marked differences between cultivars do exist. Aluminium tolerance may also be brought about by organic acids and polyphenols which detoxify Al by chelation. A typical example of this kind of tolerance is the tea crop, which takes up a large amount of Al, which is stored in the older leaves where it is detoxified by organic compounds (SIVAS-UBRAMANIAM and TALIBURDEEN [1972]). A very useful review paper on metal toxicity and especially on Al toxicity has been published by FOY et al. [1978].

20.5 Nickel

Nickel is closely related to Co both in its chemical and physiological properties. It readily forms chelate compounds and can replace other heavy metals from physiologically important centres. High Ni concentrations have a toxic effect on plants. In oats VERGNANO and HUNTER [1952] observed that Ni toxicity closely resembled Fe deficiency, a finding which may well relate to the displacement of Fe by Ni. High Ni concentrations in the nutrient medium reduce the uptake of most other nutrients (CROOKE and INKSON [1955]). According to KNIGHT and CROOKE [1956] this reduction in uptake results from the damaging effects of high Ni concentrations on the roots. The phytotoxicity of Ni has been reviewed by MISHRA and KAR [1974].

Acute Ni toxicity gives rise to chlorosis. In the cereals this shows as pale yellow stripes running the length of the leaves. Eventually the whole leaf may turn white and in extreme cases necrosis occurs at leaf margins. In the dicots Ni toxicity appears as chlorotic markings between the leaf veins, the symptoms being similar to those of Mn deficiency (HEWITT [1953]).

Most soils contain only very small quantities of Ni, usually less than 100 ppm, and well below the level at which Ni toxicity occurs. Soils derived from ultrabasic igneous rocks and particularly serpentine, however, may contain 20 to 40 times this concentration and Ni toxicity in plants is common. Serpentine soils occur in various regions throughout the world as far apart as the mountain ranges of the Pacific Coast of the U.S.A., the North of Scotland, parts of the Balkans, the South of the U.S.S.R. and Zimbabwe. On weathering, the mineral serpentine $(H_4Mg\ Fe)_5\ Si_2O$ produces a characteristic soil with a distinctive associated flora and a comparatively sparse vegetation. The soils are rich in Mg and Fe and poor in Ca. In addition they contain relatively high levels of Ni, Co and Cr. KRAUSE [1962] reported 250 ppm exchangeable Ni in the surface layer of red earth soil derived from serpentine as compared with about 1 ppm usually occurring in agricultural soils. In the serpentine soil the ratio of exchangeable Ca to Mg (Ca/Mg) was extremely low and mostly less than 0.4. The cereals, with the exception of oats, are the agricultural crops best able to cope with these conditions.

Nickel toxicity can frequently be greatly alleviated by liming. As was shown by CROOKE [1956] the effect resulted from a neutralizing of soil acidity rather than to an increase in Ca concentration *per se*. Liming not only decreases the availability of Ni and Cr, it also increases the low ratio of exchangeable Ca/Mg. Potassium application also reduces the appearance of Ni toxicity but phosphate fertilizers have the reverse effect (CROOKE and INKSON [1955]).

Normally the Ni content of plant material is about 0.1–5 ppm of the dry matter. On serpentine soils, however, values in excess of 200 ppm may occur in some plant species. Such levels are toxic to plants not adapted to these soils. In a sand culture experiment supplied with increasing levels of Ni, VERGNANO and HUNTER [1952] found Ni concentrations in the dry plant material varying from 1–1000 ppm. Toxic symptoms in oats, a Ni sensitive crop, were observed in plants with Ni contents in excess of 100 ppm (CROOKE [1956]). The uptake by less sensitive crops is lower. Nickel appears to be particularly mobile in the phloem. After uptake considerable amounts of Ni are thus transferred to seeds and fruits (CATALDO et al. [1978], MITCHELL et al. [1978]).

The biological significance of Ni as a possible micronutrient has been reviewed recently by WELCH [1981]. It is now suggested that Ni is essential for animals. Whether it is also essential for plants is still a matter of speculation. However, Ni has been shown to be an integral part of the enzyme urease (see p. 367) isolated from jack bean seeds (DIXON et al. [1975]). Furthermore several investigators have established that plants grown solely on urea N have a Ni requirement (GORDON et al. [1978]). Many plant species including N_2 fixing legumes (e.g. soya beans) accumulate large amounts of ureides (STREETER [1979]). WELCH [1981] argues that for such plants to fully utilize the N in these compounds in anaerobic reactions, urease should be required and therefore also Ni.

20.6 Chromium

There has been much interest in Cr since the relatively recent discovery that it participates in mammalian glucose metabolism and appears to be essential to man and animals (LISK [1972]). As yet, however, there is no evidence of an essential role in plant metabolism (HUFFMAN and ALLAWAY [1973]).

Total Cr levels in igneous and sedimentary rocks are usually in the range of up to about 100 ppm. Most soils have less than 100 ppm although those derived from serpentine may contain several per cent Cr. Soil Cr is largely unavailable to plants because it occurs in relatively insoluble compounds such as chromite $FeCr_2O_4$, in mixed oxides of Cr, Al and Fe, or in silicate lattices. In addition Cr^{3+} binds tenaciously to negatively charged sites on clays and organic matter. Chromates (hexavalent Cr) are relatively rare and are only stable in alkaline oxidizing conditions (ALLAWAY [1968]).

The rate of uptake and translocation of Cr by plants is low. In studying the uptake of $CrCl_3$ by detopped tomato plants from nutrient solutions, TIFFIN [1972] found Cr contents in the xylem exudates of only about 10% of the levels in the nutrient solution. Even allowing for the fact that some Cr may have become associated with exchange sites in the root, the results are indicative of a low rate of uptake. This together with the poor availability in soil means that low levels of Cr are found in plant material. These are usually in the order of 0.02 to 1 ppm.

Toxicity effects have been observed by HUNTER and VERGNANO [1953] in oats supplied with excess of 5 ppm Cr as chromium sulphate. Plants suffering from severe Cr toxicity had small roots and narrow brownish red leaves, covered in small necrotic spots. Acute infertility in some serpentine soils may result from Cr toxicity although other factors are usually involved (see p. 565). The literature of Cr toxicity in relation to serpentine soils has been discussed by PRATT [1966].

20.7 Selenium

Selenium resembles sulphur in its chemical properties. In uptake a competitive effect occurs between selenate and sulphate indicating that both ions have affiinty for the same carrier sites (LEGGETT and EPSTEIN [1956]). The incorporation of Se into amino acids analagous to those of S (selenomethionine and selenocysteine) has also been observed in a number of plant species (PETERSEN and BUTLER [1962]).

Stimulatory effects of low concentrations of Se on plant growth have occasionally been reported. However, the toxic effects of excess Se which give rise to stunting and chlorosis are more well known. Growth is retarded and the Se content increases. Selenium is concentrated particularly in the growing points and seeds, and Se contents of up to 1500 ppm can occur (TRELEASE [1945]). The reasons for Se toxicity are not clear. It is widely held that Se compounds interfere with S metabolism by replacement. However, Se is not able to replace S in all its metabolic functions. Indeed in some plant species there is evidence that Se even follows certain metabolic routes not open to S (SHRIFT [1969]).

In most soils Se occurs in very low concentrations and often less than 0.2 ppm. In acid and neutral soils, availability is low and Se is often present as selenite which may be fixed as ferric selenite. It can also form organic complexes. The element may occur in soils in a number of oxidation states depending on soil redox potential, soil pH, microbiological effects and the presence of other ions (ALLAWAY [1968]). Selenate, the form taken up by plants, occurs only under well aerated alkaline conditions. Such Se rich soils with high selenate levels are found primarily under arid climatic conditions. Seleniferous indicator plants such as the milk vetches *Astragalus bisulcatus* and *A. pectinatus* are indigenous to these soils. These species can accumulate enormous amounts of Se without any detrimental effect on plant growth and levels of several thousand ppm Se are not uncommon (GANJE [1966]). Native grasses growing on the same soils contain only a few ppm Se.

The differences between plants in their ability to accumulate and to tolerate Se have not been fully explained. It has been suggested that in non accumulator plants, Se is mostly found in the proteins (BUTLER and PETERSEN [1967]) whereas the accumulator plants have the ability to synthesize Se containing non-protein amino acids and this prevents toxicity. VIRUPAKSHA and SHRIFT [1965] proposed that the protein amino acid selenocysteine is converted into Se methyl selenocysteine and in this way Se is prevented from disturbing protein metabolism. The more recent findings of NIGAM and MCCONNELL [1976], however, using radioactive selenate found a considerable percentage of radioactivity in the proteins of the Se accumulator *Astragalus bisulcatus*. These workers suggest that differences in the toxicity of Se towards plant species are difficult to explain in terms of interspecies differences in protein incorporation.

The effect of Se in animal nutrition is particularly important. Selenium is an essential element for animals and is required in very low concentrations. Deficiency has been shown to give rise to a muscular dystrophy in livestock known as 'white muscle disease' as well as hair and feather loss. ALLAWAY [1968] has suggested that it is desirable to control the Se levels in food and feed crops to a range between 0.1–1 ppm, and cites a survey in United States which showed that one-third of forage and grain crops were below this optimum level. At higher concentrations in excess of about 5 ppm in the diet there is danger of Se toxicity. This is well known as 'alkali disease' in farm animals and occurs on Se rich alkali soils. In extreme cases it can result in the loss of hair and feathers, and in cattle may lead to misformation of hooves and teeth. As selenate and sulphate compete in uptake by plants, the uptake of selenate can be depressed by sulphate application. This is an important remedial treatment on Se toxic soils.

20.8 Lead

Lead is a major chemical pollutant of the environment, and is highly toxic to man. No other pollutant has accumulated in man to average levels so close to those which are potentially clinically poisonous.

The major source of Pb pollution arises from petrol combustion. According to LAGERWERFF [1972] this source accounts for about 80% of the total Pb in the atmosphere. Lead is added to petrol as tetra ethyl lead, and is emitted in exhaust fumes largely as minute particles of inorganic Pb compounds. About 50% of this falls somewhere within the region of 100 m from the road. The remainder is distributed widely in the biosphere. This is evident from the results of MURO-ZUMI et al. [1969] which shows the dramatic increase in the Pb content of snow over the past thirty years in core samples taken from the North Greenland Icecap. This rise must be almost entirely attributable to increased petrol consumption. Industrial regions are particularly polluted by airborne Pb. In Manchester, for example, a large industrial city in England, levels in the region of 1000 ppm have been observed in street dust (DAY et al. [1975]). The average Pb level in soils in comparison is about 15 ppm. Blood Pb levels have also been found to rise considerably in humans living near motorways. Lead toxicity in man has also been caused by water contamination from Pb piping. This can also be an important source of Pb pollution.

Lead is toxic because it mimics many aspects of the metabolic behaviour of Ca, and inhibits many enzyme systems. In man, one of the chief concerns of Pb toxicity is its effect in causing brain damage particularly to the young. There is evidence that Pb pollution can induce aggressive behaviour in animals. It is believed that this can also occur in humans and BRYCE-SMITH and WALDRON [1974] have presented a very strong case for implicating Pb as one of the causal factors for the increased rate of delinquency in large industrial cities. From the viewpoint of plant nutrition it is important to remember that Pb pollution mainly arises from airborne sources.

The total Pb content of agricultural soils lies between 2–200 ppm. Soils with levels in excess of this are limited to a relatively few regions where Pb mineral deposits occur. In such soils Pb in the upper horizons may reach over 3000 ppm. Toxic effects of Pb can result in a reduction in plant growth but this is not generally seen in the field and almost all detailed observations of Pb toxicity in plants are restricted to water culture experiments (BREWER [1966]). PAGE et al. [1971] carried out an extensive study on the Santa Ana Freeway in Southern California, a highway with a very high traffic density of 70 000 cars per 24 hrs. These workers analysed the Pb fall out and Pb contents of 27 crops at various distances from the road. It was concluded that the content of Pb contaminate was dependent on several factors including distance from the highway, nature of the collecting surface of the plant, duration of the exposure, the traffic density and the direction of the prevailing winds. Many workers have shown that Pb contamination very clearly follows the motorway areas. Vegetation at the side of the road may have levels of 50 ppm Pb but a distance of only 150 m away from the motorway the level is normally about 2 or 3 ppm. Contamination occurs only on the outer part of plant seed or leaves and stem, and a high proportion can be removed by washing. Levels of Pb in grain, tubers and roots are very little affected and do not deviate very much from normal levels for such tissues of about 0.5 ppm (FOY et al. [1978]).

Lead airborne contamination in soils is usually restricted to the top few cm of the soil profile (HEILENZ [1970]). This retention in the upper part of the profile probably relates to the strong adsorption of Pb^{2+} to organic and clay colloids as well as to the formation of insoluble Pb chelates with organic matter (LAGERWERFF [1972]). The availability of soil Pb is usually low and can be decreased even further by liming. A high soil pH may precipitate Pb as hydroxide, phosphate or carbonate, as well as possibly promoting the formation of Pb organic matter complexes. Enhanced levels of Ca^{2+} also increase competition with Pb^{2+} for exchange sites on roots and soil surfaces.

The reason for Pb toxicity in plants is not clear. More is known of the detrimental effect of Pb in animal nutrition (see BRYCE-SMITH [1975]). In animals, Pb toxicity interferes with Fe metabolism and the formation of haem. Lead inhibits two steps in the conversion of δ amino-laevulnic acid to haem (see p. 479). It inhibits the enzyme ALA dehydrase in the conversion of δ amino-laevulnic acid (ALA) to porphobilinogen (PBG). It also blocks the formation of haem from coproporphyrinogen III. In the blood and urine of Pb toxic patients there is therefore a marked increase in the levels of ALA and coproporphyrin III (the oxidation product of coproporphyrinogen III). It is not known whether Pb has the same effect in haem synthesis in plant cells. However, the organic Pb form trialkyl Pb is a powerful mutagenic agent and is known to derange the spindle fibre mechanism of cell division in both plant and animal cells (see BRYCE-SMITH [1975]).

Lead taken up by plants is accumulated in the cell wall. This may well protect the cell from the toxic effects. In maize plants, MALONE et al. [1974] have shown that Pb is first concentrated in dictyosome vesicles which fuse together to encase Pb deposits. These are then removed from the cell cytoplasm to outside the plasmalemma to fuse with the cell wall.

20.9 Cadmium

There is considerable current interest in Cd in plant nutrition. Cadmium and Zn are chemically very similar. Cadmium is thus able to mimic the behaviour of the essential element Zn in its uptake and metabolic functions. Unlike Zn, however, Cd is toxic both to plants and animals. The basic cause of the toxicity probably lies in the much higher affinity of Cd for thiol groupings (SH) in enzymes and other proteins. The presence of Cd therefore disturbs enzyme activity. In plants excess Cd may also disturb Fe metabolism and cause chlorosis.

In animal nutrition Cd is a cumulative poison. It is mainly stored in the kidneys and to some extent also in the liver and spleen. Excess Cd results in damage to the kidney tubules, rhinitis (inflammation of the mucous membrane of the nose), emphysema (a chronic disease of the lungs in which the alveoli become excessively distended) as well as other chronic disorders. In marked contrast to the effects of Pb, however, neurological disorders are not induced by Cd.

A condition of chronic Cd poisoning which has been observed in the Toyama city region of Japan is known as Itai-Itai disease. Excess Cd in the diet has been found to impair kidney function and hence disturb the metabolism of Ca and P and cause bone disease. The disease which is very painful causes excessive demineralization and embrittlement of the skeleton. It has been observed particularly in middle-aged women whose stores of Ca have been depleted by frequent childbirth. The cause of this disease has been traced back to the diet of rice grown on paddy soils polluted with Cd from a mine source.

There is now general concern that under certain conditions the Cd content of plants may be raised and thus become hazardous to man. The sources of soil Cd are varied. Cadmium is added to soils in very small amounts in phosphate fertilizers (WILLIAMS and DAVID [1973]). Along with other heavy metals, it is also present in sewage sludge. Levels from about 10 to as much as 1500 ppm Cd have been observed in the dry matter of this material (BERROW and WEBBER [1972]), which is being used more and more on agricultural land. The main source of Cd pollution to the environment, however, are metal smelters. Zinc smelters are particularly notorious in this respect as the Cd:Zn ratio in Zn ores is usually in the order of 1:350. In addition, soils along roadsides are polluted with Cd from tyres and lubricant oils (LAGERWERFF [1972]). Normal Cd levels in plant material are in the range of 0.1–1.0 ppm. Toxic effects in man have been observed from the regular consumption of plants in excess of 3 ppm Cd.

Cadmium differs markedly from lead in that it can be transported readily from the soil *via* the plant root to the upper plant parts. Its availability depends much on soil pH and the presence of other cation species. Calcium and Zn in particular depress the Cd uptake. The uptake process is probably a passive one and the movement in the plant resembles that of Ca, with exchange sites involved (see p. 446). In most plant species transport of Cd into the shoots is usually directly proportional to the external concentration (JONES *et al.* [1975], PETTERSON [1976]). However, translocation from the leaves into seeds is low and the Cd content of cereal grains from highly contaminated soils only exceeds 1 ppm (SOMMER [1979]). According to CHANEY and HORNICK [1978] this is the source of 50% of Cd in the average US diet. There is much evidence that crop species and genotypes vary markedly in Cd uptake, thus offering a means of retaining Cd at a low level in plant products. This topic along with general aspects of heavy metal toxicities has been reviewed recently by MARSCHNER [1982].

In practical terms, the two major sources of Cd pollution are from Zn ores and sewage sludges. There is no evidence that Cd is becoming a general hazard. Nevertheless, the use of sewage sludges should be carefully monitored. The findings of Dijkshoorn and Lampe [1975] show at least that the uptake of Cd from sewage sludge is considerably lower than that from an equal level of Cd-salt added to the soil. Cadmium uptake from soil is also much less effective than uptake from solution culture.

General Reading

Chapters 14-20

Amberger, A.: (G) The role of manganese in the metabolism of plants. Agrochimica *17*, 69–83 (1973)

Batey, T.: Manganese and boron deficiency. In: Ministry of Agriculture Fisheries and Food, Trace Elements in Soils and Crops, p. 137–148. Technical Bulletin 21, 1971

Bowen, H.J.M.: Trace Elements in Biochemistry, Academic Press, Inc., 1966

Bradford, G.R.: Boron. In: H.D. Chapman (ed.): Diagnostic Criteria for Plants and Soils, p. 33–61. University of California, Division of Agricultural Sciences (1966)

Brewer, R.F.: Lead. In: H.D. Chapman (ed.): Diagnostic Criteria for Plants and Soils p. 213–217. University of California, Division of Agricultural Sciences, 1966

Chapman, H.D. (ed.): Diagnostic Criteria for Plants and Soils. University of California, Division of Agricultural Sciences, 1966

Cheng, B.T.: Dynamics of soil manganese. Agrochimica *17*, 84–95 (1973)

Cheng, B.T. and Ouellette, G.T.: Molybdenum as a plant nutrient. Soils and Fertilizers, *36*, 207–215 (1973)

Dam Kofoed, A.: Copper and its utilization in Danish agriculture. Fertilizer Research *1*. 63–71 (1980)

Davies, B.E. (ed.): Applied Trace Elements. J. Wiley, 1980

Epstein, E.: Mineral Nutrition of Plants. Principles and Perspectives. John Wiley and Sons, Inc., New York, London, Sydney, Toronto 1971

Foy, C.D.: Effects of aluminium on plant growth. In: E.W. Carson (ed.): The Plant Root and its Environment, p. 601–642. University Press of Virginia, Charlottesville, 1974

Foy, C.D., Chaney, R.L. and White, M.C.: The physiology of metal toxicity in plants. Ann. Rev. Plant Physiol. *29*, 511–566 (1978)

Gauch, H.G.: Inorganic Plant Nutrition, p. 243–259. Dowden Hutchinson and Ross Inc., Stroudsburg, Pa, USA (1972)

Gupta, U.C.: Boron in nutrition of crops. Adv. Agron. *31*, 273–307 (1979)

Hewitt, E.J. and Smith, T.A.: Plant Mineral Nutrition. English University Press, 1975

Ivanova, N.N.: Molybdenum in plant nutrition. Agrochimica, *17*, 96–118 (1973)

Jackson, J.F. and Chapman, K.S.R.: The role of boron in plants. In: D.J.D. Nicholas and A.R. Egan (eds.): p. 213–225. Trace Elements in Soil-Plant-Animal Systems, Academic Press (1975)

Johnson, C.M.: Selenium in soils and plants: Contrasts in conditions providing safe but adequate amounts of selenium in the food chain. In: D.J.D. Nicholas and A.R. Egan ds(e): Trace Elements in Soil-Plant-Animal System., p. 165–180. Academic Press, London, New York, San Francisco, 1975

JONES, L.H.P. and HANDRECK, K.A.: Silica in soils plants and animals., Adv. in Agron., *19*, 107–149 (1967)

LAGERWERFF, J.V.: Lead mercury and cadmium as environmental contaminants, p. 593–636. In: Micronutrients in Agriculture. Soil Sci. Soc. America, Madison, Wisconsin, USA, 1972

LEWIN, J.C. and REIMANN, B.E.F.: Silicon and plant growth. Ann. Rev. Plant Physiol., *20*, 289–304 (1969)

LINDSAY, W.D.: Zinc in soils and plant nutrition. Adv. in Agronomy *24*, 147–186 (1972).

LINDSAY, W.L.: Chemical Equilibria in Soils. Wiley, 1980

LONERAGAN, J.F., ROBSON, A.D. and GRAHAM, R.D. (eds.), Copper in Soil and Plants. Academic Press, London, New York and San Francisco 1981

MARTIN, J.P.: Bromine. In: H.D. CHAPMAN (ed.): Diagnostic Criteria for Plants and Soils, p. 62–64. University of California, Division of Agricultural Sciences, 1966

McKENZIE, R.M.: The mineralogy and chemistry of soil cobalt. In: D.J.D. NICHOLAS and A.R. EGAN: Trace Elements in Soil-Plant-Animal Systems, p. 83–93. Academic Press.

MITCHELL, R.L.: Soil aspects of trace elements problems in plants and animals. J. Rl. Agric. Soc. *124*, 75–86 (1963)

MITCHELL, R.L.: Cobalt in soil and its uptake by plants. Agrochimica, *16*, 521–532 (1972)

MORDVEDT, J.J., GIORDANO, P.M. and LINDSAY, W.L.: Micronutrients in Agriculture. Soil Sci. Soc. of America, Madison, Wisconsin, U.S.A., 1972

NICHOLAS, D.J.D. and EGAN, A.R.: Trace Elements in Soil-Plant-Animal systems. Academic Press, Inc., London, New York, San Francisco 1975

NRIAGU, J.O.: Copper in the Environment, 2 vols, Wiley, 1979

NRIAGU, J.O.: Cadmium in the Environment. 2. vols., Wiley, 1980

OKUDA, A. and TAKAHASHI, E.: The role of silicon. In: The Mineral Nutrition of the Rice Plant, p. 123–146. Proc. Symp. Intern. Rice Res. Inst., John Hopkins Press, Baltimore, USA 1965

PAGE, A.L., GANJE, T.J. and JOSHI, M.S.: Lead quantities in plants, soils and air near some major highways in Southern California. Hilgardia, *41*, 1–31 (1971)

PEISACH, J., AISEN, P. and BLUMENBERG, W.E.: The Biochemistry of Copper. Academic Press, London and New York (1966)

PRICE, C.A., CLARK, H.E. and FUNKHOUSER, H.E.: Functions of micronutrients in plants, In: Micronutrients in Agriculture, p. 31–42. Soil Sci. Soc. of America, Madison, Wisconsin 1972

SAUCHELLI, V.: Trace Elements in Agriculture. Van Nostrand Reinhold Company, New York, 1969

SCHÜTTE, K.H.: The Biology of the Trace Elements. Their Role in Nutrition. London, Crosby and Lockwood, 1964

SHKOLNIK, M.Y.: General conception of the physiological role of boron in plants. Physiol. Rastenii, *21*, 140–150 (1974)

SHRIFT, A.: Aspects of selenium metabolism in higher plants. Ann. Rev. Plant Physiol., *20*, 475–494 (1969)

SWAINE, D.J.: The Trace Element Content of Soils. Commonwealth Bureau of Soil Science Tech. Comm., No.48, 1955

VANSELOW, A.P.: Cobalt. In: H.D. CHAPMAN (ed.): Diagnostic Criteria for Plants and Soils, p. 14.–156. University of California, Division of Agricultural Sciences, 1966

References

Publications not written in English are indicated by a letter in parenthesis.

(D) = Danish text
(F) = French text
(G) = German text
(N) = Dutch text
(P) = Polish text
(R) = Russian text
(Ru) = Rumanian text
(Y) = Yugoslavian text

ABOU-KHALED, A., HAGAN, R.M. and DAVENPORT, D.C.: Effects of kaolinite as reflective antitranspirant on leaf temperature, transpiration, photosynthesis, and water use efficiency. Water Resource Res. 6, 280–289 (1970)

ACEVEDO, E., HSIAO, TH.C. and HENDERSON, D.W.: Immediate and subsequent growth responses of maize leaves to changes in water status. Plant Physiol. 48, 631–636 (1971)

ACQUAYE, D.K., MACLEAN, A.J. and RICE, H.M.: Potential and capacity of potassium in some representative soils of Ghana. Soil Sci. 103, 79–90 (1967)

ADAMS, F.: Soil solution, p. 441–481, in E.W.Carson: The Plant Root and its Environment, University Press of Virginia (1974)

ADAMS, F. and LUND, Z.F.: Effect of chemical activity of soil solution aluminium on cotton root penetration of acid subsoils. Soil Sci. 101, 193–198 (1966)

ADDISCOTT, T.M.: Potassium and the distribution of calcium and magnesium in potato plants. J. Sci. Fd Agric. 25, 1173–1183 (1974)

ADEPTU, J.A. and AKAPA, L.K.: Root growth and nutrient uptake characteristics of some cowpea varieties. Agron J. 69, 940–943 (1977)

ADJEI-TWUM, D.C. and SPLITTSTOESSER, W.E.: The effect of soil water regimes on leaf water potential, growth and development of soybeans. Physiol. Plant. 38, 131–137 (1976)

ADRIANO, D.C., PAULSEN, G.M. and MURPHY, L.S.: Phosphorus-iron and phosphorus-zinc relationship in corn (Zea mays L.) seedlings as affected by mineral nutrition. Agron. J. 63, 36–39 (1971)

AGARWALA, S.C. and HEWITT, E.J.: Molybdenum as a plant nutrient. J. Hort. Sci. 29, 291–300 (1954)

AGARWALA, S.C. and HEWITT, E.J.: Molybdenum as a plant nutrient. III. The interrelationships of molybdenum and nitrate supply in the growth and molybdenum content of cauliflower plants grown in sand culture. J. Hort. Sci. 29, 278–290 (1954)

AGARWALA, S.C. and HEWITT, E.J.: Molybdenum as a plant nutrient. V. Effect of molybdenum supply on the growth and composition of cauliflower plants given different sources of nitrogen supply in sand culture. J. Hort. Sci. 30, 163–180 (1955)

AGARWALA, S.C. and HEWITT, E.J.: Molybdenum as a plant nutrient. J. Hort. Sci. 30, 151–162 (1955)

AGBLE, W.K.: Agronomic practices under favourable rain-fed conditions, p. 466–473, in Proc. 1. FAO/SIDA Seminar for plant scientists from Africa and Near East, Cairo 1973. FAO, Rome 1974

AHTI, E.: Correcting stem girth measures for variations induced by soil moisture changes. Communicationes Instituti Forestalis Fenniae 78.4, Helsinki (1973)

AKAZAWA, T.: Ribulose-1,5 bisphosphate carboxylase. In: Photosynthesis II, Encycl. Plant Physiol. New Series Vol 6 (M. GIBBS and E. LATZKO, eds.) p. 208–229. Springer-Verlag Berlin, Heidelberg, New York 1979

AKTAS, M. and VAN EGMOND, F.: Effect of nitrate nutrition on iron utilization by an Fe efficient and an Fe inefficient soybean cultivar Plant and Soil 51, 257–274 (1979).

ALBERDA, T.: Crop photosynthesis: methods and compilation of data obtained with a mobile field equipment. 3. Perennial ryegrass. p. 4–11. Agr. Res. Rep. 865 Centre for Agricultural Publishing and Documentation, Wageningen 1977

ALBERT, L.S.: Induction and antagonism of boron-like deficiency symptoms of tomato plants by selected nitrogen-bases. Plant Physiol. 43, S-51-4 : 15 (1968)

ALBERT, L.S. and WILSON, C.M.: Effect of boron on elongation to tomato root tips. Plant Physiol. 36, 244–251 (1961)

ALLAWAY. W.H.: Trace element cycling. Adv. Agron. 20, 235–274 (1968)

ALLEN, S.E., TERMAN, G.L. and HUNT, C.M.: Soluble and slow-release nitrogen fertilizer effects on grass forage, as influenced by rate and placement. J. agric. Sci. 77, 397–404 (1971)

ALLISON, F.W.: The fate of nitrogen applied to soils. Adv. Agron. 18, 219–258 (1966)

ALTHER, L.: Organic farming on trial. Natural History 81, 16–24 (1972)

ALTHERR, E. and EVERS, F.H.: (G) Effects of magnesia when fertilizing a spruce stand on bunter sandstone in the Odenwald. Allg. Forst- u. Jagdzeitung 146, 217–224 (1975)

AMBERGER, A.: (G) The role of manganese in the metabolism of plants. Agrochimica 17, 69–83 (1973)

AMBERGER, A.: Protein biosynthesis and effect of plant nutrients on the process of protein formation. In: Fertilizer Use and Protein Production, p. 75–89. Int. Potash Inst. Bern, 1975

AMBERGER, A and AIGNER, H.: (G) Experimental results of a straw application trial lasting eight years. Z. Acker- u. Pflanzenbau 130, 291–303 (1969)

AMBLER, J.E., BROWN, J.C. and GAUCH, H.G.: Effect of zinc on translocation of iron in soybean plants. Plant Physiol. 46, 320–323 (1970)

AMESZ, J.: Plastoquinone. In: Photosynthesis I, Encycl. Plant Physiol., New Series Vol. 5 (A. TREBST and M. ARNON eds.) p. 238–246. Springer-Verlag Berlin, Heidelberg, New York 1977

AMIN, J.V. and JOHAM, H.E.: The cations of the cotton plant in sodium substituted potassium deficiency. Soil Sci. 105, 248–254 (1968)

ANDERSON, G.D.: Potassium response of various crops in East Africa, in Potassium in Tropical Crops and Soils, p. 287–309, Proc. 10th Coll. Int. Potash Inst., Bern 1973

ANDERSON, J.W.: The function of sulphur in plant growth and metabolism, p. 87–97. In: Sulphur in Australasian Agriculture. Ed. McLachlan, Sidney Univ. Press 1975

ANDERSON, J.M. and PYLIOTIS, N.A.: Studies with manganese deficient chloroplasts. Biochim. Biophys. Acta 189, 280–293 (1969)

ANDREWS, T.J. and HATCH, M.D.: Activities and properties or ribulose diphosphate carboxylase from plants with the C4 dicarboxylic pathway of photosynthesis. Phytochemistry 10, 9–15 (1971)

ANSARI, A.Q. and BOWLING, D.J.F.: Measurement of the transroot electrical potential of plants grown in soil. New Phytol. 71, 111–117 (1972)

ANTONIW, L.D. and SPRENT, J.I.: Primary metabolites of Phaseolus vulgaris nodules. Phytochemistry 17, 675–678 (1978)

ANTONOVICS, J., BRADSHAW, A.D. and TURNER, R.G.: Heavy metal tolerance in plants. Adv. in Ecol. Res. 7, 1–85 (1971)

574

APPELQVIST, L.A.: Lipids in Cruciferae. II. Fatty acid composition of *Brassica napus* seed as affected by nitrogen, phosphorus, potassium and sulfur nutrition of the plants. Physiol. Plant. *21*, 455–465 (1968)

ARIFIN, PERKINS, H.F. and TAN, K.H.: Potassium fixation and reconstitution of micaceous structures in soils. Soil Sci. *116*, 31–35 (1973)

ARISZ, W.H.: Significance of the symplasm theory for transport across the roots. Protoplasma *46*, 1–62 (1956)

ARMSTRONG, M.J. and KIRKBY, E.A.: The influence of humidity on the mineral composition of tomato plants with special reference to calcium distribution Plant and Soil *52*, 427–435 (1979)

ARNEKE, W.W.: (G) The effect of potassium on the components of the water potential and on the growth rate of *Phaseolus vulgaris*. Ph. D. Thesis, FB 19 Nutrition Sci. Justus Liebig-University, Giessen 1980

ARNOLD, P.W.: The potassium status of some English soils considered as a problem of energy relationships. The Fertilizer Sci., London, Proc. No. 72, 25–55 (1962)

ARNON, D.I.: Functional aspects of copper in plants, p. 89–114, in Copper metabolism. The Johns Hopkins Press, Baltimore 1950

ARNON, D.I.: Phosphorus and the biochemistry of photosynthesis. Agrochimica *3*, 108–139 (1959)

ARNON, D.I.: Cell-free photosynthesis and the energy conversion process, p. 489–565, in Light and Life, ed. W.D. McElroy and Bentley Glass (John Hopkins Press) 1961

ARNON, D.I.: Photosynthetic activity of isolated chloroplasts. Physiol. Rev. *47*, 317–358 (1967)

ARNON, D.I. and STOUT, P.R.: The essentiality of certain elements in minute quantity for plants with special reference to copper. Plant Physiol. *14*, 371–375 (1939)

ARNON, D.I., FRATZKE, W.E. and JOHNSON, C.M.: Hydrogen ion concentration in relation to absorption of inorganic nutrients by higher plants. Plant Physiol. *17*, 515–524 (1942)

ARNON, D.I., LOSADA, M., WHATLEY, F.R., TSUJIMOTO, H.Y., HALL, D.O. and HORTON, A.A.: Photosynthetic phosphorylation and molecular oxygen. Proc. Nat. Acad. Sci. *47*, 1314–1334 (1961)

ARNON, D.I. and WESSEL, G.: Vanadium as an essential element for green plants. Nature *172*, 1039–1040 (1953)

ARNON, D.I.: Photosynthesis 1950–1975: Changing concepts and perspectives. In: Photosynthesis I, Plant Physiol. New Series, Vol. 5 (A. TREBST and M. AVRON, eds.) p. 7–56. Springer-Verlag Berlin, Heidelberg, New York 1977

ARNON, I.: Mineral Nutrition of Maize. Int. Potash Inst., Bern, 1975

ASHER, C.J. and OZANNE, P.G.: Growth and potassium content of plants in solution culture maintained at constant potassium concentrations Soil Sci. *103*. 155–161 (1967)

ASHER, C.J. and OZANNE, P.G.: Individual plant variability in susceptibility to potassium deficiences: Some observations on capeweed (*Arctotheca calendula* L Levyus). Austr. J. Plant Physiol. *4*, 499–503 (1977)

ASWORTH, J., BRIGGS, G.G., EVANS, A.A. and MATULA, J.: Inhibition of nitrification by nitrapyrin, carbon disulphide and trithiocarbonate. J. Sci. Fd Agric. *28*, 673–683 (1977)

ATANASIU, N.: (G) The law of growth factors and its importance for research and practical agriculture. Berlin, Sitzungsber. Bd. *111*, Heft 15, Verlag S. Hirzel, Leipzig (1954)

ATKINS, C.A., PATE, J.S. and SHARKEY, P.J.: Asparagine metabolism-key to the nitrogen nutrition of developing legume seeds. Plant Physiol. *56*, 807–812 (1975)

ATKINSON, D.E.: The energy charge of the adenylate pool as a regulatory parameter. Interaction with feed-back modifiers. Biochemistry *7*, 4030–4034 (1968)

ATKINSON, R.J., POSNER, A.M. and QUIRK, J.P.: Kinetics of isotopic exchange of phosphate at the α-Fe OOH- aqueous solution interface J. Inorg. Nucl. Chem. *34*, 2201–2211 (1972)

AUFHAMMER, W. and SOLANSKY, S.: (G) Influence of kinetin application on photosynthate storage in the ears of spring barley by kinetin application. Z. Pflanzenern. Bodenk., Heft *4*, 503–515 (1976)

AYED, I.A.: A study in the mobilization of iron in tomato roots by chelate treatments. Plant and Soil *32*, 18–26 (1970)

AYRES, A.S.: Calcium silicate slag as a growth stimulant for sugarcane on low-silicon soils. Soil Sci. *101*, 216–227 (1966)

AYRES, A.S. and HAGIHARA, H.H.: Effectiveness of raw rock phosphate for sugar cane. Soil Sci. *91*, 383–387 (1961)

BACH, M.K , MAGEE, W.F. and BURRIS, R.H.: Translocation of photosynthetic products to soybean nodules and their role in nitrogen fixation. Plant Physiol. *33*, 118–123 (1958)

BACHE, B.W. and IRELAND, C.: Desorption of phosphate from soils using anion exchange resins. J. Soil Sci. *31*, 297–306 (1980)

BACHTHALER, G.: (G) Effects of chlorocholine-chloride (CCC) foliar application on winter and spring wheat grown on sites with high rainfall. Z. Acker- u. Pflanzenbau *126*, 357–382 (1967)

BACHTHALER, G. and WAGNER, A.: (G) Long term field trial comparing straw incorporation and straw burning on different sites. Bayr. Landw. Jahrb. *50*, 436–461 (1973)

BADEN, W.: (G) Adequate potash and phosphate application to organic soils. Kali-Briefe, Fachgeb. 7, 1. Folge (1965)

BAKER, D.A. and WEATHERLEY, P.E.: Water and solute transport by exuding root systems of *Ricinus communis*. J. exp. Bot. *20*, 485–496 (1969)

BALCAR, J., BREZINOVA-DOSKAROVA, ALENA and EDER, J.: Dependence of radiostrontium uptake by pea and lupin on the content of calcium in the nutrient solution. Biol. plant. *11*, 34–40 (1969)

BALFOUR, E.: The Living Soil and the Haughley Experiment. Faber and Faber, p. 278. London 1975

BALKE, N.E. and HODGES, T.K.: Plasma membrane adenosine triphosphatase of oat roots. Plant Physiol. *55*, 83–86 (1975)

BANGERTH, F.: Calcium-related physiological disorders of plants. Ann. Rev. Phytopathol. *17*, 97–122 (1979)

BANGERTH, F., DILLEY, D.R. and DEWEY, D.H.: Effect of postharvest calcium treatment on internal breakdown and respiration of apple fruit J. Amer. Soc. Hort. Sci. *97*, 679–682 (1972)

BAR-AKIVA, A.: Chemical and biochemical measurements on plants as a mean of controlling yield and plant performance, p. 211–219. Proc. 9th Congr. Int. Potash. Inst., Bern 1970

BAR-AKIVA, A., LAVON, R. and SAGIV, J.: Ascorbic acid oxidase activity as a measure of copper nutrition requirement of citrus trees. Agrochimica *14*, 47–54 (1969)

BAR-AKIVA, A., SAGIV, J. and LESHEM, J.: Nitrate reductase activity as an indicator for assessing the nitrogen requirement of grass crops. J. Sci. Fd Agric. *21*, 405–407 (1970)

BAR-AKIVA, A. and STERNBAUM, J.: Possible use of nitrate reductase activity of leaves as a measure of the nitrogen requirement of citrus trees. Pl. Cell Physiol. *6*, 575–577 (1965)

BARANKIEWICZ, T.J.: CO_2-exchange rates and ^{14}C photosynthetic products of maize leaves as affected by potassium deficiency. Z. Pflanzenphysiol. *89*, 11–20 (1978)

BARBER, D.A.: Influence of microorganisms on assimilation of nitrogen by plants from soil and fertilizer sources. In: Nitrogen-15 in Soil Plant Studies, p. 91–101, IAEA, Vienna 1971

BARBER, D.A., EBERT, M. and EVANS, T.S.: The movement of ^{15}O through barley and rice plants. J. Exp. Bot. *13*, 397–403 (1962)

BARBER, D.A. and FRANKENBURG, U.C.: The contribution of microorganisms to the apparent absorption of ions by roots grown under non-sterile conditions. New Phytol. *70*, 1027 (1971)

BARBER, D.A. and MARTIN, J.K.: The release of organic substances by cereal roots in soil. New Phytol. *76*, 69–80 (1976)

BARBER, D.A. and SHONE, M.G.T.: The absorption of silica from aqueous solutions by plants. J. exp. Bot. *17*, 569–578 (1966)

BARBER, J.: Light induced uptake of potassium and chloride by *Chlorella pyrenoidosa*. Nature *217*, 876–878 (1968)

BARBER, S.A.: A diffusion and mass flow concept of soil nutrient availability. Soil Sci. *93*, 39–49 (1962)

BARBER, S.A.: Mechanism of potassium absorption by plants, p. 293–310. In: KILMER *et al.*: The Role of Potassium in Agriculture, Madison, USA (1968)

BARBER, S.A.: Influence of the plant root on ion movement in the soil, p. 525–564. In: E.W.CARSON: The Plant Root and its Environment, University Press of Virginia (1974)

BARBER, S.A.: Growth requirements of nutrients in relation to demand at the root surface. In: The Soil-Root Interface (J.L. HARLEY and R. SCOTT RUSSELL, eds.) p. 5–20. Academic Press London, New York, San Francisco 1979

BARBER, S.A., WALKER, J.M. and VASEY, E.H.: Mechanism for the movement of plant nutrients from the soil and fertilizer to the plant root. J. Agr. Food Chem. *11*, 204–207 (1963)

BARBER, W.D. and THOMAS, W.I.: Evaluation of the genetics of relative phosphorus accumulation by corn *(Zea mays L.)* using chromosomal translocations. Crop Sci. *12*, 755–758 (1972)

BARDZIK, J.M., MARSH, H.V., jr. and HAVIS, J.R.: Effects of water stress on the activities of three enzymes in maize seedlings. Plant Physiol. *47*, 828–831 (1971)

BARKER, A.V., MAYNARD, D.N., MIODUCHOWSKA, B. and BUCH, A.: Ammonium and salt inhibition of some physiological processes associated with seed germination. Physiol. Plant. *23*, 898–907 (1970)

BARKER, C. and HILDITCH, T.P.: The influence of environment upon the composition of sunflower seed oils. J. Sci. Fd Agric. *1*, 118–121 (1950)

BARLEY, K.P.: The configuartion of the root system in relation to nutrient uptake. Adv. Agron. *22*, 159–201 (1970)

BARLEY, K.P. and ROVIRA, A.D.: The influence of root hairs on the uptake of phosphate. Commun. Soil Sci. Plant Anal. *1*, 287–292 (1970)

BARROW, N.J.: Comparison of the adsorption of molybdate, sulfate and phosphate by soils. Soil Sci. *109*, 282–288 (1970)

BARROWS, H.L., TAYLOR, A.W. and SIMPSON, E.C.: Interaction of limestone particle size and phosphorus on the control of soil acidity. Proc. Soil Sci. Soc. Amer. *32*, 64–68 (1968)

BARTHOLOMEW, W.W.: ^{15}N in research on the availability and crop use of nitrogen. In: Nitrogen-15 in Soil Plant Studies, p. 1–20, IAEA, Vienna 1971

BARTLETT, R.J.: Iron oxidation proximate to plant roots. Soil Sci. *92*, 372–379 (1961)

BARTLETT, R.J. and RIEGO, D.C.: Toxicity of hydroxy aluminium in relation to pH and phosphorus. Soil Sci. *114*, 194–200 (1972)

BARTLETT, R.J. and SIMPSON, T.J.: Interaction of ammonium and potassium in a potassium-fixing soil. Proc. Soil Sci. Soc. Amer. *31*, 219–222 (1967)

BARTON, R.: The production and behaviour of phytoferritin particles during senescence of *Phaseolus* leaves. Planta *94*, 73–77 (1970)

BASSHAM, J.A.: The reductive pentose phosphate cycle and its regulation. In: Photosynthesis II. New Series, Vol. 6 (M. GIBBS and E. LATZKO, eds.) p. 9–30. Springer-Verlag Berlin, Heidelberg, New York 1979

BASSHAM, J.A. and CALVIN, M.: The path of carbon in photosynthesis, p. 104. Prentice Hall Inc., Englewood Cliffs, N.Y. (1957)

BATEY, T.: Manganese and boron deficiency. In Trace Elements in Soils and Crops: Techn. Bull. 21, p. 137–149, Ministry of Agric., Fisheries and Food, UK (1971)

BAULE, H.: (G) Relationships between the nutrient content and diseases in forest trees. Landw. Forsch. *23*/I. Sonderh., 92–104 (1969)

BAULE, H. and FRICKER, C.: The fertiliser treatment of forest trees. BLV-Verlagsges. München 1970

BAYZER, H. and MAYR, H.H.: (G) Amino acid composition of rye grain proteins influenced by nitrogen application and chlorine-choline-chloride. Z. Lebensmittel-Untersuchung u. -Forsch. *133*, 215–217 (1967)

BEAR, F.E. *et al.*: Hunger signs in crops, a symposium. The American Soc. Agron., The National Fertilizer Ass., Washington 1949

BEARDSELL, M.F. and COHEN, D.: Relationship between leaf water status, abscisic acid levels, stomatal resistance in maize and sorghum. Plant Physiol. *56*, 207–212 (1975)

BECKETT, P.H.T. and NAFADY, M.H.M.: Potassium-calcium exchange equilibria in soils: The location of non-specific (Gapon) and specific exchange sites. Soil Sci. *18*, 263–281 (1967)

BECKING, J.H.: A requirement of molybdenum for the symbiotic nitrogen fixation in alder. Plant and Soil *15*, 217–227 (1961)

BEEVERS, L.: Nitrogen Metabolism in Plants. Edward Arnold, London 1976

BEEVERS, L. and HAGEMAN, R.H.: Nitrate reduction in higher plants. Ann. Rev. Plant Physiol. *20*, 495–518 (1969)

BEEVERS, L. and HAGEMAN, R.H.: The role of light in nitrate metabolism in higher plants, p. 85–113. In: Photophysiology. Vol. VII. Ed. A.C.Giese, Academic Press London 1972

BELL, O.T., KOEPPE, D.E. and MILLER, R.J.: The effects of drought stress on respiration of isolated corn mitochondria. Plant Physiol. *48*, 413–415 (1971)

BENDALL, D.S. and R.HILL: Haem-proteins in photosynthesis. Ann. Rev. Plant Physiol. *19*, 167–186 (1968)

BENEDICT, C.R. and BEEVERS, H.: Formation of sucrose from malate in germinating castor beans. I. Conversion of malate to phosphoenol-pyruvate. Plant Physiol. *36*, 540–544 (1961)

BENNETT, A.C.: Toxic effects of aqueous ammonia, copper, zinc, lead, boron, and manganese on root growth. In: E.W.CARSON, ed. The Plant Root and its Environment, p.669–683. University of Virginia, Charlottesville 1974

BENNETT, A.C. and ADAMS, F.: Concentration of NH_3 (aq) required for incipient NH_3 toxicity to seedlings. Soil Sci. Soc. Amer. Proc. *34*, 259–263 (1970)

BENNETT, J.P.: Iron in leaves. Soil Sci. *60*, 91–105 (1945)

BENSON, A.A.: On the orientation of lipids in chloroplasts and cell membranes. The Journal of the American Oil Chemists' Soc. *43*, 265–273 (1966)

BEN-ZIONI, A., ITAI, C. and VAADIA, Y.: Water and salt stresses, kinetin and protein synthesis in Tobacco leaves. Plant Physiol. *42*, 361–365 (1967)

BEN-ZIONI, A., VAADIA, Y. and LIPS, S.H.: Nitrate uptake by roots as regulated by nitrate reduction products of the shoot. Physiol. Plant. *24*, 288–290 (1971)

BERGER, K.C.: Micronutrient deficiencies in the United States. J. Agric. Food Chem. *10*, 178–181 (1962)

BERGERSEN, F.J.: Biochemistry of symbiotic nitrogen fixation in legumes. Ann. Rev. Plant Physiol. *22*, 121–140 (1971)

BERGMANN, W.: (G) Occurrence, diagnosis, and prevention of nutrient deficiency in crops. Dt. Landw. Verlag, Berlin (1960)

BERGMANN, W.: (G) Recommendations for establishing fertilizer application schemes for large areas of industrialized plant production according to soil tests. VEB Chemiehandel, 113 Berlin (1969)

BERGMANN, W. and NEUBERT, P.: (G) Plant Diagnosis and Plant Analysis. VEB Gustav Fischer Verlag Jena (1976)

BERINGER, H.: (G) Uptake and effect of the micronutrient copper applied in ionic and chelated form to barley. Z. Pflanzenernähr. Düng. Bodenk. *100*, 22–34 (1963)

BERINGER, H.: Influence of temperature and seed ripening on the *in vivo* incorporation of $^{14}CO_2$ into the lipids of oat grains *(Avena sativa L.)*. Plant Physiol. *48*, 433–436 (1971)

BERINGER, H. and KOCH, K.: (G) Nitrogen metabolism in a normal and a lysine-rich barley supplied with different levels of potassium. Landw. Forsch. Sonerh. 34/II, 36–44, Kongressband (1977)

BERINGER, H. and SAXENA, N.P.: (G) Effect of temperature on the content of tocopherol in seed oils. Z. Pflanzenernähr. Bodenk. *120*, 71–78 (1968)

BERNSTEIN, L.: Osmotic adjustment of plants to saline media. II. Dynamic phase. Amer. J. Bot. *50* (4), 360–370 (1963)

BERNSTEIN, L.: Salt tolerance of plants. Agric. Inform. Bull. No. 283 (1970)

BERNSTEIN, L. and HAYWARD, H.E.: Physiology of salt tolerance. Ann. Rev. Plant Physiol. *9*, 25–46 (1958)

BERROW, M.C. and WEBBER, J.: Trace elements in sewage sludges. J. Sci. Food Agr. *23*, 93–1000 (1972)

BESFORD, R.T.: A phosphatase as a potential indicator of the phosphorus status of the glasshouse cucumber *(Cucumis sativus)*. J. Sci. Fd. Agric *29*, 87–91 (1978)

BETHLENFALVAY, G.J. and PHILLIPS, D.A.: Interactions between symbiotic nitrogen fixation, combined N application, and photosynthesis in *Pisum sativum*. Physiol. Plant. *42*, 119–123 (1978)

BHANGOO, M.S. and ALBRITTON: Effect of fertilizer nitrogen, phosphorus, and potassium on yield and nutrient content of 'Lee' soybeans. Agron. J. *64*, 743–746 (1972)

BHAT, K.K.S. and NYE, P.H.: Diffusion of phosphate to plant roots in soil. II. Uptake along the roots at different times and the effect of different levels of phosphorus. Plant and Soil *41*, 365–382 (1974)

BHAT, K.K.S. and NYE, P.H.: Diffusion of phosphate to plant roots in soil. III. Depletion around onion roots without root hairs. Plant and Soil *41*, 383–394 (1974)

BHUIJA, Z.H. and WALKER, N.: Autotrophic nitrifying bacteria in acid tea soils from Bangladesh and Sri Lanka. J. appl. Bact. *42*, 253–257 (1977)

BIDDULPH, O.: Mechanisms of translocation of plant metabolites. In: Physiological Aspects of Crop Yield, p. 143–164. American Soc. of Agron., Madison, Wisconsin, USA 1969

BIDDULPH, O., NAKAYAMA, F.S. and CORY, R.: Transpiration stream and ascension of calcium. Plant Physiol. *36*, 429–436 (1961)

BIEDERBECK, V.O., CAMPBELL, C.A., BOWREN, K.E. and MCIVER, R.N.: Effect of burning cereal straw on soil properties and grain yields in Saskatchewan. Soil Sci. Soc. Am. J. *44*, 103–111 (1980)

BIELESKI, R.L.: Effect of phosphorus deficiency on levels of phosphorus compounds in *Spirodela*. Plant Physiol. *43*, 1300–1316 (1968)

BINGHAM. F.T.: Relation between phosphorus and micronutrients in plants. Soil Sci. Soc. Amer. Proc. *27*, 389–391 (1963)

BINGHAM, F.T., ELSEEWI, A. and OERTLI, J.J.: Characteristics of boron absorption by excised barley roots. Soil Sci. Soc. Am. Proc. *34*, 613–617 (1970)

BIRKE, J.: (G) Agronomic aspects of the physiology of yield formation. Sitzungsberichte Bd. XII, Heft 13, Dt. Akad. d. Landw. Wiss. zu Berlin (1966)

BIRNBAUM, E.H., DUGGER, W.M. and BEASLEY, B.C.A.: Interaction of boron with components of nucleic acid metabolism in cotton ovules cultured *in vitro*. Plant Physiol. *59*, 1034–1038 (1977)

BISHOP, N.J.: Partial reactions of photosynthesis and photoreduction. Ann. Rev. Plant Physiol. *17*, 185–208 (1966)

BISHOP, N.J.: Photosynthesis: The electron transportsystem of green plants. Ann. Rev. Biochem. *40*, 197–226 (1971)

BJÄLFVE, G.: The effectiveness of nodule bacteria. Plant and Soil *18*, 70–76 (1963)

BLANCHAR, R.W. and CALDWELL, A.C.: Phosphate-ammonium-moisture relationships in soils. II. Ion concentrations in leached fertilizer and effect on plants. Proc. Soil Sci. Soc. Amer. *30*, 43–48 (1966)

BLANCHET, R., STUDER, R. and CHAUMONT, C.: (F) Some aspects of interactions in the water supply of plants. Ann. agron. *13*, 93–110 (1962)

BLASER, R.E. and BRADY, N.C.: Nutrient competition in plant associations. Agron. J. *42*, 128–135 (1950)

BLEVINS, D.G., HIATT, A.J. and LOWE, R.H.: The influence of nitrate and chloride uptake on expressed sap, pH, organic acid synthesis and potassium accumulation in higher plants. Plant Physiol. *54*, 82–87 (1974)

BLONDEL, A. and BLANC, D.: (F) Influence of ammonium ion uptake and reduction in young wheat plants. C.R. Acad. Sci. (Paris) Ser. D, *277*, 1325–1327 (1973)

BOARDMAN, N.K.: Trace elements in photosynthesis, p. 199–212. In: Trace Elements in Soil-Plant-Animal Systems. NICHOLAS, ED., EGAN, D.J.D. and EGAN, A.R. Academic Press 1975

BOEHLE, J. jr. and LINDSAY, W.L.: Micronutrients. The Fertilizer Shoe-Nails. Pt. 6, In the Limelight-Zinc, Fertilizer Solutions *13* (1), 6–12 (1969)

BÖHM, W.: (G) The assessment of the root system under field conditions. Kali-Briefe (Büntehof) *14* (2), 91–101 (1978)

BOGORAD, L.: The biosynthesis of protochlorophyll. In M.B. Allen (ed) Comparative biochemistry of photoreactive system, p. 227–256, Academic, New York (1968)

BOGUSLAWSKI, E. VON: (G) Law of yield formation. In: W. Ruhland: Encyclopedia of Plant Physiology, Vol. 4, p. 943–976, Springer-Verlag, Berlin, Göttingen, Heidelberg (1958)

BOGUSLAWSKI, E. VON and GIERKE, K. VON: (G) Recent investigations into nutrient removal of some crops. Z. Acker- u. Pflanzenbau *112*, 226–252 (1961)

BOGUSLAWSKI, E. VON and LACH G.: (G) The K release of soils measured by plant uptake in comparison with the exchangeable potassium. Z. Acker- u. Pflanzenbau *134*, 135–164 (1971)

BOGUSLAWSKI, E. VON and SCHILDBACH, R.: (G) Effect of sites, years, fertilizer application and irrigation on quality and yield level of sugar beets. Zucker *22*, 123–132 (1969)

BOLE, J.B.: Influence of root hairs in supplying soil phosphorus to wheat. Can. J. Soil Sci. *53*, 196–175 (1973)

BOLT, G.H.: Ion adsorption by clays. Soil Sci. *79*, 267–276 (1955)

BOMMER, D. and DAMBROTH, M.: (G) Physiology of yield formation of crops growing in the temperate zone. In: Role of Fertilization in the Intensification of Agricultural Production, p. 95–111. Proc. 9th Congr. Intern. Potash Institute, Berne 1970

BOND, G.: Fixation of nitrogen in non-legumes with alnustype root nodules. In E.A. Kirkby: Nitrogen Nutrition of the Plant, p. 1–8, University of Leeds 1970

BORST, N.P. and MULDER, C.: (N) Nitrogen contents, nitrogen fertilizer rates and yield of winter barley on sandy, clay, and silty soils in North Holland. Bedryfsontwikkeling *2*, 31–36 (1971)

BOTHE, H.: Flavodoxin. In: Photosynthesis I, Encycl. Plant Physiol. New Series, Vol. 6 (A. TREBST and M. AVRON, eds.) p. 217–221. Springer-Verlag Berlin, Heidelberg, New York 1977

BOULD, C. and TSAI-FUA CHIU: Mobility of calcium in fruit plants. In: 4th Int. Coll. on the Control of Plant Nutrition, Vol. I. (A. COTTENIE, ed.) p. 104–107. Gent (1976)

BOULD, C., NICHOLAS, D.J.D., TOLHURST, J.A.H. and WALLACE, T.: Zinc deficiencies of fruit trees in Britain. Nature *164*: 801–882 (1949)

BOUMA, D.: Nutrient uptake and distribution in subterranean clover during recovery from nutritional stresses. I. Experiments with phosphorus. Aust. J. biol. Sci. *20*: 601–612 (1967)

BOUMA, D.: Nutrient uptake and distribution in subterranean clover during recovery from nutritional stresses. II. Experiments with sulphur. Aust. J. biol. Sci. *20*, 613–621 (1967)

BOVE, J.M., BOVE, C., WHATLEY, F.R. and ARNON, D.I.: Chloride requirement for oxygen evolution in photosynthesis. Z. Naturforsch. *18b*, 683–688 (1963)

BOWDEN, J.W., POSNER, A.M. and QUIRK, J.P.: Ionic adsorption on variable charge mineral surfaces. Theoretical-charge development and titration curves. Austr. J. Soil Res. *15*, 121–136 (1977)

BOWEN, G.D.: In: Ectomycorrhizae. Their Ecology and Physiology. (G.C. MARCKS and T.T. KOWSLOWSKI, eds.) p. 151–205. Academic Press, New York 1973

BOWEN, J.E.: Absorption of copper, zinc and manganese by sugar cane tissue. Plant Physiol. *44*, 255–261 (1969)

BOWEN, J.E. and NISSEN, P.: Boron uptake by excised barley roots. I. Uptake into the free space. Plant Physiol. *57*, 353–357 (1976)

BOXMA, R.: Bicarbonate as the most important soil factor in lime-induced chlorosis in the Netherlands. Plant and Soil *37*, 233–243 (1972)

BOYD, D.A.: Some recent ideas on fertilizer response curves. In: Role of Fertilisation in the Intensification of Agricultural Production, p. 461–473, 9th Congr. Int. Potash Inst., Bern 1970

BOYER, J.S.: Relationship of water potential to growth of leaves. Plant Physiol. *43*, 1056–1062 (1968)

BOYER, J.S.: Leaf enlargement and metabolic rates in corn, soybean and sunflower at various leaf water potentials. Plant Physiol. *46*, 233–235 (1970)

BRADFORD, G.R.: Boron in Diagnostic Criteria for Plants and Soils, p. 33–61, ed. H.D.Chapman, Univ. of California 1966

BRADSHAW, A.D.: Populations of *Agrostis tenuis* resistant to lead and zinc poisoning. Nature *169*, 1098 (1952)

BRADY, N.C.: The Nature and Properties of Soils. 8th ed. MacMillan Publishing Co., Inc. New York 1974

BRAG, H.: The influence of potassium on the transpiration rate and stomatal opening in *Triticum aestivum* and *Pisum sativum*. Physiol. Plant. *26*, 250–257 (1972)

BRANTON, D. and DREAMER, D.W.: Membrane Structure. Springer-Verlag, Vienna 1972

BRAUER, A.: (G) Effect of fertilizer application on the digestibility and forage value of meadow hay. Landw. Forsch. *13*, 201–216 (1960)

BRAUNSCHWEIG, L.C. v.: (G) Results of some years lasting field trials on testing the optimum soil potassium status. Landw. Forsch. Sonderh. *35*, 219–231 (1978)

BRAY, R.H. and KURTZ, L.T.: Determination of total, organic and available forms of phosphorus in soils. Soil Sci. *59*, 39–45 (1945)

BREISCH, H., GUCKERT, A. and REISINGER, O.: (F) Electromicroscopic studies on the apical zone of maize roots. Soc. bot. Tr. Coll. Rhizosphere *122*, 55–60 (1975)

BREMNER, I. and KNIGHT, A.H.: The complexes of zinc, copper, and manganese present in ryegrass. Brit. J. Nutr. *24*, 279–290 (1970)

BREMNER, J.M.: Determination of fixed ammonium in soil. J. agric. Sci. *52*, 147–160 (1959)

BREMNER, J.M.: Nitrogen availability indexes. In C.A.Black: Methods of Soil Analysis. Agronomy 9, 1324–1325 (1965)

BREMNER, J.M.: Critique of soils and other sources of nitrous oxide. In: Nitrogen in the Environment. Soil-Plant-Nitrogen Relationships, Vol. 2 (D.R. NIELSEN and J.G. MACDONALD, eds.) p. 477–491. Academic Press, 1978

BRETELER, H.: A comparison between ammonium and nitrate nutrition of young sugar-beet plants grown in nutrient solutions at constant acidity. 1. Production of dry matter, ionic balance and chemical composition. Neth. J. agric. Sci. *21*, 227–244 (1973)

BRETELER, H.: Nitrogen fertilization, yield and protein quality of a normal and a high lysine maize variety. J. Sci. Fd Agric. *27*, 978–982 (1976)

BRETELER, H. and SMIT, A.L.: Effect of ammonium nutrition on uptake and metabolism of nitrate in wheat. Neth. J. agric. Sci. *22*, 73–81 (1974)

BREVEDAN, E.R. and HODGES, H.F.: Effects of moisture deficits on ^{14}C translocation in corn *(Zea mays L.)*. Plant Physiol. *52*, 436–439 (1973)

BREWBAKER, J.L. and KWACK, B.H.: The essential role of calcium ion in pollen germination and pollen tube growth. Amer. J. Bot. *50*, 859–865 (1963)

BREWER, R.F.: Lead, p. 213–217. In H.D.Chapman: Diagnostic Criteria for Plants and Soils. Univ. of California, Div. of Agric. Sciences (1966)

BREWER, R.F.: Fluorine p. 180–196. In H.D.Chapman. Diagnostic Criteria for Plants and Soils. Univ. of California. Div. of Agric. Sciences (1966)

BREWSTER, J.L., BHAT, K.K.S. and NYE, P.H. The possibility of predicting solute uptake and plant growth response from independently measured soil and plant characteristics. V. The growth and phosphorus uptake of rape in soil at a range of phosphorus concentrations and a comparison of results with the prediction of a simulation model. Plant and Soil 44, 295–328 (1976)

BREWSTER, J.L. and TINKER, P.B.: Nutrient flow rates into roots. Soils and Fertilizers 35, 355–359 (1972)

BROCKMAN, J.S. Quality and timing of fertiliser N for grass and grass/clover swards. Proc. Fert. Soc. 142, 5–13 (1974)

BRONNER, H.: (G) Relation between the easily soluble nitrogen in soils and the development of beets. Landw. Forsch. 30/II. Sonderh. 39–44 (1974)

BROUWER, R., KLEINENDORST, A. and LOCHER, J.TH.: Growth responses of maize plants to temperature. Proc. Uppsala Symp. 1970. Plant response to climatic factors, Unesco 1973, p. 169–174

BROWMAN, M.G., CHESTERS, G. and PIONKE, H.B.: Evaluation of tests for predicting the availability of soil manganese to plants. J. agric. Sci. 72, 335–340 (1969)

BROWN, J.C.: Iron chlorosis in soybeans as related to the genotype of rootstock. Soil Sci. 96, 387–394 (1963)

BROWN, J.C.: Mechanism of iron uptake by plants. Plant, Cell and Environment 1, 249–257 (1978)

BROWN, J.C.: Effects of boron stress on copper enzyme activity in tomato. J. of Plant Nutrition 1, 39–53 (1979)

BROWN, J.C., AMBLER, J.E., CHANEY, R.L. and FOY, C.D.: Differential responses of plant genotypes to micronutrients, p. 389–418. In: Micronutrients in Agriculture. Ed. Soil Sci. Soc. Amer. 1972

BROWN, J.C., CLARK, R.J. and JONES, W.E.: Efficient and inefficient use of phosphorus by sorghum. Soil Sci. Soc. Am. J. 41, 747–750 (1977)

BROWN, J.C., TIFFIN, O.L. and HOLMES, R.S.: Carbohydrate and organic acid metabolism with C-14 distribution affected by copper in Thatcher wheat. Plant Physiol. 33, 38–42 (1958)

BROWN, R.H.: A difference in nitrogen use efficiency in C_3 and C_4 plants and its implications in adaption and evolution. Crop Sci. 18, 93–98 (1978)

BROWNELL, P.F. and CROSSLAND, C.J.: The requirement for sodium as a micronutrient by species having the C4 dicarboxylic photosynthetic pathway. Plant Physiol. 49, 794–797 (1972)

BROYER, T.C., CARLTON, A.B., JOHNSON, C.M. and STOUT, P.R.: Chlorine: A micronutrient element for higher plants. Plant Physiol. 29, 526–532 (1954)

BROYER, T.C. and STOUT, P.R.: The macronutrient elements. Ann. Rev. Plant Physiol. 10, 277–300 (1959)

BRÜCKNER, U., HÖFNER, W. and ORLOVIUS, K.: (G) Influence of growth regulators on assimilation and yield of spring wheat. Landw. Forsch. Sonderh. 35, 291–299 (1978)

BRUIN, P. and GROOTENHUIS, J.A.: Interrelation of nitrogen, organic matter, soil structure and yield. Stikstof, Dutch Nitrogenous Fertilizer Review 12, 157–163 (1968)

BRUINSMA, J.: Root hormones and overground development. In: Plant Regulation and World Agriculture (K. SCOTT, ed.) p. 35–47. Plenum Publ. Corp. 1979

BRUN, W.A. and COOPER, R.L.: Effects of light intensity and carbon dioxide concentration on photosynthetic rate of soybean. Crop Sci. 7, 451–454 (1967)

BRUNE, H., THIER, E. and BORCHERT, E.: (G) Variability of biological protein quality of different cereals (variations in fertilizer application and sites). 3rd Comm.: Experimental results of investigations into the metabolism of pigs and rats with regard to amino acid indices. Z. Tierphysiol., Tierernähr. u. Futtermittelkd. 24, 89–107 (1968)

BRYCE-SMITH, D.: Heavy metals as contaminants of the human environment. The Educational Techniques Subject Group. Chemistry Cassette. The Chem. Soc. London 1975

BRYCE-SMITH, D. and WALDRON, H.A.: Lead, behaviour and criminality. The Ecologist *4*, 367–377 (1974)

BUCHNER, A. and STURM, H.: (G) Fertilizer application in intensive agriculture, p. 156. 3rd ed. DLG-Verlag Frankfurt/Main 1971

BUCKMAN, H.O. and BRADY, N.C.: The Nature and Properties of Soils, 7th Ed. The Macmillan Co.; Collier-Macmillan Ltd. London 1969

BUDIG, M.: (G) Fertilizer placement to overcome potassium deficiency of grapes on loess soils. Diss. d. Landw. Fakultät d. Justus-Liebig-Universität, Giessen 1970

BÜNEMANN, G. and LÜDDERS, P.: (G) Effect of seasonal nitrogen supply on the growth of apple trees. II. Bitter pit in 'Cox' related to N-timing and Ca-supply. Die Gartenbauwiss. *34*, (16), 287–302 (1969)

BUNESCU, S., TOMOROGA, P. and IANCU, C.: (Ru) The influence of some phytotechnical factors on the phytosanitary state of wheat under irrigation conditions. Problème Agricole No. 5, p. 45–52 (1972)

BURKART, N.: (G) Potassium dynamics and yield formation on potassium fixing soils in Southern Bavaria. Ph. D. Thesis, Fac. of Agriculture and Horticulture Technical University, Munich 1975

BURKE, C. and LONG, S.P.: Release of carboxylating enzymes from maize and sugar cane leaf tissue during progressive grinding. Planta *99*, 199–210 (1971)

BURR, G.O., HARTT, C.E., TANIMOTO, T., TAKAHASHI, D. and BRODIE, H.W.: The circulatory system of the sugarcane plant. Radioisotop. in scientific Res. *4*, 351–368 (1958)

BURSTRÖM, H.G.: Calcium and plant growth. Biol. Rev. *43*, 287–316 (1968)

BURT, R.L.: Carbohydrate utilization as a factor in plant growth. Aust. J. Biol. Sci. *17*, 867–877 (1964)

BUSH, L.P.: Influence of certain cations on activity of succinyl CoA synthetase from tobacco. Plant Physiol. *44*, 347–350 (1969)

BUSSLER, W.: (G) Manganese deficiency symptoms in higher plants. Z. Pflanzenernähr. Düng. Bodenk. *81* (126), 225–241 (1958)

BUSSLER, W.: (G) Manganese toxicity in higher plants. Z. Pflanzenernähr. Düng. Bodenk. *81*, 256–265 (1958)

BUSSLER, W.: (G) The development of calcium deficiency symptoms. Z. Pflanzenernähr. Düng. Bodenk. *100*, 53–58 (1963)

BUSSLER, W.: (G) Relationship between root formation and boron in sunflowers. Z. Pflanzenernähr. Düng. Bodenk. *92*, 1–14 (1960)

BUSSLER, W.: (G) Boron deficiency symptoms and their development. Z. Pflanzenernähr. Düng. Bodenk. *105*, 113–135 (1964)

BUSSLER, W.: Comparative Examinations of Plants Suffering from Potash Deficiency. Verlag Chemie, Weinheim 1964

BUSSLER, W.: (G) Development of molybdenum deficiency symptoms in cauliflower. Z. Pflanzenernähr. Bodenk. *125*, 36–50 (1970)

BUTLER, G.W. and PETERSON, P.J.: Uptake and metabolism of inorganic forms of selenium-75 by *Spirodela obligorrhiza*. Austr. J. Biol. Sci. *20*, 77–86 (1967)

CALDWELL, T.H.: Copper deficiency in crops I. Review of Part work in 'Trace Elements in Soils and Crops' Tech. Bulletin, Min. of Agric., Fisheries and Food, U.K. *21*, 62–72 (1971)

CALVIN, M.: (G) The photosynthetic cycle. Angew. Chemie *68*, 253–264 (1956)

CANDELA, M.J., FISHER, E.G. and HEWITT, E.J.: Molybdenum as a plant nutrient. X. Some factors affecting the activity of nitrate reductase in cauliflower plants growth with different nitrogen sources and molybdenum levels in sand culture. Plant Physiol. *32*, 280–288 (1957)

CANTLIFFE, D.J.: Nitrate accumulation in table beets and spinach as affected by nitrogen, phosphorus, and potassium nutrition and light intensity. Agron. J. *65*, 563–565 (1973)

CARLES, J., CALMES, J., MAGNY, J. and PULOU, R.: (F) The distribution of zinc and its toxicity in plants. C.R. Acad. Sci. (Paris), Sér. D, *268*, 516–519 (1969)

CARROLL, M.D. and LONERAGAN, J.F.: Response of plant species to concentration of zinc in solution. II. Rate of zinc absorption and their relation to growth. Austr. J. Agric. Res. *20*, 457–463 (1969)

CARTER, M.R.: Association of cation and organic anion accumulation with iron chlorosis of Scots pine on prairie soils. Plant and Soil *56*, 293–300 (1980)

CARTWRIGHT, B. and HALLSWORTH, E.G.: Effects of copper deficiency on root nodules of subterranean clover. Plant and Soil *33*, 685–698 (1970)

CASPER, H.: (G) Nitrate availability as a function of soil water content. Modell experiments with young maize plants. Diss. Fachbereich 19 Ernährungswissenschaften, Justus-Liebig-Universität Giessen 1975

CASSAGNES, P., MAGNY, J., AZALBERT, P. and CARLES, J.: (F) Contribution to investigations into the accumulation of minerals during the growth of apple fruit (Reine des Reinettes). C.R. Acad. Sci. (Paris) Sér. D, *269*, 708–711 (1969)

CATALDO, D.A., GARLAND, T.R., WILDUNG, R.E. and DRUCKER, H.: Nickel in plants. II Distribution and chemical form in soybean plants Plant. Physiol. *62*, 566–570 (1978)

CHAMPION, R.A. and BARLEY, K.P.: Penetration of clay by root hairs. Soil Sci. *108*, 402–407 (1969)

CHANDLER, R.F.: Overcoming physiological barriers to higher yields through plant breeding, p. 421–434. In: Role of Fertilization in the Intensification of Agricultural Production. Int. Potash Inst., Bern 1970

CHANEY, R.L., BROWN, J.C. and TIFFIN, L.O.: Obligatory reduction of ferric chelates in iron uptake by soybeans. Plant Physiol. *50*. 208–213 (1972)

CHANEY, R.L. and HORNICK, S.B. Accumulation and effects of cadmium on crops In: Proc 1st Int. Cadmium Conf. p. 136–150 Bulletin London 1978

CHANG-CHI CHU: Carbon dioxide in the open atmosphere and in a field of sugarcane at Tainan Taiwan. Taiwan Sugar Experiment Station, Tainan, Research Report No. 1, 1–18 (1968)

CHAPMAN, D.L.: (G) Quoted from G.Kortüm: Textbook of Electrochemistry, p. 345. Verl. Chemie, Weinheim 1957

CHAPMAN, H.D.: Diagnostic Criteria for Plants and Soils. University of California, Div. of Agric. Sciences, 1966

CHAPMAN, M.A. and KEAY, J.: The effect of age on the response of wheat to nutrient stress. Aust. J. Exp. Agric. and Animal Husbandry *11*, 223–228 (1971)

CHARLEY, J.L. and McGARITY, J.L.: High soil nitrate-levels in patterned saltbush communities. Nature *201*, 1351–1352 (1964)

CHATT, J.: Nitrogen Fixation – Future Prospects. Proceedings No. 155, Fertilizer Soc. of London 1976

CHAUDHRY, F.M. and LONERAGAN, J.F.: Effects of nitrogen, copper and zinc nutrition of wheat plants. Aust. J. Agric. Res. *21*, 865–879 (1970)

CHAUDHRY, F.M. and LONERAGAN, J.F.: Zinc absorption in wheat seedlings: Inhibition by macronutrient ions in short term experiments and its relevance to long term zinc nutrition. Soil Sci. Soc. Amer. Proc. *36*, 323–327 (1972)

CHEESEMAN, J.M. and HANSON, J.B.: Energy-linked potassium influx as related to cell potential in corn roots. Plant Physiol. *64*, 842–845 (1979)

CHEN, C.H. and LEWIN, J.: Silicon as a nutrient element for *Equisetum arvense*. Can. J. Bot. *47*, 125–131 (1969)

CHENERY, M.: A preliminary study of aluminium and the tea bush. Plant and Soil *6*, 174–200 (1955)

CHENG, B.T.: Dynamics of soil manganese. Agrochimica *17*, 84–95 (1973)

CHENG, B.T. and OULLETTE, G.J.: Molybdenum as a plant nutrient. Soil and Fertilizers *36*, 207–215 (1973)

CHENIAE, G. M.: Photosystem II and O_2 evolution. Ann. Rev. Plant Physiol. *21*, 467–498 (1976)

CHENIAE, G. M. and MARTIN, J. F.: Sites of function of manganese within photosystem II. Roles in O_2 evolution and system II. Biochim. Biophys. Acta *197*, 219–239 (1970)

CHENIAE, G. M. and MARTIN, I. F.: Effect of hydroxylamine on photosystem II. I. Factors affecting the decay of CO_2 evolution. Plant Physiol. *47*, 568–575 (1971)

CHEUNG, W.Y.: Calmodulin plays a pivotal role in cellular regulation, Science *207*, 19–27 (1980)

CHEVALIER, S. and HUGUET, C.: (F) Magnesium deficiency effects on apple trees. Ultrastructural evolution in deficient leaves of apple trees. Ann. agron. *26*, 351–362 (1975)

CHIMIKLES, P.E. and KARLANDER, E.P.: Light and calcium interactions in *Chlorella* inhibited by sodium chloride. Plant Physiol. *51*, 48–56 (1973)

CHIU, T. F. and BOULD, C.: Effect of shortage of calcium and other cations on Ca-45 mobility, growth and nutritional disorders of tomato plants *(Lycopersicon esculentum)* J. Sci. Fd. Agric. *27*, 969–977 (1976)

CHO, D.Y. and PONNAMPERUMA, F.N.: Influence of soil temperature on the chemical kinetics of flooded soils and the growth of rice. Soil Sci. *112*, 184–194 (1971)

CHRISTENSON, D. R. and DOLL, E.C.: Release of magnesium from soil clay and silt fractions during cropping. Soil Sci. *116*, 59–63 (1973)

CLAASSEN, N. and BARBER, S.A.: Simulation model for nutrient uptake from soil by growing plant root system. Agron. J. *68*, 961–964 (1976)

CLARKSON, D.T.: Calcium uptake by calciole and calcifuge species in the genus *Agrostis* L. J. Ecol. (Oxford) *53*, 427–435 (1965)

CLARKSON, D.T.: Ion Transport and Cell Structure in Plants. McGraw Hill 1974

CLARKSON, D.T.: Membrane structure and transport. In: The Molecular Biology of Plant Cells (H. SMITH, ed.) p. 24–63. Blackwell, Oxford 1977

CLARKSON, D.T. and HANSON, J.B.: The mineral nutrition of higher plants. Ann. Rev. Plant Physiol. *31*, 239–298 (1980)

CLARKSON, D.T., ROBARDS, A.W. and SANDERSON, J.: The tertiary endodermis in barley roots: fine structure in relation to radial transport of ions and water. Planta *96*, 292–305 (1971)

CLARKSON, D.T., SANDERSON, J. and RUSSELL, R.S.: Ion uptake and root age. Nature *220*, 805–806 (1968)

CLARKSON, D.T. and SANDERSON, J.: The uptake of a polyvalent cation and its distribution in the root apices of *Allium cepa*. Tracer and autoradiographic Studies. Planta *89*, 136–154 (1969)

CLARKSON, D.T. and SANDERSON, J.: Sites of absorption and translocation of iron in barley roots. Tracer and microautoradiographic studies. Plant Physiol. *61*, 731–736 (1978)

CLARKSON, D.T. and WARNER, A.J.: Relationship between root temperature and the transport of ammonium and nitrate ions by Italian and perennial ryegrass *(Lolium multiflorum and Lolium perenne)*. Plant Physiol. *64*, 557–561 (1979)

CLELAND, R.E.: A dual role of turgor pressure in auxin-induced cell elongation in *Avena coleoptiles*. Planta *77*, 182–191 (1967)

CLEMENT, C.R. and HOPPER, M.J.: The supply of potassium to high yielding cut grass. N.A.A.S. Quarterly Review No. 79, Spring (1968)

CLEMENT, C.R., HOPPER, M.J. and JONES, L.H.P.: The uptake of nitrate by *Lolium perenne* from flowing nutrient solution. J. Expt. Bot. *29*, 453–464 (1978)

COCUCCI, M.C. and DALLA ROSA, S.: Effects of canavanine on IAA- and fusicoccin-stimulated cell enlargement, proton extrusion and potassium uptake in maize coleoptiles. Physiol. Plant. *48*, 239–242 (1980)

COÏC, Y., FAUCONNEAU, G., PION, R., BUSSON, F., LESAINT, C. and LABONNE, F.: (F) Effect of the mineral nutrition on the composition of grain proteins in cereals (wheat and barley). Ann. Physiol. vég. *5* (4), 281–292 (1963)

Coïc, Y., Lesaint, C. and Le Roux, F.: (F) Effects of ammonium and nitrate nutrition and a change of ammonium and nitrate supply on the metabolism of anions and cations in tomatoes. Ann. Physiol. vég. *4*, 117–125 (1962)

Coleman, R.G.: The effect of sulfur deficiency on the free amino acids of some plants. Aust. J. Biol. Sci. *10*, 50–56 (1957)

Collander, R.: Selective absorption of cations by higher plants. Plant Physiol. *16*, 691–720 (1941)

Connell, W.E. and Patrick, W.H.: Reduction of sulfate to sulfide in waterlogged soil. Proc. Soil Sci. Soc. Amer. *33*, 711–715 (1969)

Cooke, G.W.: Phosphorus and potassium fertilizers: their forms and their places in agriculture. The Fertilizer Soc. Proc. No. 92 (1966)

Cooke, G.W.: The Control of Soil Fertility. Crosby, Lockwood and Son Ltd., London (1967)

Cooke, G.W.: Fertilizing for Maximum Yield. Crosby Lockwood and Son Ltd. London 1972

Cooke, G.W.: Change in the amounts of fertilizers used and the forms in which they are produced, together with comments on current problems in valuing fertilizers and using them efficiently. Cento Seminar on Fertilizer Analytical Methods, Sampling and Quality Control, Pakistan 1974

Cooke, G.W.: The role of organic manures and organic matter in managing soils for higher crop yields – a review of the experimental evidence. Proc. Int. Seminar on Soil Environment and Fertility Management in Intensive Agriculture, p. 53–64. Tokyo 1977

Cooke, G.W. and Williams, R.J.B.: Losses of nitrogen and phosphorus from agricultural land. Water Treatm. Exam. *19*, 253–276 (1970)

Coombs, J.: Enzymes of C_4 metabolism In: Photosynthesis II, Encycl. Plant Physiol. New Series Vol. 6 (M. Gibbs and E. Latzko, eds.) p. 251–262, Springer-Verlag Berlin, Heidelberg, New York 1979

Cooper K.M. and Tinker, P.B.: Translocation and transfer of nutrients in vesicular-arbuscular mycorrhizas. II Uptake and transfer of phosphorus, zinc and sulphur. New Phytol. *81*, 43–52, 1978

Cooper, T.G., Filmer, D., Wishnick, M. and Lane, M.D.: The active species of 'CO_2' utilized by ribulose diphosphate carboxylase. J. Biol. Chem. *244*, 1081–1083 (1969)

Coppenet, M.: (F) Results from observations of a twelve years lasting lysimeter experiment in Quimper (1954–1965). Ann. agron. *20*, 111–143 (1969)

Cottenie, A. and Kiekens, L.: Quantitative and qualitative plant response to extreme nutritional conditions. In: Wehrmann, J.: Plant Analysis and Fertilizer Problems, p. 543–556, Vol. 2. German Soc. Plant Nutrition, Hannover 1974

Coulson, C.L., Christy, A.L., Cataldo, D.A. and Swanson, C.A.: Carbohydrate translocation in sugar beet petioles in relation to petiolar respiration and adenosine 5'-triphosphate. Plant Physiol. *49*, 919–923 (1972)

Cowling, D.W. and Lockyer, D.R.: Growth of perennial ryegrass *(Lolium perenne L.)* exposed to a low concentration of sulphur dioxide. J. Exp. Bot. *27*, 411–417 (1976)

Cox, G., Moran, K.J., Sanders, F., Nockolds, C. and Tinker, P.B.: Translocation and transfer of nutrients in vesicular-arbuscular mycorrhizas. III. Polyphosphate granules and phosphorus translocation. New Phytol. *84*, 649–659 (1980)

Cox, W.J. and Reisenauer, H.M.: Growth and ion uptake by wheat supplied nitrogen as nitrate, or ammonium, or both. Plant and Soil *38*, 363–380 (1973)

Cram, W.J.: Chloride fluxes in cells of the isolated root cortex of *Zea mays*. Aust. J. biol. Sci. *26*, 757–779 (1973)

Cramer, W.A.: Cytochromes. In: Photosynthesis I, Encycl. Plant Physiol. New Series Vol. 5 (A. Trebst and M. Arnon, eds.) p. 227–237. Springer-Verlag Berlin, Heidelberg, New York 1977

Crawford, R.M.M.: Alcohol dehydrogenase activity in relation to flooding tolerance in roots. J. exp. Bot. *18*, 458–464 (1967)

CRESS, W.A., THRONEEERRY, G.O. and LINDSEY, D.L.: Kinetics of phosphorus absorption by mycorrhizal and non-mycorrhizal tomato roots. Plant Physiol. *64*, 484–487, 1979

CRIPPS, E.G.: Boron nutrition of the hop. J. hort. Sci. *31*, 25–34 (1956)

CRISP, P., COLLIER, G.F. and THOMAS, T.H.: The effect of boron on tipburn and auxin activity in lettuce. Sci. Hortic. *5*, 215–226 (1976)

CROMPTON, E.: Some morphological features associated with poor soil drainage. J. of Soil Sci. *3*, 277–289 (1952)

CROMPTON, E.: Soil structure. N.A.A.S. Quarterly Review, No. 41, 6–14 (1958)

CROOKE, W.M.: Effect of soil reaction on uptake of nickel from a serpentine soil. Soil Sci. *81*, 269–276 (1956)

CROOKE, W.M. and INKSON, R.H.E.: The relationship between nickel toxicity and major nutrient supply. Plant and Soil *6*, 1–15 (1955)

CROY, L.I. and HAGEMAN, R.H.: Relationship of nitrate reductase activity to grain protein production in wheat. Crop Sci. *10*, 280–285 (1970)

CUNNINGHAM, R.K. and NIELSEN, K.F.: Evidence against relationships between root cation exchange capacity and cation uptake by plants. Nature *200*, 1344–1345 (1963)

CUPINA, T. and SARIC, M.: Assimilation of carbon into some organic matters in young corn plants grown under various conditions of nutrition. J. Sci. Agric. Res. *20*, 48–62 (1967)

CURRIER, W.W. and STROBEL, G.A.: Chemotaxis of *Rhizobium* spp. to plant root exudates. Plant Physiol. *57*, 820–823 (1976)

DAINTY, J.: Ion transport and electrical potentials in plant cells. Ann. Rev. Plant Physiol. *13*, 379–402 (1962)

DALAL, R.C.: Soil organic phosphorus. Adv. Agron. *29*, 83–117 (1977)

DALLING, M.J., TOLBERT, N.E. and HAGEMAN, R.H.: Intracellular location of nitrate reductase and nitrite reductase. II. Wheat roots. Biochem. Biophys. Acta *283*, 513–519 (1972)

DALY, G.T.: Nitrogen fixation by nodulated *Alnus rugosa*. Can. J. Bot. *44*, 1607–1621 (1966)

DAM KOFOED, A.: Potassium and the environment, p. 331–350. In: Potassium Research and Agricultural Production. Int. Potash Inst., Bern 1974

DAM KOFOED, A.: Copper and its utilization in Danish agriculture. Fertilizer Research *1*, 63–71 (1980)

DAM KOFOED, A. and FOGH, H.T.: (D) The sulphur nutrition of plants. Tidsskrift for Planteavl *72*, 503–512 (1968)

DAM KOFOED, A. and HØJMARK, J.V.: (D) Field experiments with magnesium fertilizers. Tidsskrift for Planteavl *75*, 349–376 (1971)

DAM KOFOED, A. and KJELLERUP, V.: (D) Movements of fertilizer nitrogen in soil. Tidesskrift for Planteavl *73*, 659–686 (1970)

DAM KOFOED, A. and LARSEN, K.E.: (D) Experiments with Peraform, a slowly acting nitrogenous fertilizer. Tidsskrift for Planteavl *73*, 172–179 (1969)

DAM KOFOED, A. and LINDHARD, J.: (D) Removal of plant nutrients from grass-covered soils in lysimeters. Tidsskrift for Planteavl *72*, 417–437 (1968)

DAM KOFOED, A., LINDHARD, J. and SØNDERGARD KLAUSEN, P.: (D) Experiments with anhydrous ammonia as a nitrogenous fertilizer. Tidsskrift for Planteavl *71*, 145–225 (1967)

DAM KOFOED, A. and SØNDERGAARD KLAUSEN, P.: (D) Field application of fertilizer nitrogen to grass and to clover-grass mixtures. Tidsskrift for Planteavl *73*, 203–246 (1969)

DANIEL, C. and OCHS, R.: (F) Improvement of production of young oil palms in Peru by chloride fertilizer application. Oléagineux *30*, 295–298 (1975)

DANIELLI, J.F. and DAVSON, H.A.: A contribution to the theory of the permeability of thin films. J. Cellular comp. Physiol. *5*, 495–508 (1935)

DANIELS, R.R., STUCKMEYER, B.E. and PETERSON, L.A.: Copper toxicity in *Phaseolus vulgaris* L. as influenced by iron nutrition. I. An anatomical study. J. Amer. Soc. Hort. Sci. *9*, 249–254 (1972)

DAVIES, D.B., HOOPER, L.J. and CHARLESWORTH, R.R. et al.: Copper deficiency in crops: III Copper disorders in cereals grown in chalk soils in South Eastern and Central Southern England in 'Trace Elements in Soils and Crops', Tech. Bulletin, Min. of Agric., Fisheries and Food 21, 88–118 (1971)

DAVIES, D.D.: Control of and by pH. Sym. Soc. Exp. Biol. 27, 513–529 (1973)

DAVIS, R.F. and HIGINBOTHAM: Electrochemical gradients and K^+ and Cl^- fluxes in excised corn roots. Plant Physiol. 57, 129–136 (1976)

DAVISON, A. and JEFFERIES, B.J.: Some experiments on the nutrition of plants growing on coal mine waste heaps. Nature 210, 649–650 (1966)

DAY, A.D. and INTALAP, S.: Some effects of soil moisture stress on the growth of wheat (Triticum aestivum L. em Thell). Agron. J. 62, 27–29 (1970)

DAY, J.P., HART, H. and ROBINSON, M.S.: Lead in urban street dust. Nature 253, 343–345 (1975)

DE, R.: Cultural practices for maize, sorghum and millets. 1. FAO/SIDA Seminar for plant scientists from Africa and Near East, FAO Rome 1974, p. 440–451

DEAR, J.M. and ARNOFF, S.: The nonessentiality of boron for Scenedesmus. Plant Physiol. 43, 997–998 (1968)

DE BOODT, M. and DE LEENHEER, L.: (N) Investigations into pore distribution in soils. Medelingen Landbouwhogeschool, Gent 98–130 (1955)

DECAU, J. and POLLACSEK, M.: Improving plant protein by nuclear techniques. Intern. Atomic Energy Agency, 132/17, 357–366 (1970)

DECAU, J. and PUJOL, B.: (F) Comparative effects of irrigation and nitrogen fertilizer on the qualitative and quantitative production of different maize cultivars. Ann. agron. 24, 359–373 (1973)

DE CORMIS, L.: (F) Contribution to the study of sulphur absorption by plants exposed to an atmosphere of sulphur dioxide. Ann. Physiol. vég. 10 (2), 99–112 (1968)

DEJAEGERE, R. and NEIRINCKX, L.: Proton extrusion and ion uptake: Some characteristics of the phenomenon in barley seedlings. Z. Pflanzenphysiol. 89, 129–140 (1978)

DEKOCK, P.C.: Heavy metal toxicity and iron chlorosis. Ann. Bot. NS 20, 133–141 (1956)

DEKOCK, P.C.: Nutrient balance in plant leaves. Agric. Progress 33, 88–95 (1958)

DEKOCK, P.C., CHESHIRE, M.V. and HALL, A.: Comparison of the effect of phosphorus and nitrogen on Cu deficient and suffering oats. J. Sci. Food Agric. 22, 431–440 (1971)

DEKOCK, P.C., COMMISIONG, K., FARMER, V.C. and INKSON, R.H.E.: Interrelationships of catalase, peroxidase, hematin and chlorophyll. Plant Physiol. 35, 599–604 (1960)

DEKOCK, P.C., DYSON, P.W., HALL, A. and GRABOWSKA, F.: Metabolic changes associated with calcium deficiency in potato sprouts. Potato Res. 18, 573–581 (1975)

DEKOCK, P.C., HALL, A., INKSON, R.H.E. and ROBERTSON, R.A.: Blossom end rot in tomatoes. J. Sci. Food Agric. 30, 508–514 (1979)

DELA GUARDIA, M.D. and BENLLOCH, M.: Effects of potassium and gibberellic acid on stem growth of whole sunflower plants. Physiol. Plant. 49, 443–448 (1980)

DELAS, J.: (F) The toxicity of copper accumulated in soils. Agrochimica 7, 258–288 (1963)

DELOCH, H.W.: (G) Analytical determination of sulphur in biochemical materials and the uptake of sulphur by crops in relation to fertilizer application. Diss. Landw. Fakultät Giessen 1960

DELWICHE, C.C.: The Biosphere. Scientific Amer., p. 71–80, Inc. W.H. Freeman, San Francisco 1970

DENAEYER-DE SMET, S.: (F) Aspects about the accumulation of zinc in plants growing on calamine soils. Bull. Inst. r. Sci. nat. Belg. 46, 1–13 (1970)

DE WIT, C.T., DIJKSHOORN, W. and NOGGLE, J.C.: Ionic balance and growth of plants. Verslagen van landbouwkundige onderzoekingen, Wageningen, 68 pages, 1963

DHINDSA, R.S. and CLELAND, R.E.: Water stress and protein synthesis. Plant Physiol. 55, 778–781 (1975)

DICKINSON, D. B.: Permeability and respiratory properties of germinating pollen. Physiol. Plant. 20, 118–127 (1967)

DIEST, A. VAN: Soil-structural problems associated with intensive farming in the Netherlands. In: Proc. of the Intern. Seminar on Soil Environment and Fertility Management in Intensive Agriculture. p. 145–153, Tokyo 1977

DIJK, H. VAN: (G) The C/N ratio in the A_1(p) horizon of cultivated sandy soils in relation to the mineralization of carbon and nitrogen. Stikstof, Dutch nitrogenous fertilizer review 12, 89–96 (1968)

DIJKSHOORN, W. and ISMUNADJI, M.: Nitrogen nutrition of rice plants measured by growth and nutrient content in pot experiments. 2. Uptake of ammonium and nitrate from a water-logged soil. Neth. J. agric. Sci. 20, 44–57 (1972)

DIJKSHOORN, W. and LAMPE, J. E. M.: Availability for ryegrass of cadmium and zinc from dressings of sewage sludge. Neth. J. Agric. Sci. 23, 338–344 (1975)

DIJKSHOORN, W. and VAN WIJK, A. L.: The sulphur requirements of plants as evidenced by the sulphur-nitrogen ratio in the organic matter, a review of published data. Plant and Soil 26, 129–157 (1967)

DILZ, K. and WOLDENDORP, J. W.: Distribution and nitrogen balance of ^{15}N labelled nitrate applied on grass sods. Proc. Intern. Grassl. Congr. 8th, p. 150–152, Reading 1960

DION, H. G. and MANN, P. J. G.: Trivalent manganese in soils. J. Agric. Sci. 36, 239–245 (1946)

DITTMER, H. J.: A quantitative study of the roots and root hairs of a winter rye plant (Secale cereale). Am. J. Bot. 24, 417–420 (1937)

DIXON, N. E., GAZZOLA, C., BLAKELEY, R. L. and ZERNER, B.: Jack bean urease (EC 3.5.1.5.) a metalloenzyme. A simple biological role for nickel? J. Am. Chem. Soc. 97, 4131–4132 (1975)

DOBEREINER, J., DAY, J. M. and DART, P. J.: Nitrogeneous activity and oxygen sensitivity of the Paspalum notatum Azotobacter paspali association. J. Gen. Microbiol. 71, 103–116 (1972)

DOBLER, M., DUNITZ, J. D. and KRAJEWSKI, J.: Structure of the K^+ complex with Enniatin B, a macrocyclic antibiotic with K^+ transport properties. J. Mol. Biol. 42, 603–606 (1969)

DOLL, E. C.: Nitrogen fertilization of alfalfa and alfalfa-orchardgrass hay. Agron. J. 54, 469–471 (1962)

DOLL, E. C. and LUCAS, R. E.: Testing soils for potassium, calcium, and magnesium, p. 133–151. In L. M. Walsh and J. D. Beaton: Soil Testing and Plant Analysis. Soil Science Soc. of America, Madison/USA 1973

DOMPERT, W. and BERINGER, H.: (G) Oil synthesis in sunflower seeds exposed to different oxygen concentrations. Die Naturwiss. 57, 40 (1970)

DRAKE, M. and WHITE, J. M.: Influence of nitrogen on the uptake of calcium. Soil Sci. 91, 66–69 (1961)

DRAYCOTT, A. P. and DURRANT, M. J.: Plant and soil magnesium in relation to response of sugar beet to magnesium applications. J. of the Int. Inst. for Sugar Beet Research 5, 129–135 (1971)

DRAYCOTT, A. P. and FARLEY, R. F.: Response by sugar beet to soil dressings and foliar sprays of manganese. J. Sci. Fd Agric. 24, 675–683 (1973)

DRAYCOTT, A. P., MARSH, J. A. P. and TINKER, P. B. H.: Sodium and potassium relationships in sugar beet. J. agric. Sci. 74, 567–573 (1970)

DREW, M. C. and BIDDULPH, O.: Effect of metabolic inhibitors and temperature on uptake and translocation of [45]Ca and [45]K by intact bean plants Plant Physiol 48, 426–432 (1971)

DREW, M. C. and GOSS, M. J.: Effect of soil physical factors on root growth. Chem and Ind. No. 14, 679–684 (1973)

DREW, M.C. and NYE, H.P.: The supply of nutrient ions by diffusion to plant roots in soil. II. The effect of root hairs on the uptake of potassium by roots of rye grass *(Lolium multiflorum)*. Plant and Soil *31*, 407–424 (1969)

DREW, M.C., NYE, P.H. and VAIDYANATHAN, L.Y.: The supply of nutrient ions by diffusion to plant roots in soil. I. Absorption of potassium by cylindrical roots of onion and leek. Plant and Soil *30*, 252–270 (1969)

DROUINEAU, G. and BLANC, D.: (F) Influence of the nitrogen nutrition on the development and on the metabolism of plants. Agrochimica *5*, 49–58 (1961)

DROUINEAU, G. and MAZOYER, R.: (F) Contribution to the study of copper toxicity in soils. Ann. agronom. *13*, 31–53 (1962)

DUISBERG, P.C. and BUEHRER, T.F.: Effect of ammonia and its oxidation products on rate of nitrification and plant growth. Soil Sci. *78*, 37–49 (1954)

DUNCAN, W.G.: Maize. In: Crop Physiology (L.T. EVANS ed.) p. 23–50. Cambridge University Press 1975

DUNLAP, D.B. and THOMPSON, A.H.: Effect of boron sprays on the development of bitter-pit in the York Imperial apple. Maryland Agr. Exp. Sta Bull. A 102 (1959)

DUNLOP, J. and BOWLING, D.J.F.: The movement of ions to the xylem exudate of maize roots. II. A comparison of the electrical potential and electrochemical potentials of ions in the exudate and in the root cells. J. Exp. Bot. *22*, 445–452 (1971).

DURING, C. and DUGANZICH, D.M.: Simple empirical intensity and buffering capacity measurements to predict potassium uptake by white clover. Plant and Soil *51*, 167–176 (1979)

DURRANT, M.J. and DRAYCOTT, A.P.: Uptake of magnesium and other fertilizer elements by sugar beet grown on sandy soils. J. agric. Sci. *77*, 61–68 (1971)

DUTHION, M.: (F) Potassium in soils. Revue Agricol. France – Fertilisation No. 2 (1966)

DUVIGNEAUD, P. and DENAEYER-DE SMET, S.: (F) Effect of some heavy metals in the soil (copper, cobalt, manganese, uranium) on the vegetation in Upper Katanga. Ier Colloq. Soc. Bot. France 121 (1959)

DYBING, C.D. and ZIMMERMANN, D.C.: Fatty acid accumulation in maturing flaxseeds as influenced by environment. Plant Physiol. *41*, 1465–1470 (1966)

DYER, B.: On the analytical determination of probably available mineral plant food in soils. J. Chem. Soc. *23*, 799–810 (1894)

EAGLES, C.F.: Apparent photosynthesis and respiration in populations of *Lolium perenne* from contrasting climatic regions. Nature *215*, 100–101 (1967)

EAKIN, J.H.: Food and fertilizers, p. 1–21. In: The Fertilizer Handbook, The Fertilizer Inst., Washington 1972

EATON, F.M.: Chlorine, p. 98–135. In: H.D.Chapman: Diagnostic Criteria for Plants and Soils. Univ. of California, Div. of Agric. Sciences 1966

EDELBAUER, A.: (G) Investigations on the effect of various KCl/K_2SO_4 ratios on grape yield, juice quality and amino acid pattern in the juice of *Vitis vinifera* grown in solution culture. In: 4th Int. Coll. on the Control of Plant Nutrition, Vol. I (A. COTTENIE, ed.) p. 293–303. Gent 1976

EDELBAUER, A.: (G) Composition of juice of *Vitis vinifera* at different chloride/sulphate ratios in the nutrient solution. Mitt. Klosterneuburg, Rebe u. Wein, Obstbau u. Früchteverwertung, Jahrg. *27*, 217–222 (1977)

EDWARDS, G.E. and HUBER, S.C.: C_4 metabolism in isolated cells and protoplasts. In: Photosynthesis II, New Series, Vol. 8 (M. GIBBS and E. LATZKO, eds.) p. 102–112. Springer-Verlag Berlin, Heidelberg, New York 1979

EFFMERT, E.: (G) The effect of fertilizer application on the phosphate content of potato starch (I). Effect of fertilizer application on the ratio of amylose/amylopectin in potato starch. Thaer-Archiv *11*, 745–753 u. 755–759 (1967)

EGMOND, F. VAN, and BRETELER, H.: Nitrate reductase activity and oxalate content of sugarbeet leaves. Neth. J. agric. Sci. *20*, 193–198 (1972)

EGNER, H.: (G) Recent contributions to chemical soil tests with particular regard to the lactate method. Landw. Forsch., 6. Sonderh., 28–32 (1955)

EHLERS, W., GEBHARDT, H. and MEYER, B.: (G) Investigations into the position specific bonds of potassium to illite, kaolinite, montmorillonite, and humus. Z. Pflanzenernähr. Bodenk. *119*, 173–186 (1968)

EHLERS, W., MEYER, B. and SCHEFFER, F.: (G) K selectivity and fractionation of the exchangeable potassium. Z. Pflanzenernähr. Bodenk. *117*, 1–29 (1967)

EHRLER, W.L.: Transpiration of alfalfa as affected by low root temperature and other factors of a controlled environment. Plant Physiol. *37*, Supplm. 843 (1962)

EILRICH, G.L. and HAGEMAN, R.H.: Nitrate reductase activity and its relationship to accumulation of vegetative and grain nitrogen in wheat *(Triticum aestivum L.)*. Crop Sci. *13*, 59–66 (1973)

ELGAWHARY, S.M., LINDSAY, W.L. and KEMPER, W.D.: Effect of complexing agent and acids on the diffusion of zinc to a simulated root. Soil Sci. Soc. Amer. Proc. *34*, 211–214 (1970)

EL-SHEIKH, A.M. and ULRICH, A.: Interactions of rubidium, sodium and potassium on the nutrition of sugar beet plants. Plant Physiol. *46*, 645–649 (1970)

ELZAM, O.E. and EPSTEIN, E.: Absorption of chloride by barley roots: kinetics and selectivity. Plant Physiol. *40*, 620–624 (1965).

ELZAM, O.E. and HODGES, T.K.: Calcium inhibition of potassium absorption in corn roots. Plant Physiol. *42*, 1483–1488 (1967)

EMBLETON, T.W.: Magnesium. In: Diagnostic Criteria for Plants and Soils. Ed. H.D.Chapman, Univ. of California, Div. of Agric. Sci., p. 225–263 (1966)

ENGEL, W.: (G) Investigations into the Si compounds in the culm of rye. Planta *41*, 358–390 (1953)

EPPENDORFER, W.: The effect of nitrogen and sulphur on changes in nitrogen fractions of barley plants at various early stages of growth and on yield and amino acid composition of grain. Plant and Soil *29*, 424–438 (1968)

EPSTEIN, E.: Dual pattern of ion absorption by plant cells and by plants. Nature *212*, 1324–1327 (1966)

EPSTEIN, E.: Mineral Nutrition of Plant: Principles and Perspectives. John Wiley and Sons, Inc., New York, London, Sydney, Toronto 1972

EPSTEIN, E.: Ion absorption by roots: The role of micro-organisms. New Phytol. *71*, 873–874 (1972)

EPSTEIN, E.: Flow in the phloem and the immobility of calcium and boron: A new hypothesis in support of an old one. Experimentia *29*, 133 (1973)

EPSTEIN, E. and HAGEN, C.E.: A kinetic study of the absorption of alkali cations by barley roots. Plant Physiol. *27*, 457–474 (1952)

EPSTEIN, E. and LEGGETT, J.E.: The absorption of alkaline earth cations by barley roots: kinetics and mechanism. Am. J. Bot. *41*, 785–791 (1954)

ERDEI, L., TOTH, I., and ZSOLDOS, F.: Hormonal regulation of Ca^{2+} stimulated K^+ influx and Ca^{2+}, K^+-ATPase in rice roots: in vivo and in vitro effects of auxins and reconstitution of the ATPase. Physiol. Plant. *45*, 448–452 (1979)

ERGLE, D.R. and EATON, F.M.: Sulfur nutrition of cotton. Plant Physiol. *26*, 639–654 (1951)

ERGLE, D.R. and GUINN, G.: Phosphorus compounds of cotton embryos and their changes during germination. Plant Physiol. *34*, 476–482 (1959)

ERICKSON, A.E. and VAN DOREN, D.M.: The Relation of Plant Growth and Yield to Soil Oxygen Availability, p. 428–434. Trans. 7th Int. Congr. Soil Sci., Madison, Wisc., USA, Vol. III, 1960

ETHERTON, B.: Relationship of cell transmembrane electropotential to potassium and sodium acculmulation ratios in oat and pea seedlings. Plant Physiol. *38*, 581–585 (1963)

ETHERTON, B. and HIGINBOTHAM, N.: Transmembrane potential measurements of cells of higher plants as related to salt uptake. Science *131*, 409–410 (1961)

EVANS, C.E. and KAMPRATH, E.J.: Lime response as related to percent aluminium saturation, solution aluminium and organic matter content. Soil Sci. Soc. Amer. Proc. *34*, 893–896 (1970)

EVANS, H. and NASON, A.: Pyridine nucleotide-nitrate reductase from extracts of higher plants. Plant Physiol. *28*, 233–254 (1953)

EVANS, H.J. and RUSSELL, S.A.: Physiological Chemistry of Symbiotic Nitrogen Fixation by Legumes, p. 191–244. In J.R.Postgate: The Chemistry and Biochemistry of Nitrogen Fixation, Plenum Publishing Co. 1971   •

EVANS, H.J. and SORGER, G.J.: Role of mineral elements with emphasis on the univalent cations. Ann. Rev. Plant Physiol. *17*, 47–77 (1966)

EVANS, L.T. and RAWSON, H.M.: Photosynthesis and respiration by the flag leaf and components of the ear during grain development in wheat. Aust. J. Biol. Sci. *23*, 245–254 (1970)

EVANS, L.T., WARDLAW, I.F. and FISCHER, R.A.: Wheat. In: L.T.EVANS: Crop Physiology, p. 101–149. Cambridge University Press, Cambridge 1975

EVERS, F.H.: (G) Effect of ammonium and nitrate nitrogen on growth and mineral content of *Picea* and *Populus*. I. Growth at different acidity levels and Ca concentration in the nutrient medium. Z. f. Bot. *51*, 61–79 (1963)

EVERT, R.F.: Vascular anatomy of angiospermous leaves, with special consideration of the maize leaf. Ber. Deutsch. Bot. Ges. *93*, 43–55 (1980)

EWART, J.A.D.: Glutenin and dough tenacity. J. Sci. Fd Agric. *29*, 551–556 (1978)

FALLER, N.N.: (G) The sulphur dioxide content of the air as a factor of the sulphur supply of plants. Diss. Landw. Fakultät d. Justus-Liebig-Universität, Giessen 1968

FALLER, N., HERWIG, K. and KÜHN, H.: (G) The uptake of sulphur dioxide ($^{35}SO_2$) from the air. I. Effect on crop yield. Plant and Soil *33*, 177–191 (1970)

FARLEY, R.F. and DRAYCOTT, A.P.: Manganese deficiency of sugar beet in organic soil. Plant and Soil *38*, 235–244 (1973)

FARLEY, R.F. and DRAYCOTT, A.P.: Diagnosis of manganese deficiency in sugar beet and response to manganese applications. J. Sci. Fd. Agric. *27*, 991–998 (1976)

FARMER, V.C. and WILSON, M.J.: Experimental conversion of biotite to hydrobiotite. Nature *226*, 841–842 (1970)

FARQUHAR, G.D., FIRTH, P.M., WETSELAR, R. and WEIR, B.: On the gaseous exchange of ammonia between leaves and the environment: determination of the ammonia compensation point. Plant Physiol. *66*, 710–714 (1980)

FARRAR, K.: A review of extraction techniques used to determine available boron in soils. ADAS Q Rev. *19*, 93–100 (1975)

FAUST, M. and SHEAR, C.B.: Biochemical changes during the development of cork spot of apples. Qual. Plant Mater. Veg. *19*, 255–265 (1969)

FEIGENBAUM, S. and MENGEL, K.: The effect of reduced light intensity and sub-optimal potassium supply on N_2 fixation and N turnover in Rhizobium infected lucerne. Physiol. Plant. *45*, 245–249 (1979)

FINCK, A.: (G) Manganese requirement of oats at various growth stages. Plant and Soil 7, 389–396 (1956)

FINCK, A.: (G) Critical nutrient contents in plants and their evaluation with regard to fertilizer requirement. Z. Pflanzenernähr. Bodenk. *119*, 197–208 (1968)

FINGER, H. and WERK, O.: (G) Increase of the sodium and magnesium content in pasture herbage and the influence of Magnesia-Kainite application on the forage uptake by cows. Landw. Forsch. *28*/II. Sonderh., 190–196 (1973)

FISCHER, R.A.: Stomatal opening: role of potassium uptake by guard cells. Science *160*, 784–785 (1968)

FISCHER, R.A. and HSIAO, T.C.: Stomatal opening in isolated epidermal strips of *Vicia faba*. II. Responses to KCl concentration and the role of potassium absorption. Plant Physiol. *43*, 1953–1958 (1968)

FISHER, D.B.: Structure of functional soybean sieve elements. Plant Physiol. *56*, 555–569 (1975)

FISHER, J.D., HANSEN, D. and HODGES, T.K.: Correlation between ion fluxes and ion-stimulated adenosine triphosphatase activity of plant roots. Plant Physiol. *46*, 812–814 (1970)

FISHER, R.A.: A preliminary note on the effect of sodium silicate in increasing the yield of barley. J. Agric. Sci. *19*, 132–139 (1929)

FLEMING, G.: Mineral disorders associated with grassland farming, In Proc. Intern. Meeting on Animal Production from Temperate Grassland, p. 88–95 An Foras Taluntais, Dublin 1977

FLOWERS, T.J., TROKE, P.F. and YEO, A.R.: The mechanism of salt tolerance in halophytes. Ann. Rev. Plant Physiol. *28*, 89–121 (1977)

FOCHT, D.D.: Methods for analysis of denitrification in soil. In: Nitrogen in the Environment. Soil-Plant-Nitrogen Relationships, Vol. 1 (D.R. NIELSEN and J.G. MACDONALD, eds.) p. 433–490. Academic Press 1978

FOLLETT, R.H. and LINDSAY, W.L.: Profile distribution of zinc, iron, manganese and copper in Colorado soils. Colorado Exp. Station Techn. Bull. 110 (1970)

FOROUGHI, M., MARSCHNER, H. and DÖRING, H.W.: (G) Occurence of boron deficiency in *Citrus aurantium* L. (Bitter orange) at the Caspian Sea (Iran). Z. Pflanzenernähr. Bodenk. *136*, 220–228 (1973)

FORSTER, H.: (G) Effect of some interruptions in the nutrient supply on the development of yield and quality characteristics in sugar beets. Landw. Forsch. *25/II*. Sonderh., 99–105 (1970)

FORSTER, H.: Relationship between the nutrition and the appearance of 'greenback' and 'blossom-end rot' in tomato fruits. Acta Hort. *29*, 319–326 (1973)

FORSTER, H.: (G) Effect of the potassium and nitrogen supply to plants on yield components and yield formation of cereals. Landw. Forsch. *26*, 221–227 (1973)

FORSTER, H. and MENGEL, K.: (G) The effect of a short term interruption in the K supply during the early stage on yield formation, mineral content and soluble amino acid content. Z. Acker- u. Pflanzenbau *130*, 203–213 (1969)

FORSTER, H. and VENTER, F.: (G) The effect of the K nutrition on 'green back' in tomato fruits. Gartenbauwiss. *40*, 75–78 (1975)

FOWDEN, L.: Aspects of amino acid metabolism in plants. Ann. Rev. Plant Physiol. *18*, 85–106 (1967)

FOY, C.D.: Effect of aluminium on plant growth. In: E.W.CARSON: The Plant Root and its Environment, p. 601–642. Univ. Press of Virginia, Charlottesville 1974

FOY, C.D.: Effects of soil calcium availability on plant growth. In: E.W.CARSON: The Plant Root and its Environment, p. 565–600. Univ. Press of Virginia, Charlottesville 1974

FOY, C.D.: General principles involved in screening plants for aluminium and manganese tolerance. In: M.J. WRIGHT, ed., Plant Adaptation to Mineral Stress in Problem Soils, p. 255–267, Cornell University 1976

FOY, C.D., ARMINGER, W.H., BRIGGLE, L.W. and REID, D.A.: Differential aluminium tolerance of wheat and barley varieties in acid soils. Agron. J. *57*, 413–417 (1965)

FOY, C.D., CHANEY, R.L. and WHITE, M.C.: The physiology of metal toxicity in plants. Ann. Rev. Plant Physiol. *29*, 511–566 (1978)

FOY, C.D., FLEMING, A.L., BURNS, G.R. and ARMINGER, W,H.: Characterization of differential aluminium tolerance among varieties of wheat and barley. Agron. J. *31*, 513–521 (1967)

FRANKE, W.: Mechanisms of foliar penetration of solutions. Ann. Rev. Plant Physiol. *18*, 281–300 (1967)

FRÉMOND, Y. and OUVRIER, M.: (F) Importance of an adequate mineral nutrition for the establishment of a coco plantation on sandy soils. Oléagnieux, 26ᵉ année, No. 10, 609–616 (1971)

FRENEY, J.R. and STEVENSON, F.J.: Organic sulphur transformations in soils. Soil Sci. *101*, 307–316 (1966)

FRIDOVICH, I.: Superoxide dismutases. Ann. Rev. Biochem. *44*, 147–159 (1975)

FRIED, M.: 'E', 'L', and 'A' values. 8th Intern. Congress of Soil Science, Bucharest, Romania IV, 29–39 (1964)

FRIED, M. and BROESHART, H.: The Soil-Plant System, p. 183–206. Academic Press, New York, London 1969

FRIED, M. and DEAN, L.A.: A concept concerning the measurement of available soil nutrients. Soil Sci. *73*, 263–271 (1952)

FRIED, M. and SHAPIRO, R.E.: Soil-plant relationships in ion uptake. Ann. Rev. Plant Physiol. *12*, 91–112 (1961)

FRIEDRICH, J.W. and SCHRADER, L.E.: Sulphur deprivation and nitrogen metabolism in maize seedlings. Plant Physiol. *61*, 900–903 (1978)

FRIES, L.: Vitamin B_{12} in *Pisum sativum* L. Physiol. Plant. *15*, 566–571 (1962)

FRIIS-NIELSEN, B.: An approach towards interpreting and controlling the nutrient status of growing plants by means of chemical plant analyses. Plant and Soil *24*, 63–80 (1966)

FRITZ, D.: (G) Effect of technical measurements on the quality of some vegetable crops. Bayr. Jahrb. *54*, 78–87 (1977)

FÜRCHTENICHT, K., HOFFMANN, G. and VETTER, H.: (G) Is fertilizer application correct with regard to soil fertility, yield, and profit? In: Düngung, Umwelt, Nahrungsqualität, p. 152–168. VDLUFA, Darmstadt 1978

FUCHS, W.: (G) Investigations on the effect of nitrogen fertilization on the setting and the development of the yield character 'number of spikelets per ear' in case of winter rye, winter wheat, and two row spring barley. Arch. Acker- u. Pflanzenbau and Bodenkd. *19*, (4) 277–286 (1975)

FULTON, J.M.: Stomatal aperture and evapotranspiration from field grown potatoes. Canad. J. Plant Sci. *47*, 109–111 (1967)

GÄRTEL, W.: (G) Investigations into the potassium and magnesium contents of grapes. Weinberg u. Keller *2*, 368–375 (1955)

GÄRTEL, W.: (G) The cause of chlorosis in compact calcareous soils. Weinberg u. Keller *12*, 143–164 (1965)

GÄRTEL, W.: (G) Excess phosphate application – the reason for zinc deficiency in grapes. Der Deutsche Weinbau *23*, 916–918 (1968)

GÄRTEL, W.: (G) The micronutrients – their importance for the nutrition of grapes with particular regard to deficiency and toxicity symptoms. Weinberg u. Keller *21*, 435–507 (1974)

GALE, J. and HAGAN, R.M.: Plant antitranspirants. Ann. Rev. Plant Physiol. *17*, 269–282 (1966)

GALE, M.D.: Genetic variation for hormonal activity and yield. In: Crop Physiology and Cereal Breeding, p. 29–34. Proc. Eucarpia Workshop, Wageningen, Netherlands, Nov. 1978

GANJE, T.J.: Selenium, p. 394–404. In H.D. CHAPMAN: Diagnostic Criteria for Plants and Soils. Univ. of California, Div. of Agric. Sciences (1966)

GANRY, F., GUIRAUD, G. and DOMMERGUES, Y.: Effect of straw incorporation on the yield and nitrogen balance in the sandy-pearl millet cropping system of Senegal. Plant and Soil *50*, 647–662 (1978)

GANSSMANN, W.: (G) Investigations into the influence of silicic acid on the uptake of phosphoric acid and other nutrients. Die Phosphorsäure *22*, 223–241 (1962)

GAPON, E.N.: On the theory of exchange adsorption in soils. J. Gen. Chem. (USSR) *3*, 144–163 (1933)

GARDNER, D.J.C. and PEEL, A.J.: ATP in sieve tube sap from willow. Nature *222*, 774 (1969)

GARDNER, E.H.: Potassium relationship in some British Columbia soils. Can. J. Soil Sci. *47*, 49–53 (1967)

GARDNER, W.R.: Dynamic aspects of soil-water availability to plants. Ann. Rev. Plant Physiol. *16*, 323–342 (1965)

GARTNER, J.A.: Effect of fertilizer nitrogen on a dense sward of Kikuyu. *Paspalum* and carpet grass. 2. Interactions with phosphorus and potassium. Queensl. J. of Agric. and Anim. Sci. *26*, 365–372 (1969)

GASSER, J.K.R.: The efficiency of energy used in the production of carbohydrates and lipids. In: Fertilizer Use and Production of Carbohydrates and Lipids, p. 341–352. Int. Potash Inst., Bern 1977

GASSER, J.K.R., GREENLAND, D.J. and RAWSON, R.A.C.: Measurement of losses from fertilizer nitrogen during incubation in acid sandy soils and during subsequent growth of ryegrass, using ^{15}N-labelled fertilizers. J. Soil Sci. *18*, 289–300 (1967)

GASSER, J.K.R. and IORDANOU, I.G.: Effects of ammonium sulphate and calcium nitrate on the growth yield and nitrogen uptake of barley, wheat and oats. J. agric. Sci. *68*, 307–316 (1967)

GEERING, H.R., HODGSON, J.F. and SDANO, C.: Micronutrient cation complexes in soil solution: IV. The chemical state of manganese in soil solution. Soil Sci. Soc. Amer. Proc. *33*, 81–85 (1969)

GEIGER, D.R.: Phloem loading, p. 396–431. In: M.H. ZIMMERMANN and J.A. MILBURN: Transport in Plants I, Phloem Transport. Springer-Verlag Berlin, Heidelberg, New York 1975

GEIGER, D.R.: Control of partitioning and export of carbon in leaves of higher plants. Bot. Gaz. *140*, 241–248 (1979)

GEIGER, D.R. and CATALDO, D.A.: Leaf structure and translocation in sugar beet. Plant Physiol. *44*, 45–54 (1969)

GEIGER, D.R., SOVONICK, S.A., SHOCK, T.L. and FELLOWS, R.J.: Role of free space in translocation in sugar beet. Plant Physiol. *54*, 892–898 (1974)

GEIJN, S.C. VAN DEN and PETIT, C.M.: Transport of divalent cations. Plant Physiol. *64*, 954–958 (1979)

GEORGE, J.R., PINHEIRO, M.E. and BAILEY, T.B.: Long-term potassium requirements of nitrogen fertilized smooth brome-grass. Agron. J. *71*, 586–591 (1979)

GERDEMANN, J.W.: Mycorrhizae. In: The Plant Root and its Environment (E.W. CARSON, ed.) p. 205–217. University Press of Virginia, Charlottesville 1974

GERLOFF, G.C.: Plant efficiencies in the use of nitrogen, phosphorus, and potassium. In: Plant Adaption to Mineral Stress in Problem Soils. (M.J. WRIGHT and S.A. FERRARI, eds.) p. 161–173. Beltsville Maryland 1976

GERSON, D.F. and POOLE, R.J.: Chloride accumulation by mung bean root tips. A low affinity active transport system at the plasmalemma. Plant Physiol. *50*, 603–607 (1972)

GIAQUINTA, R.: Possible role of pH gradient and membrane ATPase in the loading of sucrose into the sieve tubes. Nature *267*, 369–370 (1977)

GIAQUINTA, R.: Phloem loading of sucrose. Involvement of membrane ATPase and proton transport. Plant Physiol. *63*, 744–748 (1979)

GIAQUINTA, R.T. and GEIGER, D.R.: Mechanism of inhibition of translocation by localized chilling. Plant Physiol. *51*, 372–377 (1973)

GIBBON, D.P., HOLLIDAY, R., MATHEI, F. and LUPI, G.: Crop production potential and energy conversion efficiency in different crops. Ex. Agric. *6*, 197–204 (1970)

GIBBS, M. and CALO, N.: Factors affecting light induced fixation of carbon dioxide by isolated spinach chloroplasts. Plant Physiol. *34*, 318–323 (1959)

GIORDANO, P.M., KOONTZ, H.V. and RUBINS, E.J.: C-14 distribution in photosynthate of tomato as influenced by substrate copper and molybdenum level and nitrogen source. Plant and Soil *24*, 437–446 (1966)

GIORDANO, P.M. and MORTVEDT, J.J.: Agronomic effectiveness of micronutrients in macronutrient fertilizers. In: Micronutrients in Agriculture, p. 505–524 (1972)

GIORDANO, P. M., NOGGLE, J. C. and MORTVEDT, J. J.: Zinc uptake by rice as affected by metabolic inhibitors and competing cations. Plant and Soil *41*, 637–646 (1974)

GISIGER, L. and HASLER, A.: (G) wauses of grey speck in oats. Plant and Soil *1*, 19–30 (1949)

GISKIN, M. and MAJDAN, A.: Problems of plant nutrition and fertilizer use on Huleh muck soils, p. 249–252. In: Transition from Extensive to Intensive Agriculture with Fertilizers. Proc. 7th Colloq. Intern. Potash Institute, Berne 1969

GLASS, A.D.M.: Regulation of potassium absorption, in barley roots. An allosteric model. Plant Physiol. *58*, 33–37 (1976)

GLASS, A.D.M. and DUNLOP, J.: The influence of potassium content on the kinetics of K^+ influx into excised ryegrass and barley roots. Planta *141*, 117–119 (1978)

GLASS, A.D.M. and PERLEY, J.E.: Varietal differences in potassium uptake by barley. Plant Physiol. *65*, 160–164 (1980)

GLYNNE, M. D.: Effect of potash on powdery mildew in wheat. Plant Path. *8*, 15–16 (1959)

GÖRING, H. and BUI HUY THIEN: Influence of nutrient deficiency on prolins accumulation in the cytoplasm of *Zea mays* L. seedlings. Biochem. Physiol. Pflanzen *174*, 9–16 (1979)

GÖRLITZ, H.: (G) Effect of fertilizer application on properties of potato starch. In: Mineralstoffversorgung von Pflanze und Tier, S. 93–100, Tagungsberichte Nr. 85, Dt. Akad. d. Landw. Wiss. Berlin 1966

GOLDBACH, H. and MICHAEL, G.: Abscisic acid content of barley grains during ripening as affected by temperature and variety. Crop Sci. *16*, 797–799 (1976)

GOLDBACH, E., GOLDBACH, H., WAGNER, H. and MICHAEL, G.: Influence of N-deficiency on the abscisic acid content of sunflower plants. Physiol. Plant. *34*, 138–140 (1975)

GOLDSCHMIDT, V. M.: Geochemistry. Oxford Univ. Press (Clarendon), London and New York 1954

GOLLMICK, F., NEUBERT, P. and VIELEMEYER, H.P.: (G) Possibilities and limitations of plant analysis in estimating the nutrient requirement of crops. Fortschrittsberichte f.d. Landw. u. Nahrungsgüterwirtschaft 8, H. 4 (1970), Dt. Akad. d. Landw. Wiss. Berlin

GOOR, B.J. VAN, and WIERSMA, D.: Redistribution of potassium, calcium, magnesium and manganese in the plant. Physiol. Plant. *31*, 163–168 (1974)

GORDON, W.R., SCHWEMMER, S.S. and HILLMAN W.S.: Nickel and the metabolism of urea by *Lemna pancicostata*. Hegelm 6746. Planta *140*, 265–268 (1978)

GOSS, R.L.: The effects of potassium on disease resistance, p. 221–241. In: The Role of Potassium in Agriculture, Madison, USA, 1968

GOSWAMI, A.K. and WILLCOX, J.S.: Effect of applying increasing levels of nitrogen to ryegrass. I. Composition of various nitrogenous fractions and free amino acids. J. Sci. Food Agric. *20*, 592–595 (1969)

GOUY, G.: (G) quoted from D. KORTÜM: Textbook of Electrochemistry, p. 345. Verl. Chemie, Weinheim 1957

GRAFF, O. and KÜHN, H.: (G) Influence of the earthworm *Lumbricus terrestris* L. on the yield and nutrient effect of a straw application. Landw. Forsch. *30*, 86–93 (1977)

GRAHAM, E. R. and FOX, R. L.: Tropical soil potassium as related to labile pool and calcium exchange equilibria. Soil Sci. *111*, 318–322 (1971)

GRAHAM, E. R. and KAMPBELL, D. H.: Soil potassium availability and reserve as related to the isotopic pool and calcium exchange equilibria. Soil Sci. *106*, 101–106 (1968)

GRAHAM, E. R. and LOPEZ, P. L.: Freezing and thawing as a factor in the release and fixation of soil potassium as demonstrated by isotopic exchange and calcium exchange equilibria. Soil Sci. *108*, 143–147 (1969)

GRAHAM-BRYCE, I. J.: The movements of potassium and magnesium ions in soil in relation to their availability. Techn. Bull. Nr. 14 'Soil Potassium and Magnesium', p. 20–32; Ministry of Agriculture, Fisheries and Food, London 1967

GRAUPE, B.: (G) Molybdenum metabolism of ruminants, p. 309–317. In: Mineralstoffversorgung von Pflanze und Tier, Tagungsberichte Nr. 85, Dt. Akad. d. Landw. Wiss., Berlin 1966

GRAVEN, E.H., ATTOE, O.J. and SMITH, D.: Effect of liming and flooding on manganese toxicity in alfalfa. Soil Sci. Soc. Amer. Proc. *29*, 702–706 (1965)

GREEN, J.F. and MUIR, R.M.: The effect of potassium on cotyledon expansion induced by cytokinins. Plant Physiol. *43*, 213–218 (1978)

GREENWAY, H. and MUNNS, R.: Mechanism of salt tolerance in non halophytes. Ann. Rev. Plant Physiol. *31*, 149–190 (1980)

GREENWAY, H. and PITMAN, M.G.: Potassium retranslocation in seedlings of *Hordeum vulgare*. Aust. J. biol. Sci. *18*, 235–247 (1965)

GREENWOOD, D.J.: Studies on the distribution of oxygen around the roots of mustard seedlings *(Sinapis alba* L.*)*. New Phytol. *70*, 97–101 (1971)

GREENWOOD, D.J.: Fertilizer food production: world scene. Fertilizer Research *2*, 31–51 (1981)

GREENWOOD, D.J., CLEAVER, I.J. and TURNER, M.K.: Fertilizer requirements of vegetable crops, p. 4–30. The Fertilizer Soc., London 1974

GREENWOOD, D.J., CLEAVER, T.J., TURNER, M.K., HUNT, J., NIENDORF, K.B. and LOQUENS, S.M.H.: Comparison of the effects of nitrogen fertilizer on the yield, nitrogen content and quality of 21 different vegetable and agricultural crops. J. agric. Sci. *95*, 471–485 (1980)

GRIMME, H.: (G) Adsorption of Mn, Co, Cu, and Zn to goethite in dilute solutions. Z. Pflanzenernähr. Bodenk. *121*, 58–65 (1968)

GRIMME, H.: Potassium release in relation to crop production. In: Potassium Research and Agricultural Production, p. 113–118, 10th Congr. Int. Potash Inst., Bern 1974

GRIMME, H.: Magnesium diffusion in soils at different water and magnesium contents. Z. Pflanzenernähr. Bodenk. *134*, 9–19 (1973)

GRIMME, H., VON BRAUNSCHWEIG, L.C. and NEMETH, K.: (G) Potassium, calcium and magnesium interactions as related to cation uptake and yield. Landw. Forsch. *30*/II. Sonderh., 93–100 (1974)

GRIMME, H., NEMETH, K. and VON BRAUNSCHWEIG, L.C.: (G) Relationships between the behaviour of potassium in the soil and the potassium nutrition of plants. Landw. Forsch. *26*/I. Sonderh., 165–176 (1971)

GROSSE-BRAUCKMANN, E.: (G) Influence of N, CaO and P_2O_5 on SiO_2 uptake by cereals. Landw. Forsch. *9*, 196–203 (1956)

GRUNWALDT, H.S.: (G) Investigations into the sulphur content of soils in Schleswig-Holstein. Diss. Landw. Fakultät, Kiel 1969

GUCKERT, A., BREISCH, H. and REISINGER, O.: (F) Interface soil-roots I. Electron microscopic study on the relationship between mucilage, clay minerals and microorganisms. Soil Biol. Biochem. *7*, 241–250 (1975)

GUERRERO, M.G., VEGA, J.M. and LOSADA, M.: The assimilatory nitrate reducing system and its regulation. Ann. Rev. Plant Physiol. *32*, 169–204 (1981)

GUIRAUD, G. and BERLIER, Y.: (F) Investigations with N-15 on denitrification in soils particularly in association with incorporated straw. Compt. Rend. 1000–1007 (1969)

GUKOVA, M.M. and TJULINA, O.V.: (R) Effect of potassium on the nitrogen uptake by leguminous crops. Izvestija Timirjazevskoy sel'skochozjajstvennoj akademii, Moskva Nr. 3, 100–109 (1968)

GUNSALUS, I.C., PEDERSEN, T.C. and SLIGAR, S.G.: Oxygenase catalysed biological hydroxylations. Ann. Rev. Biochem. *44*, 317–340 (1975)

GUPTA, U.C.: Boron nutrition of crops. Adv. Agron. *31*, 273–307 (1979)

GUPTA, U.C. and CUTCLIFFE, J.A.: Effects of methods of boron application on leaf tissue concentration of boron and control of brown-heart in rutabaga. Can. J. Plant Sci. *58*, 63–68 (1978)

GUSTAFSON, F.G. and SCHLESSINGER, M.J.: Absorption of ^{60}Co by bean plants in the dark. Plant Physiol. *31*, 316–318 (1956)

GUTSTEIN, Y.: The uptake of nitrogen, potassium and sodium and their interrelated effects on yield and quality composition of sugar beet. Qualit. plant. materiae veg. *15*, 1–28 (1967)

597

HABER, A.H. and TOLBERT, N.E.: Metabolism of C-14-bicarbonate, P-32-phosphate or S-35-sulfate by lettuce seed during germination. Plant Physiol. *34*, 376–380 (1959)

HACKETT, C.: Ecological aspects of the nutrition of *Deschampsia flexuosa* (L.) Triu. I. The effect of aluminium, manganese and pH on germination. J. Ecol. (Oxford) *52*, 159–167 (1964)

HADAS, A. and KAFKAFI, U.: Kinetics of the mineralization of ureaform as influenced by temperature. Soil Sci. *118*, 16–21 (1974)

HAEDER, H.E.: (G) Potassium release of maturing barley. Z. Pflanzenernähr. Bodenk. *129*, 125–132 (1971)

HAEDER, H.E.: (G) The influence of chloride nutrition in comparison with sulphate nutrition on assimilation and translocation of assimilates in potato plants. Landw. Forsch. *32*/I. SH, 122–131 (1975)

HAEDER, H.E.: Effect of potassium nutrition on sink intensity and duration. In: Physiological Aspects of crop productivity, p. 185–194 Int. Potash Inst., Bern 1980

HAEDER, H.E., BERINGER, H. and MENGEL, K.: (G) Redistribution of ^{14}C into the grains of two spring-wheat cultivars. Z. Pflanzenernähr. Bodenk. *140*, 409–419 (1977)

HAEDER, H.E. and MENGEL, K.: (G) The absorption of potassium and sodium in dependence on the nitrogen nutrition level of the plant. Landw. Forsch. *23*/I. Sonderh., 53–60 (1969)

HAEDER, H.E. and MENGEL, K.: Translocation and respiration of assimilates in tomato plants as influenced by K nutrition. Z. Pflanzenernähr. Bodenk. *131*, 139–148 (1972)

HAEDER, H.E., MENGEL, K. and FORSTER, H.: The effect of potassium on translocation of photosynthates and yield pattern of potato plants. J. Sci. Fd Agric. *24*, 1479–1487 (1973)

HAGEMAN, R.H. and FLESHER, D.: Nitrate reductase activity in corn seedlings as affected by light and nitrate content of nutrient media. Plant Physiol. *35*, 700–708 (1960)

HAGEMANN, O. and MÜLLER, S.: (G) Investigations into the effect of pH on the recovery of fertilizer phosphate and on the metabolization of soil phosphates. Arch. Acker- u. Pflanzenbau u. Bodenk. *20*, 805–815 (1976)

HAGSTROM, G.R. and BERGER, K.C.: Molybdenum deficiencies of Wisconsin soils. Soil Sci. *99*, 52–56 (1965)

HAI, TANG VAN, and LAUDELOUT, H.: (F) Absorption of phosphate by rice roots. Ann. Physiol. vég. *8*, 13–24 (1966)

HAK, T.A.: Diseases of wheat, barley and rice and their control. 1. FAO/SIDA Seminar for plant scientists from Africa and Near East, Cairo 1973, p. 542–549. FAO, Rome 1974

HALE, M.G. and MOORE, L.D.: Factors affecting root exudation II: 1970–1978. Adv. Agron. *31*, 93–124 (1979)

HALL, D.A.: The influence of varied calcium nutrition on the growth and ionic compostion of plants. Ph. D. Thesis. University of Leeds 1971

HALL, D.O.: Solar energy and biology for fuel food and fibre. TIBS *2*, 99–101 (1977)

HALL, D.O., CAMMACK, R. and RAO, K.K.: Role for ferredoxins in the origin of life and biological evolution. Nature *233*, 136–138 (1971)

HALL, S.M. and BAKER, D.A.: The chemical composition of *Ricinus* phloem exudate. Planta *106*, 131–140 (1972)

HALLSWORTH, E.G., WILSON, S.B. and ADAMS, W.A.: Effect of cobalt on the non nodulated legume. Nature *205*, 307 (1965)

HALLSWORTH, E.G., WILSON, S.B. and GREENWOOD, E.A.N.: Copper and cobalt in nitrogen fixation. Nature *187*, 79–80 (1960)

HAMISSA, M.R.: Fertilizer requirements for broadbeans and lentils. First FAO/SIDA Seminar for Plant Scientists from Africa and Near East, Cairo 1973, p. 410–416. FAO, Rome 1974

HAMMOND, L.L., CHIEN, S.H. and POLO, J.R.: Phosphorus availability from partial acidulation of two phosphate rocks. Fertilizer Research *1*, 37–49 (1980)

HANOTIAUX, G.: (F) Soil sampling for chemical analysis. Bull. Rech. Agron. de Gembloux, N.S. 1, Nr. 3 (1966)

HANOTIAUX, G. and MANIL, G.: (F) Investigations into the dynamics of phosphorus and potassium in the soil. Pédologie *13*, 73–91 (1963)

HANSON, J.B. and BONNER, J.: The relationship between salt and water uptake in Jerusalem artichoke tuber tissue. Ann. J. Bot. *41*, 702–710 (1954)

HAQ, A.U. and MILLER, M.H.: Prediction of available soil Zn, Cu and Mn using chemical extractants. Agron. J. *64*, 779–782 (1972)

HARLEY, J.L.: Mycorrhiza. Oxford University Press 1971

HARMSEN, G.W.: (G) What does the content of soluble nitrogen in the soil mean? Z. Pflanzenernähr. Düng. Bodenk. *84*, 98–102 (1959)

HARRIS, P. and JAMES, A.T.: Effect of low temperature on fatty acid biosynthesis in seeds. Biochim. Biophys. Acta *187*, 13–18 (1969)

HARRISON, M.A. and WALTON, D.C.: Abscisic acid in water stressed bean leaves. Plant Physiol. *56*, 250–254 (1975)

HARTT, C.E.: Effect of potassium deficiency upon translocation of ^{14}C in attached blades and entire plants of sugarcane. Plant Physiol. *44*, 1461–1469 (1969)

HARTT, C.E.: Effect of potassium deficiency upon translocation of ^{14}C in detached blades of sugarcane. Plant Physiol. *45*, 183–187 (1970)

HARTT, C.E.: Translocation of carbon-14 in sugarcane plants supplied with or deprived of phosphorus. Plant Physiol. *49*, 569–571 (1972)

HAUCK, R.D.: Quantitative estimates of nitrogen-cycle-processes: Concepts and review. In: Nitrogen-15 in Soil Plant Studies, p. 65–80. IAEA, Vienna 1971

HAY, R.K.M.: The temperature of the soil under a barley crop. J. Soil Sci. *27*, 121–128 (1976)

HAYAISHI, O.: Biological oxidations. Ann. Rev. Biochem. *31*, 25–46 (1962)

HAYMAN, D.S.: Mycorrhiza and crop production. Nature *287*, 487–488 (1980)

HAYNES, R.J. and GOH, K.M.: Ammonium and nitrate nutrition of plants. Biol. Rev. *53*, 465–510 (1978)

HEATHCOTE, R.C.: (G) Fertilization with potassium in the Savanna zone of Nigeria. Potash Review, Subject 16, 57th suite (1972)

HEATHERLY, L.G. and RUSSELL, W.J.: Effect of soil water potential of two soils on soybean emergence. Agron. J. *71*, 980–982 (1979)

HEBER, U., KIRK, M.R., GIMMLER, H. and SCHÄFER, G.: Uptake and reduction of glycerate by isolated chloroplasts. Planta *120*, 32–46 (1974)

HEBER, U. and PURCZELD, P.: Substrate and product fluxes across the chloroplast envelope during bicarbonate and nitrite reduction. Proc. 4th Int. Congr. on Photosynthesis, p. 107–118 (1977)

HECHT-BUCHHOLZ, CH. and MARSCHNER, H.: (G) Changes in the fine structure of cells of maize root tips deprived of potassium. Z. Pflanzenphysiol. *63*, 416–427 (1970)

HECHT-BUCHHOLZ, Ch., MIX, G. and MARSCHNER, H.: Effect of NaCl on mineral content and fine structure of cells in plants with different salt tolerance. In: Plant Analysis and Fertilizer Problems (J. WEHRMANN, ed.) p. 147–156. Greman Soc. Plant Nutrition, Hannover 1974

HEHL, G. and MENGEL, K.: (G) The effect of varied applications of potassium and nitrogen on the carbohydrate content of several forage crops. Landw. Forsch. *27*/II. Sonderh., 117–129 (1972)

HEILENZ, S.: (G) Investigations into the lead content of plants on sites with heavy traffic. Landw. Forsch. *25*/I. Sonderh., 73–78 (1970)

HELAL, H.M. and MENGEL, K.: Nitrogen metabolism of young barley plants as affected by NaCl-salinity and potassium. Plant and Soil *51*, 457–462 (1979)

HELAL, H.M. and MENGEL, K.: Interaction between light intensity and NaCl salinity and their effects on growth, CO_2 assimilation, and photosynthetic conversion in young broad beans. Plant Physiol. *67*, 999–1002 (1981)

HELDT, H.W., JA CHONG, C., MARONDE, D., HEROLD, A., STANKOVIC, Z.S., WALKER, D.A., KRAMINER, A., KIRK, M.R. and HEBER, U.: Role of orthophosphate and other factors in the regulation of starch formation in leaves and isolated chloroplasts. Plant Physiol. *59*, 1146–1155 (1977)

HENCKEL, P. A. and SOLOVYOV, V. A.: Accumulation and distribution of sodium and potassium im pumpkin plants as a result of substrate salinization by sodium chloride and sodium sulphate. Fiziol. Rastenij *15*, 521–529 (1968)

HENDERSON, G.S. and STONE, E.L. jr.: Interactions of phosphorus availability, mycorrhiza and soil fumigation on coniferous seedlings. Proc. Soil Sci. Soc. Am. *34*, 314–318 (1970)

HENDRICKSON, L.L., WALSH, L.M. and KEENEY, D.R.: Effectiveness of nitrapyrin in controlling nitrification of fall and spring applied anhydrous ammonia. Agron. J. *70*, 704–708 (1978a)

HENDRICKSON, L.L., KEENEY, D.R., WALSH, L.M. and LIEGEL, E.A.: Evalution of nitrapyrin as a means of improving N efficiency in irrigated sands. Agron J. *70*, 699–704 (1978b)

HENDRIX, J.E.: The effect of pH on the uptake and accumulation of phosphate and sulfate ions by bean plants. Amer. J. Bot. *54*, 560–564 (1967)

HENKENS, C.H.: (G) General lines for the application of trace elements in Holland. Landw. Forsch. *18*, 108–116 (1965)

HENTSCHEL, G.: The uptake of ^{15}N-labelled urea by bush beans. In: E.A. KIRKBY: Nitrogen Nutrition of the Plant, p. 30–34. University of Leeds, Agricultural Chemistry Symposium 1970

HERRMANN, B.: (G) Fatty acid composition of the crude fat fraction of winter rape seed as influenced by nitrogen fertilization. Arch. Acker- und Pflanzenbau und Bodenk. *21*, 141–148 (1977)

HERZOG, H. and GEISLER, G.: (G) Effect of cytokinin application on assimilate storage and endogenous cytokinin activity in the caryopsis of two spring wheat cultivars. Z. Acker- und Pflanzenbau *144*, 230–242 (1977)

HESSE, P.R.: A Textbook of Soil Chemical Analysis, John Murray London 1971

HEWITT, E.J.: Relation of manganese and other metal toxicities to the iron status of plants. Nature *161*, 489–490 (1948)

HEWITT, E.J.: Metal interrelationship in plant nutrition. J. Exper. Bot. *4*, 59–64 (1953)

HEWITT, E.J.: Essential nutrient elements for plant, p. 137–360. In: Plant Physiology, Vol. III, Inorganic Nutrition of Plant. Academic Press 1963

HEWITT, E.J.: Physiological and biochemical factors which control the assimilation of inorganic nitrogen supplies by plants, p. 78–103. In: E.A. KIRKBY: Nitrogen Nutrition of the Plant, The University Leeds 1970

HEWITT, E.J.: Assimilatory nitrate-nitrite reduction. Ann. Rev. Plant Physiol. *26*, 73–100 (1975)

HEWITT, E.J. and AGARWALA, S.C.: Reduction of triphenyltetrazolium chloride by plant tissue and its relation to the molybdenum status. Nature *169*, 545–546 (1952)

HEWITT, E.J., BOLLE-JONES, E.W. and MILES, P.: The production of copper, zinc and molybdenum deficiencies in crop plants grown in sand culture with special reference to some effects of water supply and seed reserves. Plant and Soil *5*, 205–222 (1954)

HEWITT, E.J. and GUNDRY, C.S.: The molybdenum requirement of plants in relation to nitrogen supply. J. Hort. Sci. *45*, 351–358 (1970)

HEWITT, E.J. and SMITH, T.A.: Plant Mineral Nutrition. English Univ. Press London 1975

HIATT, A.J.: Reactions *in vitro* of enzymes involved in CO_2 fixation accompanying salt uptake by barley roots. Z. Pflanzenphysiol. *56*, 233–245 (1967)

HIATT, A.J.: Relationship of cell sap pH to organic acid change during ion uptake. Plant Physiol. *42*, 294–298 (1967)

HIATT, A.J. and LEGGETT, J.E.: Ionic interactions and antagonism in plants, p. 101–134. In: E.W. CARSON: The Plant Root and Its Environment. University Press of Virginia, Charlottesville 1974

HIGINBOTHAM, N.: The mineral absorption process in plants. The Botanical Review *99*, 15–69 (1973)

HIGNETT, T.P.: Liquid fertilizer production and distribution. UNO, Second Interregional Fertilizer Symposium, Kiev, Ukraine, 1971; New Delhi, India, 1971

600

HILDEBRANDT, E.A.: (G) Uptake and degradation of nitrosamines in sunflower seedlings. Landw. Forsch. Sonderh. *36*, 187–195 (1979)

HILL, J.M.: The changes with age in the distribution of copper and some copper containing oxidase in red clover *(Trifolium pratense* L. cv Dorset Marlgrass). J. Exp. Bot. *24*, 525–536 (1973)

HINKLE, P.C. and McCARTY, R.E.: How cells make ATP. Sci. American *238*, 104–123 (1978)

HINGSTON, F.J., POSNER, A.M. and QUIRK, J.P.: Anion adsorption by goethite and gibbsite. I. The role of the proton in determining adsorption envelopes. J. Soil Sci. *23*, 177–193 (1972)

HIPP, B.W. and THOMAS, G.W.: Method for predicting potassium uptake by grain sorghum. Agron. J. *60*, 467–469 (1968)

HOAGLAND, D.R.: Lectures on the inorganic nutrition of plants, p. 48–71. Chronica Botanica Company, Waltham, Mass. USA 1948

HODGES, T.K.: Ion absorption by plant roots. Advances in Agronomy *25*, 163–207 (1973)

HODGES, T.K., LEONARD, R.T., BRACKER, C.E. and KEENAN, T.W.: Purification of an ion stimulated adenosine triphosphatase from plant roots: association with plasma membranes. Proc. Nat. Acad. Sci. USA *69*, 3307–3311 (1972)

HODGSON, J.F., LINDSAY, W.L. and TRIERWEILER, J.F.: Micronutrient cation complexing in soil solution. II. Complexing of zinc and copper in displacing solution from calcareous soils. Soil Sci. Soc. Amer. Proc. *30*, 723–726 (1966)

HÖLL, W.: (G) The symbiosis between legumes and bacteria of the genus *Rhizobium*. Naturw. Rdsch. *8*, 281–289 (1975)

HOJJATI, S.M. and MALEKI, M.: Effect of potassium and nitrogen fertilization on lysine, methionine and total protein contents of wheat grain, *Triticum aestivum* L. em. Thell. Agron. J. *64*, 46–48 (1972)

HOJMARK, J.V.: Placement of NPK fertilizer for potatoes. Tidsskrift for Planteavl *76*, 196–208 (1972)

HOLDER, C.B. and BROWN, K.W.: The relationship between oxygen and water uptake by roots of intact bean plants. Soil Sci. Soc. Am. J. *44*, 21–25 (1980)

HOLFORD, I.C.R.: Effects of phosphate buffer capacity of soil on the phosphate requirements of plants. Plant and Soil *45*, 433–444 (1976)

HOLFORD, I.C.R. and MATTINGLY, G.E.G.: Phosphate sorption by jurassic oolitic limestones Geoderma *13*, 257–264 (1975)

HOLLIDAY, R.: Effects of fertilisers upon potato yields and quality. In: J.D. IVINS and F.L. MILTHORPE: The Growth of the Potato, p. 248–264. Butterworths, London 1963

HOLLIDAY, R.: The efficiency of solar energy conversion by the whole crop. In: DUCKHAM, A.N., JONES, J.G.W. and ROBERTS, E.H.: Food Production and Consumption. P. 127–146. North Holland Publishing Company, Amsterdam, Oxford 1976

HOLM-HANSEN, O., GERLOFF, G.C. and SKOOG, F.: Cobalt as an essential element for bluegreen algae. Physiol. Plant. *7*, 665–675 (1954)

HOMANN, P.E.: Studies on the manganese of the chloroplast. Plant Physiol. *42*, 997–1007 (1967)

HONERT, TH. VAN DEN: Water transport in plants as a catenary process. Disc. Faraday Soc. *3*, 146–153 (1948)

HOOGERKAMP, M.: Ley, periodically reseeded grassland or permanent grassland. Agric. Res. Rep. *812*, 5–35 (1974)

HOOKER, A.L.: Plant nutrients on stalk rot and lodging. Better Crops with Plant Food *50*, 6–9 (1966)

HOOKER, M.L., SANDER, D.H., PETERSON, G.A. and DAIGGER, L.A.: Gaseous N losses from winter wheat. Agron. J. *72*, 789–792 (1980)

HOPKINS, H.T.: Absorption of ionic species of orthophosphate by barley roots: effects of 2,4-dinitrophenol and oxygen tension. Plant Physiol. *31*, 155–161 (1956)

HOPKINS, H.T., SPECHT, A.W. and HENDRICKS, S.B.: Growth and nutrient accumulation as controlled by oxygen supply to plant roots. Plant Physiol. *25*, 193–208 (1950)

HORST, W.J. and MARSCHNER, H.: Effect of excessive manganese supply on uptake and translocation of calcium in bean plants *(Phaseolus vulgaris* L.). Z Pflanzenphysiol. *87*, 137–148 (1978a)

HORST, W.J. and MARSCHNER, H.: Effect of silicon in manganese tolerance of bean plants *(Phaseolus vulgaris* L). Plant on Soil *50*, 287–303 (1978b)

HOSSNER, L.R., FREEOUF, J.A. and FOLSOM, B.L.: Solution phosphorus concentration and growth of rice *(Oryza sativa* L.) in flooded soils. Proc. Soil Sci. Soc. Amer. *37*, 405–408 (1973)

HSIAO, T.C.: Rapid changes in levels of polyribosomes in *Zea mays* in response to water stress. Plant Physiol. *46*, 281–285 (1970)

HSIAO, T.C.: Plant responses to water stress. Ann. Rev. Plant Physiol. *24*, 519–570 (1973)

HSIAO, T.C., ACEVEDO, E., FERERES, E. and HENDERSON, D.W.: Water stress, growth and osmotic adjustment. Phil. Trans. Royal Soc. London *273*, 479–500 (1976)

HSIAO, T.C., HAGEMAN, R.H. and TYNER, E.H.: Effects of potassium nutrition on protein and total free amino acids in *Zea mays*. Crop Sci. *10*, 78–82 (1970)

HUBER, D.M., WARREN, H.L., NELSON, D.W. and TSAI, C.Y.: Nitrification inhibitors – new tools for food production. Bio Science *27*, 523–529 (1977)

HUBER, D.M., WARREN, H.L., NELSON, D.W., TSAI, C.Y. and SHANER, G.E.: Response of winter wheat to inhibiting nitrification of fall-applied nitrogen. Agron. J. *72*, 632–637 (1980)

HUFFMAN, E.W.D. and ALLAWAY, W.H.: Growth of plants in solution culture containing low levels of chromium Plant Physiol. *52*, 72–75 (1973)

HUGHES, J.C. and SWAIN, T.: After-cooking blackening in potatoes. 11. Core experiments. J. Sci. Fd Agric. *13*, 229–236 (1962)

HUGHES, J.D. and SEARLE, P.G.E.: Observations on the residual value of accumulated phosphorus in a red loam. Aust. J. Agric. Res. *15*, 377–383 (1964)

HULPOI, N., PICU, I. and TIANU, A.: (Ru) Researches concerning the application of fertilizers to irrigated field crops. Probleme Agricole Nr.8, August 1971, Ministerul Agriculturii, Industriei Alimentare, Silviculturii Si Apeor, Rumania

HUMBLE, G.D. and HSIAO, T.C.: Specific requirement of potassium for light-activated opening of stomata in epidermal strips. Plant Physiol. *44*, 230–234 (1969)

HUMBLE, G.D. and HSIAO, T.C.: Light-dependent influx and efflux of guard cell potassium during stomatal opening and closing. Plant Physiol., Suppl. 44, Nr. 97, p. 21 (1969)

HUMBLE, G.D. and HSIAO, T.C.: Light -dependent influx and efflux of potassium of guard cells during stomatal opening and closing. Plant Physiol. *46*, 483–487 (1970)

HUMBLE, G.D. and RASCHKE, K.: Stomatal opening quantitatively related to potassium transport. Plant Physiol. *48*, 447–453 (1971)

HUNDT, I., SCHILLING, G., FISCHER, F. and BERGMANN, W.: (G) Investigations on the influence cf the micro-nutrient boron on nucleic acid metabolism. Thaer-Arch. *14:* 725–737 (1970)

HUNTER, T.G. and VERGNANO, O.: Trace element toxicities in oats. Ann. App. Biol. *40*, 761–777 (1953)

HUPPERT, V. and BUCHNER, A.: (G) Recent experimental results on the effect of several N forms with particular regard to environmental conditions. Z. Pflanzenernähr. Düng. Bodenk. *60*, 62–92 (1953)

HURD-KARRER, A.M.: Comparative fluorine uptake by plants in limed and unlimed soil. Soil Sci. *70*, 153–159 (1950)

HUTCHIN, M.E. and VAUGHAN, B.E.: Relation between simultaneous Ca and Sr transport rates in isolated segments of vetch, barley and pine roots. Plant Physiol. *43*, 1913–1918 (1968)

HUTCHINSON, T.C.: Lime-chlorosis as a factor in seedling establishment on calcareous soils. I. A comparative study of species from acidic and calcareous soils in their susceptibility to lime-chlorosis. New Phytol. *66*, 697–705 (1967)

HYDE, B.B., HODGE, A.J., KAHN, A. and BIRNSTIEL, M.L.: Studies in phytoferritin. I. Identification and localization. J. Ultrastruc. Res. *9*, 248–258 (1963)

HYLTON, L.O., ULRICH, A. and CORNELIUS, D.R.: Potassium and sodium interrelations in growth and mineral content of Italian ryegrass. Agron. J. *59*, 311–314 (1967)

ILJIN, W.S.: Metabolism of plants affected with lime-induced chlorosis (calciose). Plant and Soil *3*, 239–256 and 339–351 (1951)

ISERMANN, K.: (G) The effect of adsorption processes in the xylem on the calcium distribution in higher plants. Z. Pflanzenernähr. Bodenk. *126*, 191–203 (1970)

ITAI, C., RICHMOND, A. and VAADIA, Y.: The role of root cytokinins during water and salinity stress. Israel J. Bot. *17*, 187–195 (1968)

IVANOV, S.: (G) The climatic zones of the earth and the chemical activities of plants. In: ABDERHALDEN: Fortschr. d. naturwiss. Forsch. N.F. Heft 5, S. 1, Berlin u. Wien 1929

JACKSON, B.L.J. and DURING, C.: Studies of slowly available potassium in soils of New Zealand. I. Effects of leaching, temperature and potassium depletion on the equilibrium concentration of potassium in solution. Plant and Soil *51*, 197–204 (1979)

JACKSON, M.L.: Soil Chemical Analysis, Constable 1958

JACKSON, P.C. and EDWARDS, D.G.: Cation effects on chloride fluxes and accumulation levels in barley roots. J. Gen. Physiol. *50*, 225–241 (1966)

JACKSON, P.C. and HAGEN, C.E.: Products of orthophosphate absorption by barley roots. Plant Physiol. *35*, 326–332 (1960)

JACKSON, W.A. and VOLK, R.J.: Role of potassium in photosynthesis. In: The role of Potassium in Agriculture. (V.J. KILMER, S.E. YOUNTS and N.C. BRADY, eds.) p. 109–145. Am. Soc. Agron. Madison, USA 1968

JACKSON, W.A. and VOLK, R.J.: Photorespiration. Ann. Rev. Plant Physiol. *21*, 385–432 (1970)

JACOB, A. and v. UEXKÜLL, H.: Fertilizer use, nutrition and manuring of tropical crops. 3rd ed. Verlagsges. f. Ackerbau, Hannover 1963

JACOBSON, B.S., FONG, F. and HEATH, R.L.: Carbonic anhydrase of spinach. Studies on its location, inhibition and physiological function. Plant Physiol. *55*, 468–474 (1975)

JACOBSON, J.A., OVERSTREET, L., KING, R. and HANDLEY, H.M.: A study of potassium absorption by barley roots. Plant Physiol. *25*, 639–647 (1950)

JACOBSON, K.: Iron in the leaves and chloroplasts of some plants in relation to their chlorophyll content. Plant Physiol. *20*, 233–245 (1945)

JACOBSON, L.: Carbon dioxide fixation and ion absorption in barley roots. Plant Physiol. *30*, 264–269 (1955)

JACOBSON, L., MOORE, D.P. and HANNAPEL, R.J.: Role of calcium in absorption of monovalent cations. Plant Physiol. *35*, 352–358 (1960)

JACOBSON, L. and OERTLI, J.J.: The relation between iron and chlorophyll contents in chlorotic sunflower leaves. Plant Physiol. *31*, 199–204 (1956)

JACOBY, B., ABAS, S. and STEINITZ, B.: Rubidium and potassium absorption by bean-leaf slices compared to sodium absorption. Physiol. Plant. *28*, 209–214 (1973)

JAGENDORF, A.T.: Photophosphorylation. In: Photosynthesis I, Encycl. Plant Physiol. New Series, Vol. 5 (A. TREBST and M. ARNON, eds.) p. 307–337. Springer-Verlag Berlin, Heidelberg, New York 1977

JAHN-DEESBACH, W. and MAY, H.: (G) The effect of variety and additional late nitrogen application on the thiamin (vitamin B_1) content of the total wheat grain, various flour types, and secondary milling products. Z. Acker- u. Pflanzenbau *135*, 1–18 (1972)

JAHN-DEESBACH, W. and WEIPERT, D.: (G) Investigations into the influence of nitrogen application on the yield and technological properties of wheat. Landw. Forsch. *18*, 132–145 (1965)

JAMES, D.W., JACKSON, T.L. and HARWARD, M.E.: Effects of molybdenum content of alfalfa grown in acid soils. Soil Sci. *105*, 397–402 (1968)

JAMES, D. W., WEAVER, W. H. and REEDER, R. L.: Chloride uptake by potatoes and the effects of potassium, chloride, nitrogen and phosphorus fertilization. Soil Sci. *109*, 48–52 (1970)

JARVIS, S. C., JONES, L. H. P. and HOPPER, M. J.: Cadmium uptake from solution by plants and its transport from roots to shoots. Plant and Soil *44*, 179–191 (1976)

JASPER, D. A., MANDAL, R., OSMAN, K.T.: Phosphorus and the formation of vesicular arbuscular mycorrhizas. Soil Biol. Biochem. *11*, 501–505, 1979.

JEFFREYS, R. A. and WALLACE, A.: Detection of iron ethylene-diamine di (o-hydroxy-phenylacetate) in plant tissue. Agron. J. *60*, 613–616 (1968)

JENKINSON, D.S., NOWAKOWSKI, T.Z. and MITCHELL, J.D.D.: Growth and uptake of nitrogen by wheat and ryegrass in fumigated and irradiated soil. Plant and Soil *36*, 149–158 (1972)

JENNER, C.F.: The conversion of sucrose to starch in developing fruits. Ber. Deutsch. Bot. Ges. *93*, 289–298 (1980)

JENNER, C.F. and RATHJEN, A.J.: Factors regulating the accumulation of starch in ripening wheat grain. Aust. J. Plant Physiol. *2*, 311–322 (1975)

JENNINGS, D.H.: The effects of sodium chloride on higher plant Biol. Rev. *51*, 453–486 (1976)

JENNY, H. and OVERSTREET, R.: Contact effects between plant roots and soil colloids. Proc. Nat. Sci. *24*, 384–392 (1938)

JENSEN, H.L.: A survey of biological nitrogen fixation in relation to the world supply of nitrogen. Trans. 4th Int. Congr. Soil Sci. (Amsterdam) *1*, 165–172 (1950)

JESCHKE, W. D.: (G) Cyclic and non cyclic photophosphorylation as energy source for the light dependent chloride uptake of *Elodea*. Planta *73*, 161–174 (1967)

JOHAM, H.J.: Accumulation and distribution of molybdenum in the cotton plant. Plant Physiol. *28*, 275–280 (1953)

JOHANSEN, C., EDWARDS, D.G. and LONERAGAN, J.F.: Potassium fluxes during potassium absorption by intact barley plants of increasing potassium content. Plant Physiol. *45*, 601–603 (1970)

JOHNSON, C.M.: Molybdenum, p. 286–301. In: Diagnostic Criteria for Plants and Soils, ed. Chapman, 1966

JOHNSON, C.M., STOUT, P.R., BROYER, T.C. and CARLTON, A.B.: Comparative chlorine requirements of different plant species. Plant and Soil *8*, 337–353 (1957)

JOHNSON, D.L. and ALBERT, L.S.: Effect of selected nitrogen bases and boron on the ribonucleic acid content, elongation and visible deficiency symptoms in tomato root tips. Plant Physiol. *42*, 1307–1309 (1967)

JOHRI, B.M. and VASIL, I.K.: Physiology of pollen. Bot. Rev. *27*, 325–381 (1961)

JONES, J.B. jr.: Distribution of 15 elements in corn leaves. Commun Soil Sci. Plant Anal. *1*, 27–34 (1970)

JONES, L.H.P.: Effect of liming a neutral soil on the cycle of manganese. Plant and Soil *8*, 315–327 (1957)

JONES, L.H.P. and HANDRECK, K.A.: Silica in soils, plants and animals. Adv. in Agronomy *19*, 107–149 (1967)

JONES, L.H.P. and HANDRECK, K.A.: Studies of silica in the oat plant. III. Uptake of silica from soils by the plant. Plant and Soil *23*, 79–96 (1965)

JONES, R.L. HINESLY, T.D., ZIEGLER, E.L. and TYLER, J.J.: Cadmium and zinc contents of corn leaf on grain produced by sluge amended soil. J. Environ. Qual. *4*, 509–514 (1975)

JUDEL, G.K.: (G) Fixation and mobilization of boron in soils with high B contents toxic to crops. Landw. Forsch. Sonderh. *34*/II, 103–108 (1977)

JUNG, J. and DRESSEL, J.: (G) Behaviour of magnesium in soil and plants studied in a lysimeter experiment lasting 10 years. Z. Acker- u. Pflanzenbau *130*, 122–135 (1969)

JUNG, J., KOCH, H., RIEBER, N. and WÜRZER, B.: (G) Growth regulating action of triazoline and aziridine derivatives of norborneno-diazetine. Z. Acker- und Pflanzenbau *149*, 128–136 (1980)

JUNGK, A.: (G) Effect of ammonium and nitrate nitrogen on the cation-anion balance in plants and its relationship to the yield. Landw. Forsch., Sonderh. 21, 50–63 (1967)

JUNGK, A.: (G) Content of minerals and water in dependence on the development of plants. Z. Pflanzenernähr. Bodenk. *125*, 119–129 (1970)

JURINAK, J.J. and INOUYE, T.S.: Some aspects of zinc and copper phosphate formation in aqueous systems. Soil Sci. Amer. Proc. *26*, 144–147 (1962)

JYUNG, W.H., EHMANN, A., SCHLENDER, K.K. and SCALA, J.: Zinc nutrition and starch metabolism in *Phaseolus vulgaris* L. Plant Physiol. *55*, 414–420 (1975)

KAILA, A.: Forms of newly retained phosphorus in mineral soils. J. Sci. agric. Soc. Finland *36*, 65–76 (1964)

KAILA, A.: Potassium status in different particle size fractions of some finnish soils. J. Sci. Agric. Soc. Finland *39*, 45–56 (1967)

KANDLER, O.: (G) On the question of aerobic fermentation in root meristems. Planta *51*, 544–546 (1958)

KANNAN, S. and JOSEPH, B.: Absorption and transport of Fe and Mn in germinating Sorghum. Plant Physiol. *55*, 1006–1008 (1975)

KANWAR, J.S. and SHAH SINGH, S.: Boron in normal and saline-alkali soils of the irrigated areas of the Punjab. Soil Sci. *92*, 207–211 (1961)

KARLEN, D.L., ARNY, D.C. and WALSH, L.M.: Incidence of chocolate spot *(Pseudomonas syringae)*, Northern corn leaf blight *(Helminthosporium turcicum)* and lodging of corn as influenced by soil fertility. Comm. in: Soil Science and Plant Analysis *4*, 359–368 (1973)

KATZNELSON, H.: The rhizosphere effect of mangels on certain groups of microorganisms. Soil Sci. *62*, 343–354 (1946)

KAVANAU, J.L.: Structure and function in biological membranes, Vol. I, p. 132 ff. Holden-Day, Inc., San Francisco, London, Amsterdam 1965

KAWAI, K.: The relationship of phosphorus adsorption to amorphous aluminium for characterizing andosols. Soil Sci. *129*, 186–190 (1980)

KEENEY, D.R.: Protein and amino acid composition of maize grain as influenced by variety and fertility. J. Sci. Fd Agric. *21*, 182–184 (1970)

KEERTHISINGHE, G. and MENGEL, K.: (G) Phosphate buffer power in various soils and its change due to phosphate ageing. Mitteilung. Dtsch. Bodenkundl. Gesellschaft *29*, 217–230 (1979)

KELLER, P. and DEUEL, H.: (G) Cation exchange equilibrium with dead plant roots. Trans. Comm. II and IV. Int. Soc. Soil Sci., Vol. II, p. 164–168, Hamburg 1958, Verlag Chemie, Weinheim/Bergstr. 1958

KELLEY, P.M. and IZAWA, S.: The role of chloride ion in photosystem II I. Effects of chloride on photosystem II electron transport and hydroxylamine inhibition. Biochim. Biophys. Acta *502*, 198–210 (1978)

KELLY, G.J., LATZKO, E. and GIBBS, M.: Regulatory aspects of photosynthetic carbon metabolism. Ann. Rev. Plant Physiol. *27*, 181–205 (1976)

KEMMLER, G.: (G) Fertilizer application to modern rice- and wheat cultivars in developing countries, p. 545–563. In: Proc. VIIth Fertilizer World Congress, Vienna 1972

KEMP, A.: The effects of K and N dressings on the mineral supply of grazing animals. Potassium and Systems of Grassland Farming. The Potassium Institute, Ltd., 1971, Proc. 1st Colloq. Potass. Inst. Ltd., p. 1–14 (1971)

KEMP, A., DEIJS, W.B., HEMKES, O.J. and VAN ES, A.J.H.: Hypomagnesaemia in milking cows: intake and utilization of magnesium from herbage by lactating cows. Neth. J. agric. Sci. *9*, 134–149 (1961)

KEYS, A.J., BIRD, I.F., CORNELIUS, M.J., LEA, P.J., WALLSGROVE, R.M. and MIFLIN, B.J.: Photorespiratory nitrogen cycle. Nature *275*, 741–743 (1978)

KHAN, A.A. and SAGAR, G.R.: Translocation in tomato: The distribution of the products of photosynthesis of the leaves of a tomato plant during the phase of food production. Hort. Res. *7*, 60–69 (1967)

KHASAWNEH, F.E. and DOLL, E.C.: The use of phosphate rock for direct applications to soils. Adv. Agron. *30*, 159–206 (1978)

KICK, K.: (G) On th nutrient content of Egyptian soils with particular reference to the micronutrients Cu, Zn and B. Z. Pflanzenernähr. Düng. Bodenk. *100*, 102–114 (1963)

KILBOURN, B.T., DUNITZ, J.D., PIODA, L.A.R. and SIMON, W.: Structure of the K+ complex with nonactin, a macrotetrolide antibiotic possessing highly specific K^+ transport properties. J. Mol. Biol. *30*, 559–563 (1967)

KIRKBY, E.A.: Influence of ammonium and nitrate nutrition on the cation-anion balance and nitrogen and carbohydrate metabolism of white mustard plants grown in dilute nutrient solutions. Soil Sci. *105*, 133–141 (1968)

KIRKBY, E.A.: Ion uptake and ionic balance in plants in relation to the form of nitrogen nutrition. In: I.H.RORISON: Ecological Aspects of the Mineral Nutrition of Plants, p. 215–235. British Ecological Society, Symposium No. 9 (1969)

KIRKBY, E.A.: Recycling of potassium in plants considered in relation to ion uptake and organic acid accumulation. In: Plant Analysis and Fertilizer Problems, Vol. 2, p. 557–568. Proc. 7th Intern. Colloq. Hanover 1974

KIRKBY, E.A.: Maximizing calcium uptake. Comm. Soil Sci Plant Anal. *10*, 89–113 (1979)

KIRKBY, E.A.: Plant growth in relation to nitrogen supply. In: CLARKE, F.E. and ROSSWALL, T. eds. Terrestrial Nitrogen Cycles, Processes, Ecosystem Strategies and Management Impacts, p. 249–267, Ecol Bull Stockholm *33* (1981)

KIRKBY, E.A. and ARMSTRONG, M.J.: Nitrate uptake by roots as regulated by nitrate assimilation in the shoot of castor oil plants. Plant Physiol *65*, 286–290 (1980)

KIRKBY, E.A., ARMSTRONG, M.J. and LEGGETT, J.E.: Potassium recirculation in tomato plants in relation to potassium supply. J. Plant Nutr. *3*, 955–966 (1981)

KIRKBY, E.A. and HUGHES, A.D.: Some aspects of ammonium and nitrate nutrition in plant metabolism, p.69–77. In: E.A. KIRKBY: Nitrogen Nutrition of the Plant, Univ. of Leeds 1970

KIRKBY, E.A. and KNIGHT, A.H.: The influence of the level of nitrate nutrition on ion uptake and assimilation, organic acid accumulation and cation-anion balance in whole tomato plants. Plant Physiol. *60*, 349–353 (1977)

KIRKBY, E.A. and MENGEL, K.: Ionic balance in different tissues of the tomato plant in relation to nitrate, urea or ammonium nutrition. Plant Physiol. *42*, 6–14 (1967)

KIRKBY, E.A. and MENGEL, K.: Preliminary observations on the effect of urea nutrition on the growth and nitrogen metabolism of sunflower plants. In: E.A. KIRKBY: Nitrogen Nutrition of the Plant, p. 35–38. The University of Leeds 1970

KIRKBY, E.A. and MENGEL, K.: The role of magnesium in plant nutrition. Z. Pflanzenern. Bodenk. H. 2, 209–222 (1976)

KLAPP, E.: (G) Textbook of Husbandry and Crop. Science. 3rd. ed., p. 63. P.-Parey-Verlag, Berlin 1951

KLEPPER, L. and HAGEMAN, R.H.: The occurrence of nitrate reductase in apple leaves. Plant Physiol. *44*, 110–114 (1969)

KLIEWER, M. and EVANS, H.J.: Physiological studies on the B_{12} coenzyme content of nodules from legumes and alder of *Rhizobium* species. Plant Physiol. *37*, 6–7 (1962)

KLIEWER, M. and EVANS, H.J.: B_{12} coenzyme content of the nodules from legumes, alder and of *Rhizobium meliloti*. Nature *194*, 108 (1962)

KLIEWER, M. and EVANS, H.J.: Identification of cobamide coenzyme in nodules of symbionts and isolation of the B_{12} coenzyme from *Rhizobium meliloti*. Plant Physiol. *38*, 55–59 (1963)

KLIEWER, M. and EVANS, H.J.: Cobamide coenzyme contents of soybean nodules and nitrogen fixing bacteria in relation to physiological conditions. Plant Physiol. *38*, 99–104 (1963)

KLIEWER, W.M.: Influence of environment on metabolism of organic acids and carbohydrates in *Vitis vinifera*. I. Temperature. Plant Physiol. *39*, 869–880 (1964)

KLUGE, M.: The flow of carbon in Crassulacean Acid Metabolism (CAM). In: Photosynthesis II, Encycl. Plant Physiol. New Series, Vol. 6 (M. GIBBS and E. LATZKO eds.) p. 112–123. Springer-Verlag Berlin, Heidelberg, New York 1979

KNAUER, N.: (G) The effect of increasing phosphate rates on soil and plant during a long term fertilizer trial. Z. Acker- u. Pflanzenbau *124*, 41–58 (1966)

KNAUER, N. and SIMON, C.: (G) The effect of nitrogen application on the yield and on the content of nitrate, minerals and oxalic acid in spinach. Z. Acker- u. Pflanzenbau *128*, 197–220 (1968)

KNIGHT, A. H. and CROOKE, W. M.: Interaction between nickel and calcium in plants. Nature *178*, 220 (1956)

KOBLET, W.: (G) Translocation of assimilates in grapes and the effect of the leaf area on the yield and the quality of grapes. Die Weinwissenschaft *24*, 277–319 (1969)

KOCH, K.: (G) Culm stability and lodging susceptibility of cereals supplied with chloro-choline-chloride (CCC). Diss. Justus-Liebig-Universität Giessen 1968

KOCH, K. and MENGEL, K.: The influence of potassium nutritional status on the absorption and incorporation of nitrate nitrogen. In: Plant Analysis and Fertiliser Problems, Vol. I, p. 209–218. Proc. 7th Intern. Colloq. Hanover 1974

KOCH, K. and MENGEL, K.: The effect of K on N utilization by spring wheat during grain formation. Agron. J. *69*, 477–480 (1977)

KÖHN, W.: (G) Effect of long term tillage-fertilization and rotation measurements on chemical and physical properties and on the yield level of a loamy sand soil. Part 2. Long term changes in yield and investigations on yield components of cereals. Bayerisch. Landw. Jahrbuch Heft 4, 419–442 (1976)

KÖHNLEIN, J. and KNAUER, N.: (G) Results of long term fertilizer trials with phosphate and potash. Schriftenreihe der Landw. Fakultät der Univ. Kiel, Heft 39 (1965)

KÖTTGEN, P.: (G) Determination of easily soluble nutrients released by electrical current, a means of estimation of the fertility status of agricultural soils. Z. Pflanzenernähr. Düng. Bodenk. *29A*, 275–290 (1933)

KOLENBRANDER, G. J.: Does leaching of fertilizers affect the quality of ground water at the waterworks? Stikstof *15*, 8–15 (1972)

KOMOR, E., ROTTER, M., WALDHAUSER, J., MARTIN, E. and CHO, B. H.: Sucrose proton symport for phloem loading in the *Ricinus* seedling. Ber. Deutsch. Bot. Ges. *93*, 211–219 (1980)

KOMOR, E. and TANNER, W.: Can energy generated by sugar efflux be used for ATP synthesis in *Chlorella*. Nature *248*, 511–512 (1974)

KONZAK, C. F., POLLE, E. and KITTRICK, J. A.: Screening several crops for aluminium tolerance. In: M. J. WRIGHT, ed. Plant Adaptation to Mineral Stress in Problem Soils p. 311–327 Cornell University 1976

KOONTZ, H. V. and FOOTE, R. E.: Transpiration and calcium deposition by unifoliate leaves of *Phaseolus vulgaris* differing in maturity. Physiol. Plant. *19*, 313–321 (1966)

KORENSKY, F. and NEUBERG, J.: Autumn application of anhydrous ammonia for spring cultures in Czechoslovakia. Rostlinná Výroba *14*, 803–814 (1968)

KOVANCI, I., HAKERLERLER, H. and HÖFNER, W.: (G) Cause of iron chlorosis in mandarins *(Citrus reticulata blanco)* in the Aegean area. Plant and Soil *50*, 193–205 (1978)

KOWALENKO, C. G. and CAMERON, D. R.: Nitrogen transformations in soil-plant systems in three years of field experiments using tracer and non-tracer methods on an ammonium-fixing soil. Can. J. Soil Sci. *58*, 195–208 (1977)

KOZMA, P.: Control of the Nutrition of the Cultivated Plants. 3rd International Colloqu. on the Control of Plant Nutrition, Vol. I and II, Akademiai Kiado, Budapest (1975)

KRAMER, D., RÖMHELD, V., LANDSBERG, E. and MARSCHNER, H.: Induction of transfer-cell formation by iron deficiency in the root epidermis of *Helianthus annuus* L. Planta, *147*, 335–339 (1980)

KRAMER, P. J.: Water relations of plant cells and tissues. Ann. Rev. Plant Physiol. *6*, 253–272 (1955)

KRAUSE, W.: (G) Flora and vegetation on serpentine sites of the Balkan. Z. Pflanzenernähr. Düng. Bodenk. *99*, 97–107 (1962)

KRAUSE, W.: (G) Soils and plant Communities. In: Encyclopedia of Plant Physiology. W. Ruhland ed. Springer-Verlag, Berlin, Vol. 4, 807–850 (1958)

KRAUSKOPF, K.B.: Geochemistry of Micronutrients. In: Micronutrients in Agriculture, p. 7–40. Soil Sci. Soc. of America, Madison/USA 1972

KRAUSS, A.: Influence of nitrogen nutrition on tuber initiation of potatoes. In: Physiological Aspects of Crop Productivity, p. 175–184 Int. Potash Inst., Bern 1980

KRAUSS, A. and MARSCHNER, H.: (G) Influence of the nitrogen nutrition of potatoes on tuber induction and tuber growth rate. Z. Pflanzenernähr. Bodenk. *128*, 153–168 (1971)

KRAUSS, A. and MARSCHNER, H.: (G) Influence of nitrogen nutrition and application of growth regulators on tuber initiation in potato plants. Z. Pflanzenern. Bodenk. Heft *2*, 143–155 (1976)

KRENZER, E.G., MOSS, D.N. and CROOKSTON, R.K.: Carbon dioxide compensation points of flowering plants. Plant Physiol. *56*, 194–206 (1975)

KRÜGER, W.: The influence of fertilizers on fungal disease of maize. In: Fertilizer Use and Plant Health, p. 145–156. Int. Potash Inst., Bern 1976

KUBOTA, J. and ALLAWAY, W.H.: Geographic distribution of trace element problems, p. 525–554. In: Micronutrients in Agriculture, ed. by J.J.Mortvedt, P.M.Giordano and W.L.Lindsay. Soil Sci. Soc. America, Madison/USA 1972

KÜHN, H.: (G) Possibilities for the enrichment of vegetables with micronutrients by fertilizer application. Landw. Forsch., 16. Sonderh., 112–120 (1962)

KÜHN, H., HÖFNER, W. and LINSER, H.: (G) Increased shortening of cereal plants by combined application of growth regulators (CCC, Ethephon, Ancymidol). Landw. Forsch. Sonderh. 35, 271–276 (1978)

KÜHN, H. and SCHAUMLÖFFEL, E.: (G) The effect of high copper application on the growth of cereals. Landw. Forsch. *14*, 82–98 (1961)

KÜHN, H., SCHUSTER, W. and LINSER, H.: (G) Marked reduction in culm length of winter rye by combined application of CCC and ethephon under field conditions. Z. Acker- und Pflanzenbau *145*, 22–30 (1977)

KÜRTEN, P.W.: (G) Fertilizer application for the production of wheat with high baking quality, p. 32–49. In: Qualität im Getreidebau, Landw. Schriftenreihe Boden und Pflanze der Ruhr-Stickstoff AG, Bochum Nr. 11, 1964

KUNTZE, H. and BARTELS, R.: (G) Nutrient status and yield production on peat grassland. Landw. Forsch. Sonderh. *31*/I, 208–219 (1975)

KURSANOV, A.L. and VYSKREBENTZEVA, E.: (F) The role of potassium in plant metabolism and the biosynthesis of compounds important for the quality of agricultural products. In: Potassium and the Quality of Agricultural Products. Proc., p. 401–420. 8th Congr. Intern. Potash Institute, Berne 1966

KURSANOV, A.L.: Transport of assimilates and sugar storage in sugar beet. Z. Zuckerind. *24*, 478–487 (1974)

KURVITS, A. and KIRKBY, E.A.: The uptake of nutrients by sunflower plants *(Helianthus annuus)* growing in a continuous flowing culture system supplied with nitrate or ammonium as nitrogen source Z. Pflanzenernähr. Bodenk. *143*, 140–149 (1980)

KYLIN, A.: The uptake and metabolism of sulfate by deseeded wheat plants. Physiol. Plant *6*, 775–795 (1953)

KYLIN, A. and QUATRANO, R.S.: Metabolic and biochemical aspects on salt tolerance. In: A. POLJAKOFF-MAYBER and J.GALE: Ecological Studies *15*, p. 147–167. Springer-Verlag, Berlin, Heidelberg, New York 1975

LABANAUSKAS, C.K.: Manganese, p. 264–285. In: H.D.CHAPMAN: Diagnostic criteria for plant and soils. University of California 1966

LACHANCE, R. O. and OUELLETTE, G. J.: Pathological histology of boron-deficient alfalfa stems and leaves as an aid in diagnosing alfalfa yellows. Canad. J. Agr. Sci. *34*, 488–493 (1954)

LACHOVER, D. and ARNON, I.: (F) Observations on the relationship between heavy potassium deficiency and poor quality of several agricultural products of major crops. In: Potassium and the Quality of Agricultural Products, p. 439–464. Proc. 8th Congr. Int. Potash Inst., Bern 1966

LAETSCH, W. M.: The C-4 syndrome: A structural analysis. Ann. Rev. Plant Physiol. *25*, 27–52 (1974)

LÄUCHLI, A.: Translocation of inorganic solutes. Ann. Rev. Plant Physiol. *23*, 197–218 (1972)

LÄUCHLI, A.: Function of the root in relation to the structural aspects and localization of ions. XII. Intern. Botanical Congr. Leningrad 1975

LÄUCHLI, A., KRAMER, D., PITMAN, M. G. and LÜTTGE, U.: Ultrastructure of xylem parenchyma cells of barley roots in relation to ion transport to the xylem. Planta *119*, 85–99 (1974)

LÄUCHLI, A. and PFLÜGER, R.: Potassium transport through plant cell membranes and metabolic role of potassium in plants. In: Potassium Research – Review and Trends. p. 111–163. Potash Inst., Bern 1978

LÄUCHLI, A., SPURR, A. R. and EPSTEIN, E.: Lateral movement of ions into the xylem of corn roots. II. Evaluation of a stelar pump. Plant Physiol. *48*, 118–124 (1971)

LÅG, J.: Relationships between the chemical composition of the precipitation and the contents of exchangeable ions in the humus layer of natural soils. Acta Agric. Scand. *18*, 148–152 (1968)

LAGERWERFF, J. V.: Lead, mercury and cadmium as environmental contaminants, p. 593–636. In: Micronutrients in Agriculture, ed. by J. J. Mortvedt, P. M. Giordano and W. L. Lindsay. Soil Sci. Soc. America, Madison/USA 1972

LAGERWERFF, J. V. and BOLT, G. H.: Theoretical and experimental analysis of Gapon's equation for ion exchange. Soil Sci. *87*, 217–222 (1959)

LAGERWERFF, J. V. and EAGLE, H. E.: Osmotic and specific effects of excess salts on beans. Plant Physiol. *36*, 472–477 (1961)

LAMBERT, R. G. and LINCK, A. J.: Comparison of the uptake of P-32 and K-42 intact alfalfa and oat roots. Plant Physiol. *39*, 920–924 (1964)

LANGSTON, R.: Studies on marginal movement of cobalt-60 in cabbage. Proc. Amer. Soc. hort. Sci. *68*, 366–369 (1956)

LARCHER, W.: (G) The efficiency of CO_2 assimilation of higher plants under laboratory conditions and field conditions. Festschrift f. Prof. Dr. O. Stocker, Stolzen/Weser 1963

LARKUM, A. W. D.: Ionic relations of chloroplasts *in vivo*. Nature *218*, 447–449 (1968)

LARSEN, S.: The use of ^{32}P in studies on the uptake of phosphorus by plants. Plant and Soil *4*, 1–10 (1952)

LARSEN, S.: Isoionic exchange of phosphate in paddy soils. Plant and Soil *27*, 401–407 (1967a)

LARSEN, S.: Soil phosphorus. Adv. in Agron. *19*, 131–206 (1967)

LARSEN, S. and COOKE, J. J.: The influence of radioactive phosphate levels on the absorption of phosphate by plants and on the determination of labile soil phosphate. Plant and Soil *14*, 43–48 (1961)

LARSEN, S. and SUTTON, C. D.: The influence of soil volume on the absorption of soil phosphorus by plants and on the determination of labile soil phosphorus. Plant and Soil *18*, 77–84 (1963)

LARSEN, S. and WIDDOWSON, A. E.: Chemical composition of soil solution. J. Sci. Fd Agric. *19*, 693–695 (1968)

LATHWELL, D. J. and PEECH, M.: Interpretation of chemical soil tests. Cornell Univ. Agric. Exp. Stat., New York State College of Agriculture, Ithaca, New York, Bulletin 995, October 1964

LATIMORE, M., GIDDENS, J. and ASHLEY, D. A.: Effect of ammonium and nitrate nitrogen upon photosynthate supply and nitrogen fixation by soybeans. Crop Sci. *17*, 399–404 (1977)

LAVES, D.: (G) Potassium transformation in soil. Arch. Acker- u. Pflanzenbau u. Bodenk. *22* (8), 521–528 (1978)

LAVY, T.L. and BARBER, S.A.: Movement of molybdenum in the soil and its effect on availability to the plant. Soil Sci. Soc. Amer. Proc. *28*, 93–97 (1964)

LAWRENCE, T., WARDER, F.G. and ASHFORD, R.: Nitrate accumulation in intermediate wheatgrass. Canad. J. Plant Sci. *48*, 85–88 (1968)

LAZAROFF, N. and PITMAN, M.G.: Calcium and magnesium uptake by barley seedlings. Aust. J. biol. Sci. *19*, 991–1005 (1966)

LEA, P.J. and MIFLIN, B.J.: Alternative route for nitrogen assimilation in higher plants. Nature *251*, 614–616 (1974)

LEACH, G.: Energy and Food Production. IPC Science and Technology Press, Guildford 1976

LEE, C., MILLER, G.W. and WELKIE, G.W.: The effects of hydrogen fluoride and wounding on respiratory enzymes in soybean leaves. Air Water Pollut. Int. J. *10*, 169–181 (1965)

LEE, S.G. and ARNOFF, S.: Boron in plants: A biochemical role. Science *158*, 798–799 (1967)

LEGGETT, J.E. and EPSTEIN, E.: Kinetics of sulfate absorption by barley roots. Plant Physiol. *31*, 222–226 (1956)

LEGGETT, J.E. and GILBERT, W.A.: Magnesium uptake by soybeans. Plant Physiol. *44*, 1182–1186 (1969)

LEHNINGER, A.L.: Biochemistry, the Molecular Basis of Cell Structure and Function. Worth Publishers, Inc., New York 1975

LEHR, J.J. and VAN WESEMAEL, J.G.: (N) Volatilization of ammonia on calcareous soils. Landbouwk. Tijdschr. *73*, 1156–1168 (1961)

LEMON, E. and HOUTTE, R. VAN: Ammonia exchange at the land surface. Agron. J. *72*, 876–883 (1980)

LENDZIAN, K. and BASSHAM, J.A.: NADPH/NADH ratios in photosynthesizing reconstituted chloroplasts. Biochim. Biophys. Acta *430*, 478–489 (1976)

LENKA, D. and DASTANE, N.G.: Water management practises for rice. Ann. Rep. Chakuli Centre, Irri. Res. Scheme, Major River Valley Project Areas. ICAR, New Delhi 1970

LEONARD, R.T. and HODGES, T.K.: Characterization of plasma membrane-associated adenosine triphosphatase activity of oat roots. Plant Physiol. *52*, 6–12 (1973)

LESSANI, H. and MARSCHNER, H.: Relation between salt tolerance and long distance transport of sodium and chloride in various crop species. Aust. J. Plant Physiol. *5*, 27–37 (1978)

LETEY, J., STOLZY, L.H., BLANK, G.B. and LUNT, O.R.: Effect of temperature on oxygen-diffusion rates and subsequent shoot growth, root growth and mineral content of two plant species. Soil Sci. *92*, 314–321 (1961)

LEWIN, J.C.: Physiological studies of the boron requirement of the diatom *Cylindrotheca fusiformis*. J. Exp. Bot. *17*, 473–479 (1966)

LEWIN, J. and REIMANN, B.E.F.: Silicon and plant growth. Ann. Rev. Plant Physiol. *20*, 289–304 (1969)

LEWIS, D.A. and TATCHELL, J.A.: Energy in UK agriculture. J. Sci. Food Agric. *30*, 449–457 (1979)

LEWIS, D.G. and QUIRK, J.P.: Phosphate diffusion in soil and uptake by plants. III. P^{31}-movement and uptake by plants as indicated by P^{32}-autoradiography. Plant and Soil *26*, 445–453 (1967)

LEWIS, D.G. and QUIRK, J.P.: Phosphate diffusion in soil and uptake by plants. IV. Computed uptake by model roots as a result of diffusive flow. Plant and Soil *26*, 454–468 (1967)

LEWIS, J.C. and POWERS, W.L.: Antagonistic action of chlorides on the toxicity of iodides to corn. Plant Physiol. *16*, 393–398 (1941)

LIEBIG, J.: (G) The Organic Chemistry and its Application on Agriculture and Physiology. p. 167 Verlag Viehweg, Braunschweig 1841

LIN, W. and HANSON, J.B.: Cell potentials, cell resistance, and proton fluxes in corn root tissues. Plant Physiol. *58*, 276–282 (1976)

610

LINDSAY, W. L.: Zinc in soils and plant nutrition. Adv. in Agron. *24*, 147–186 (1972)

LINDSAY, W. L.: Inorganic phase equilibria of micronutrients in soils, p. 41–57. In: Micronutrients in Agriculture, Soil Sci. Soc. America, Inc., Madison/USA 1972

LINDSAY, W. L.: Role of chelation in micronutrient availability. In: E. W. CARSON: The Plant Root and Its Environment, p. 507–524. University Press of Virginia 1974

LINDSAY, W. L., HODGSON, J. F. and NORVELL, W. A.: The physicochemical equilibrium of metal chelates in soils and their influence on the availability of metal cations. Trans. Comm. II and IV. Int. Soc. Soil Sci. (Aberdeen 1966), p. 305–316 (1967)

LINDSTROM, E. S., NEWTON, J. W. and WILSON, P. W.: The relationship between photosynthesis and nitrogen fixation. Proc. Nat. Acad. Sci. US *38*, 392–396 (1952)

LINGLE, J. C., TIFFIN, L. O. and BROWN, J. C.: Iron-uptake transport of soybeans as influenced by other cations. Plant Physiol. *38*, 71–76 (1963)

LINSER, H. and HERWIG, K.: (G) Investigations into the relationship between nutrient uptake and the osmotic pressure of the outer solution. Protoplasma *LVII*, 588–600 (1963)

LINSER, H. and HERWIG, K.: (G) Relationships between wind, transpiration and nutrient translocation in flax with particular regard to a varied water and potash application. Kali-Briefe, Fachgeb. 2, 2. Folge (1968)

LINSER, H. and KÜHN, H.: (G) Levels and timing of chlorocholine chloride application to spring wheat, in order to shorten the length of the culm. Z. Pflanzenernähr. Düng. Bodenk. *101*, 206–210 (1963)

LINSER, H., KÜHN, H. and SCHLÖGL, G.: (G) A field technique for distinguishing between sulphur and nitrogen deficiency. p. 90–103 V. Simposio Internazionale di Agrochimica su 'Lo zolfo in agricoltura', Palermo 1964

LINSER, H., MAYR, H. and BODO, G.: (G) Effect of chlorocholine chloride on spring wheat. Bodenkultur *12*, 279–280 (1961)

LISK, D. J.: Trace metals in soils, plants & animals. Adv. in Agron. *24*, 261–325 (1972)

LOCASCIO, S. J., WARREN, G. F. and WILCOX, G. E.: The effect of phosphorus placement on uptake of phosphorus and growth of direct seeded tomatoes. Amer. Soc. Hort. Sci. *76*, 503–514 (1960)

LOCHER, J. T. and BROUWER, R.: Preliminary data on the transport of water, potassium and nitrate in intact and bleeding maize plants. Mededeling 238 van het I.B.S. (Wageningen), p. 41–49 (1964)

LODISH, H. F. and ROTHMAN, J. E.: The assembly of cell membranes Sci. American *240:* 38–53 (1979)

LÖHNIS, M. P.: Effect of magnesium and calcium supply on the uptake of manganese by various crop plants. Plant and Soil *12*, 339–376 (1960)

LONERAGAN, J. F.: The availability and absorption of trace elements in soil-plant systems and their relation to movement and concentrations of trace elements in plants. In D. J. D. Nicholas and A. R. Egan: Trace Elements in Soil-Plant-Animal Systems, p. 109–134. Academic Press London 1975

LONERAGAN, J. F. and ASHER, C. J.: Response of plants to phosphate concentration in solution culture. II. Rate of phosphate absorption and its relation to growth. Soil Sci. *103*, 311–318 (1967)

LONERAGAN, J. F., GLADSTONES, J. S. and SIMMONS, W. J.: Mineral elements in temperate crop and pasture plants. II. Calcium. Aust. J. agric. Res. *19*, 353–364 (1968)

LONERAGAN, J. F. and SNOWBALL, K.: Calcium requirements of plants. Aust. J. agric. Res. *20*, 465–478 (1969)

LOUGHEED, E. C., MURR, D. P. and MILLER, S. R.: Effects of calcium and daminozide on ethylene production and softening of apple fruits Experientia *35*, 43–45 (1979)

LOOMIS, R. S., WILLIAMS, W. A. and HALL, A. E.: Agricultural productivity. Ann. Rev. Plant Physiol. *22*, 431–463 (1971)

LORENZ, H.: Nitrate ammonium and amino acids in bleeding sap of tomato plants in relation to the form and concentration of nitrogen in the medium. Plant and Soil *45*, 169–176 (1976)

611

LOUÉ, A.: (F) Investigations into the potash nutrition and fertilization of grapes. Expérimentation et études agronomiques (1968). Société Commerciale des Potasses d'Alsace, Services Agronomiques

LOUÉ, A.: (F) Plant analysis for the estimation of nutrient requirement, especially the potash requirement of potatoes. In: Le contôrle de l'alimentation des plantes cultivées (PAL KOZMA, ed.) p. 265–282. Akademiai Kiado, Budapest 1975

LOUÉ, A.: (F) Average effect of potassium fertilization to arable crops in long term field trials. Potash Review (Berne) Subj. 16, Suite 79th No. 4 (1979)

LOW, A.J. and ARMITAGE, E.R.: The composition of the leachate through cropped and uncropped soils in lysimeters compared with that of the rain. Plant and Soil 33, 393–411 (1970)

LOWTHER, W.L. and LONERAGAN, J.F.: Calcium and nodulation in subterranean clover (Trifolium subterraneum L.). Plant Physiol. 43, 1362–1366 (1968)

LUCAS, R.E. and DAVIS, J.F.: Relationships between pH values of organic soils and availabilities of 12 plant nutrients. Soil Sci. 92, 177–182 (1961)

LUCAS, R.E. and KNEZEK, B.D.: Climatic and soil conditions promoting micronutrient deficiencies in plants. In: Micronutrients in Agriculture, p. 265–288 (1972)

LÜTTGE, U., CRAM, W.J. and LATIES, G.G.: The relationship of salt stimulated respiration to localized ion transport in carrot tissue. Z. Pflanzenphysiol. 64, 418–426 (1971)

LÜTTGE, U., KLUGE, M. and BALL, E.: Effects of osmotic gradients on vacuolar malic acid storage. Plant Physiol. 56, 613–616 (1975)

LUNDEGÅRDH, H.: (G) The nutrient uptake of plants. Verlag G. Fischer, Jena 1932

LUNDEGÅRDH, H.: (G) Leaf analysis. Verlag G. Fischer, Jena 1945

MAAS, E.V.: Calcium uptake by excised maize roots and interactions with alkali cations. Plant Physiol. 44, 985–989 (1969)

MAAS, E.V. and LEGGETT, J.E.: Uptake of ^{86}Rb and K by excised maize roots. Plant Physiol. 43, 2054–2056 (1968)

MAAS, E.V., MOORE, D.P. and MASON, B.J.: Influence of calcium and magnesium on manganese absorption. Plant Physiol. 44, 796–800 (1969)

MacDONALD, I.R., MACKLON, A.E.S. and MacLEOD, R.W.G.: Energy supply and light-enhanced chloride uptake in wheat laminae. Plant Physiol. 56, 699–702 (1975)

MACHOLD, O.: (G) Investigations on metabolically defective tomato mutants. III Effect of ammonium and nitrate nitrogen on the chlorophyll content. Flora, Abt. A 157, 536–551 (1967)

MACHOLD, O.: (G) Effect of nutritional conditions on the status of iron in leaves, on the chlorophyll content, and on the activity of catalase and peroxidase. Flora, Ab. A. 159, 1–25 (1968)

MACHOLD, O. and SCHOLZ, G.: (G) Iron status and chlorophyll synthesis in higher plants. Naturwiss. 56, 447–452 (1969)

MACHOLD, O. and STEPHAN, U.W.: The function of iron in porphyrin and chlorophyll biosynthesis. Phytochemistry 8, 2189–2192 (1969)

MACKLON, A.E.S. and DEKOCK, P.C.: Physiological gradients in the potato tuber. Physiol. Plant. 20, 421–429 (1967)

MacLEOD, L.B.: Effects of N, P, and K and their interactions on the yield and kernel weight of barley in hydroponic culture. Agron. J. 61, 26–29 (1969)

MacLEOD, L.B. and JACKSON, L.P.: Effect of concentration of the Al ion on root development and establishment of legume seedlings. Can. J. Soil Sci. 45, 221–234 (1965)

MAERTENS, M.C.: (F) Experimental investigation into the nutrition of maize with minerals and water. Comparison between the requirement of the plant and the uptake potential of the roots for nitrogen, phosphorus, and potassium. C.R. Acad. Sc. (Paris) 273, Serie D, 682–684 (1971)

MAGISTAD, O.C., REITEMEIER, R.F. and WILCOX, L.V.: Determination of soluble salts in soils. Soil Sci. 59, 65–75 (1945)

MAHAPATRA, J.C., PRASAD, R. and LEELAVATHI, C.R.: Proc. FAJ Symposium on use of NPK-Complex Fertilizers based on nitrophosphate process. Fertilizer Ass. of India, New Delhi (1973)

MAIZEL, J.V., BENSON, A.A. and TOLBERT, N.E.: Identification of phosphoryl choline as an important constituent of plant saps. Plant Physiol. *31*, 407–408 (1956)

MAJOR, D.J. and CHARNETSKI, W.A.: Distribution of C-14 labelled assimilates in rape plants. Crop Sci. *16*, 530–532 (1976)

MAKMUR, A., GERLOFF, G.G. and GABELMAN, W.H.: Physiology and inheritance of efficiency in potassium utilization in tomatoes grown under potassium stress. J. Amer. Soc. Hort. Sci. *103* (4), 545–549 (1978)

MALAVOLTA, E., DANTAS, J.P., MORIAS, R.S. and NOGUEIRA, F.D.: Calcium problems in Latin America. Comm. in Soil Sci. and Plant Anal. *10*, 29–40 (1979)

MALEK, F. and BAKER, D.A.: Proton co-transport of sugars in phloem loading. Planta *135*, 297–299 (1977)

MALLISSIOVAS, N.: (G) Iron chlorosis of vine – causal relationships between inducing factors and processes. Diss. Fachbereich 19 Ernährungswissenschaften, Justus Liebig-University Giessen 1980

MALONE, C., KOEPPE, D.E. and MILLER, R.J.: Localization of lead accumulated in corn plants. Plant Physiol. *53*, 388–394 (1974)

MALOTH, S. and PRASAD, R.: Relative efficiency of rock phosphate and superphosphate for cowpea *(Vigna sinensis Savi)* fodder. Plant and Soil *45*, 295–300 (1976)

MALQUORI, A., RISTORI, G. and VIDRRICH, V.: Biological weathering of potassium silicates: I. Biotite. Agrochimica *19*, 522–529 (1975)

MANDAL, S.C.: Phosphorus management of our soils. Need for a more rational approach. 40th Sess. Indian Soc. of Soil Science, Bhubaneswar 1975

MARC, J. and PALMER, J.H.: Relationship between water potential and leaf inflorescence initiation in *Helianthus annuus*. Physiol. Plant. *36*, 101–104 (1976)

MARCELLE, R. and BODSON, M.: Greenback disease and mineral content of tomato fruit. Journal of Plant Nutrition *1*, 207–217 (1979)

MARINOS, N.C.: Studies on submicroscopic aspects of mineral deficiencies. I. Calcium deficiency in the shoot apex of barley. Am. J. Bot. *49*, 834–849 (1962)

MARQUARD, R., KÜHN, H. and LINSER, H.: (G) The effect of the sulphur nutrition on the synthesis of mustard oils. Z. Pflanzenernähr. Bodenk. *121*, 221–230 (1968)

MARSCHNER, H.: Why can sodium replace potassium in plants? In: Potassium in Biochemistry and Physiology, p. 50–63. Proc. 8th Collow. Int. Potash Inst., Bern 1971

MARSCHNER, H.: (G) Effect of O_2 supply to roots on mineral uptake and plant growth. In: Pseudogley & Gley, Trans. Comm. V and VI of the Int. Soc. Soil Sci., 541–555 (1972)

MARSCHNER, H.: Mechanisms of regulation of mineral nutrition in higher plants, p. 99–109. In: Mechanisms of Regulation of Plant Growth, ed. R.L.Bieleski. A.R.Ferguson and M.M.Cresswell. Bulletin 12, The Royal Society of New Zealand 1974

MARSCHNER, H.: Calcium nutrition of higher plants. Neth. J. agric. Sci. *22*, 275–282 (1974)

MARSCHNER, H.: (G) Nutritional and yield physiological aspects of plant nutrition. Angew. Botanik *52*, 71–87 (1978)

MARSCHNER, H.: General Introduction to the Mineral Nutrition of Plants. In LÄUCHLI, A. and BIELESKI, R.L., eds., Encyclopedia of Plant Physiology, New Series Vol. 12, Inorganic Plant Nutrition. Springer-Verlag 1982 (in press)

MARSCHNER, H., HANDLEY, R. and OVERSTREET, R.: Potassium loss and changes in the fine structure of corn root tips induced by H-ion. Plant Physiol. *41*, 1725–1735 (1966)

MARSCHNER, H., KALISCH, K. and RÖMHELD, V.: Mechanism of iron uptake in different plant species. In: Proc. 7th Int. Colloq. Plant Analysis and Fertilizer Problems, p. 273–281. Hannover 1974

MARSCHNER, H. and MENGEL, K.: (G) The effect of Ca and H ions at different metabolic conditions on the membrane permeability of young barley roots. Z. Pflanzenernähr. Düng. Bodenk. *112*, 39–49 (1966)

MARSCHNER, H. and OSSENBERG-NEUHAUS, H.: (G) Effect of 2, 3, 5 tri iodobenzoic acid (TIBA) on calcium transport and cation exchange capacity in sun flowers. Z. Pflanzenphysiologie *85*, 29–44 (1977)

MARSCHNER, H. and POSSINGHAM, J. V.: Effect of K$^+$ and Na$^+$ on growth of leaf discs of sugar beet and spinach. Z. Pflanzenphysiol. *75*, 6–16 (1975)

MARSCHNER, H. and RICHTER, CH.: (G) Calcium translocation in roots of maize and bean seedlings. Plant and Soil *40*, 193–210 (1974)

MARSCHNER, H. and SCHROPP, A.: (G) Comparative studies on the sensitivity of six rootstock varieties of grapevine to phosphate-induced Zn deficiency. Vitis *16*, 79–88 (1977)

MARSH, H. V. jr., EVANS, H. J. and MATRONE, G.: Investigations on the role of iron in chlorophyll metabolism. II. Effect of iron deficiency on chlorophyll synthesis. Plant Physiol. *38*, 638–642 (1963)

MARTIN, J. P.: Bromine, p. 62–64. In: H. D. CHAPMAN: Diagnostic Criteria for Plants and Soils. Univ. of California, Div. of Agric. Sciences 1966

MARTIN, P.: Pathway of translocation of ^{15}N from labelled nitrate or ammonium in kidney bean plants. In; E. A. KIRKBY: Nitrogen Nutrition of the Plant, p. 104–112. The Univ. of Leeds, 1970

MARTIN, W. E. and MATOCHA, J. E.: Plant analysis as an aid in the fertilization of forage crops, p. 393–426. In: Soil Testing and Plant Analysis. Soil Soc. Amer. Inc., Madison, USA 1973

MASCARENHAS, J. P. and MACHLIS, L.: Chemotropic response of the pollen of *Antirrhinum majus* to calcium. Plant Physiol. *39*, 70–77 (1964)

MASSUMI, A.: (G) Investigations into the molybdenum status of plants and soils in Schleswig-Holstein. Diss. d. Landw. Fakultät d. Univ. Kiel 1967

MATHUR, B. N., AGRAWAL, N. K. and SINGH, V. S.: Effect of soil versus foliar application of urea on the yield of American cotton variety '320'. Indian J. agric. Sci. *38*, 811–815 (1968)

MATSUBAYASHI, M., ITO, R., NOMOTO, T., TAKASE, T. and YAMADA, N.: Some properties of paddy field soils. In: Theory and practice of fertilizer application, p. 183–227 (1963)

MAYNARD, D. N.: Nutritional disorders of vegetable crops: A review. Journal of Plant Nutrition *1*, 1–23 (1979)

MAYNARD, D. N. and BARKER, A. V.: Studies in the tolerance of plants to ammonium nutrition. J. Amer. Soc. Hort. Sci. *94*, 235–239 (1969)

MAYNARD, D. N. and BARKER, A. V.: Nitrate content of vegetable crops. Hortscience *7*, 224–226 (1972)

MAYNARD, D. N., BARKER, A. V., MINOTTI, P. L. and PECK, N. H.: Nitrate accumulation in vegetables. Adv. Agron. *28*, 71–118 (1976)

MCAULIFFE, C. F., HALL, N. S., DEAN, L. A. and HENDRICKS, S. B.: Exchange reactions between phosphates and soils. Hydroxylic surfaces of soil minerals. Soil Sci. Soc. Amer. Proc. *12*, 119–123 (1947)

MCCORD, J. M., KEELE, B. B. and FRIDOVICH, I.: An enzyme based theory of obligate anaerobiosis: The physiological function of superoxide dismutase. Proc. Nat. Acad. Sci. USA *68*, 1024–1027 (1971)

MCKENZIE, R. M.: Soil cobalt, p. 83–93. In: D. J. D. NICHOLAS and A. R. EGAN: Trace Elements in Soil-Plant-Animal Systems. Academic Press London 1975

MCLACHLAN, K. D. and DE MARCO, D. G.: The influence of gypsum particle size on pasture response on a sulphur deficient soil. Aust. J. exp. Agric. Anim. Husbandry *8*, 203–209 (1968)

MCLAREN, R. G. and CRAWFORD, D. V.: Studies on soil copper I. The fractionation of Cu in soils. J. Soil Sci. *24*, 172–181 (1973)

MᴄLᴇᴀɴ, E. O., Aᴅᴀᴍs, D. and Fʀᴀɴᴋʟɪɴ, R. E.: Cation exchange capacities of plant roots as related to their nitrogen contents. Soil Sci. Soc. Am. Proc. *20*, 345–347 (1956)

MᴄMɪᴄʜᴀᴇʟ, B. L., Jᴏʀᴅᴀɴ, W. R. and Pᴏᴡᴇʟʟ, R. D.: An effect of water stress of ethylene production by intact cotton petioles. Plant Physiol. *49*, 658–660 (1972)

MᴄNᴇᴀʟ, F. H., Wᴀᴛsᴏɴ, C. A. and Kɪᴛᴛᴀᴍs, H. A.: Effects of dates and rates of nitrogen fertilisation on the quality and field performance of five hard red spring wheat varieties. Agron. J. *55*, 470–472 (1963)

Mᴇɪʀɪ, A., Kᴀᴍʙᴜʀᴏғғ, J. and Pᴏʟᴊᴀᴋᴏғғ-Mᴀʏʙᴇʀ, A.: Response of bean plants to sodium chloride and sodium sulphate salinization. Ann. Bot. *35*, 837–847 (1971)

Mᴇɪʀɪ, A. and Pᴏʟᴊᴀᴋᴏғғ-Mᴀʏʙᴇʀ, A.: Effect of variations in substrate salinity on the water balance and ionic composition of bean leaves. Israel J. Bot. *18*, 99–112 (1969)

Mᴇɪʀɪ, A. and Sʜᴀʟʜᴇᴠᴇᴛ, J.: Crop growth under saline conditions. Ecological Studies Vol. 5, p. 277–290. Springer-Verlag Berlin, Heidelberg, New York 1973

Mᴇɴɢᴇʟ, D. B. and Bᴀʀʙᴇʀ, S. A.: Rate of nutrient uptake per unit of corn root under field conditions. Agron. J. *66*, 399–402 (1974)

Mᴇɴɢᴇʟ, K.: (G) The Donnan distribution of cations in the free space of plant roots and its significance for the active cation uptake. Z. Pflanzenernähr. Düng. Bodenk. *95*, 240–259 (1961)

Mᴇɴɢᴇʟ, K.: Effect of potassium on assimilate conduction to storage tissue. Ber. Deutsch. Bot. Gⴀs. *93*, 353–362 (1980)

Mᴇɴɢᴇʟ, K. and ᴠᴏɴ Bʀᴀᴜɴsᴄʜᴡᴇɪɢ, L. C.: The effect of soil moisture upon the availability of potassium and its influence on the growth of young maize plants *(Zea mays* L.*)*. Soil Sci. *134*, 142–148 (1972)

Mᴇɴɢᴇʟ, K. and Bᴜsᴄʜ, R.: The importance of the potassium buffer power on the critical potassium level in soil. Soil Sci. in press (1982)

Mᴇɴɢᴇʟ, K. and Cᴀsᴘᴇʀ, H.: The effect of soil moisture on the availability of soil nitrate. Pflanzenernähr. Bodenkd. *143*, 617–626 (1980)

Mᴇɴɢᴇʟ, K., Gʀɪᴍᴍᴇ, H. and Nᴇᴍᴇᴛʜ, K.: (G) Potential and actual availability of plant nutrients in soils. Landw. Forsch. *23*/I. Sonderh., 79–91 (1969)

Mᴇɴɢᴇʟ, K. and Hᴀᴇᴅᴇʀ, H. E.: The effect of the nitrogen nutritional status of intact barley plants on the retention of potassium. Z. Pflanzenernähr. Bodenk. *128*, 105–115 (1971)

Mᴇɴɢᴇʟ, K. and Hᴀᴇᴅᴇʀ, H. E.: (G) Photosynthesis and translocation of photosynthates during grain filling in wheat supplied with different K levels. Z. Acker- u. Pflanzenbau *140*, 206–213 (1974)

Mᴇɴɢᴇʟ, K. and Hᴀᴇᴅᴇʀ, H. E.: The effect of potassium and light intensity on the grain yield production of spring wheat. 4th Int. Colloq. on the Control of Plant Nutrition, p. 463–475 (1976)

Mᴇɴɢᴇʟ, K. and Hᴀᴇᴅᴇʀ, H. E.: Effect of potassium supply on the rate of phloem sap exudation and the composition of phloem sap of *Ricinus communis.* Plant Physiol. *59*, 282–284 (1977)

Mᴇɴɢᴇʟ, K., Hᴀɢʜᴘᴀʀᴀsᴛ, M. R. and Kᴏᴄʜ, K.: The effect of potassium on the fixation of molecular nitrogen by root nodules of *Vicia faba.* Plant Physiol. *54*, 535–538 (1974)

Mᴇɴɢᴇʟ, K. and Hᴇʟᴀʟ, M.: (G) The effect of the exchangeable Ca^{++} of young barley roots on the flux of K^+ and phosphate – an interpretation of the Viets effect. Z. Pflanzenphysiol. *57*, 223–234 (1967)

Mᴇɴɢᴇʟ, K. and Hᴇʟᴀʟ, M.: The effect of increasing nitrogen supply on the composition of the soluble amino fraction and yield of spring wheat. In: E. A. Kɪʀᴋʙʏ: Nitrogen Nutrition of the Plant, p. 162–173. The University of Leeds 1970

Mᴇɴɢᴇʟ, K and Mᴀʟʟɪssɪᴏᴠᴀs, N.: (G) Bicarbonate as inducing factor of iron chlorosis in vine *(Vitis vinifera).* Vitis, 20, 235–243 (1981)

Mᴇɴɢᴇʟ, K. and Pғʟüɢᴇʀ, R.: (G) The influence of several salts and several inhibitors on the root pressure of *Zea mays.* Physiol. Plant. *22*, 840–849 (1969)

MENGEL, K. and PFLÜGER, R.: The release of potassium and sodium from young excised roots of *Zea mays* under various efflux conditions. Plant Physiol. *49*, 16–19 (1972)

MENGEL, K. and SCHERER, H.W.: Release of non exchangeable (fixed) soil NH_4^+ under field conditions during the growing season. Soil Sci., *131*, 226–232, 1981

MENGEL, K., SCHERER, H.W. and MALISSIOVAS, N.: (G) Chlorosis from the aspect of soil chemistry and vine nutrition. Mitt. Klosterneuburg *29*, 151–156 (1979)

MENGEL, K., SEÇER, M. and KOCH, K.: Potassium on protein formation and amino acid turnover in developing wheat grain. Agron. J. 73, 74–78 (1981)

MENGEL, K. and VIRO, M.: Effect of potassium supply on the transport of photosynthates to the fruits of tomatoes *(Lycopersicon esculentum)*. Physiol. Plant *30*, 295–300 (1974)

MENGEL, K. and VIRO, M.: The significance of plant energy status for the uptake and incorporation of NH_4-nitrogen by young rice plants. Soil Sci. Plant Nutr. *24*, (3) 407–416 (1978)

MENGEL, K., VIRO, M. and HEHL, G.: Effect of potassium on uptake and incorporation of ammonium-nitrogen of rice plants. Plant and Soil *44*, 547–558 (1976)

MENGEL, K. and WIECHENS, B.: (G) Importance of the non exchangeable soil K fraction on the yield production of rye-grass. Z. Pflanzenernähr. Bodenk. *142*, 836–847 (1979)

MENZEL, R.G. and HEALD, W.R.: Distribution of potassium, rubidium, cesium, calcium and strontium within plants grown in nutrient solutions. Soil Sci. *80*, 287–293 (1955)

MERCER, E.R. and RICHMOND, J.L.: Fate of nutrients in soil: Copper, p. 9. In: Letcombe Laboratory Annual Report (1970)

MERTZ, E.T., BATES, L.S. and NELSON, O.E.: Mutant gene that changes protein composition and increases lysine content of maize endosperm. Science *145*, 279–280 (1964)

MEYER, B.S.: A critical evaluation of the terminology of diffusion phenomena. Plant Physiol. *20*, 142–164 (1945)

MICHAEL, G.: (G) Phosphate fractions in oat grains and spinach related to a varied application of phosphorus. Bodenk. u. Pflanzenernähr. *14*, 148–171 (1939)

MICHAEL, G.: (G) Uptake and distribution of magnesium and its role in higher green plants. Bodenk. u. Pflanzenernähr. *25*, 65–120 (1941)

MICHAEL, G.: (G) The selection potential of plants in mineral uptake. Dt. Akad. d. Landw. Wiss. *VIII*, Heft 4, Berlin 1959

MICHAEL, G. and BERINGER, H.: The role of hormones in yield formation. In: Physiological Aspects of Crop Productivity. p. 85–116, 15th Colloq. Int. Potash Inst., Bern 1980

MICHAEL, G. and BLUME, B.: (G) The influence of a nitrogen application on the protein composition of barley grains. Z. Pflanzenernähr. Düng. Bodenk. *88*, 237–250 (1960)

MICHAEL, G. and MARSCHNER, H.: (G) Phosphate exchange at root surfaces. Z. Bot. *46*, 37–52 (1958)

MICHAEL, G. and MARSCHNER, H.: (G) Influence of varied air humidity and transpiration on mineral uptake and distribution. Z. Pflanzenernähr. Düng. Bodenk. *96*, 200–212 (1962)

MICHAEL, G., MARTIN, P. and OWASSIA, I.: The uptake of ammonium and nitrate from labelled ammonium nitrate in relation to the carbohydrate supply of the roots. In: E.A. KIRKBY: Nitrogen Nutrition of the Plant, Univ. of Leeds, p. 22–29 (1970)

MICHAEL, G., SCHUMACHER, H. and MARSCHNER, H.: (G) Uptake of ammonium and nitrate nitrogen from labelled ammonium nitrate and their distribution in the plant. Z. Pflanzenernähr. Düng. Bodenk. *110*, 225–238 (1965)

MICHAEL, G., WILBERG, E. and KOUHSIAHI-TORK, K.: (G) Boron deficiency induced by high air humidity. Z. Pflanzenernähr. Bodenk. *122*, 1–3 (1969)

MIFLIN, B.J.: Potential for improvement of quantity and quality of plant proteins through scientific research. In: Fertilizer Use and Protein Production, p. 41–62. Intern. Potash Inst., Berne 1975

MIFLIN, B.J. and LEA, P.J.: Amino acid metabolism. Ann. Rev. Plant Physiol. *28*, 299–329 (1977)

616

MILLER, F.P.: Fertilizers and our environment, p. 23–46. In: The Fertilizer Handbook. The Fertilizer Institute, Washington 1972

MILLER, G.W.: Carbon dioxide-bicarbonate absorption, accumulation, effects on various plant metabolic reactions, and possible relations to lime induced chlorosis. Soil Sci. 89, 241–245 (1960)

MILLER, J.E. and MILLER, G.W.: Effects of fluoride on mitochondrial activity in higher plants. Physiol Plant. 32, 115–121 (1974)

MILLER, K.R.: Die photosynthetisierende Membran. Spektrum d. Wissenschaft 12, 37–45 (1979)

MILLER, L.P. and FLEMION, F.: The role of minerals in phytochemistry. Phytochemistry Van Nostrand Reinhold Co., Vol. III, 12–19 (1973)

MILTHORPE, F.L. and MOORBY, J.: Vascular transport and its significance in plant growth. Ann. Rev. Plant Physiol. 20, 117–138 (1969)

MINDERMAN, G. and LEEFLANG, K.W.F.: The amounts of drainage water and solutes from lysimeters planted with either oak, pine or natural dune vegetation, or without any vegetation cover. Plant and Soil 28, 61–80 (1968)

MINER, G.S., LILLY, J.P. and TERRY, D.L.: Nitrogen release characteristics of isobutylidene diurea and its effectiveness as a source of N for flue-cured tobacco Agron. J. 70, 434–438 (1978)

MINISTRY OF AGRICULTURE FISHERIES AND FOOD. Technical Bulletin No. 209. Fertilizer Recommendations. H.M.S.O. (1973)

MINOTTI, P.L., WILLIAMS, D. CRAIG and JACKSON, W.A.: Nitrate uptake by wheat as influenced by ammonium and other cations. Crop Sci. 9, 9–14 (1969)

MISHRA, D. and KAR, M.: Nickel in plant growth and metabolism. Bot. Rev. 40, 395–452 (1974)

MITCHELL, G.A., BINGHAM, E.T. and PAGE, A.L.: Yield and metal composition of lettuce and wheat grown on soils amended by sewage sludge enriched with cadmium, copper, nickel, and zinc. J. Environ. Qual. 7, 165–171 (1978)

MITCHELL, H.H. and EDMAN, M.: Fluorine in soils, plants and animals. Soil Sci. 60, 81–90 (1945)

MITCHELL, H.H., HAMILTON, T.S. and BEADLES, J.R.: The relationship between the protein content of corn and the nutritional value of the protein. J. Nutr. 48, 461–476 (1952)

MITCHELL, P.: Coupling of phosphorylation to electron and hydrogen transfer by a chemiosmotic type of mechanism. Nature 191, 144–148 (1961)

MITCHELL, P.: Chemiosmotic coupling in oxidative and photosynthetic phosphorylation. Biol. Rev. 41, 445–502 (1966)

MITCHELL, P.: Promotive chemiosmotic mechanisms in oxidative and photosynthetic phosphorylation. Trends in Biochemical Sciences 3, N58–N61 (1978)

MITCHELL, R.L.: Trace elements in Scottish peats. Int. Peat Symp. Dublin 1954, Sect. B 3

MITCHELL, R.L.: Trace elements in Soil, p. 320–368. In: F.E. BEAR: Chemistry of the Soil, New York, Reinhold, 1964

MITCHELL, R.L.: Cobalt in soil and its uptake by plants. Agrochimica 16, 521–532 (1972)

MITSCHERLICH, E.A.: (G) Soil Science for Farmers, Foresters and Gardeners. 6. ed. Max Niemeyer Verlag, Halle (1950)

MITSCHERLICH, E.A.: (G) Soil Science for Farmers, Foresters and Gardeners. 7th ed., Verlag P. Parey, Berlin, Hamburg 1954

MITSCHERLICH, E.A. and BEUTELSPACHER, H.: (G) Investigations into the water consumption of some crops and the water economy of a natural soil profile. Bodenk. u. Pflanzenernähr. 9/10, 337–395 (1938)

MIZRAHI, Y., BLUMENFELD, A. and RICHMOND, A.E.: Abscisic acid and transpiration in leaves in relation to osmotic root stress. Plant Physiol. 46, 169–171 (1970)

MOGHIMI, A., TATE, M.E. and OADES, J.M.: Phosphate dissolution by rhizosphere products. II Characterization of rhizosphere products especially α ketogluconic acid. Soil Biol. Biochem. 10, 283–286 (1978)

MOHR, H.D.: (G) Soil penetration by roots in relation to important soil characteristics. Kali-Briefe (Büntehof) *14*, (2) 103–113 (1978)

MØLLE, K.G. and JESSEN, T.: (D) Increasing amounts of nitrogen to spring cereals grown on low areas 1960–67. T. Planteavl *72*, 489–502 (1968)

MOORBY, J.: The influence of carbohydrate and mineral nutrient supply on the growth of potato tubers. Ann. Bot. *32*, 57–68 (1968)

MORARD, P.: (F) Distribution of phosphorus, studied with the radioactive isotope and with colorimetry, in buckwheat *(Fagopyrum esculentum,* var. La Harpe*)*, grown in nutrient solution. C.R. Acad. Sci. Sér. D, *270*, 2075–2077 (1970)

MORARD, P.: (F) Contribution to the study of the potassium nutrition of sorghum. Thesis, University Toulouse 1973

MORESHET, S., STANHILL, G. and FUCHS, M.: Effect of increasing foliage reflectance on the CO_2 uptake and transpiration resistance of a grain Sorghum crop. Agron. J. *69*, (2) 246–250 (1977)

MORGAN, M.A., VOLK, R.J. and JACKSON, W.A.: Simultaneous influx and efflux of nitrate during uptake by perennial reygrass. Plant Physiol. *51*, 267–272 (1973)

MORGAN, P.W., JOHAM, H.E. and AMIN, J.V.: Effect of manganese toxicity on the indole-acetic acid oxidase system in cotton. Plant Physiol. *41*, 718–724 (1966)

MORIMURA, S., TAKAHASHI, E. and MATSUMOTO, H.: Association of aluminium with nuclei and inhibition of cell division in onion *(Allium cepa)* roots. Z. Pflanzenphysiologie *88*, 395–401 (1978)

MORRÉ, D.J.: Membrane biogenesis. Ann. Rev. Plant Physiol. *26*, 441–481 (1975)

MOORE, D.P.: Mechanism of micronutrient uptake by plants, p. 171–198. In: Micronutrients in Agriculture. Soil Sci. Soc. Amer. Inc., Madison 1972

MOORE, D.P.: Physiological effects of pH on roots. In E.W.Carson. The Plant Root and Its Environment, p. 135–151. University Press Virginia, Charlottesville (1974)

MOTHES, K.: (G) Sulphur metabolism of plants. Planta *29*, 67–109 (1939)

MUELLER, P. and RUDIN, D.O.: Development of K+-Na+ discrimination in experimental bimolecular lipid membranes by macrocyclic antibiotics. Biochem. Biophys. Res. Commun. *26*, 398–405 (1967)

MÜNCH, E.: (G) Translocation of materials in plants. Fischer Verlag, Jena 1930

MULDER, D.: Mg-deficiency in fruit trees on sandy and clay soils in Holland. Plant and Soil *2*, 145–157 (1950)

MULDER, E.G.: Importance of molybdenum in the nitrogen metabolism of microorganisms and higher plants. Plant and Soil *1*, 94–119 (1948)

MULDER, E.G.: Effect of the mineral nutrition of potato plants on the biochemistry and the physiology of the tubers. Neth. J. Agric. Sci. *4*, 333–356 (1956)

MUMFORD, F.E., STARK, H.M. and SMITH, D.H.: A naturally-occurring cofactor for indole-acetic acid oxidase. Plant Physiol. *37*, XIV (1962)

MUNDEL, G. and KRELL, W.: (G) Changes in chemical criteria of a grassland soil due to long term application of high nitrogen rates. Arch. Acker- u. Pflanzenbau u. Bodenkd. *22*, 643–651 (1978)

MUNK, H.: (G) The nitrification of ammonium salts in acid soils. Landw. Forsch. *11*, 150–156 (1958)

MUNK, H.: (G) Vertical migration of inorganic phosphate under conditions of a high phosphate application. Landw. Forsch. *27*/I. Sonderh., 192–199 (1972)

MUNN, D.A. and JACKSON, W.A.: Nitrate and ammonium uptake by rooted cuttings of sweet potato. Agron. J. *70*, 312–316 (1978)

MURAKA, I.P., JACKSON, T.L. and MOORE, D.P.: Effects of N, K and Cl on N components of Russet Burbank potatoes. Agron. J. *65*, 868 (1973)

MURATA, Y. and MATSUSHIMA, S.: Rice In: Crop Physiology (L.T. EVANS, ed.), p. 73–99. Cambridge University Press 1975

MUROZUMI, M., CHOW, T.J. and PATTERSON, C.: Chemical concentrations of pollutant lead aerosols, terrestrial dust and sea salts in Greenland and Antarctic snow strata. Geochim. Cosmochim. Acta 33, 1247–1294 (1969)

MURPHY, L.S. and WALSH L.M.: Correction of micronutrient deficiencies with fertilizers. In: Micronutrients in Agriculture, p. 347–387 (1972)

MURPHY, M.J. and SIEGEL, L.M., TOVE, S.R. and KAMIN, H.: Siroheme: A new prosthetic group participating in six-electron reduction reactions catalyzed by both sulphite and nitrite reductases. Proc. Nat. Acad. Sci. U.S.A., 71, 612–616 (1974)

MURPHY, R.P.: Some factors influencing cation uptake by excised roots of perennial ryegrass. Plant and Soil 10, 242–249 (1959)

MYERS, R.J.K. and PAUL, E.A.: Nitrate ion electrode methode for soil nitrate nitrogen determination. Canad. J. Soil Sci. 48, 369–371 (1968)

MYERS, R.J.K. and PAUL, E.A.: Plant uptake and immobilization of ^{15}N-labelled ammonium nitrate in a field experiment with wheat. In: Nitrogen-15 in Soil Plant Studies, p. 55–64, I.A.E.A. Vienna 1971

MYTTENAERE, C.: (F) Effect of the strontium-calcium ratio on the localisation of strontium and calcium in Pisum sativum. Physiol. Plant 17, 814–827 (1964)

NEALES, T.F.: Components of the total magnesium content within the leaves of white clover and perennial rye grass. Nature 177, 388–389 (1956)

NEISH, A.C.: Studies on chloroplasts. Biochem. J. 33, 300–308 (1939)

NELSON, W.L.: Plant factors affecting potassium availability and uptake, p. 355–380. In: The Role of Potassium in Agriculture. Madison/USA 1968

NÉMETH, K.: The effect of K fertilization and K removal by rye-grass in pot experiments on the K concentration of the soil solution of various soils. Plant and Soil 42, 97–107 (1975)

NÉMETH, K.: The availability of nutrients in the soil as determined by electroultrafiltration (EUF). Adv. Agron. 31, 155–188 (1979)

NÉMETH, K. and HARRACH, T.: (G) Interpretation of chemical soil tests in loess soil eroded to a different degree. Landw. Forsch. 30/I. Sonderh., 131–137 (1974)

NÉMETH, K., MENGEL, K. and GRIMME, H.: The concentration of K, Ca and Mg in the saturation extract in relation to exchangeable K, Ca and Mg. Soil Sci. 109, 179–185 (1970)

NEUBAUER, H. and SCHNEIDER, W.: (G) The nutrient uptake of seedlings and its application for the estimation of the nutrient content in soils. Z. Pflanzenernähr. Düng. Bodenk. A 2, 329–362 (1923)

NEUBERT, P., WRAZIDLO, W., VIELEMEYER, H.P., HUNDT, I., GOLLMICK, F. and BERGMANN, W.: (G) Tables of plant analysis. Inst. of Plant Nutrition, Jena 1970

NEWMAN, A.C.D.: Cation exchange properties of micas. I. The relation between mica composition and potassium exchange in solutions of different pH. J. Soil Sci. 20, 357–373 (1969)

NEWMAN, E.I.: Root and soil water relations. In: E.W.CARSON: The Plant Root and Its Environment, p. 362–440. University Press of Virginia, Charlottesville 1974

NEWMAN, E.I.: Water relations, p. 157–196. In: Plant Structure Function and Adaptation. Ed. M.A.Hall. Macmillan Press London 1976

NEWMAN, E.I. and ANDREWS, R.E.: Uptake of phosphorus and potassium in relation to root growth and root density. Plant and Soil 38, 49–69 (1973)

NEYRA, C.A. and DÖBEREINER, J.: Nitrogen fixation in grasses. Adv. in Agron. 29, 1–38 (1977)

NICHOLAS, D.J.D.: Determination of minor element levels in soils with the Aspergillus niger method. Trans. Intern. Congr. Soc. Soil Sci. Vol. III, p. 168–182, Madison, Wisc. 1960

NICHOLAS, D.J.D.: Minor mineral nutrients. Ann. Rev. Plant Physiol. 12, 63–90 (1961)

NICHOLAS, D.J.D. and NASON, A.: Role of molybdenum as a constituent of nitrate reductase from soybean leaves. Plant Physiol. 30, 135–138 (1955)

NICHOLAS, D.J.D. and THOMAS, W.D.E.: Some effects of heavy metals on plants grown in soil culture. Part I. The effect of cobalt on fertiliser and soil phosphate uptakes and the iron and cobalt status of tomato. Plant and Soil 5, 67–80 (1954)

619

NICHOLAS, D.J.D. and THOMAS, W.D.: Some effects of heavy metals on plants grown in soil culture. Part II. The effect of nickel on fertiliser and soil phosphate uptakes and iron and nickel status of tomato. Plant and Soil 5, 182–193 (1954)

NIENSTEDT, E.F.: (G) Influence of nitrogen on the formation of some constituents in green oats. Z. Acker- u. Pflanzenbau 129, 331–354 (1969)

NIGAM, S.N. and McCONNELL, W.B.: Metabolism of Na_2SeO_4 in *Astragalus bisulcatus*, lima bean and wheat: a comparative study. J. Exp. Bot. 27, 565–571 (1976)

NISSEN, P.: Uptake of sulfate by roots and leaf slices of barley. Mediated by single, multiphasic mechanisms. Physiol. Plant 24, 315–324 (1971)

NISSEN, P.: Uptake and mechanisms: Inorganic and organic. Ann. Rev. Plant Physiol. 25, 53–79 (1974)

NITSOS, R.E. and EVANS, H.J.: Effects of univalent cations on the activity of particulate starch synthetase. Plant Physiol. 44, 1260–1266 (1969)

NOBEL, P.S.: Relation of light-dependent potassium uptake by pea leaf fragments to the pK of the accompanying organic acid. Plant Physiol. 46, 491–493 (1970)

NOBEL, P.S.: Relation of swelling and photophosphorylation to light-induced ion uptake by chloroplasts *in vitro*. Biochim. Biophys. Acta 131, 127–140 (1967)

NOMMIK, H.: The residual effects of nitrogen fertilizers in relation to the quantities of mineral nitrogen recovered in the soil profile. Acta agric. scand. 16, 163–178 (1966)

NOWAKOWSKI, T.Z.: Effects of nitrogen fertilizers on total nitrogen soluble nitrogen and soluble carbohydrate contents of grass. J. Agric. Sci. 59, 387–392 (1962)

NUTTALL, W.F., WARKENTIN, B.P. and CARTER, A.L.: 'A' values of potassium related to other indexes of soil potassium availability. Soil Sci. Soc. Am. Proc. 31, 344–348 (1967)

NYATSANGA, T. and PIERRE, W.H. Effect of nitrogen fixation by legumes on soil acidity. Agron. J. 65, 936–940 (1973)

NYE, P.H.: The measurement and mechanism of ion diffusion in soil. I. The relation between self diffusion and bulk-diffusion. J. Soil Sci. 17, 16–23 (1966)

NYE, P.H.: Processes in the root environment. J. Soil Sci. 19, 205–215 (1968)

NYE, P.H.: The rate limiting step in plant nutrient absorption from the soil. Soil Sci. 123, 292–297, 1977

NYE, P.H.: Soil properties controlling the supply of nutrients to the root surface. p. 39–49. In: J.L. HARLEY and R. SCOTT RUSSELL (eds.). The Soil – Root Interface. Academic Press 1979

NYE, P.H. and TINKER, P.B.: Solute Movement in the Soil Root System. Blackwell Scientific Publications, Oxford, London, Edinburgh, Melbourne 1977

OADES, J.M.: The nature and distribution of iron compounds in soils. Soil and Fertilizers 26, 69–80 (1963)

OAKS, A. and BIDWELL, R.G.S.: Compartimentation of intermediary metabolites. Ann. Rev. Plant Physiol. 21, 43–66 (1970)

OAKS, A., WALLACE, W. and STEVENS, D.: Synthesis and turnover of nitrate reductase in corn roots. Plant Physiol. 50, 649–654 (1972)

OBIGBESAN, G.O.: (G) Investigations into the question of the phosphorus status of Central African soils and the phosphorus response of some phosphate fertilizers. Diss. Agric. Fac. Justus-Liebig-Universität Giessen 1970

OBIGBESAN, G.O.: The influence of potassium nutrition on the yield and chemical composition of some tropical root and tuber crops. In: Potassium in Tropical Crops and Soils, p. 311–322. 10th Colloq. Intern. Potash Institute, Berne 1973

O'CONNOR, G.A., LINDSAY, W.L. and OLSEN, S.R.: Diffusion of iron and iron chelates in soil. Soil Sci. Soc. Amer. Proc. 35, 407–410 (1971)

ODHNOFF, C.: Boron deficiency and growth. Physiol. Plant. 10, 984–1000 (1957)

OERTLI, J.J.: Loss of boron from plants through guttation. Soil Sci. 94, 214–219 (1962)

620

OERTLI, J.J.: The influence of certain environmental conditions on water and nutrient uptake and nutrient distribution in barley seedlings with special reference to boron. In: Advancing Frontiers Plant Sciences 6, 55–85, L. Chandra ed. Inst. for the Advancement of Science and Culture, New Delhi 1963

OERTLI, J.J.: Controlled-release fertilizers. Fertilizer Research 1, 103–123 (1980)

ÖZBEK, N.: Studies on the chemical methods will be used for determining the phosphorus status of different regions in Turkey. Univ. Ankara Yearbook of the Faculty of Agric., p. 124–162 (1969)

OGUS, L. and FOX, R.L.: Nitrogen recovery from a soil profile by Bromus inermis. Agron. J. 62, 69–71 (1970)

OHKI, K.: Manganese and zinc status related to maximum growth for selected agronomic crops. Proc. of the International Seminar on Soil Environment and Fertility Management in Intensive Agriculture. Tokyo p. 659–668 (1977)

OHLROGGE, A.J.: Plant growth regulators in intensive agricultural systems. In: Proc. Int. Sem. on Soil Environment and Fertility Management in Intensive Agriculture. (The Soc. Sci. Soil and Manure, Japan, ed.) p. 590–593. Tokyo 1977

OKUDA, A. and TAKAHASHI, E.: The role of silicon, p. 123–146. In: The Mineral Nutrition of the Rice Plant, Proc. Symp. Intern. Rice Res. Inst., John Hopkins Press, Baltimore/USA 1965

OLDENKAMP, L. and SMILDE, K.W.: Copper deficiency in douglas fir Pseudotsuga menziesii Mirb. Franco). Plant and Soil 25, 150–152 (1966)

OLLAGNIER, M. and OCHS, R.: (F) The chlorine nutrition of oil palm and coconut. Oléagineux, 26e année, No. 6, 367–372 (1971)

OLSEN, S.R.: Micronutrient interactions. In: 'Micronutrients in Agriculture'. Ed. Soil Sci. Soc. Amer. Inc., Madison/Wisconsin, p. 243–264 (1972)

OLSEN, S.R., COLE, C.V., WATANABE, F.S. and DEAN, C.A.: Estimation of available phosphorus in soils by extraction with sodium bicarbonate. US. Dep. Agric. Cir. No. 939, 19 (1954)

OLSEN, S.R. and WATANABE, F.S.: Diffusive supply of phosphorus in relation to soil texture variations. Soil Sci. 110, 318–327 (1970)

ORLOVIUS, K. and HÖFNER, W.: (G) Effect of a varied nitrogen application on the rate of assimilation and on the yield formation of spring wheat. Z. Pflanzenernähr. Bodenkd., Heft 5, 631–640 (1976)

OSMOND, C.B.: Ion absorption and carbon metabolism in cells of higher plants, p. 347–372. In: Encyclop. Plant Physiol. Vol. 2, Part A. Ed. Lüttge and Pitman, Springer Berlin, Heidelberg, New York 1976

OSMOND, C.B.: Crassulacean acid metabolism: A curiosity in context. Ann. Rev. Plant Physiol. 29, 379–414 (1978)

O'TOOLE, J.C., OZBUN, J.L. and WALLACE, D.H.: Photosynthetic response to water stress in Phaseolus vulgaris. Physiol. Plantarum 40, 111–114 (1977)

OUELLETTE, G.J. and LACHANCE, R.O.: Soil and plant analysis as means of diagnosing boron deficiency in alfalfa in Quebec. Canad. J. agric. Sci. 34, 494–503 (1954)

OZAKI, L.G.: Effectiveness of foliar manganese sprays on peas and beans. Amer. Soc. Hort. Proc. 66, 313–316 (1955)

OZANNE, P.G., WOOLEY, J.T. and BROYER, T.C.: Chlorine and bromine in the nutrition of higher plants. Austr. J. Biol. Sci. 10, 66–79 (1957)

OZOLINA, G. and LAPINA, L.: Effect of copper and nitrogen nutrition of maize and flax on dynamics of nucleic acids. Microélem Prod. Rast. 75–102 (1965)

PAAUW, F. VAN DER: Relations between the potash requirements of crops and meteorological conditions. Plant and Soil 3, 254–268 (1958)

PAAUW, F. VAN DER: Fertilization with phosphorus. Intern. superphosphate manufacturers' association. Extr. Bull. Docum. No. 32, Paris (1962)

PAAUW, F. VAN DER: Factors controlling the efficiency of rock phosphates for potatoes and rye on humic sandy soils. Plant and Soil 22, 81–98 (1965)

PAAUW, F. VAN DER: (G) Development and evaluation of a new water extraction technique for the determination of available phosphate. Landw. Forsch. *23*/II.Sonderh., 102–109 (1969)

PADURARIU, A., HOROVITZ, C.T., PALTINEANU, R. and NEGOMIREANU: On the relationship between soil moisture and osmotic potential in maize and sugar beet plants. Physiol. Plant. *22*, 850–860 (1969)

PÄTZOLD, C. and DAMBROTH, M.: (G) Sensitivity to injury. Der Kartoffelbau *15*, 291–292 (1964)

PAGE, A.L., GANJE, T.J. and JOSHI, M.S.: Lead quantities in plants, soils and air near some major highways in Southern California. Hilgardia *41*, 1–31 (1971)

PAGE, E.R.: Studies in soil and plant manganese. II. The relationship of soil pH to manganese availability. Plant and Soil *16*, 247–257 (1962)

PAGE, E.R. and GERWITZ, A.: Phosphate uptake by lettuces and carrots from different soil depths in the field. J. Sci. Fd Agric. *20*, 85–90 (1969)

PAGE, M.B. and TALIBUDEEN, O.: Nitrate concentrations under winter wheat and in fallow soil during summer at Rothamsted. Plant and Soil *47*, 527–540 (1977)

PARFITT, R.L.: Anion adsorption by soils and soil materials. Adv. Agron. *30*, 1–50 (1978)

PARFITT, R.L. and SMART, R.S.C.: The mechanism of sulfate adsorption on iron oxides. Soil Sci. Soc. Am. J. *42*, 48–50 1978

PARK, C.S.: The micronutrient problem of Korean Agriculture. In: Proc of Internat. Symp. commemorating the 30th Anniversary of Korean Liberation (Nat. Acad Sci. Rep. Korea, ed.) p. 847–862, Seoul 1975

PARKER, J.H.: How fertilizer moves and reacts in the soil. Crops and Soils Magazine, Nov. 1972

PARSONS, J.W. and TINSLEY, J.: Nitrogenous Substances. In: GIESEKING J.E. (ed.). Soil Components, Vol. I. Organic Components p. 263–304, Springer 1975

PARTHIER, B.: (G) The biological fixation of atmospheric nitrogen. Biol. Rdsch. *16*, 345–364 (1978)

PATE, J.S.: Movement of nitrogenous solutes in plants, p. 165–187, IAEA-PI-341/13. In: Nitrogen-15 in Soil-Plant Studies. International Atomic Energy Agency, Vienna 1971

PATE, J.S.: Transport and partitioning of nitrogenous solutes. Ann. Rev. Plant Physiol. *31*, 313–340 (1980)

PATE, J.S., ATKINS, C.A., HAMEL, K., McNEIL, D.L. and LAYZELL, D.B.: Transport of organic solutes in phloem and xylem of a nodulated legume. Plant Physiol. *63*, 1082–1088 (1979)

PATRICK, W.H. jr. and MAHAPATRA, I.G.: Transformation and availability to rice of nitrogen and phosphorus in waterlogged soils. Ad. Agron. *20*, 323–359 (1968)

PATRICK, W.H. jr. and REDDY, K.R.: Fertilizer nitrogen reactions in flooded soils. Proc. Intern. Seminar on Soil Environment and Fertility Management in Intensive Agriculture, p. 275–281, Tokyo 1977

PAUL, R.E. and JONES, R.L.: Studies on the secretion of maize root cap slime. II Localization of slime production. Plant Physiol. *56*, 307–312 (1975)

PAUL, R.E. and JONES, R.L.: Studies on the secretion of maize root cap slime. IV Evidence for the involvement of dictyosomes. Plant Physiol. *57*, 249–256 (1976)

PAUL, R.E., JOHNSON, C.M. and JONES, R.L.: Studies on the secretion of maize root cap slime. I Some properties of the secreted polymer. Plant Physiol. *56*, 300–306 (1975)

PEDRO, G.: (F) Pedogenesis in the humid tropics and the dynamics of potassium, p. 23–49. In: Potassium in Tropical Crops and Soils. Proc. 10th Colloq. Intern. Potash Institute, Berne 1973

PEECH, M.: Lime requirements vs. soil pH curves for soils of New York State. Ithaca, N.Y. Agronomy, Cornell University 1961

PELTON, W.L.: Influence of low rates on wheat yield in southwestern Saskatchewan. Canad. J. Plant Sci. *49*, 607–614 (1969)

PENNINGSFELD, F.: (G) CO_2-application. In: J. BECKER-DILLINGEN, p. 178–180, Festschrift zum 150jährigen Bestehen der Staatl. Lehr- u. Forschungsanstalt f. Gartenbau in Weihenstephan, Bayr. Landw. Verlag 1954

PENNINGSFELD, F. and FORCHTHAMMER, L.: (G) Response of the most important vegetables on a varied nutrient ratio in fertilizer application. Die Gartenbauwiss. 8, 347–372 (1961)

PENNINGSFELD, F. and KURZMANN, P.: (G) Response of some important fruits on deficiency in macronutrients. Jahresbericht 1966/67 der Staatl. Lehr- u. Forschungsanstalt f. Gartenbau in Weihenstephan, S. 1–50 (1966/67)

PENNY, M.G. and BOWLING, D.J.F.: A study of potassium gradients in the epidermis of intact leaves of Commelina communis L. in relation to stomatal opening. Planta 119, 17–25 (1974)

PEOPLES, T.R. and KOCH, D.W.: Role of potassium in carbon dioxide assimilation in Medicago sativa L. Plant Physiol. 63, 878–881 (1979)

PERUR, N.G., SMITH, R.L. and WIEBE, H.H.: Effect of iron chlorosis on protein fractions of corn leaf tissues. Plant Physiol. 36, 736–739 (1961)

PETER, A. v.: Fertilizer requirement in developing countries. The Fertilizer Society, Proc., No. 188, London 1980

PETERSON, P.J.: The distribution of Zn-65 in Agrostis tenuis and A. stolonifera tissues. J. Exp. Bot. 20, 863–875 (1969)

PETERSON, P.J. and BUTLER, G.W.: The uptake and assimilation of selenite by higher plants. Aust. J. Biol. Sci. 15, 126–146 (1962)

PETTERSON, A.: Heavy metal uptake by plants from solutions with metal ion, plant species and growth period variations. Plant and Soil 45, 445–459 (1976)

PFAFF, C.: (G) The behaviour of nitrogen in the soil after a long term lysimeter experiment. Z. Acker- u. Pflanzenbau 117, 77–99 (1963)

PFAFF, C.: (G) The leaching of calcium, magnesium, chloride, and sulphate out of the soil profile (lysimeter experiments). Z. Acker- u. Pflanzenbau 117, 117–128 (1963)

PFLÜGER, R.: (G) Investigations on light-induced cation fluxes of isolated chloroplasts. Ber. Deutsch. Bot. Ges. 87, 383–388 (1974)

PFLÜGER, R. and MENGEL, K.: (G) The photochemical activity of chloroplasts obtained from plants with a different potassium nutrition. Plant and Soil 36, 417–425 (1972)

PFLÜGER, R. and WIEDEMANN, R.: (G) Effect of monovalent cations on the nitrate reduction in Spinacia oleracea L. Z. Pflanzenphysiol. 85, 125–133 (1977)

PIERCE, W.S. and HIGINBOTHAM, N.: Compartments and fluxes of K^+, Na^+, and Cl^- in Avena coleoptile cells. Plant Physiol. 46, 666–672 (1970)

PIMENTEL, D., HURD, L.E., BELLOTTI, A.C., FORSTER, M.J., OKA, I.N., SHOLES, O.D. and WHITMAN, R.J.: Food production and the energy crisis. Science 182, 443–449 (1973)

PISSAREK, H.P.: (G) The development of potassium deficiency symptoms in spring rape. Z. Pflanzenernähr. Bodenk. 136, 1–96 (1973)

PISSAREK, H.P.: (G) Influence of intensity and performance of Mg deficiency on the grain yield of oats. Z. Acker- u. Pflanzenbau 148, 62–71 (1979)

PITMAN, M.G.: Uptake and transport of ions in barley seedlings. III. Correlation between transport to the shoot and relative growth rate. Aust. J. biol. Sci. 25, 905–919 (1972)

PLANT, W.: The effects of molybdenum deficiency and mineral toxicities on crop in acid soils. J. hort. Sci. 31, 163–176 (1956)

PLATT, S.G., PLAUT, Z. and BASSHAM, J.A.: Ammonia regulation of carbon metabolism in photosynthesizing leaf discs. Plant Physiol. 60, 739–742 (1977)

PLUENNEKE, R.H. and JOHAM, H.E.: The influence of low substrate sodium levels upon the free amino acid content of cotton leaves. Plant Physiol. 49, 502–505 (1972)

POLJAKOFF-MAYBER, A. and GALE, J.: Plants in Saline Environments. Ecological Studies, Vol. 15. Springer-Verlag, Berlin, Heidelberg, New York 1975

POLLARD, A.S., PARR, A.J. and LOUGHMAN, B.C.: Boron in relation to membrane function in higher plants. J. Exp. Bot. 28, 831–841 (1977)

PONNAMPERUMA, F.N.: Dynamic aspects of flooded soils and the nutrition of the rice plant. In: The Mineral Nutrition of the Rice Plant, Proc. of a Symposium at The Intern. Rice Res. Inst., Febr. 1964, p. 295–328. The Johns Hopkins Press, Baltimore, Maryland 1965

PONNAMPERUMA, F.N.: The chemistry of submerged soils. Adv. Agron. *24*, 29–96 (1972)

PONNAMPERUMA, F.N.: Electrochemical changes in submerged soils and the growth of rice. In: Soils and Rice. (The Intern. Rice Research Institute, ed.) p. 421–441, Los Baños, Philippines 1978

POOLE, R.J.: Energy coupling for membrane transport. Ann. Rev. Plant Physiol. *29*, 437–460 (1978)

POOVAIAH, B.W.: Role of calcium in ripening and senescence. Comm. Soil Sci. Plant Anal. *10*, 83–88 (1979)

POOVAIAH, B.W. and LEOPOLD, A.C.: Inhibition of abscission by calcium. Plant Physiol. *51*, 848–851 (1973)

PORTIS, A.R. and McCARTY, R.E.: Effects of adenine nucleotides and of phosphorylation on H^+ uptake and the magnitude of the H^+ gradient in illuminated chloroplasts. J. Biol. Chem. *249*, 6250–6254 (1974)

POSKUTA, J. and KOCHANSKA, K.: The effect of potassium glycidate on the rates of CO_2-exchange and photosynthetic products of bean leaves. Z. Pflanzenphysiol. *89*, 393–400 (1978)

POSSINGHAM, J.V.: Mineral nutrition and amino acids in tomato. Aust. J. Biol. Sci. *9*, 539–551 (1956)

POSSINGHAM, J.V., VESK, M. and MERCERI, F.V.: The fine structure of leaf cells of manganese-deficient spinach. J. Ultrastructure Res. *11*, 68–83 (1964)

POWRIE, J.K.: The effect of cobalt on the growth of young lucerne on a siliceous sand. Plant and Soil *21*, 81–93 (1964)

PRAAG, H.J. VAN, FISCHER, V. and RIGA, A.: Fate of fertilizer nitrogen applied to winter wheat as $Na^{15}NO_3$ and ($^{15}NH_4)_2SO_4$ studied in microplots through a four-course rotation: 2. Fixed ammonium turnover and nitrogen reversion. Soil Sci. *130*, 100–105 (1980)

PRASKE, J.A. and PLOCKE, D.J.: A role for zinc in the structural integrity of the cytoplasmic ribosomes of *Euglena gracilis*. Plant Physiol. *48*, 150–155 (1971)

PRATT, P.F.: Chromium, p. 136–141. In: H.D. CHAPMAN: Diagnostic Criteria for Plants and Soils. University of California, Div. of Agric. Sciences, 1966

PRATT, P.F.: Vanadium, p. 480–483. In: H.D. CHAPMAN: Diagnostic Criteria for Plants and Soils, University of California, Riverside 1966

PRAUSSE, A.: (G) Results of a three years trial with phosphorus following the application of various phosphate forms. Thaer-Archiv *12*, 97–114 (1968)

PREISS, J. and LEVI, C.: Metabolism of starch in leaves. In: Photosynthesis II, New Series, Vol. 6 (M. GIBBS and E. LATZKO, eds.) p. 282–312. Springer-Verlag Berlin, Heidelberg, New York 1979

PRICE, C.A.: RNA-synthesis, zinc deficiency and the kinetics of growth. Plant Physiol. *37*, XXI (1962)

PRICE, C.A.: Iron compounds and plant nutrition. Ann. Rev. Plant Physiol. *19*, 239–248 (1968)

PRICE, C.A.: Molecular Approaches to Plant Physiology. McGraw-Hill, p. 398, 1970

PRICE, C.A., CLARK, H.E. and FUNKHOUSER, H.E.: Functions of micronutrients in plants. In: Micronutrients in Agriculture. Soil Sci. Soc. of America, Madison/Wisconsin, p. 731–742 (1972)

PRIMOST, E.: (G) The dependence of grain yield, gluten content and swelling capacity of wheat on nitrogen application and soil class. Plant and Soil *16*, 94–107 (1962)

PRIMOST, E.: (G) The influence of fertilizer application on the quality of wheat. Landw. Forsch., 22. Sonderh., 149–157 (1968)

PRIMOST, E. and RITTMEYER, G.: (G) Changes in the structure of wheat culms, resulting from CCC application, in relation to cultivars and sites. Z. Acker- u. Pflanzenbau *128*, 117–138 (1968)

PRINCE, A. L., ZIMMERMAN, M. and BEAR, F. E.: The magnesium supplying powers of 20 New Jersey soils. Soil Sci. *63*, 69–78 (1947)

PRISCO, J. T. and O'LEARY, J. W.: The effect of humidity and cytokinin on growth and water relations of salt-stressed bean plants. Plant and Soil *39*, 263–276 (1973)

PRUMMEL, J.: Fertilizer placement experiments. Plant and Soil *8*, 231–253 (1957)

PUCKETT, K. J., NIEBOER, E., FLORA, W. P. and RICHARDSON, D. H. S.: Sulfur dioxide: its effect on photosynthetic C-14 fixation in lichens and suggested mechanisms of phytotoxicity. New Phytol. *72*, 141–154 (1973)

PULSS, G. and HAGEMEISTER, H.: (G) Hypomagnesaemie after the feeding of wilted silage of pasture herbage during the stable period. Z. Tierphysiol., Tierernähr. u. Futtermittelk. *25*, 32–42 (1969)

PURITCH, G. S. and BARKER, A. V.: Structure and function of tomato leaf chloroplasts during ammonium toxicity. Plant Physiol. *42*, 1229–1238 (1967)

QUASTEL, J. H.: Soil metabolism. Ann. Rev. Plant Physiol. *16*, 217–240 (1965)

RADMER, R. and KOK, B.: Energy capture in photosynthesis: Photosystem II. Ann. Rev. Biochem. *44*, 409–433 (1975)

RAGGIO, M. and RAGGIO, N.: Root nodules. Ann. Rev. Plant Physiol. *13*, 109–128 (1962)

RAGHAVENDRA, A. S. and DAS, V. S. R.: Photochemical activities of chloroplasts isolated from plants with the C-4 pathway of photosynthesis and from plants with the Calvin cycle. Z. Pflanzenphysiol. *88*, 1–11 (1978)

RAHIMI, A. and BUSSLER, W.: (G) Physiological hypotheses in the formation of copper deficiency. Z. Pflanzenernähr. Bodenkd. *136*, 25–32 (1973)

RAIKOV, L.: Reclamation of solonetz soils in Bulgaria, p. 35–47. In: I. SZABOLCS: European Solonetz Soils and Their Reclamation. Akadémiai Kiadó, Budapest 1971

RAINS, D. W.: Salt transport by plants in relation to salinity. Ann. Rev. Plant Physiol. *23*, 367–388 (1972)

RAMAN, K. V. and JACKSON, M. L.: Vermiculite surface morphology. In: Clays and clay minerals, p. 423–429. 12th Natl. Conf. Pergamon Press, New York 1964

RANDALL, G. W. and SCHULTE, E. E.: Manganese fertilization of soybeans in Wisconsin. Proc. Wis. Fert. and Aglime Conf. *10*, 4–10 (1971)

RANDHAWA, N. S., SINHA, M. K. and TAKKAR, P. N.: Micronutrients. In: Soils and Rice (Intern. Rice Research Institute, ed.) p. 581–603, Los Baños, Philippines 1978

RAO, K. P. and RAINS, D. W.: Nitrate absorption by barley. Plant Physiol. *57*, 55–58 (1976)

RAPP, A., FRANCK, H. and ULLEMEYER, H.: (G) The aromatic compounds of various wines. Deutsche Lebensmittel-Rundsch. *3*, 81–85 (1971)

RASCHKE, R.: Stomatal action. Ann. Rev. Plant Physiol. *26*, 309–340 (1975)

RATHORE, V. S., BAJAJ, Y. P. S. and WITTWER, S. H.: Sub cellular localization of zinc and calcium in bean *(Phaseolus vulgaris L.)* tissues. Plant Physiol. *49*, 207–211 (1972)

RATHSACK, R.: (G) The nitrification inhibiting effect of dicyan diamide. Landw. Forsch. *31*, 347–358 (1978)

RATNER, A. and JACOBY, B.: Effect of K^+, its counter anion, and pH on sodium efflux of barley root tips. J. Exp. Botany *27*, 843–852 (1976)

RAUSER, W. E.: Zinc toxicity in hydroponic culture. Can. J. Bot. *51*, 301–304 (1973)

RAVEN, J. A. and SMITH, F. A.: Nitrogen assimilation and transport in vascular land plants in relation to intracellular pH regulation. New Phytol *76*, 415–431 (1976)

RAY, T. B. and BLACK, C. C.: The C_4 pathway and its regulation. In: Photosynthesis II, Encycl. Plant Physiol. New Series Vol. 6 (M. GIBBS and E. LATZKO, eds.) p. 77–101. Springer-Verlag Berlin, Heidelberg, New York 1979

REICHENBACH, H. VON: Factors of mica transformation. In: Potassium in Soil, p. 33–42. Proc. 9th Colloq. Int. Potash Inst., Bern 1972

REILLY, C.: The uptake and accumulation of copper by *Becium homblei* (De Wild). Duvig and Planke. New Phytologist *68*, 1081–1087 (1969)

REISENAUER, H. M.: Cobalt in nitrogen fixation by a legume. Nature *186*, 375–376 (1960)

REISENAUER, H. M.: The effect of sulfur on the absorption and utilization of molybdenum by peas. Soil Sci. Soc. Amer. Proc. *34*, 871–875 (1963)

REISENAUER, H. M., TABIKH, A. A. and STOUT, P. R.: Molybdenum reactions with soils and the hydrous oxides of iron, aluminium and titanium. Soil Sci. Soc. Amer. Proc. *26*, 23–27 (1962)

REISENAUER, H. M., WALSH, L. M. and HOEFT, R. G.: Testing soils for sulphur, boron, molybdenum and chlorine, p. 173–200. In: L. M. WALSH and J. D. BEATON: Soil Testing and Plant Analysis. Soil Sci. Soc. of America Inc., Madison/Wisconsin 1973

REISSIG, H.: (G) The influence of liming on the Sr-90 uptake by crops under field conditions. Kernenergie *5*, 678–684 (1962)

REITH, J. W. S.: Fertilizer placement for swedes and turnips. Emp. J. exp. Agric. *27*, 300–312 (1959)

REITH, J. W. S.: Soil properties limiting the efficiency of fertilizers, p. 275–278. VIIth Fertilizer World Congress, Vienna 1972

RENDIG, V. V., OPUTA, C. and MCCOMB, E. A.: Effects of sulphur deficiency on non-protein nitrogen, soluble sugars and N/S ratios in young corn plants. Plant and Soil *44*, 423–437 (1976)

RENGER, M. and STREBEL, O.: (G) Nitrate supply to plant roots as a function of depth and time. Landw. Forsch. Sonderh. 33/II, 13–19 (1976)

RENSING, L. and CORNELIUS, G.: (G) Biological membranes as components of oscillating systems. Biol. Rdsch. *18*, 197–209 (1980)

REUTHER, W. and LABANAUSKAS, C. K.: Copper, p. 157–179. In: H. C. CHAPMAN: Diagnostic Criteria for Plants. Univ. of California, Agric. Pub. Berkley U.S. 1966

REZK, A. I. and AMER, F.: Exchangeable potassium and its selectivity by soils as quantity-intensity parameters for soil potassium. Soil Sci. Soc. Amer. Proc. *33*, 876–880 (1969)

RHOADES, J. D., INGVALSON, R. D. and HATCHER, J. T.: Adsorption of boron by ferromagnesian minerals and magnesium hydroxide. Soil Sci. Soc. Amer. Proc. *34*, 934–941 (1970)

RIBAILLIER, D. and AUZAC, J. d': (F) New perspectives in hormonale stimulation of the production of *Hevea brasiliensis*. R.G.C.P. *47* (4), 433–439 (1970)

RICH, C. J.: Mineralogy of soil potassium. In: The Role of Potassium in Agriculture, p. 79–96. Amer. Soc. Agron., Madison/USA 1968

RICH, C. J.: Potassium in soil minerals, p. 15–31. In: Potassium in Soil, Intern. Potash Inst., Berne 1972

RICH, C. J. and BLACK, W. R.: Potassium exchange as affected by cation size, pH and mineral structure. Soil Sci. *97*, 384–390 (1964)

RICHARDS, L. A.: A pressure-membrane extraction apparatus for soil solution. Soil Sci. *51*, 377–386 (1941)

RICHARDS, I. R.: A review of FAO data responses of tropical crops to fertilizers 1961–1977. Fisons Ltd. Felixstowe 1979

RIEHLE, G. and JUNG, J.: (G) The process of nitrite formation in spinach. Landw. Forsch. *19*, 231–242 (1966)

RIEHM, H.: (G) The ammonium lactate acetic acid method for the determination of easily soluble phosphates in calcareous soils. Agrochimica *3*, 49–65 (1959)

RIEHM, H. and QUELLMALZ, E.: (G) The determination of plant nutrients in rain water and in the air and their importance for the agriculture, p. 171–183. In: H. RIEHM: 100 Jahre Staatl. Landw. Versuchs- und Forschungsanstalt Augustenberg 1959

RILEY, D. and BARBER, S. A.: Effect of ammonium and nitrate fertilization on phosphorus uptake as related to root-induced pH changes at the root-soil interface. Soil Sci. Soc. Am. Proc. *35*, 301–306 (1971)

RINNE, R. W. and LANGSTON, R. G.: Effect of growth on redistribution of some mineral elements in peppermint. Plant Physiol. *35*, 210–215 (1960)

Rios, M.A. and Pearson, R.W.: The effect of some chemical environmental factors on cotton behavior. Soil Sci. Soc. Amer. Proc. *28*, 232–235 (1964)

Rivière, J.: (F) Studies on the rhizosphere of wheat. Ann. Agron. *11*, 397–440 (1960)

Robards, A.W., Jackson, S.M., Clarkson, D.T. and Sanderson, J.: The structure of barley roots in relation to the transport of ions into the stele. Protoplasma *77*, 291–312 (1973)

Robertson, G.A. and Loughman, B.C.: Reversible effects of boron on the absorption and incorporation of phosphate in *Vicia faba* L. New Phytol. *73*, 291–298 (1974)

Robinson, F.A.: Vitamins, p. 195–220. In: Phytochemistry. Vol. III. Ed. L.P. Miller, 1973

Roemer, T. and Scheffer, F.: (G) Textbook of Agronomy, 5. ed., p. 149, Verlag P. Parey, Berlin and Hamburg 1959

Römer, W.: (G) Investigations into the capacity of the photosynthetic apparatus of barley *(Hordeum distichon* L.*)* and in relation to environmental conditions. Arch. Bodenfruchtbarkeit u. Pflanzenprodukt. *15*, 415–423 (1971)

Römheld, V. and Marschner, H.: Fine regulation of iron uptake by the Fe-efficient plant *Helianthus annuus.* In: The Soil-Root Interface (J.L. Harley and R.S. Russell, eds.) p. 405–417. Academic Press, London 1979

Römheld, V. and Marschner, H.: Rhythmic iron stress reactions in sunflower. Physiol. Plant *53* in press (1981)

Roland, J.C. and Bessoles, M.: (F) Detection of calcium in the cells of the collenchym. C.R. Acad. Sci., Sér. D, *267*, 589–592 (1968)

Roll-Hansen, J.: Steaming of soil for tomatoes. State Experiment Station Kvitzmar, Stjördal, Norway, Report No. 10 (1952)

Rolston, D.E.: Measuring nitrogen loss from denitrification. California Agriculture *31*, 12–13 (1977)

Rorison, I.H.: Some experimental aspects of the calcicole-calcifuge problem. I. The effects of competition and mineral nutrition upon seedling growth in the field. J. Ecol. *48*, 585–599 (1960)

Rorison, I.H.: The calcicole-calcifuge problem. II. The effects of mineral nutrition on seedling growth in solution culture. J. Ecol *48*, 679–688 (1960)

Rorison, I.H.: Ecological Aspects of the Mineral Nutrition of Plants. Blackwell Scientific Publ. Oxford and Edinburgh 1969

Rorison, I.H.: The effects of soil acidity on nutrient availability and plant response. In: Hutchinson, T.C. and Havas, M. (eds.). Effects of Acid Precipitation on Terrestrial Ecosystems, p. 283–304. Plenum Press 1980

Roscoe, B.: The distribution and condition of soil phosphate under old permanent pasture. Plant and Soil *12*, 17–29 (1960)

Roubelakis, K.A. and Kliewer, W.M.: Changes in the activities of ornithine transcarbamylase and arginase, and concentrations of nitrogenous substances during germination and seedling development of *Vitis vinifera* L. Vitis *17*, 377–385 (1978)

Roussel, N., van Stallen, R. and Vlassak, K.: (F) Results of experimentation over two years with unhydrous ammonia. J. Intern. Inst. Sugar Beet Res., Tienen *2*, 35–52 (1966)

Roux, L.: (F) Condensed phosphates in mineral nutrition. Application of a highly condensed potassium polyphosphate to barley grown in solution culture. Ann. Physiol. vég. *10*, 83–98 (1968)

Rovira, A.D. and Davey, C.B.: Biology of the rhizosphere. In: The Plant Root and its Environment (E.W. Carson, ed.), p. 153–204. University Press of Virginia, Charlottesville 1974

Rowell, D.L., Martin, M.W. and Nye, P.H.: The measurement and mechanism of ion diffusion in soils. III. The effect of moisture content and soil-solution concentration on the self-diffusion of ions in soils. J. Soil Sci. *18*, 204–222 (1967)

Rush, D. W. and Epstein, E.: Differences between salt-sensitive and salt-tolerant genotypes of the tomato. Plant Physiol. *57*, 162–166 (1976)

Russ, E.: (G) The determination of available copper and manganese in soils with particular regard to the seedling method. Diss. d. Landw. Fakultät, Giessen 1958

Russell, E. W.: Soil Conditions and Plant Growth, 10th Edition, Longman 1973

Russell, R. S. and Barber, D. A.: The relationship between salt uptake and the absorption of water by intact plants. Ann. Rev. Plant Physiol. *11*, 127–140 (1960)

Russell, R. S. and Clarkson, D. T.: Ion transport in root systems. In: N. Sunderland: Perspectives in Experimental Biology. Vol. 2. Botany, p. 401–411, Pergamon Press, Oxford and New York 1976

Russell, R. S., Rickson, J. B. and Adams, S. N.: Isotopic equilibria between phosphates in soil and their significance in the assessment of fertility by tracer methods. J. Soil Sci. *5*, 85–105 (1954)

Rutland, R. B.: Radioisotopic evidence of immobilization of iron in *Azalea* by excess calcium bicarbonate. J. Amer. Soc. Hort. Sci. *96* (5), 653–655 (1971)

Rutland, R. B. and Bukovac, M. J.: The effect of calcium bicarbonate on iron absorption and distribution by *Chrysanthemum morifolium* (Ram). Plant and Soil *35*, 225–236 (1971)

Ryan, P. F.: Fertilizer placement for kale. Irish J. Agric. Res. *1*, 231–236 (1962)

Ryden, J. C., Syers, J. K. and Harris, R. F.: Phosphorus in runoff and streams. Adv. in Agron. *25*, 1–45 (1973)

Sabey, B. R.: Influence of soil moisture tension on nitrate accumulation in soils. Proc. Soil Sci. Soc. Amer. *33*, 263–266 (1969)

Sadeghian, E. and Kühn, H.: (G) Effect of ancymidol and ethrel on the gibberellic acid content (GA_3) of cereal species. Z. Pflanzenernähr. Bodenkd. *135*, 309–314 (1976)

Saglio, P.: (F) Iron nutrition of grapes. Ann. Physiol. vég. *11*, 27–35 (1969)

Salami, U. A. and Kenefick, D. G.: Stimulation of growth in zinc deficient corn seedlings by the addition of tryptophan. Crop Sci. *10*, 291–294 (1970)

Salmon, R. C. and Arnold, P. W.: The uptake of magnesium under exhaustive cropping. J. Agric. Sci. *61*, 421–425 (1963)

San Valentin, G. O., Robertson, W. K., Johnson, J. T. and Weeks, W. W.: Effect of slow-release fertilizer in fertilizer residues and on yield and composition of flue-cured tobacco. Agron. J. *70*, 345–348 (1978)

Sanders, F. E. and Tinker, P. B.: Phosphate flow into mycorrhizal roots. Pestic. Sci. *4*, 385–395 (1973)

Sanders, J. L. and Brown, D. A.: A new fiber optic technique for measuring root growth of soybeans under field conditions. Agron. J. *70*, 1073–1076 (1978)

Sanderson, G. W. and Cocking, E. C.: Enzymic assimilation of nitrate in tomato plants. I. Reduction of nitrate to nitrite. Plant Physiol. *39*, 416–422 (1964)

Santarius, K. A.: (G) Dependance of Hill reaction and photophosphorylation on water content and their importance for draught and frost resistance of plants. Ber. Deutsch. Bot. Ges. *80*, 133–135 (1967)

Sauerbeck, D. and Johnen, B.: (G) The turnover of plants during the growth period and its influence on 'soil respiration'. Z. Pflanzenern. Bodenk. Heft *3*, 315–328 (1976)

Sauter, J. J.: Analysis of the amino acids and amides in the xylem sap of *Salix caprea* L. in early spring. Pflanzenphysiol. *79*, 276–280 (1976)

Scaife, M. A. and Clarkson, D. T.: Calcium related disorders in plants – a possible explanation for the effect of weather. Plant and Soil. *50*, 723–725 (1978)

Schachtschabel, P.: (G) Investigations into the sorption of clay minerals and organic soil colloids and the determination of the proportion of these colloids on the total sorption of soils. Kolloid-Beiheft *51*, 199–276 (1940)

Schachtschabel, P.: (G) The available magnesium in soils and its determination. Z. Pflanzenernähr. Düng. Bodenk. *67*, 9–23 (1954)

SCHACHTSCHABEL, P.: (G) Manganese in the soil. Die Phosphorsäure *15*, 133–139 (1955)

SCHACHTSCHABEL, P.: (G) Optimum pH, phosphorus and potassium in arable soils. Landw. Forsch., 17. Sonderheft, 60–82 (1963)

SCHACHTSCHABEL, P.: (G) The influence of the pH on soil structure and the turnover of fertilizer phosphates in the soil. Landw. Forsch. *21*, Sonderh., 40–49 (1967)

SCHÄFER, P. and SIEBOLD, M.: (G) Influence of increasing potash application rates on yield and quality of the spring wheat 'Kolibri'. Results from a potash fixing location. Bayer. Landw. Jahrb. *49*, 19–39 (1972)

SCHARPF, H.C. and WEHRMANN, J.: (G) Importance of mineral nitrogen quantity in the soil profile at the beginning of the growth period for the N-application rate for winter wheat. Landw. Forsch. *32*/I, Sonderheft, 100–114 (1975)

SCHARRER, K. and BÜRKE, R.: (G) The influence of nutrition on the vitamin A (carotene) synthesis in crops. Z. Pflanzenernähr. Düng. Bodenk. *62*, 244–262 (1953)

SCHARRER, K. and JUNG, J.: (G) The influence of nutrition on the cation/anion ratio in plants. Z. Pflanzenernähr. Düng. Bodenk. *71*, 76–94 (1955)

SCHARRER, K. and MENGEL, K.: (G) On the transient occurrence of visible magnesium deficiency in oats. Agrochimica *4*, 3–24 (1960)

SCHARRER, K. and PREISSNER, R.: (G) The vitamin B_1 content of plants in relation to nutrition. Z. Pflanzenernähr. Düng. Bodenk. *67*, 166–179 (1954)

SCHARRER, K. and SCHAUMLÖFFEL, E.: (G) The uptake of copper by spring cereals grown on copper deficient soils. Z. Pflanzenernähr. Düng. Bodenk. *89*, 1–17 (1960)

SCHARRER, K. and WERNER, W.: (G) Dependence of ascorbic acid content on the nutrition of the plant. Z. Pflanzenernähr. Düng. Bodenk. *77*, 97–110 (1957)

SCHECHTNER, G. and DEUTSCH, A.: Nitrogen efficiency in field trials and its economic significance for milk production. In: Nitrogen and Grassland, p. 199–219. Wageningen, Proc. 1st General Meeting, European Grassland Fed., Centre for Agricultural Publications and Documentation 1966

SCHEFFER, F. and SCHACHTSCHABEL, P.: (G) Textbook of Soil Science. 9th ed. F.-Enke-Verlag, Stuttgart 1976

SCHEFFER, F. and WELTE, E.: (G) Plant Nutrition, 3rd ed., p. 163, P.-Enke-Verlag, Stuttgart 1955

SCHEFFER, F., WELTE, E. and VON REICHENBACH, H.: (G) Potassium content and mineral composition of the 'Göttinger E-Feld'. Z. Pflanzenernähr. Düng. Bodenk. *88*, 115–128 (1960)

SCHERER, H.W.: (G) Influence of Fe and Mn on the content of minerals and organic acids in maize and sun flower. Ph. D. Thesis, FB 19 Fac. Nutritional Sci., Justus Liebig-University, Giessen 1978

SCHERER, H.W.: (G) Dynamics and availability of non exchangeable NH_4^+ in soils. Landw. Forsch., Sonderh. *37*, 217–225, Kongressband 1980

SCHERER, H.W. and DANZEISEN, L.: (G) The effect of increasing nitrogen fertilizer rates on the development of root nodules, on the symbiotic N_2 assimilation, and on growth and yield of broad beans *(Vicia faba* L.). Z. Pflanzenernähr. Bodenkd. *143*, 464–470 (1980)

SCHERER, H.W. and MENGEL, K.: (G) Contents of fixed ammonium nitrogen of twelve representative soils in Hessia. Landw. Forsch. *32*, 416–424 (1979)

SCHIFF, J.A. and HODSON, R.C.: The metabolism of sulfate. Ann. Rev. Plant Physiol. *24*, 381–414 (1973)

SCHILDBACH, R.: (G) Relationships between fertilizer application to brewing barley and the beer quality. Z. Acker- u. Pflanzenbau *136*, 219–237 (1972)

SCHIMANSKY, C.: (G) Investigations into the translocation of magnesium (Mg-28) in sun flowers. Z. Pflanzenernähr. Bodenk. *136*, 68–81 (1973)

SCHLECHTE, G.: (G) Nutrient uptake of plants and mycorrhiza. I Ectotrophic mycorrhiza. Kali-Briefe, (Büntehof) Fachgeb. 2, 6. Folge (1976)

SCHLICHTING, E.: (G) The phosphate and molybdate bond in soil profiles with iron congregations. Z. Pflanzenernähr. Düng. Bodenk. *90*, 204–208 (1960)

629

SCHLICHTING, E. and SCHWERTMANN, U.: (G) Pseudogley and Gley. Verlag Chemie, Weinheim 1973

SCHMALFUSS, K.: (G) Plant Nutrition and Soil Science. 9th ed., p. 160. S.-Hirzel-Verlag, Stuttgart 1963

SCHMALFUSS, K. and KOLBE, G.: (G) The farmyard manure. Albrecht-Thaer-Archiv 7, 199–213 (1963)

SCHMALFUSS, K. and REINICKE, I.: (G) The effect of increasing potassium rates in the form of KCl and K_2SO_4 on yield and content of water, N-compounds, K, Cl and S fractions of spinach grown in pot experiments. Z. Pflanzenernähr. Düng. Bodenk. 91, 21–29 (1960)

SCHMID, R.: (G) Nitrogen fixing plants. Naturw. Rdsch. 21, 384–386 (1968)

SCHMID, W.E., HAAG, H.P. and EPSTEIN, E.: Absorption of zinc by excised barley roots. Physiol. Plant 18, 860–869 (1965)

SCHMIDT, A.: Photosynthetic assimilation of sulfur compounds. In: Photosynthesis II, Encycl. Plant Physiol. New Series Vol. 6 (M. GIBBS and E. LATZKO, eds.) p. 481–486. Springer-Verlag Berlin, Heidelberg, New York 1979

SCHMIDT, K. and UNGER, H.: (G) Comparative investigations into the effects of straw and farmyard manure application on crop yield and the cellulytic activity in the soil. Albrecht-Thaer-Archiv 12, 227–239 (1968)

SCHMITT, L. and BRAUER, A.: (G) Compound fertilizers and straight fertilizers in trials lasting 10 years. Landw. Forsch. 22, 244–261 (1969)

SCHMITT, L. and BRAUER, A.: (G) Seventy-five years Fertilizer Application Experiments on Meadows of the Agricultural Experimental Station of Darmstadt – Results of the oldest exact Experiments of the European Continent. J.D. Sauerländer's Verlag Frankfurt/Main 1979

SCHNITZER, M. and SKINNER, S.I.M.: Organo-metallic interactions in soils. IV. Carboxyl and hydroxyl groups in organic matter and metal retention. Soil Sci. 99, 278–284 (1965)

SCHÖN, M., NIEDERBUDDE, E.A. and MAHKORN, A.: (G) Results of a 20 years lasting experiment with mineral fertilization and farm yard manure application in the loess area near Landsberg (Lech). Z. Acker- u. Pflanzenbau 143, 27–37 (1976)

SCHOEN, R. and RYE, R.O.: Sulfur isotope distribution in solfataras, Yellowstone National Park. Science 170, 1082–1084 (1971)

SCHOFIELD, R.K.: A ratio law governing the equilibrium of cations in the soil solution. Proc. 11th Int. Congr. pure appl. Chem. London 3, 257–261 (1947)

SCHOFIELD, R.K.: Can a precise meaning be given to 'available' soil phosphorus? Soils and Fertilizers 28, 373–375 (1955)

SCHOUWENBURG, J. Ch. and SCHUFFELEN, A.C.: Potassium exchange behaviour of an illite. Neth. J. Agric. Sci. 11, 13–22 (1963)

SCHRADER, L.E., RITENOUR, G.L., EILRICH, G.L. and HAGEMAN, R.H.: Some characteristics of nitrate reductase from higher plants. Plant Physiol. 43, 930–940 (1968)

SCHREIBER, R.: (G) Effect of magnesium on the yield and the nutrient uptake of K_2O and MgO by cereals. Z. Pflanzenernähr. Düng. Bodenk. 48, 37–64 (1949)

SCHROEDER, D.: (G) Potassium fixation and potassium release of loess soils. Landw. Forsch. 8, 1–7 (1955)

SCHROEDER, D.: (G) Potassium in soils and potassium nutrition of plants. Kali-Briefe (Büntehof), Fachgeb. 1. 3. Folge (1976)

SCHROEDER, D.: Structure and weathering of potassium containing minerals. In: Potassium Research-Review and Trends. p. 43–63. Proc. 11th Congr. Int. Potash Inst., Bern 1978

SCHROEDER, D. and ZAHIROLESLAM, S.: (G) Magnesium contents of Schleswig-Holstein soils. Z. Pflanzenernähr. Düng. Bodenk. 100, 207–215 (1963)

SCHUBERT, K.R. and EVANS, H.J.: Hydrogen evolution a major factor affecting the efficiency of nitrogen fixation in nodulated symbionts. Proc. Natl. Acad. Sci. USA 73, 1207–1211 (1976)

SCHUBERT, K.R., JENNINGS, N.T. and EVANS, H.J.: Hydrogen reactions of nodulated leguminous plants. Plant Physiol. *61*, 398–401 (1978)

SCHÜLLER, H., REICHARD, Th. and NÉMETH, K.: (G) Relationship between P fertilization, yield, P uptake and soil tests. Landw. Forsch. *28*, 147–157 (1975)

SCHUFFELEN, A.C.: (G) Nutrient content and nutrient release in soils. Vortragstagung Chemie und Landwirtschaftliche Produktion. 100 Jahre Landwirtschaftlich-chemische Bundesversuchsanstalt Wien, 27–42 (1971)

SCHUMACHER, R. and FRANKENHAUSER, F.: (G) Fight against bitter pit. Schweiz. Z. f. Obst-u. Weinbau *104*, No 16 424 (1968)

SCHUPHAN, W.: (G) Quality of Crops for Human Nutrition. BLV-Verlagsges. München, Bonn, Wien 1961

SCHUPHAN, W., KLING, M. and OVERBECK, G.: (G) Effect of genetic and environmental factors on the contents of vitamin B_1, vitamin B_2 and niacin in winter and spring wheat. Qualit. plant. materiae veg. (Den Haag) *15*, 177–214 (1968)

SCHUURMAN, J.J.: Effects of density of top and subsoil on root and top growth of oats. Z. Acker- u. Pflanzenbau *134*, 185–199 (1971)

SCHWERTMANN, U.: (G) The selective cation adsorption of the clay fraction of some soils developed from sediments. Z. Pflanzenernähr. Düng. Bodenk. *97*, 9–25 (1962)

SCOTT, N.M.: Sulphate contents and sorption in Scottish soils. J. Sci. Fd. Agric. *27*, 367–372 (1976)

SCOTT, N.M. and ANDERSON, G.: Organic sulphur fractions in Scottish soils. J. Sci. Fd. Agric. *27*, 358–366 (1976)

SEÇER, M.: (G) Effect of potassium on nitrogen metabolization and grain protein formation in spring wheat. Kali-Briefe (Büntehof) *14* (6), 393–402 (1978)

SEELIG, J.: (G) Structure of lipids in biological membranes. Paper presented at the Biophys. Colloq. Giessen, 1980

SENTENAC, H., MOUSIN, D. and SALSAC, L.: (F) Measurement of phosphatase activity in cellulose cell wall material obtained with the help of a non ionic detergent. C.R. Acad. Sci. Paris, *290* (7 janvier), Serie D-21 (1980)

SERRY, A., MAWARDI, A., AWAD, S. and AZIZ, I.A.: Effect of zinc and manganese on wheat production. 1. FAO/SIDA Seminar for Plant Scientists from Africa and Near East, FAO Rome 1974, p. 404–409

SERVAITES, J.C., SCHRADER, L.E. and JUNG, D.M.: Energy dependent loading of amino acids and sucrose into the phloem of soybean. Plant Physiol. *64*, 546–550 (1979)

SHANMUGAM, K.T., O'GARA, F., ANDERSEN, K. and VALENTINE, R.C.: Biological nitrogen fixation. Ann. Rev. Plant Physiol. *29*, 263–276 (1978)

SHARPLES, R.O.: The structure and composition of apples in relation to storage quality. Rep. E. Malling Res. Stn for 1967, 185–189 (1968)

SHAW, K.: Loss of mineral nitrogen from soil. J. Agric. Sci. *58*, 145–151 (1962)

SHEAR, C.B.: Calcium-related disorders of fruits and vegetables. Hort. Sci. *10*, 361–365 (1975)

SHIMSHI, D.: Interaction between irrigation and plant nutrition. In: Transition from extensive to intensive agriculture with fertilizers, p. 111–120. Proc. 7th Colloq. Int. Potash Inst., Bern 1969

SHKOLNIK, M.Y.: General conception of the physiological role of boron in plants. Physiol. Rastenii *21*, 140–150 (1974)

SHOMER, ILAN, A. and WAISEL, Y.: The effect of sodium chloride on the balance between the C_3- and C_4-carbon fixation pathways Physiol. Plant. *29*, 190–193 (1973)

SHRIFT, A.: Aspects of selenium metabolism in higher plants. Ann. Rev. Plant Physiol. *20*, 475–494 (1969)

SIBBESEN, E.: A simple ion exchange resin procedure for extracting plant available elements from soil. Plant and Soil *46*, 665–669 (1977)

SIBBESEN, E.: An investigation of the anion exchange resin method for soil phosphate extraction. Plant and Soil *50*, 305–321 (1978)

SIDERIS, C.P. and YOUNG, H.J.: Growth and chemical composition of *Ananas comusus* in solution cultures with different iron-manganese ratios. Plant Physiol. *24*, 416–440 (1949)

SILVIUS, J.E., INGLE, M. and BAER, C.H.: Sulphur dioxide inhibition of photosynthesis in isolated spinach chloroplasts. Plant Physiol. *56*, 434–437 (1975)

SIMMELSGAARD, S.E.: Adaption to water stress in wheat. Physiol. Plant. *37*, 167–174 (1976)

SIMON-SYLVESTRE, G.: First results of a survey on the total sulphur content of arable soils in France. Annales agron. *20*, 609–625 (1969)

SIMS, J.R. and BINGHAM, F.T.: Retention of boron by layer silicates, sesquioxides and soil materials: II. Sesquioxides. Soil Sci. Soc. Amer. Proc. *32*, 364–369 (1968)

SINGER, S.J.: A fluid lipid-globular protein mosaic model of membrane structure. Ann. N.Y. Acad. Sci. *195*, 16–23 (1972)

SINGH, B. and BRAR, S.P.S.: Dynamics of native and applied potassium in maize-wheat rotation. Potash Review, subj. 9, 35th suite, No. 6 (1977)

SINGH, T.N., PALEG, L.G. and ASPINALL, D.: Stress metabolism III. Variations in response to water deficit in the barley plant. Austr. J. Biol. Sci. *26*, 65–76 (1973)

SIONIT, N., TEARE, I.D. and KRAMER, P.J.: Effects of repeated application of water stress and water status and growth of wheat. Physiol. Plant. *50*, 11–15 (1980)

SIPPOLA, J., ERVIÖ, R. and ELEVELD, R.: The effects of simultaneous addition of ammonium and potassium on their fixation in some Finnish soils. Ann. Agriculturae Fenniae *12*, 185–189 (1973)

SKELTON, B.J. and SHEAR, G.M.: Calcium translocation in the peanut *(Arachis hypogea L.)*. Agron. J. *63*, 409–412 (1971)

SKOKUT, T.A., WOLK, C.P., THOMAS, J., MEEKS, J.C., SHAFFER, P.W., and CHIEN W.S.: Initial organic products of assimiliation of (N-13) ammonium and (N-13) nitrate by tobacco cells cultured in different sources of nitrogen. Plant Physiol. *62*, 299–304 (1978)

SLACK, A.V.: Chemistry and Technology of Fertilizers. John Wiley and Sons, New York, London, Sidney 1967

SLACK, C.R. and HATCH, M.D.: Comparative studies on the activity of carboxylases and other enzymes in relation to the new pathway of photosynthetic carbon dioxide fixation in tropical grasses. Biochem. J. *103*, 660–665 (1967)

SLATYER, R.O.: Plant-Water Relationships. Academic Press, London, New York 1967

SLUIJSMANS, C.M.J. and KOLENBRANDER, G.J.: The significance of animal manure as a source of nitrogen in soils. In: Proc. Intern. Seminar on Soil Environment and Fertility Management in Intensive Agriculture. p. 403–411. Tokyo 1977

SMITH, A.M. and REES, A.P.T.: Pathways of carbohydrate fermentation in the roots of marsh plants. Planta *146*, 327–334 (1979)

SMITH, F.A. and RAVEN, J.A.: H$^+$ transport and regulation of cell pH, p. 317–346. In: Encyclop. Plant Physiol, Vol. 2, Part A. Ed. Lüttge and Pitmann. Springer, Berlin, Heidelberg, New York 1976

SMITH, F.A. and RAVEN, J.A.: Intercellular pH and its regulation. Ann. Rev. Plant Physiol. *30*, 289–311 (1979)

SMITH, P.F.: Mineral analysis of plant tissues. Ann. Rev. Plant Physiol. *13*, 81–108 (1962)

SMITH, T.A. and GARRAWAY, J.L.: N-carbamylputrescine – an intermediate in the formation of putrescine by barley. Phytochemistry *3*, 23–26 (1964)

SMITH, T.A. and SINCLAIR, C.: The effect of acid feeding on amine formation in barley. Ann. Bot. *31*, 103–111 (1967)

SODEK, L. and DA SILVA, W.J.: Glutamate synthase: A possible role in nitrogen metabolism of developing maize endosperm. Plant Physiol. *60*, 602–605 (1977)

SOMERS, J.J. and SHIVE, J.W.: The iron-manganese relation in plant metabolism. Plant Physiol. *17*, 582–602 (1942)

SOMMER, G.: (G) Pot experiments to establish the danger levels of cadmium copper, lead and zinc in relation is the application of refuse materials in agriculture. Landw. Forschung, Sonderheft *35*, 350–364 (1979)

SOMMER, K. and ROSSIG, K.: (G) Nitrification inhibition influencing yields in association with varied N fertilization and a proposal for classification of inhibitors. Landw. Forsch. *31*, 291–299 (1978)

SONNTAG, C. and MICHAEL, G.: (G) Influence of a late nitrogen application on the protein content and protein composition of grains obtained from conventional and lysine rich varieties of maize and barley. Z. Acker- u. Pflanzenbau *138*, 116–128 (1973)

SOPER, R.J. and HUANG, P.M.: The effect of nitrate nitrogen in the soil profile on the response of barley to fertilizer nitrogen. Can. J. Soil Sci. *43*, 350–358 (1962)

SOVONICK, S.A., GEIGER, D.R. and FELLOWS, R.J.: Evidence for active phloem loading in the minor veins of sugar beet. Plant Physiol. *54*, 886–891 (1974)

SPANNER, D.C.: Electroosmotic flow. In: Transport in Plants I, New Serie, Vol. 1 (M.H. ZIMMERMANN and J.A. MILBURN, eds.) p. 301–327. Springer-Verlag Berlin, Heidelberg, New York 1975

SPANSWICK, R.M. and WILLIAMS, E.J.: Electrical potentials and Na, K and Cl concentrations in the vacuole and cytoplasm of *Nitella translucens*. J. Exp. Bot. *15*, 193–200 (1964)

SPILLER, H., BOOKJANS, G. and BÖGER, P.: The influence of oxygen on nitrite reduction in a reconstituted system. Z. f. Naturforschung *31c*, 565–568 (1976)

STÄHLIN, A.: (G) Response of grassland and forage crops on 'Floranid'. Z. Acker- u. Pflanzenbau *126*, 301–316 (1967)

STANACEV, S.: Effect of vegetation space on sugar beet yield and quality. Savremena Poljoprivreda *15*, 403–413 (1967)

STANFORD, G., LEGG, J.O. and CHICHESTER, F.W.: Transformations of fertilizer nitrogen in soil. I. Interpretation based on chemical extractions of labelled and unlabelled nitrogen. Plant and Soil *33*, 425–435 (1970)

STANIER, R.Y., DOUDOROFF, M. and ADELBERG, E.A.: General Microbiology, 3rd ed. 1971

STAPP, C. and WETTER, C.: (G) Contributions to the quantitative microbiological determination of magnesium, zinc, iron, molybdenum and copper in soils. Landw. Forsch. *5*, 167–180 (1953)

STEFFENS, D.: (G) Comparative investigations on the potassium uptake potential and the development of root system of *Lolium perenne* and *Trifolium pratense*. Diss. Fachbereich 19, Ernährungswissenschaften, Justus Liebig-University Giessen 1981

STEFFENS, D. and MENGEL, K.: (G) The uptake potential of *Lolium perenne* and *Trifolium pratense* for interlayer K^+ of clay minerals. Landw. Forsch. Sonderh. *36*, 120–127 (1979)

STEGEMANN, H., FRANCKSEN, H. and MACKO, V.: Potato proteins: Genetic and physiological changes, evaluated by one- and two-dimensional PAA-Gel-techniques. Z. Naturforsch. *28*, 722–732 (1973)

STELZER, R., LÄUCHLI, A. and KRAMER, D.: (G) Intercellular pathways of chloride in roots of intact barley plants. Cytobiologie *10*, 449–457 (1975)

STENUIT, D.F.: (G) Relationship between magnesium content and yield of Belgian soils. Landw. Forsch., 13. Sonderh., 23–29 (1959)

STEPHEN, C.J.: Copper uptake and accumulation by perennial ryegrass grown in soil and solution culture. J. Sci. Fd Agric. *29*, 12–18 (1978)

STEPHEN, C.J.: The uptake and distribution of copper in perennial ryegrass and white clover grown in flowing solution culture with a controlled supply of copper. J. Sci. Fd Agric. *31*, 870–876 (1980)

STEPHENS, O.: Changes in yields and fertilizer responses with continuous cropping in Uganda. Experimental Agriculture *5*, 263–269 (1969)

STEUCEK, C.G. and KOONTZ, H.V.: Phloem mobility of magnesium. Plant Physiol. *46*, 50–52 (1970)

STEVENINCK, R.F.M. VAN: The significance of calcium on the apparent permeability of cell membranes and the effects of substitution with other divalent ions. Physiol. Plant. *18*, 54–69 (1965)

STEVENSON, F.J. and ARDAKANI, M.S.: Organic matter reactions envoling micronutrients in soils, p. 79–114. In: Micronutrients in Agriculture, ed. Soil Sci. Soc. of America Inc., Madison/Wisconsin 1972

STEWART, W.D.P.: Nitrogen Fixation in Plants. University of London, The athlone Press 1966

STEWART, W.D.P.: Nitrogen-fixing plants. Science *158*, 1426–1432 (1967)

STOCKER, O.: (G) Water and photosynthetic status of Central European grasses, a contribution to the general problem of grass types. Flora (Jena) B *157*, 56–96 (1967)

STONER, C.D., HODGES, T.K. and HANSON, J.B.: Chloramphenicol as an inhibitor of energy-linked processes in maize mitochondria. Nature *203*, 258–269 (1964)

STOREY, H.H. and LEACH, R.: Sulphur deficiency disease in the tea bush. Ann. Appl. Biol. *20*, 23–56 (1933)

STOUT, P.R. and MEAGHER, W.R.: Studies of the molybdenum nutrition of plants with radioactive molybdenum. Science *108*, 471–473 (1948)

STOUT, P.R., MEAGHER, W.R., PEARSON, G.A. and JOHNSON, C.M.: Molybdenum nutrition of crop plants. I. The influence of phosphate and sulfate on the absorption of molybdenum from soils and solution cultures. Plant and Soil *3*, 51–87 (1951)

STOY, V.: (G) Assimilate synthesis and distribution as components for the yield formation of cereals. Symp. German Ass. Appl. Botany, Hanover 1972

STREETER, J.G.: Allantoin and allantoic acid in tissues and stem exudate from field grown soybean plants. Plant Physiol. *63*, 478–480 (1979)

STUTTE, C.A., WEILAND, R.T. and BLEM, A.R.: Gaseous nitrogen loss from soybean foliage. Agron. J. *71*, 95–97 (1979)

SUBBA RAO, N.S.: Prospects of bacterial fertilisation in India. Fertil. News *19*, 32–36 (1974)

SUBBA RAO, N.S. and VASANTHA, P.: Nodulation of *Trifolium alexandrinum in vitro* and nitrate effect on the amino acid composition of the plant and its root exudate. Canad. J. Bot. *43*, 1189–1194 (1965)

SUELTER, C.H.: Enzymes activated by monovalent cations. Science *168*, 789–795 (1970)

SUTCLIFFE, J.: Plants and Water, 2nd edition (ARNOLD, ed.). Studies in Biology 14, 1979

SWAINE, D.J.: The trace element content of soils. Soil Sci. Techn. Comm. No. 48. Herald Printing Works, Coney St., York (England). 1955

SYWOROTKIN, G.S.: (G) The boron content of plants with a latex system. Spurenelemente in der Landwirtschaft, 283–288, Akademie-Verlag Berlin 1958

SZABOLCS, I.: Solonetz soils in Europe, their formation and properties with particular regard to utilization, p. 9–33. In: I.SZABOLCS: European Solonetz Soils and their Reclamation. Akadémiai Kiadó Budapest 1971

SZALAY, A. and SZILAGYI, M.: Laboratory experiments on the retention of micronutrients by peat humic acids. Plant and Soil *29*, 219–224 (1968)

TAKAHASHI, E. and MIYAKE, Y.: Silica and plant growth. In: Proc. Intern. Seminar on Soil Environment and Fertility Management in Intensive Agriculture p. 603–611. Nippon Dojohiryo Gakkai, Tokyo 1977

TAKAI, Y., KOYAMA, T. and KAMURA, T.: Microbial metabolism of paddy soils. J. Agr. Chem. Soc. Japan *31*, 211–220 (1957)

TAKAKI, H. and KUSHIZAKI, M.: Accumulation of free tryptophan and tryptamine in zinc deficient maize seedlings. Plant and Cell Physiol. II, 793–804 (1970)

TAKKAR, P.N. and SINGH, T.: Zn nutrition of rice as influenced by rates of gypsum and Zn fertilization of alkali soils. Agron. J. *70*, 447–450 (1978)

TANAKA, A.: The relative importance of the source and the sink as the yield-limiting factors of rice. ASPAC, Technical Bulletin No. 6, p. 1–18 (1972)

TANAKA, A.: Influence of special ecological conditions on growth, metabolism and potassium nutrition of tropical crops as exemplified by the case of rice. In: Potassium in Tropical Crops and Soils. 10th Colloq. Int. Potash Inst., p. 97–116, Bern 1973

TANAKA, A., YAMAGUCHI, J. and KAWAGUCHI, K.: A note on the nutritional status of the rice plant in Italy, Portugal, and Spain. Soil Sci. Plant Nutr. *19*, (3) 161–171 (1973)

TANAKA, A. and YOSHIDA, S.: Nutritional disorders of the rice plant in Asia. Intern. Rice Res. Inst., Technical Bulletin 10 (1970)

TANAKA, H.: Boron adsorption by plant roots. Plant and Soil 27, 300–302 (1967)

TANNENBAUM, S.R., FETT, D., YOUNG, V.R., LAND, P.D. and BRUCE, W.R.: Nitrite and nitrate are formed by endogenous synthesis in the human intestine. Science 20, 1487–1489 (1978)

TAYLOR, D.M., MORGAN, P.W., JOHAM, H.E. and AMIN, J.V.: Influence of substrate and tissue manganese on the IAA-oxidase system in cotton. Plant Physiol. 43, 243–247 (1968)

TAYLOR, H.M. and KLEPPER, B.: The role of rooting characteristics in the supply of water to plants. Adv. Agron. 30, 99–128 (1978)

TAYLOR, R.M. and GILES, J.B.: The association of vanadium and molybdenum with iron oxides in soils. J. Soil Sci. 21, 203–215 (1970)

TAYLOR, R.M. and McKENZIE, R.M.: The association of trace elements with manganese minerals in Australian soils. Aust. J. Soil Res. 4, 29–39 (1966)

TERMAN, G.J.: Effect of rate and source of potash on yield and starch content of potatoes. Maine Agric. Expt. Sta. Bull. 581, 1–24 (1950)

TERMAN, G.L.: Volatilization losses of nitrogen as ammonia from surface-applied fertilizers, organic amendments, and crop residues. Adv. Agron. 31, 189–223 (1979)

TERMAN, G.L. and ALLEN, S.E.: Leaching of soluble and slow-release N and K fertilizers from lakeland sand under glass and fallow. Soil and Crop Science Society of Florida, Proceed. 30, 130–140 (1970)

TERMAN, G.L. and BROWN, M.A.: Uptake of fertilizer and soil nitrogen by rye grass, as affected by carbonaceous residues. Proc. Soil Sci. Soc. Am. 32, 86–90 (1968)

TERMAN, G.L., MORENO, E.C. and OSBORN, G.: Acidulation of phosphate rock in soil. Soil Sci. Soc. Am. Proc. 28, 104–107 (1964)

TERRY, N.: Photosynthesis growth and the role of chloride. Plant Physiol 60, 69–75 (1977)

TERRY, N.: Limiting factors in photosynthesis I. Use of iron stress to control phytochemical capacity in vivo. Plant Physiol 65, 114–120 (1980)

TERRY, N. and ULRICH, A.: Effects of potassium deficiency on the photosynthesis and respiration of leaves of sugar beet. Plant Physiol. 51, 783–786 (1973)

TESKE, W. and MATZEL, W.: (G) Nitrogen leaching and nitrogen utilization by the plants as established in field lysimeters using 15-N urea. Arch. Acker- u. Pflanzenbau u. Bodenk. 20, 489–502 (1976)

THOMSON, I., THORNTON, I. and WEBB, J.S.: Molybdenum in black shales and the incidence of bovine hypocuprosis. J. Sci. Fd Agric. 23, 879–891 (1972)

THOMSON, W.W. and WEIER, T.E.: The fine structure of chloroplasts from mineral-deficient leaves of Phaseolus vulgaris. Am. J. Bot. 49, 1047–1055 (1962)

THOMSON, W.W. and WEIER, T.E.: An electron microscope study of chloroplasts from leaves deficient in nitrogen, phosphorus, magnesium, potassium and zinc. Plant Physiol. 37, XI (1962)

TIFFIN, L.O.: Iron Translocation. I. Plant culture exudate sampling, iron/citrate analysis. Plant Physiol. 41, 510–514 (1966)

TIFFIN, L.O.: Translocation of manganese, iron, cobalt and zinc in tomato. Plant Physiol. 42, 1427–1432 (1967)

TIFFIN, L.O.: Translocation of micronutrients in plants, p. 199–229. In: Micronutrients in Agriculture. Soil Sci. Soc. America Inc., Madison 1972

TIFFIN, L.O. and BROWN, J.C.: Selective absorption of iron from iron chelates by soybean plants. Plant Physiol. 36, 710–714 (1961)

TINKER, P.B..: The effects of magnesium sulphate on sugar beet yield and its interactions with other fertilizers. J. agric. Sci. Camb. 68, 205–212 (1967)

TOLBERT, N.E.: (2-chloroethyl) trimethylammonium chloride and related compounds as plant growth substances. II. Effect of growth on wheat. Plant Physiol. 35, 380–385 (1960)

TOLBERT, N.E.: Glycolate metabolism by higher plants and algae. In: Photosynthesis II, Encycl. Plant Physiol. New Series, Vol. 6 (M. GIBBS and E. LATZKO, eds.) p. 338–352. Springer-Verlag Berlin, Heidelberg, New York 1979

TORIYAMA, K.: Development of agronomic practices for production of field crops under irrigated conditions-rice. In: 1. FAO/SIDA Seminar for Plant Scientists from Africa and the Near East, Cairo 1973, p. 452–456. FAO, Rome 1974

TOUCHTON, J.T., HOEFT, R.G. and WELCH, L.F.: Nitrapyrin degradation and movement in soil. Agron. J. 70, 811–816 (1978)

TRAVIS, R.L. and BOOZ, M.L.: Partial characterisation of a potassium-stimulated adenosine trophosphatase from the plasma membrane of meristematic and mature soybean root tissue. Plant Physiol. 63, 573–577 (1979)

TREBST, A.: Energy conservation in photosynthetic electron transport of chloroplasts. Ann. Rev. Plant Physiol. 25, 423–458 (1974)

TREBST, A. and PISTORIUS, E.: (G) Role of plastocyanin in the photosynthesis of isolated chloroplasts. Beiträge zur Biochemie und Physiologie von Naturstoffen. Festschrift Kurt Mothes zum 65. Geburtstag - Fischer-Verlag, Jena 1965

TRELEASE, S.F.: Selenium in soils, plants and animals. Soil Sci. 60, 125–131 (1945)

TRIP, P.: Sugar transport in conducting elements of sugar beet leaves. Plant Physiol. 44, 717–725 (1969)

TROCMÉ, S. and BARBIER, G.: (F) Influence of 'old' and 'young' potassium on the sugar content of sugar beets, p. 127–129. Int. Potash Inst., Bern 1966

TROLLDENIER, G.: (G) Cereal diseases and plant nutrition. Potash Review Subj. 23, suite 24 (1969)

TROLLDENIER, G.: Recent aspects of the influence of potassium on stomatal opening and closing, p. 130–133. In: Potassium in Biochemistry and Physiology. Proc. 8th Colloq. Int. Potash Inst., Bern 1971

TROLLDENIER, G.: (G) Soil Biology, the Soil Organisms in the Economy of Nature, p. 116. Franckh'sche Verlagshandlung, Stuttgart 1971

TROLLDENIER, G.: Secondary effects of potassium and nitrogen on rice: Change in microbial activity and iron reduction in rhizosphere. Plant and Soil 38, 267–279 (1973)

TROLLDENIER, G.: Secondary effects of potassium and nitrogen nutrition of rice: Change in microbial activity and iron reduction in the rhizosphere. Plant and Soil 38, 267–279 (1973)

TROLLDENIER, G. and ZEHLER, E.: Relationship between plant nutrition and rice diseases. In: Fertilizer Use and Plant Health, p. 85–93. Proc. 12th Colloq. Int. Potash Inst., Bern 1976

TRUOG, E.: The determination of the readily available phosphorus of soils. J. Am. Soc. Agr. 22, 879–890 (1930)

TS'O, P.O.P.: The ribosomes-ribonucleoprotein particles. Ann. Rev. Plant Physiol. 13, 45–80 (1962)

TSUI, C.: The role of zinc in auxin synthesis in the tomato plant. Amer. J. Bot. 35, 172–179 (1948)

TUBB, R.S.: Glutamine synthetase and ammonium regulation of nitrogenase synthesis in Klebsiella. Nature 251, 481–485 (1974)

TUKEY, H.B., WITTWER, S.H. and BUKOVAC, M.J.: The uptake and loss of materials by leaves and other above-ground plant parts with special reference to plant nutrition. Nutrient Uptake of Plants, 4. Intern. Symposium, Agrochimica Pisa, Florenz, p. 384–413 (1962)

TURNER, D.W. and BARKUS, B.: The effect of season, stage of plant growth and leaf position on nutrient concentrations in the banana leaf on a Kraznozem in New South Wales. Aust. J. Exp. Agric and An Husb. 14, 112–117 (1974)

TURNER, R.G.: The subcellular distribution of zinc and copper within the roots of metal-tolerant clones of Agrostis tenuis Sibth. New Phytol. 69, 725–731 (1969)

TURNER, R.G. and MARSHALL, C.: The accumulation of Zn-65 by root homogenates of Zn tolerant and non tolerant clones of Agrostis tenuis Sibth. New Phytol. 70, 539–545 (1972)

UEXKÜLL, H.R. VON: Response of coconuts to potassium chloride in the Philippines. Oléagineux *27*, 31–91 (1972)

ULRICH, A.: Metabolism of non-volatile organic acids in excised barley roots as related to cation-anion balance during salt accumulation. Amer. J. Bot. *28*, 523–537 (1941)

ULRICH, A. and FONG, K.H.: Effects of potassium nutrition on growth and cation content of potato leaves and tubers relative to plant analysis. J. Amer. Sci. *94*, 356–359 (1969)

ULRICH, A. and HILLS, F.J.: Plant analysis as an aid in fertilizing supar crops. Part I: Sugar beets, p. 271–288. In: Soil Testing and Plant Analysis. Ed. L.M.Walsh and J.D.Beaton. S.S.S.A. 1973

ULRICH, A. and HYLTON, L.O. jr.: Sulphur nutrition of Italian ryegrass measured by growth and mineral content. Plant and Soil *29*, 274–284 (1968)

ULRICH, A. and OHKI, K.: Chlorine, bromine and sodium as nutrients for sugar beet plants. Plant Physiol. *31*, 171–181 (1956)

ULRICH, A. and OHKI, K.: Potassium, p. 362–393. In: H.D.CHAPMAN: Diagnostic Criteria for Plants and Soils. University of California, Riverside, Dif. of Agric. Sciences 1966

ULRICH, A., RIRIE, D., HILLS, F.J., GEORGE, A.G. and MORSE, M.D.: Principles and practices of plant analysis. In: Soil Testing and Plant Analysis. II. Plant Analysis. Soil Sci. Soc. America, Madison, Wisc., p. 11–24 (1967)

ULRICH, A., TABATABAI, M.A., OHKI, K. and JOHNSON, C.M.: Sulfur content of alfalfa in relation to growth in filtered and unfiltered air. Plant and Soil *26*, 235–252 (1967)

UNDERWOOD, E.J.: Trace Elements in Human and Animal Nutrition. Academic Press, New York 1971

VAADIA, Y., RANEY, F.C. and HAGAN, R.M.: Plant water deficits and physiological processes. Ann. Rev. Plant Physiol. *12*, 265–292 (1961)

VALLEE, B.L. and WACKER, W.E.C.: Metalloprotein: in H.Neurath (ed.). The Proteins (2nd ed.), Vol. 5, Academic Press, New York, p. 192 (1970)

VAN DEENEN, L.L.M.: (G) Phospholipids. Relationships between their chemical structure and biological membranes. Naturwissenschaften *59*, 485–491 (1972)

VANSELOW, A.P.: Cobalt, p. 142–156. In: H.D.CHAPMAN: Criteria for Plants and Soils. University of California, Div. of Agric. Sciences 1966

VEIHMEYER, F.J. and HENDRICKSON, A.H.: The moisture equivalent as a measure of the field capacity of soils. Soil Sci. *32*, 181–193 (1931)

VENKATESWARLU, P., ARMSTRONG, W.D. and SINGER, L.: Absorption of fluoride and chloride by barley roots. Plant Physiol. *40*, 255–261 (1965)

VENKAT RAJU, K. and MARSCHNER, H.: Regulation of iron uptake from relatively insoluble iron compounds by sunflower plants. Z. Pflanzenernähr. Bodenk. *133*, 227–241 (1972)

VENTER, H.A. VAN DE and CURRIER, H.B.: The effect of boron deficiency on callose formation and ^{14}C translocation in bean *(Phaseolus vulgaris)* and cotton *(Gossypium hirsutum* L.) Am. J. Bot. *64*, 861–865 (1977)

VERGNANO, O. and HUNTER, J.G.: Nickel and cobalt toxicities in oat plants. Ann. Bot. NS *17*, 317–328 (1952)

VERTREGT, N.: Relation between black spot and composition of the potato tuber. Eur. Potato J. *11*, 34–44 (1968)

VESK, M., POSSINGHAM, J.V. and MERCER, F.V.: The effect of mineral nutrient deficiencies on the structure of leaf cells of tomato, spinach and maize. Aust. J. Bot. *14*, 1–18 (1966)

VETTER, H. and KLASINK, A.: (G) Nutrient contents in slurries and faeces. In: Wieviel düngen? p. 189–194. DLG-Verlag Frankfurt 1977

VETTER, H. and TEICHMANN, W.: (G) Field trials with varied copper and nitrogen treatments in Weser-Ems. Z. Pflanzenernähr. Bodenkd. *121*, 97–111 (1968)

VIETS, F.G.: Calcium and other polyvalent cations as accelerators of ion accumulation by excised barley roots. Plant Physiol. *19*, 466–480 (1944)

VIETS, F.G.: Water quality in relation to farm use of fertilizer. Bio. Science *21*, 460–467 (1971)

VIETS, F.G., BOAWN, L.C. and CRAWFORD, C.L.: Zinc contents and deficiency symptoms of 26 crops grown on a zinc deficient soil. Soil Sci. *78*, 305–316 (1954)

VINCENT, J., LEGGETT, J.E. and EGLI, D.B.: Cation accumulation by Glycine max. (L) Merr. as related to maturity stages. In: The Soil Root Interface (J.L. HARLEY and R. SCOTT RUSSELL, eds.) p. 440. Academic Press, London, New York, San Francisco, 1979

VINES, H.M. and WEDDING, R.T.: Some effects of ammonia on plant metabolism and a possible mechanism for ammonia toxicity. Plant Physiol. *35*, 820–825 (1960)

VIRO, M.: (G) The effect of a varied nutrition with potassium on the translocation of assimilates and minerals in *Lycopersicon esculentum*. Diss. Fachbereich 19 Ernährungswissenschaften, Justus-Liebig-Universität Giessen 1973

VIRUPAKSHA, T.K. and SHRIFT, A.: Biochemical differences between selenium accumulator and non-accumulator *Astragalus* species. Biochim. Biophys. Acta *107*, 69–80 (1965)

VLAMIS, J.: Acid soil infertility as related to soil solution and solid-phase effects. Soil Sci. *75*, 383–394 (1953)

VLAMIS, J. and WILLIAMS, D.E.: Manganese and silicon interactions in the *gramineae*. Plant and Soil *27*, 131–140 (1967)

VÖLKER, L.: (G) Influence of a late additional nitrogen application on the content of several amino acids in grain proteins. Landw. Forsch. *13*, 307–316 (1960)

VÖMEL, A.: (G) Nutrient balance in various lysimeter soils. I. Water leaching and nutrient balance. Z. Acker- u. Pflanzenbau *123*, 155–188 (1965/66)

VORM VAN DER, P.D.J. and DIEST VAN A.: Aspects of the Fe and Mn nutrition of rice plants. II. Iron and manganese uptake by rice plants grown on aerobic water cultures. Plant and Soil *52*, 12–29 (1979)

WAGGONER, P.E. and ZELITCH, I.: Transpiration and stomata of leaves. Science *150*, 1413–1420 (1965)

WAGNER, H. and MICHAEL, G.: (G) Effect of a varied nitrogen supply on the synthesis of cytokinins in roots of sunflower. Biochem. Physiol. Pflanzen (BPP) *162*, 147–158 (1971)

WAHLE, K.W.J. and DAVIES, N.T.: Involvement of copper in microsomal mixed-function oxidase reactions: a review. J. Si. Fd. Agric. *28*, 93–97 (1977)

WAHUA, T.A.T. and MILLER, D.A.: Effects of shading on the N_2-fixation, yield and plant composition of field-grown soybeans. Agron. J. *70*, 387–392 (1978)

WAINWRIGHT, S.J. and WOOLHOUSE, H.W.: Physiological mechanisms of heavy metal tolerance in plants, p. 231–257. In: M.J.CHADWICK and G.T.GOODMAN: The Ecology of Resource Degradation and Renewal. Blackwell, Oxford 1975

WALKER, D.A.: Three phases of chloroplast research. Nature *226*, 1204–1208 (1970)

WALKER, D.A.: Chloroplast and cell – The movement of certain key substances across the chloroplast envelope, p. 1–49. In: D.H.NORTHCOTE: Int. Review of Science, Plant Biochemistry Series I, Vol. *II*, Butterworths 1974

WALKER, D.A.: Regulation of starch synthesis in leaves – the role of orthophosphate. In: Physiological Aspects of Crop Productivity, p. 195–207. Proc. 15th Colloq. Int. Potash Inst., Bern 1980

WALKER, N.: Report of the Rothamsted Experimental Station, Part I. p. 283 (1976)

WALKER, N.A.: The structure of biological membranes. In: U.LÜTTGE and M.G.PITMAN: Transport in Plants II, Part A Cells. Enc. of Plant Physiology, New Series, Vol. 2, p. 3–11, Springer-Verlag, Berlin, Heidelberg, New York (1976)

WALKER, T.W.: Relations between the soil, the soil solutions and inorganic plant nutrition. Agric. Progress *20*, 74–87 (1946)

WALKER, T.W. and ADAMS, A.F.R.: Competition for sulphur in a grass-clover association. Plant and Soil *9*, 353–366 (1958)

WALKER, T.W., ORCHISTON, H.D. and ADAMS, A.F.R.: The nitrogen economy of grass legume associations. J. Brit. Grassl. Soc. *9*, 240–274 (1954)

WALKER, T.W. and SYERS, J.K.: The fate of phosphorus during pedogenesis. Geoderma *15*, 1–19 (1976)

WALLACE, A., FROLICH, E. and LUNT, O. R.: Calcium requirements of higher plants. Nature *209*, 634 (1966)

WALLACE, T.: The Diagnosis of Mineral Deficiencies in Plants by Visual Symptoms. A colour Atlas and Guide. Her Majesty's Stationery Office, London 1961

WALLACE, W. and PATE, J.S.: Nitrate reductase in the field pea *(Pisum arvense* L.*)*. Ann. Bot. (London) N.S., *29*, 655–671 (1965)

WALLACE, W. and PATE, J.S.: Nitrate assimilation in higher plants with special reference to cocklebur *(Xanthium pennsylvaticum* Wallr). Ann. of Bot. *31*, 213–228 (1967)

WALSH, T. and GOLDEN, J.D.: The boron status of Irish soils in relation to the occurrence of boron deficiency in some crops in acid and alkaline soils. Int. Soc. Soil Trans (Comm II and IV) II, 167–171 (1952)

WALTER, B., BATGEN, D., PATENBURG, H. and KOCH, W.: (G) Effect of gas and salt on soil and plant. Das Gartenamt *10*, 578–581 (1974)

WALTER, B., KOCH, W. and BASTGEN, D.: (G) Experiences and results of urea foliar applications to grapes. Weinberg und Keller *20*, 265–274 (1973)

WANASURIA, S., DE DATTA, S.K. and MENGEL, K.: Rice yield in relation to electroultrafiltration extractable soil potassium. Plant and Soil *59*, 23–31 (1981)

WANASURIA, S., MENGEL, K. and DE DATTA, S.K.: Use of electro-ultrafiltration (EUF) technique to study the potassium dynamics of wetland soils and potassium uptake by rice. Soil Sci. Plant Nutr. (Tokyo) in press (1981)

WARD, G.M. and MILLER, M.J.: Magnesium deficiency in greenhouse tomatoes. Canad. J. Plant Sci. *49*, 53–59 (1969)

WARDLAW, J.F.: The effect of water stress on translocation in relation to photosynthesis and growth. II. Effect during leaf development in *Lolium temulentum.* Aust. J. biol. Sci. *22*, 1–16 (1969)

WARNOCK, R.E.: Micronutrient uptake and mobility within corn plants *(Zea mays* L.*)* in relation to P induced zinc deficiency. Soil Sci. Soc. Amer. Proc. *34*, 765–769 (1970)

WARREN-WILSON, J.: Maximum yield potential. In: Transition from Extensive to Intensive Agriculture with Fertilisers, p. 34–56. Proc. VIIth Colloq. Int. Potash Inst., Bern 1969

WARRINGTON, K.: The influence of iron supply on toxic effects of manganese molybdenum and vanadium on soybeans, peas and flax. Ann. Appl. Biol. *41*, 1–22 (1955)

WATANABE, H. and YOSHIDA, S.: Effects of nitrogen, phosphorus, and potassium on photophosphorylation in rice in relation to the photosynthetic rate of single leaves. Soil Sci. Plant Nut. *16*, 163–166 (1970)

WATANABE, I., BERJA, N.S. and DEL ROSARIO, D.C.: Growth of *Azolla* in paddy fields as affected by phosphorus fertilizer. Soil. Sci. Plant Nutr. *26*, 301–307 (1980)

WATANABE, I., ESPINAS, C.R., BERJA, N.S. and ALIMAGNO, B.V.: Utilization of the *Azolla-Anabaena* complex as a nitrogen fertilizer for rice. IRRI Research Paper Series No. 11, 3.–14. November (1977)

WATSON, D.J.: The physiological basis of variation in yield. Adv. Agron. *4*, 101–144 (1952)

WATSON, J.D.: Molecular Biology of the Gene. Benjamin, New York, p. 494 (1965)

WEBLEY, D.M. and DUFF, R.B.: The incidence in soils and other habitats of microorganisms producing α-ketogluconic acid. Plant and Soil *22*, 307–313 (1965)

WEHRMANN, J. and SCHARPF, H.C.: (G) The mineral content of the soil as a measure of the nitrogen fertilizer requirement (N_{min} method). Plant and Soil *52*, 109–126 (1979)

WEIGL, J.: (G) Proof of the participation of mobile carriers in ion transport through plant membranes and the kinetics of anion transport in *Elodea* in light and dark. Planta *75*, 327–342 (1967)

WEINSTEIN, L.H.: Fluoride and plant life. J. of Occupational Medicine *19*, 49–78 (1977)

WEISSMAN, G.S.: Glutamine synthetase regulation by energy charge in sunflower roots. Plant Physiol. *57*, 339–343 (1976)

WELCH, L. F., JOHNSON, P. E., McKIBBEN, G. E., BOONE, L.V. and PENDLETON, I.W.: Relative efficiency of broadcast versus banded potassium for corn. Agron. J. *58*, 618–621 (1966)
WELCH, R.M.: The biological significance of nickel. J. Plant Nutrition. in press, 1982
WELCH, R.M. and HUFFMAN, W.D.: Vanadium and plant nutrition. Plant Physiol. *52*, 183–185 (1973)
WELCH, R.W.: Genotypic variation in oil and protein in barley grain. J. Sci. Fd Agric *29*, 953–958 (1978)
WELLBURN, A.R., MAJERNIK, O. and WELLBURN, F.A.M.: Effects of SO_2 and NO_2-polluted air upon the ultrastructure of chloroplasts. Environ. Pollution 3, 37–49 (1972)
WELLER, F.: A method for studying the distribution of absorbing roots of fruit trees. Expl. Agric. 7, 351–361 (1971)
WERNER, D.: (G) Investigations into the role of silicic acid for the development of higher plants and analysis of the inhibition by germanium acid. Planta *76*, 25–36 (1967)
WERNER, D.: (G) Dinitrogen fixation and primary production. Angew. Botanik *54*, 67–75 (1980)
WERNER, W.: (G) Characterization of the available phosphate after an application of different phosphate forms for some years. Z. Pflanzenernähr. Bodenk. *122*, 19–32 (1969)
WEST, K.R. and PITMAN, M.G.: Rubidium as a tracer for potassium in the marine algae *Ulva lactuca* L. and *Chaetomorpha darwinii* (Hooker) Kuetzing. Nature *214*, 1262–1263 (1967)
WHEELER, A.W.: Changes in growth-substance content during growth of wheat. J. appl. Biol. *72*, 327–334 (1972)
WHITE, D.J.: Energy use in agriculture. In: Aspects of Energy conversion (BLAIR, JONES and VAN HORN, eds.) Pergamon Press, Oxford and New York 1976
WHITE, G.C. and GREENHAM, D.W.P.: Seasonal trends in mineral nitrogen content of the soil in a long-term NPK trial on dessert apples. J. horticult. Sci. *42*, 419–428 (1967)
WHITEHEAD, D.C.: Soil and plant nutrition aspects of the sulphur cycle. Soils Fert. *29*, 1–9 (1964)
WICKE, H.J.: (G) Effect of high potassium rates on yield and quality parameters of crops (results of field trials). Albrecht-Thaer-Archiv *12*, 889–902 (1968)
WIDDOWSON, F.V., PENNY, A. and WILLIAMS, R.J.B.: Experiments measuring effects of ammonium and nitrate fertilizers, with and without sodium and potassium, on spring barley. J. agric. Sci. *69*, 197–207 (1967)
WIEBE, H.H. and AL-SAADI, H.A.: Matric bound water of water tissue from succulents. Plant Physiol. *36*, 47–51 (1976)
WIERSUM, I.K.: Calcium content of the phloem sap in relation to the Ca status of the plant. Acta bot. neerl. *28*, 221–224 (1979)
WIKLANDER, L.: Forms of potassium in the soil, p. 109–121. 2nd Congr. Int. Potash Inst., Bern 1954
WIKLANDER, L.: The soil, p. 118–164. In: Encyclopedia of Plant Physiology, Vol. 4, Springer-Verlag, Berlin, Göttingen, Heidelberg 1958
WIKLANDER, L. and HALLGREN, G.: Studies on gyttja soils. Kungl. Lantbeukshögsk. Ann. *16*, 811–827 (1949)
WILO, A., SKARLOU, V., CLEMENT, C.R. and SNAYOON, R.W.: Comparison of potassium uptake by four plant species grown in sand and in flowing culture. J. appl. Ecol. *II*, 801–802 (1974)
WILKINSON, B.: Boron in the glasshouse tomato plant. Nature *180*, 666 (1957)
WILKINSON, B.G.: Mineral composition of apples. IX. Uptake of calcium by the fruit. J. Sci. Fd. Agric. *19*, 446–447 (1968)
WILLIAMS, C.H. and DAVID, D.J.: The effects of superphosphate on the cadmium content of soils and plants. Australian J. Soil Research II, 43–56 (1973)
WILLIAMS, D.E. and VLAMIS, J.: The effect of silicon on yield and manganese 54 uptake and distribution in the leaves of barley plants grown in culture solutions. Plant Physiol. *32*, 404–409 (1957)

WILLIAMS, E.G.: Influences of parent material and drainage conditions on soil phosphorus relationships. Agrochimica *3*, 279 (1959)

WILLIAMS, E.G.: Factors affecting the availability of soil phosphate and efficiency of phosphate fertilizers. Anglo-Soviet Symposium on Agrochemical Research on the Use of Mineral Fertilizers, Moscow (1970)

WILLIAMS, E.G. and KNIGHT, A.H.: Evaluations of soil phosphate status by pot experiments, conventional extraction methods and labile phosphate values estimated with the aid of phosphorus 32. J. Sci. Fd. Agric. *14*, 555–563 (1963)

WILLIAMS, R.J.B.: The chemical composition of water from land drains at Saxmundham and Woburn, and the influence of rainfall upon nutrient losses. Rep. Roth. Exp. Sta. part 2, p. 36–67 (1970)

WILLIAMS, W.A., MORSE, M.D. and RUCKMAN, J.R.: Burning vs incorporation of rice crop residues. Agron. J. *64*, 467–468 (1972)

WILSON, D.O. and REISENAUER, H.M.: Cobalt requirement of symbiotically grown alfalfa. Plant and Soil *19*, 364–373 (1967)

WILSON, L.G., BRESSAN, R.A. and FILNER, P.: Light-dependent emission of hydrogen sulfide from plants. Plant Physiol. *61*, 184–189 (1978)

WILSON, S.B. and HALLSWORTH, E.G.: Studies of the nutrition of the forage legumes. IV. The effect of cobalt on the growth of nodulated and non nodulated *Trifolium subterraneum* L. Plant and Soil *22*, 260 (1965)

WILSON, S.B. and NICHOLAS, D.J.D.: A cobalt requirement for non-nodulated legumes and for wheat. Phytochemistry *6*, 1057–1060 (1967)

WINNER, C.: (G) Questions concerning the choice of cultivars and fertilizer application in relation to beet quality in modern sugar beet cultivation. Zucker *21*, 521–530 (1968)

WINSOR, G.W.: Potassium and the quality of glasshouse crops. In: Potassium and the Quality of Agricultural Products, p. 303–312, Proc. 8th Congr. Int. Potash Inst., Bern 1966

WINTER, H.C. and BURRIS, R.H.: Nitrogenase Ann. Rev. Biochemistry *45*, 409–426 (1976)

WITTWER, S.H. and TEUBNER, F.G.: Foliar absorption of mineral nutrients. Ann. Rev. Plant Physiol. *10*, 13–32 (1959)

WITTWER, S.H. and TOLBERT, N.E.: 2-Chloroethyl trimethyl-ammonium chloride and related compounds as plant growth substances. Plant Physiol. *35*, 871–877 (1960)

WOLDENDORP, J.W.: Losses of soil nitrogen. Stikstof, Dutch Nitrogenous Fertilizer Review, Nr. 12, 32–46 (1968)

WOLLNY, E.: (G) Investigations into the capillary movement of water in soils. Forsch.-Gebiete Agr.-Phys. *8*, 206–220 (1885)

WOOLEY, J.T.: Sodium and silicon as nutrients for the tomato plant. Plant Physiol. *32*, 317–321 (1957)

WOOLHOUSE, H.W.: Light gathering and carbon assimilation processes in photosynthesis; their adaptive modifications and significance for agriculture. Endeavour, New Series 2, 35–46 (1978)

WRIGHT, J.P. and FISHER, D.B.: Direct measurement of sieve tube turgor pressure using severed aphid stylets. Plant Physiol. *65*, 1133–1135 (1980)

WU, M.M.H., WANG, Y.P. and TANG, C.N.: Appraisal of the effectiveness of a native strain of soybean bacteria on powdered carrier by Island-wide field inoculation. J. Agric. and Forestry *18*, 1–9 (1969)

WUNDERLICH, F.: (G) The nucleus matrix: Dynamic protein-structure in cell nucleus. Naturw. Rdsch. *31*, 282–288 (1978)

WYN JONES, R.G. and LUNT, O.R.: The function of calcium in plants. Bot. Rev. *33*, 407–426 (1967)

WYN JONES, R.G., SUTCLIFFE, M. and MARSHALL, C.: Physiological and biochemical basis for heavy metal tolerance in clones of *Agrostis tenuis*, In: R.M.SAMISH: Recent Advances in Plant Nutrition. Gordon and Breach, New York 1971

YOSHIDA, S. and CASTANEDA, L.: Partial replacement of potassium by sodium in the rice plant under weakly saline conditions. Soil Sci. Plant Nutr. *15*, 183–186 (1969)

YOSHIDA, S., FORNO, D.A. and BHADROCHALM, A.: Zinc deficiency of the rice plant on calcareous and neutral soils in the Philippines. Soil Sci. Plant Nutr. *17*, 83–87 (1971)

YOSHIDA, S., OHNISHI, Y. and KITAGISHI, K.: Chemical forms, mobility and deposition of silicon in rice plant. Soil Sci. Plant Ntr. *8*, 15–21 (1962)

ZECH, W.: (G) Needle analytical investigations into the lime chlorosis of the pine *(Pinus silvestris)*. Z. Pflanzenernähr. Bodenk. *125*, 1–16 (1970)

ZECH, W., KOCH, W. and FRANZ, F.: (G) Net assimilation and transpiration of pine twigs in dependence on potassium supply and light intensity. Kali-Briefe, Fachgeb. 6, 1. Folge (1971)

ZEEH, B., KÖNIG, K.H. and JUNG, J.: Development of new plant growth regulators with biological activity related to CCC. Kemia-Kemi 1 (Helsinki) *9*, 621–623 (1974)

ZELITCH, I.: Photorespiration: Studies with whole tissues. In: Photosynthesis II, Encycl. Plant Physiol. New Series, Vol. 6 (M. GIBBS and E. LATZKO, eds.) p. 351–367. Springer-Verlag Berlin, Heidelberg, New York 1979

Subject Index